D1211805

theory of networks
and lines

ac 9036

PRENTICE-HALL INTERNATIONAL, INC., *London*
PRENTICE-HALL OF AUSTRALIA, PTY., LTD., *Sydney*
PRENTICE-HALL OF CANADA, LTD., *Toronto*
PRENTICE-HALL FRANCE, S.A.R.L., *Paris*
PRENTICE-HALL OF INDIA PRIVATE LIMITED, *New Delhi*
PRENTICE-HALL OF JAPAN, INC., *Tokyo*
PRENTICE-HALL DE MEXICO, S.A., *Mexico City*

james l. potter

chairman and professor
department of electrical engineering
rutgers, the state university

sylvan fich

professor
department of electrical engineering
rutgers, the state university

theory of networks

and lines

prentice-hall, inc.
englewood cliffs, new jersey

prentice-hall electrical engineering series

william l. everitt, editor

preface

Engineering education is faced with the necessity of teaching an ever increasing amount of scientific material in a period of time that in most institutions remains constant. The only way in which this can be accomplished without sacrificing the distinguishing characteristics of the engineering curriculum, namely design and synthesis, is by increasing the efficiency of instruction. This text is written for the purpose of increasing the efficiency of instruction in networks and transmission lines while preserving the engineering characteristics of such a course. An attempt has been made to accomplish these results by integrating the basic material in network analysis, design, and synthesis. The text is written for a junior or senior course. The only prerequisites are a first course in circuits or networks and the usual preparation in mathematics obtained during the first two years of an engineering curriculum. It is assumed that the student is familiar with the elements of determinants.

The subject matter begins with the development of the parameters of two-terminal pair networks. Chapter One also includes the derivation and application of the bisection theorem. Frequent use is made of this theorem throughout the text. A portion of the material developed in Chapter One is applied in Chapter Two to the design of resistance attenuators. Chapter Three is devoted to the synthesis of lossless networks from a specification of their poles and zeros. These results are applied in Chapter Four to the design of conventional filters. Synthesis of networks with losses is developed in Chapter Five, but is limited to either resistance-inductance or resistance-capacitance configurations. An introduction to matrix algebra is given in Chapter Six. The results are applied to impedance transformation, impedance leveling, and the analysis of special networks. The small-signal equivalent circuits of electron tubes and transistors are derived and analyzed in Chapter Seven. A feature of this analysis is the use of hybrid parameters developed in Chapter One for both electron tube and transistor

v

circuits. This integrated development is novel and is believed to have considerable pedagogic value.

Chapters Eight, Nine, and Ten constitute a self-contained course in the circuit theory of transmission lines. This material has been included because transmission lines in normal application can be satisfactorily analyzed without recourse to field theory. Another reason is that the miniaturization of electronic circuitry often makes it necessary to consider the essentially distributed parameters caused by the proximity of apparently lumped circuit components to each other. Both the time and phasor response of transmission lines are developed. This development includes the derivation and solution of the wave equation, with emphasis on the physical interpretation of the results. Methods for reducing distortion and the use of lines for impedance transformation are considered. In the study of high frequency lines, several methods of analysis similarly used for wave guides and resonators are presented. This presentation provides an introduction to future work in field theory. A brief introduction to the transient analysis of networks and lines is given in Chapter Eleven.

We are deeply grateful for the generous counsel and assistance of Professor D. A. Molony. Dr. J. P. Newton made many valuable suggestions resulting from his use of the text material in mimeographed form. Our appreciation is extended to Drs. W. L. Everitt and T. J. Higgins for their constructive criticism in reviewing the manuscript. It is impossible to acknowledge specifically all the stenographic services involved in preparing the manuscript and the notes upon which it is based. However, we wish emphatically to express our appreciation of these often undervalued services. We thank the International Telephone and Telegraph Corporation for allowing us to reproduce the tables of hyperbolic functions and exponentials.

The preparation and revision of the notes upon which this book is based has been a stimulating experience. The stimulation resulted in no small measure from the cooperation of our students, who displayed genuine interest and offered constructive criticism. It is our earnest hope that this book may evoke as much interest in other students.

JAMES L. POTTER
SYLVAN FICH

contents

two-terminal pair networks

1.0 INTRODUCTION

A network that has a pair of input terminals and a pair of output terminals is termed a two-terminal pair or a two-port network. A two-terminal pair network is a transmission type of network. Such types include attenuators for reducing voltage, current, or power by known amounts; electric wave filters that transmit certain frequencies with low attenuation while highly attenuating other frequencies; amplitude equalizers with a prescribed amplitude ratio between input and output as a function of frequency; phase equalizers with a prescribed phase difference between input and output as a function of frequency; transmission lines; phase lag and lead networks used in servomechanisms; and many others. The theory necessary for the design of these networks is presented in this text. In some cases the ultimate network consists of a number of two-terminal pair networks connected in cascade. In order to form a foundation for the analysis and design of practical networks such as those mentioned previously, it is necessary first to study general two-terminal pair networks.

In earlier circuit work it was shown that an n-mesh or n-node network may be reduced to an equivalent T or π configuration at a single frequency. It is also possible to have networks equivalent to each other at all frequencies, but they may not always be physically realizable. It is the purpose here to study network equivalence at all frequencies. In addition to T and π networks, networks such as bridged-T and lattice structures will be considered.

Various methods for relating the input and output voltages and currents of two-terminal pair networks are to be developed, and several ways for specifying the transmission characteristics of two-terminal pair networks will be established. The intrinsic value of this rather extended and somewhat tedious development will not be immediately apparent to the student, but will be appreciated in the analysis and design of the practical two-

1

terminal pair networks to be considered in later chapters. A certain amount of patience is essential to the successful study of the material that is about to be presented. This will be rewarded by the ability to analyze and design the basic components of communication and power systems. The theory developed in this chapter is also to be applied to the construction of the equivalent circuits for electron tubes and transistors.

1.1 MESH-CURRENT AND NODE-VOLTAGE EQUATIONS

The analysis of this section is confined to a general two-terminal pair passive network. Special types of networks will be considered later. Relations between the input and output voltages and currents are developed in terms of the admittance and impedance parameters. Relations between the two-terminal pair admittances and impedances are also derived. Figure 1-1 shows a general n-mesh or n-node network with the assumed voltage polarities and reference current directions.

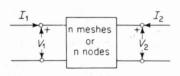

Figure 1-1 An n-mesh or n-node network.

The mesh-current equations for any network can be written in terms of the circuit parameters as follows:

$$
\begin{aligned}
Z_{11}I_1 + Z_{12}I_2 + Z_{13}I_3 + \ldots + Z_{1n}I_n &= V_1 \\
Z_{21}I_1 + Z_{22}I_2 + Z_{23}I_3 + \ldots + Z_{2n}I_n &= V_2 \\
Z_{31}I_1 + Z_{32}I_2 + Z_{33}I_3 + \ldots + Z_{3n}I_n &= V_3 \\
\cdots\cdots\cdots\cdots\cdots\cdots\cdots\cdots\cdots\cdots\cdots \\
Z_{n1}I_1 + Z_{n2}I_2 + Z_{n3}I_3 + \ldots + Z_{nn}I_n &= V_n
\end{aligned}
\qquad [1.1\text{-}1]
$$

The signs of the mutual impedance terms and the voltages are determined in the usual manner after the reference directions for the mesh currents are established.* The self-impedance terms are always positive.

The node-voltage equations for any linear network can be written in terms of the circuit parameters as follows:

$$
\begin{aligned}
Y_{11}V_1 + Y_{12}V_2 + Y_{13}V_3 + \ldots + Y_{1n}V_n &= I_1 \\
Y_{21}V_1 + Y_{22}V_2 + Y_{23}V_3 + \ldots + Y_{2n}V_n &= I_2 \\
Y_{31}V_1 + Y_{32}V_2 + Y_{33}V_3 + \ldots + Y_{3n}V_n &= I_3 \\
\cdots\cdots\cdots\cdots\cdots\cdots\cdots\cdots\cdots\cdots\cdots \\
Y_{n1}V_1 + Y_{n2}V_2 + Y_{n3}V_3 + \ldots + Y_{nn}V_n &= I_n
\end{aligned}
\qquad [1.1\text{-}2]
$$

* In connection with the material presented here, the student may desire to review *Theory of A-C Circuits* by S. Fich and J. L. Potter (Prentice-Hall, Inc., Englewood Cliffs, N.J., 1958), Chapters 5 and 6; or *Electrical Engineering Circuits* by H. H. Skilling (John Wiley & Sons, Inc., New York, 1957), Chapters 9 and 10.

The signs attached to the mutual admittance terms and the currents are determined in the usual manner after the assumed polarities of the node voltages are established. The self-admittance terms are always positive.

For the purpose of this discussion, it is assumed that the network under consideration is an n-mesh or n-node system with a pair of input terminals and a pair of output terminals, and that the network consists of passive elements; that is, it contains no voltage or current sources within the network.

It will be assumed for convenience that the input mesh or node is 1, and the output mesh or node is 2. The meshes or nodes can be numbered in any manner as long as the network determinant is set up accordingly.

If we confine ourselves to the meshes or nodes 1 and 2, as the input pair and output pair, then, referring to Eqs. 1.1-1, all voltage sources other than V_1 and V_2 are zero. It might also be stated that V_1 and V_2 are not necessarily sources; one may be a voltage drop external to the network proper.

Likewise, in Eqs. 1.1-2, all current sources other than I_1 and I_2 are equal to zero. Again, I_1 and I_2 need not both be sources; I_2 may be a current in a load external to the network, where I_1 is the current source.

Using determinant methods to solve Eqs. 1.1-1 for the input and output currents I_1 and I_2 resulting from the voltages V_1 and V_2, with all other voltages zero, the following results are obtained:

$$I_1 = \left(\frac{\Delta_{11}}{\Delta_z}\right)V_1 + \left(\frac{\Delta_{21}}{\Delta_z}\right)V_2$$

$$I_2 = \left(\frac{\Delta_{12}}{\Delta_z}\right)V_1 + \left(\frac{\Delta_{22}}{\Delta_z}\right)V_2$$

[1.1-3]

where

$$\Delta_z = \begin{vmatrix} Z_{11} & Z_{12} & \ldots & Z_{1n} \\ Z_{21} & Z_{22} & \ldots & Z_{2n} \\ \ldots & \ldots & \ldots & \ldots \\ Z_{n1} & Z_{n2} & \ldots & Z_{nn} \end{vmatrix}$$

[1.1-4]

and Δ_{11}, Δ_{12}, Δ_{21}, and Δ_{22} are cofactors of the elements of Δ_z indicated by their respective subscripts.

Equations 1.1-3 constitute a node or Y set having the same general form as Eqs. 1.1-2. Thus Eqs. 1.1-3 may be written as

$$I_1 = y_{11}V_1 + y_{12}V_2$$

$$I_2 = y_{21}V_1 + y_{22}V_2$$

[1.1-5]

where the lower-case letters denote the two-terminal pair admittances. Comparison of Eqs. 1.1-3 and 1.1-5 establishes the following relations:

$$y_{11} = \frac{\Delta_{11}}{\Delta_z}$$

$$y_{12} = \frac{\Delta_{21}}{\Delta_z}$$

$$y_{21} = \frac{\Delta_{12}}{\Delta_z}$$ [1.1-6]

$$y_{22} = \frac{\Delta_{22}}{\Delta_z}$$

When the two-port network satisfies the reciprocity theorem, that is, if the ratio of excitation to response is independent of whether the excitation exists at terminals 1 or 2, $\Delta_{12} = \Delta_{21}$. Such a network is termed a *reciprocal network*. All networks considered in this text are reciprocal except those in Chapter 7, where networks containing electron devices are considered. Equations 1.1-6 are general, but $y_{12} = y_{21}$ only when the network is reciprocal. The same condition exists for the two-terminal impedance parameters that are derived later in this section. Reciprocity will be assumed throughout this text, unless otherwise specified. In reciprocal networks, Δ_{12} and Δ_{21} will be used interchangeably.

For a π network composed of admittances Y_A, Y_B, and Y_C as shown

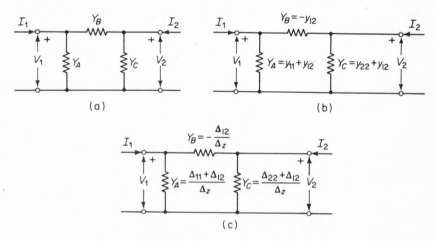

Figure 1-2 Equivalent π network derived from Z system.

in Fig. 1-2(a), the node voltage equations are written for the assumed reference voltage polarities and current directions as follows:

$$I_1 = (Y_A + Y_B)V_1 - Y_B V_2$$
$$I_2 = -Y_B V_1 + (Y_B + Y_C)V_2 \qquad [1.1\text{-}7]$$

Comparison of Eqs. 1.1-5, 1.1-6, and 1.1-7 establishes the following relations:

$$y_{11} = \frac{\Delta_{11}}{\Delta_z} = Y_A + Y_B$$

$$y_{12} = y_{21} = \frac{\Delta_{12}}{\Delta_z} = -Y_B \qquad [1.1\text{-}8]$$

$$y_{22} = \frac{\Delta_{22}}{\Delta_z} = Y_B + Y_C$$

The components of the equivalent π network are shown in Figs. 1-2(b) and 1-2(c).

It has been shown that the solution of the mesh-current equations for a two-terminal pair network yields a pair of node-voltage equations, or a Y set, leading to the equivalent π network. The components of the π network are expressed in terms of the elements of the Z determinant of the original network. When these node-voltage equations are solved for the voltages, V_1 and V_2, the result is a pair of mesh-current equations, leading to the equivalent T network. The components of the T network may also be expressed in terms of the elements of the Z determinant of the original network. This will be shown in the derivation that follows.

Solution of Eqs. 1.1-3 for V_1 and V_2 yields

$$V_1 = \left(\frac{\dfrac{\Delta_{22}}{\Delta_z}}{\dfrac{\Delta_{11}\Delta_{22} - \Delta_{21}\Delta_{12}}{\Delta_z^2}} \right) I_1 - \left(\frac{\dfrac{\Delta_{21}}{\Delta_z}}{\dfrac{\Delta_{11}\Delta_{22} - \Delta_{21}\Delta_{12}}{\Delta_z^2}} \right) I_2 \qquad [1.1\text{-}9]$$

$$V_2 = -\left(\frac{\dfrac{\Delta_{12}}{\Delta_z}}{\dfrac{\Delta_{11}\Delta_{22} - \Delta_{21}\Delta_{12}}{\Delta_z^2}} \right) I_1 + \left(\frac{\dfrac{\Delta_{11}}{\Delta_z}}{\dfrac{\Delta_{11}\Delta_{22} - \Delta_{21}\Delta_{12}}{\Delta_z^2}} \right) I_2 \qquad [1.1\text{-}10]$$

It is shown in Appendix A that

$$\frac{\Delta_{11}\Delta_{22} - \Delta_{21}\Delta_{12}}{\Delta} = \Delta_{1122} \qquad [1.1\text{-}11]$$

where the cofactor Δ_{1122} is obtained by cancelling the first two rows and columns of Δ. Application of the relation in Eq. 1.1-11 to Eqs. 1.1-9 and 1.1-10 gives the following result:

$$V_1 = \left(\frac{\Delta_{22}}{\Delta_{1122}}\right) I_1 - \left(\frac{\Delta_{12}}{\Delta_{1122}}\right) I_2 \qquad [1.1\text{-}12]$$

$$V_2 = -\left(\frac{\Delta_{21}}{\Delta_{1122}}\right) I_1 + \left(\frac{\Delta_{11}}{\Delta_{1122}}\right) I_2 \qquad [1.1\text{-}13]$$

where the cofactors are those of Δ_z.

The solution of Eqs. 1.1-5 for V_1 and V_2 yields

$$V_1 = \left(\frac{y_{22}}{|y|}\right) I_1 - \left(\frac{y_{12}}{|y|}\right) I_2$$

$$V_2 = -\left(\frac{y_{21}}{|y|}\right) I_1 + \left(\frac{y_{11}}{|y|}\right) I_2 \qquad [1.1\text{-}14]$$

where

$$|y| = \begin{vmatrix} y_{11} & y_{12} \\ y_{21} & y_{22} \end{vmatrix} = y_{11}y_{22} - y_{12}y_{21} = y_{11}y_{22} - y_{12}^2 \qquad [1.1\text{-}15]$$

Since Eqs. 1.1-12, and 1.1-14 are Z sets, they may be written as follows:

$$V_1 = z_{11}I_1 + z_{12}I_2$$

$$V_2 = z_{21}I_1 + z_{22}I_2 \qquad [1.1\text{-}16]$$

Comparison of Eqs. 1.1-12, 1.1-13, 1.1-14, and 1.1-16 establishes the following relations:

$$z_{11} = \frac{y_{22}}{|y|} = \frac{\Delta_{22}}{\Delta_{1122}}$$

$$z_{12} = z_{21} = -\frac{y_{12}}{|y|} = -\frac{\Delta_{12}}{\Delta_{1122}} \qquad [1.1\text{-}17]$$

$$z_{22} = \frac{y_{11}}{|y|} = \frac{\Delta_{11}}{\Delta_{1122}}$$

If a T network is composed of impedances Z_1, Z_2, and Z_3 as shown in Fig. 1-3(a), the mesh current equations are

$$V_1 = (Z_1 + Z_2)I_1 + Z_2I_2$$

$$V_2 = Z_2I_1 + (Z_2 + Z_3)I_2 \qquad [1.1\text{-}18]$$

Use of Eqs. 1.1-17 and 1.1-18 yields the following relations:

$$z_{11} = \frac{\Delta_{22}}{\Delta_{1122}} = \frac{y_{22}}{|y|} = Z_1 + Z_2$$

$$z_{12} = z_{21} = -\frac{\Delta_{12}}{\Delta_{1122}} = -\frac{y_{12}}{|y|} = Z_2 \qquad [1.1\text{-}19]$$

$$z_{22} = \frac{\Delta_{11}}{\Delta_{1122}} = \frac{y_{11}}{|y|} = Z_2 + Z_3$$

where the cofactors are of Δ_z. The equivalent T networks are shown in Fig. 1-3.

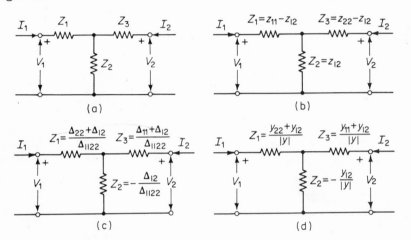

Figure 1-3   Equivalent T network derived from Z system.

Starting with Eqs. 1.1-2, and obtaining the solution for the Y system of equations, we have

$$V_1 = \left(\frac{\Delta_{11}}{\Delta_y}\right) I_1 + \left(\frac{\Delta_{21}}{\Delta_y}\right) I_2$$

$$V_2 = \left(\frac{\Delta_{12}}{\Delta_y}\right) I_1 + \left(\frac{\Delta_{22}}{\Delta_y}\right) I_2 \qquad [1.1\text{-}20]$$

where $\Delta_{12} = \Delta_{21}$ in a reciprocal network,

$$\Delta_y = \begin{vmatrix} Y_{11} & Y_{12} & \cdots & Y_{1n} \\ Y_{21} & Y_{22} & \cdots & Y_{2n} \\ \cdots & \cdots & \cdots & \cdots \\ Y_{n1} & Y_{n2} & \cdots & Y_{nn} \end{vmatrix} \qquad [1.1\text{-}21]$$

and Δ_{11}, Δ_{12}, and Δ_{22} are cofactors of Δ_y.

Equations 1.1-20 constitute a mesh or Z set having the same general form as Eqs. 1.1-1. Thus, Eqs. 1.1-20 may be written as

$$V_1 = z_{11}I_1 + z_{12}I_2$$
$$V_2 = z_{21}I_1 + z_{22}I_2$$

[1.1-22]

where the lower-case letters denote the two-terminal pair impedances. Comparison of Eqs. 1.1-20 and 1.1-22 establishes the following relations:

$$z_{11} = \frac{\Delta_{11}}{\Delta_y}$$

$$z_{12} = \frac{\Delta_{21}}{\Delta_y}$$

[1.1-23]

$$z_{21} = \frac{\Delta_{12}}{\Delta_y}$$

$$z_{22} = \frac{\Delta_{22}}{\Delta_y}$$

If a T network is composed of impedances Z_1, Z_2, and Z_3, as shown in Fig. 1-4(a), the equations for the network are Eqs. 1.1-18. A comparison

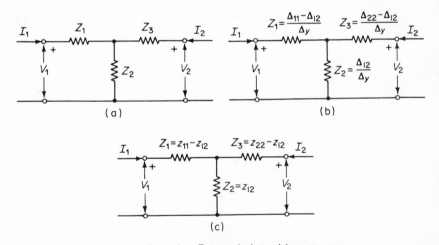

Figure 1-4 Equivalent T network derived from Y system.

of Eqs. 1.1-18 and Eqs. 1.1-20 and 1.1-22 gives the equivalent T network in terms of Δ_y, and its cofactors and z parameters as shown in Fig. 1-4.

When Eqs. 1.1-20 are solved for I_1 and I_2, the result is a pair of node-voltage equations leading to the equivalent π network. The components of the equivalent π network will be expressed in terms of the elements of the Y determinant of the original network. Solution of Eqs. 1.1-20 yields

$$I_1 = \left(\frac{\dfrac{\Delta_{22}}{\Delta_y}}{\dfrac{\Delta_{11}\Delta_{22} - \Delta_{21}\Delta_{12}}{\Delta_y^2}} \right) V_1 - \left(\frac{\dfrac{\Delta_{21}}{\Delta_y}}{\dfrac{\Delta_{11}\Delta_{22} - \Delta_{21}\Delta_{12}}{\Delta_y^2}} \right) V_2 \qquad [1.1\text{-}24]$$

$$I_2 = -\left(\frac{\dfrac{\Delta_{12}}{\Delta_y}}{\dfrac{\Delta_{11}\Delta_{22} - \Delta_{21}\Delta_{12}}{\Delta_y^2}} \right) V_1 + \left(\frac{\dfrac{\Delta_{11}}{\Delta_y}}{\dfrac{\Delta_{11}\Delta_{22} - \Delta_{21}\Delta_{12}}{\Delta_y^2}} \right) V_2 \qquad [1.1\text{-}25]$$

Applying the relation

$$\frac{\Delta_{11}\Delta_{22} - \Delta_{21}\Delta_{12}}{\Delta_y} = \Delta_{1122} \qquad [1.1\text{-}26]$$

to Eqs. 1.1-24 and 1.1-25 gives the following result:

$$I_1 = \left(\frac{\Delta_{22}}{\Delta_{1122}} \right) V_1 - \left(\frac{\Delta_{21}}{\Delta_{1122}} \right) V_2$$

$$I_2 = -\left(\frac{\Delta_{12}}{\Delta_{1122}} \right) V_1 + \left(\frac{\Delta_{11}}{\Delta_{1122}} \right) V_2 \qquad [1.1\text{-}27]$$

where the cofactors in this case are of those of Δ_y.

Likewise, solving Eqs. 1.1-22 for I_1 and I_2, we have

$$I_1 = \left(\frac{z_{22}}{|z|} \right) V_1 - \left(\frac{z_{12}}{|z|} \right) V_2$$

$$I_2 = -\left(\frac{z_{21}}{|z|} \right) V_1 + \left(\frac{z_{11}}{|z|} \right) V_2 \qquad [1.1\text{-}28]$$

where

$$|z| = \begin{vmatrix} z_{11} & z_{12} \\ z_{21} & z_{22} \end{vmatrix} = z_{11}z_{22} - z_{12}z_{21} = z_{11}z_{22} - z_{12}^2 \qquad [1.1\text{-}29]$$

Since Eqs. 1.1-27 and 1.1-28 are a y set, they may be written as

$$I_1 = y_{11}V_1 + y_{12}V_2$$

$$I_2 = y_{21}V_1 + y_{22}V_2 \qquad [1.1\text{-}30]$$

where

$$y_{11} = \frac{z_{22}}{|z|} = \frac{\Delta_{22}}{\Delta_{1122}}$$

$$y_{12} = y_{21} = -\frac{z_{12}}{|z|} = -\frac{\Delta_{12}}{\Delta_{1122}} \qquad [1.1\text{-}31]$$

$$y_{22} = \frac{z_{11}}{|z|} = \frac{\Delta_{11}}{\Delta_{1122}}$$

A comparison of Eqs. 1.1-27, 1.1-28, 1.1-30, and 1.1-31 with Eqs. 1.1-7 gives the equivalence shown in Fig. 1-5.

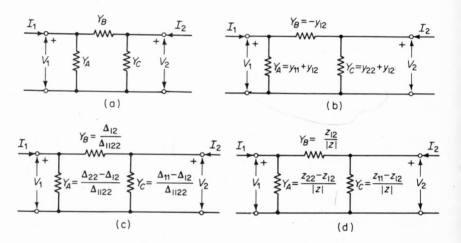

Figure 1-5 Equivalent π network derived from Y system.

The significance of the results obtained will now be summarized. The solution of the mesh-current equations of a two-terminal pair network yields a pair of node-voltage equations that lead to the equivalent π network. The solution of these node-voltage equations yields a pair of mesh-current equations that lead to the equivalent T network. The components of the equivalent T and π networks are expressed in terms of the elements of the Z determinant of the original network. The solution of the node-voltage equations of a two-terminal pair network yields a pair of mesh-current equations that lead to the equivalent T network. The solution of these mesh-current equations yields a pair of node-voltage equations that lead to the equivalent π network. The components of the latter T and π network are expressed in terms of the elements of the Y determinant of the original network. It follows that any of these two-terminal pair networks can be reduced to either a T or a π network having its components expressed in terms of the elements of either the Z or Y determinant of the original network.

The node-voltage and mesh-current equations expressed in terms of the two-terminal pair admittances and impedances are repeated here for convenience:

$$y_{11}V_1 + y_{12}V_2 = I_1$$
$$y_{21}V_1 + y_{22}V_2 = I_2 \qquad [1.1\text{-}32]$$

$$z_{11}I_1 + z_{12}I_2 = V_1$$
$$z_{21}I_1 + z_{22}I_2 = V_2 \qquad [1.1\text{-}33]$$

The physical significance of the coefficients in Eqs. 1.1-32 and 1.1-33 will now be examined. It is seen from Eqs. 1.1-32 that y_{11} is the ratio of the current I_1 to the voltage V_1 when the voltage V_2 is zero. Hence y_{11} is called the *input short-circuit admittance*, and y_{22} is defined in a similar manner. It should be carefully noted that, in an n-node network, y_{11} is not equal to Y_{11}, the self-admittance of node 1, unless $n = 2$ as in a π network. It is also seen that y_{12} is the ratio of the current I_1 to the voltage V_2 when V_1 is zero. Therefore, y_{12} is termed the *mutual short-circuit admittance*, and y_{21} is defined in a similar manner. It is again stressed that y_{12} does not in general equal Y_{12}, the mutual admittance between nodes 1 and 2 of an n-node system. It follows from Eqs. 1.1-33 that z_{11} is the ratio of the voltage V_1 to the current I_1 when the current I_2 is zero. For this reason, z_{11} is called the *input open-circuit impedance*, and z_{22} is similarly defined. It should be carefully noted that in a general n-mesh system, z_{11} is not equal to Z_{11}, the self-impedance of mesh 1, unless $n = 2$ as in a T network. It is also seen that z_{12} is the ratio of the voltage V_1 to the current I_2 when the current I_1 is zero. Therefore, z_{12} is known as the *mutual open-circuit impedance*, and z_{21} is defined in a like manner. The above definitions are summarized in Table 1-1.

TABLE 1-1

DEFINITIONS OF IMPEDANCE AND ADMITTANCE PARAMETERS

Condition	Impedance or admittance	Physical definition
$I_2 = 0$	$z_{11} = V_1/I_1$	Input open-circuit impedance
$I_1 = 0$	$z_{22} = V_2/I_2$	Output open-circuit impedance
$I_1 = 0$	$z_{12} = V_1/I_2$	Mutual or transfer open-circuit impedances
$I_2 = 0$	$z_{21} = V_2/I_1$	
$V_2 = 0$	$y_{11} = I_1/V_1$	Input short-circuit admittance
$V_1 = 0$	$y_{22} = I_2/V_2$	Output short-circuit admittance
$V_1 = 0$	$y_{12} = I_1/V_2$	Mutual or transfer short-circuit admittances
$V_2 = 0$	$y_{21} = I_2/V_1$	

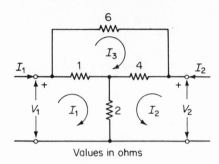

Values in ohms

Figure 1-6 Resistance network for mesh-current analysis.

An example using a simple resistance network shown in Fig. 1-6 will illustrate the material given in this section. In Fig. 1-6 the network has been set up for mesh current analysis. Setting up the mesh determinant by inspection, we have

$$\Delta_z = \begin{vmatrix} 3 & 2 & -1 \\ 2 & 6 & 4 \\ -1 & 4 & 11 \end{vmatrix}$$

where the input is at mesh 1 and the output is at mesh 2. Then, referring to Eqs. 1.1-3, the desired cofactors are Δ_{11}, Δ_{22}, Δ_{12}, and Δ_{21}. Evaluation of these cofactors follows:

$$\Delta_{11} = \begin{vmatrix} 6 & 4 \\ 4 & 11 \end{vmatrix} = 66 - 16 = 50$$

$$\Delta_{22} = \begin{vmatrix} 3 & -1 \\ -1 & 11 \end{vmatrix} = 33 - 1 = 32$$

$$\Delta_{12} = \Delta_{21} = - \begin{vmatrix} 2 & 4 \\ -1 & 11 \end{vmatrix} = -(22 + 4) = -26$$

The determinant Δ_z can be evaluated by use of Eq. 1.1-11 if solved for Δ_z. Thus

$$\Delta_z = \frac{\Delta_{11}\Delta_{22} - \Delta_{12}\Delta_{21}}{\Delta_{1122}} \qquad [1.1\text{-}34]$$

Cancelling the first two rows and columns of Δ_z, we have

$$\Delta_{1122} = 11$$

Hence

$$\Delta_z = \frac{50 \times 32 - (-26)^2}{11} = 84$$

Then, according to Eqs. 1.1-6, we have

$$y_{11} = \frac{\Delta_{11}}{\Delta_z} = \frac{50}{84}$$

$$y_{22} = \frac{\Delta_{22}}{\Delta_z} = \frac{32}{84}$$

$$y_{12} = y_{21} = \frac{\Delta_{12}}{\Delta_z} = -\frac{26}{84}$$

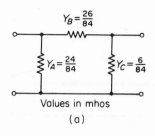
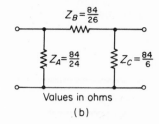

Figure 1-7 π network equivalent to Figure 1-6 and derived from Z system.

If reference is made to Fig. 1-2, the π network is constructed as shown in Fig. 1-7.

The values for the equivalent T network are obtained from Eqs. 1.1-19, using Δ_z cofactors. The cofactors have been determined in the previous example as

$$\Delta_{11} = 50 \qquad\qquad \frac{\Delta_{11}}{\Delta_{1122}} = \frac{50}{11}$$

$$\Delta_{22} = 32 \qquad\qquad \frac{\Delta_{22}}{\Delta_{1122}} = \frac{32}{11}$$

$$\Delta_{12} = -26 \qquad\qquad \frac{\Delta_{12}}{\Delta_{1122}} = -\frac{26}{11}$$

$$\Delta_{1122} = 11$$

With reference to Fig. 1-3(c), the equivalent T network is constructed as shown in Fig. 1-8.

It is seen that it is simpler to construct the T network from the Z system of equations than it is to construct the π network, since the value of the determinant is not required for the T network.

The same network as Fig. 1-6 will be used for the node voltage network example; it is shown in Fig. 1-9 with the values given in mhos.

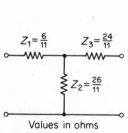
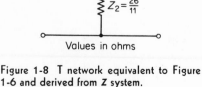

Figure 1-8 T network equivalent to Figure 1-6 and derived from Z system.

Figure 1-9 Resistance network for node-voltage analysis.

Setting up the node determinant by inspection, we have

$$\Delta_y = \begin{vmatrix} \frac{7}{6} & -1 & -\frac{1}{6} \\ -1 & \frac{7}{4} & -\frac{1}{4} \\ -\frac{1}{6} & -\frac{1}{4} & \frac{5}{12} \end{vmatrix}$$

Since the input is taken at node 1 and the output at node 3, the desired cofactors of Δ_y in this case are Δ_{11}, Δ_{33}, Δ_{13}, and Δ_{1133}, where

$$\Delta_{11} = \begin{vmatrix} \frac{7}{4} & -\frac{1}{4} \\ -\frac{1}{4} & \frac{5}{12} \end{vmatrix} = \frac{16}{24}$$

$$\Delta_{33} = \begin{vmatrix} \frac{7}{6} & -1 \\ -1 & \frac{7}{4} \end{vmatrix} = \frac{25}{24}$$

$$\Delta_{13} = \begin{vmatrix} -1 & \frac{7}{4} \\ -\frac{1}{6} & -\frac{1}{4} \end{vmatrix} = \frac{13}{24}$$

$$\Delta_{1133} = \frac{7}{4}$$

Using Eq. 1.1-34 for evaluating Δ_y, the following result is obtained:

$$\Delta_y = \frac{\Delta_{11}\Delta_{33} - \Delta_{13}^2}{\Delta_{1133}} = \frac{\frac{16}{24} \times \frac{25}{24} - \left(\frac{13}{24}\right)^2}{\frac{7}{4}} = \frac{11}{48}$$

Using Eqs. 1.1-23 to determine the values for the equivalent T network, we have

$$z_{11} = \frac{\Delta_{11}}{\Delta_y} = \frac{\frac{16}{24}}{\frac{11}{48}} = \frac{32}{11}$$

$$z_{33} = \frac{\Delta_{33}}{\Delta_y} = \frac{\frac{25}{24}}{\frac{11}{48}} = \frac{50}{11}$$

$$z_{13} = \frac{\Delta_{13}}{\Delta_y} = \frac{\frac{13}{24}}{\frac{11}{48}} = \frac{26}{11}$$

The equivalent T network is shown in Fig. 1-10. It is seen that Fig. 1-10 is identical with Fig. 1-8 as obtained from the Z system.

The equivalent π network is obtained from the Y system by Eqs. 1.1-31 with subscript 3 replacing 2.

$$y_{11} = \frac{\Delta_{33}}{\Delta_{1133}} = \frac{\frac{25}{24}}{\frac{7}{4}} = \frac{50}{84}$$

$$y_{22} = \frac{\Delta_{11}}{\Delta_{1133}} = \frac{\frac{16}{24}}{\frac{7}{4}} = \frac{32}{84}$$

$$y_{12} = -\frac{\Delta_{13}}{\Delta_{1133}} = -\frac{\frac{13}{24}}{\frac{7}{4}} = -\frac{26}{84}$$

The equivalent π network is shown in Fig. 1-11; it is identical to Fig. 1-7(a) as obtained from the Z system.

In Fig. 1-9, the input node is labelled 1 and output node, 3. Nodes 2 and 3 can be interchanged so that 2 is the output node. When the determinant Δ_y is written accordingly, the same results are obtained as given above.

Values in ohms

Figure 1-10 T network equivalent to Figure 1-6 and derived from Y system.

Values in mhos

Figure 1-11 π network equivalent to Figure 1-6 and derived from Y system.

1.2 TRANSMISSION EQUATIONS

A set of equations that is of considerable importance in the analysis of two-terminal pair networks is obtained by finding the relations between the input voltage and current and the output voltage and current. The solution of Eqs. 1.1-32 for I_1 and V_1 in terms of V_2 and I_2 yields

$$\begin{aligned} V_1 &= -\left(\frac{y_{22}}{y_{21}}\right) V_2 + \left(\frac{1}{y_{21}}\right) I_2 \\ I_1 &= -\left(\frac{y_{11}y_{22} - y_{12}^2}{y_{21}}\right) V_2 + \left(\frac{y_{11}}{y_{21}}\right) I_2 \end{aligned} \qquad [1.2\text{-}1]$$

The input voltage and current can also be related to the output voltage and current by solving Eqs. 1.1-33. The solution gives the following results:

$$\begin{aligned} V_1 &= \left(\frac{z_{11}}{z_{12}}\right) V_2 - \left(\frac{z_{11}z_{22} - z_{12}^2}{z_{12}}\right) I_2 \\ I_1 &= \left(\frac{1}{z_{12}}\right) V_2 - \left(\frac{z_{22}}{z_{12}}\right) I_2 \end{aligned} \qquad [1.2\text{-}2]$$

Equations 1.2-1 and 1.2-2 have the general form of

$$\begin{aligned} V_1 &= AV_2 - BI_2 \\ I_1 &= CV_2 - DI_2 \end{aligned} \qquad [1.2\text{-}3]$$

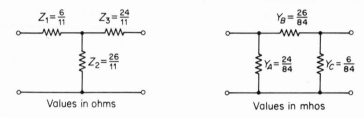

where the coefficients have the following values:

$$A = \frac{z_{11}}{z_{12}} = -\frac{y_{22}}{y_{12}} \qquad [1.2\text{-}4]$$

$$B = \frac{|z|}{z_{12}} = -\frac{1}{y_{12}} \qquad [1.2\text{-}5]$$

$$C = \frac{1}{z_{12}} = -\frac{|y|}{y_{12}} \qquad [1.2\text{-}6]$$

$$D = \frac{z_{22}}{z_{12}} = -\frac{y_{11}}{y_{12}} \qquad [1.2\text{-}7]$$

The relations, $y_{12} = y_{21}$ and $z_{12} = z_{21}$, have been used in Eqs. 1.2-1 through 1.2-7.

The constants A, B, C, and D in Eqs. 1.2-4 through 1.2-7 are related as follows:

$$\begin{vmatrix} A & B \\ C & D \end{vmatrix} = \frac{y_{22}y_{11}}{y_{12}^2} - \frac{y_{11}y_{22} - y_{12}^2}{y_{12}^2} = 1 = AD - BC$$

$$\begin{vmatrix} A & B \\ C & D \end{vmatrix} = \frac{z_{11}z_{22}}{z_{12}^2} - \frac{z_{11}z_{22} - z_{12}^2}{z_{12}^2} = 1 = AD - BC \qquad [1.2\text{-}8]$$

Since $AD - BC = 1$, only three independent parameters are required to define a two-terminal pair network, because the fourth can be obtained from the other three. Note also that A equals D when z_{11} equals z_{22}, or when y_{11} equals y_{22}. Under these conditions, the network is symmetrical with respect to the input and output terminals, and is termed a *symmetrical network*.

Expressions for V_2 and I_2 in terms of V_1 and I_1 can readily be obtained from Eqs. 1.2-3 with the aid of Eqs. 1.2-8. The resulting equations are

$$V_2 = DV_1 - BI_1$$
$$I_2 = CV_1 - AI_1 \qquad [1.2\text{-}9]$$

Equations 1.2-3 and 1.2-9 are inverse sets.

A much easier way to relate the coefficients is by the short-circuit conditions, when V_1 or V_2 equals zero; or by the open-circuit conditions, when I_1 or I_2 equals zero. For example, in Eqs. 1.2-3

$$\frac{V_1}{V_2} = A \quad \text{when } I_2 = 0 \quad \text{(open circuit)}$$

In Eqs. 1.1-32

$$\frac{V_1}{V_2} = \frac{y_{22}}{y_{21}} \quad \text{when } I_2 = 0$$

In Eqs. 1.1-33

$$\frac{V_1}{V_2} = \frac{z_{11}}{z_{12}} \quad \text{when } I_2 = 0$$

Therefore

$$A = -\frac{y_{22}}{y_{21}} = \frac{z_{11}}{z_{12}} \qquad \text{[1.2-10]}$$

For the B coefficient

$$\frac{V_1}{I_2} = -B \quad \text{when } V_2 = 0 \quad \text{(short circuit)}$$

In Eqs. 1.1-32

$$\frac{V_1}{I_2} = \frac{1}{y_{21}} = \frac{1}{y_{12}} \quad \text{when } V_2 = 0$$

As shown in Eqs. 1.1-31, $\dfrac{1}{y_{12}} = -\dfrac{|z|}{z_{12}}$ Hence

$$B = -\frac{1}{y_{12}} = \frac{|z|}{z_{12}} \qquad \text{[1.2-11]}$$

For the C coefficient

$$\frac{I_2}{V_1} = C \quad \text{when } I_1 = 0$$

In Eqs. 1.1-33

$$\frac{I_2}{V_1} = \frac{1}{z_{12}} \quad \text{when } I_1 = 0$$

As shown in Eqs. 1.1-17 $\dfrac{1}{z_{12}} = -\dfrac{|y|}{y_{12}}$. Hence

$$C = \frac{1}{z_{12}} = -\frac{|y|}{y_{12}} \qquad \text{[1.2-12]}$$

For the coefficient D

$$\frac{I_1}{I_2} = -D \quad \text{when } V_2 = 0$$

In Eqs. 1.1-32

$$\frac{I_1}{I_2} = \frac{y_{11}}{y_{21}} \quad \text{when } V_2 = 0$$

In Eqs. 1.1-33

$$\frac{I_1}{I_2} = -\frac{z_{22}}{z_{21}} \quad \text{when } V_2 = 0$$

Therefore

$$D = -\frac{y_{11}}{y_{21}} = \frac{z_{22}}{z_{21}} \qquad [1.2\text{-}13]$$

1.3 HYBRID EQUATIONS

In addition to the mesh-current and node-voltage equations discussed in Sec. 1.1, and the transmission equations treated in Sec. 1.2, there are other relationships that are called "mixed" or "hybrid" equations. Such hybrid equations are widely used in the analysis of electron-tube and transistor equivalent networks, as considered later in this book. One hybrid set, known as the g set,* is based on expressing the input current in terms of the input voltage and the output current, and expressing the output voltage in terms of the input voltage and the output current, as follows:

$$I_1 = g_{11}V_1 + g_{12}I_2$$
$$V_2 = g_{21}V_1 + g_{22}I_2 \qquad [1.3\text{-}1]$$

In Eqs. 1.3-1, $g_{11} = I_1/V_1$ when $I_2 = 0$. It follows directly from Eqs. 1.1-33 that

$$g_{11} = \frac{1}{z_{11}} \qquad [1.3\text{-}2]$$

It also follows from Eqs. 1.2-4 and 1.2-6 that

$$g_{11} = \frac{1}{z_{11}} = \frac{|y|}{y_{22}} = \frac{C}{A} \qquad [1.3\text{-}3]$$

In Eqs. 1.3-1, $g_{12} = I_1/I_2$ when $V_1 = 0$. It follows directly from Eqs. 1.1-33 that

$$g_{12} = -\frac{z_{12}}{z_{11}} \qquad [1.3\text{-}4]$$

It also follows from Eq. 1.2-4 that

* The letter g is used to distinguish this set from the inverse set, discussed later in this section, which is identified by the letter h. The g in the immediate frame of reference is not related to the g of conductance.

$$g_{12} = -\frac{z_{12}}{z_{11}} = \frac{y_{12}}{y_{22}} = -\frac{1}{A} \qquad [1.3\text{-}5]$$

The other two coefficients in Eqs. 1.3-1 can be evaluated in a similar manner; they are tabulated in Table 1-2. Their derivation is left to the student as an exercise.

The inverse set of equations corresponding to Eqs. 1.3-1 is found by solving Eqs. 1.3-1 for V_1 and I_2 in terms of V_2 and I_1. The result is as follows:

$$V_1 = -\left(\frac{g_{12}}{|g|}\right) V_2 + \left(\frac{g_{22}}{|g|}\right) I_1$$
$$I_2 = \left(\frac{g_{11}}{|g|}\right) V_2 - \left(\frac{g_{21}}{|g|}\right) I_1 \qquad [1.3\text{-}6]$$

where

$$|g| = \begin{vmatrix} g_{11} & g_{12} \\ g_{21} & g_{22} \end{vmatrix} \qquad [1.3\text{-}7]$$

Equations 1.3-6 can be written as

$$V_1 = h_{11}I_1 + h_{12}V_2 \qquad [1.3\text{-}8]$$
$$I_2 = h_{21}I_1 + h_{22}V_2 \qquad [1.3\text{-}9]$$

for the inverse mixed set of equations.

In Eq. 1.3-8, $h_{11} = V_1/I_1$ when $V_2 = 0$. It follows directly from Eqs. 1.1-32 that

$$h_{11} \doteq \frac{1}{y_{11}} \qquad [1.3\text{-}10]$$

It also follows from Eqs. 1.2-5 and 1.2-7 that

$$h_{11} = \frac{1}{y_{11}} = \frac{|z|}{z_{22}} = \frac{B}{D} \qquad [1.3\text{-}11]$$

It is seen from Eq. 1.3-9 that $h_{21} = I_2/I_1$ when $V_2 = 0$. It follows from Eqs. 1.1-32 that

$$h_{21} = \frac{y_{21}}{y_{11}} \qquad [1.3\text{-}12]$$

It also follows from Eq. 1.2-7 that

$$h_{21} = \frac{y_{21}}{y_{11}} = -\frac{z_{21}}{z_{22}} = -\frac{1}{D} \qquad [1.3\text{-}13]$$

TABLE 1-2

RELATIONS AMONG TWO-TERMINAL PAIR NETWORK PARAMETERS

	Z n-mesh	Y n-node	z	y	g	h	$A\ B$ / $C\ D$
z	$\begin{matrix} \dfrac{\Delta_{22}}{\Delta_{1122}} & -\dfrac{\Delta_{21}}{\Delta_{1122}} \\[4pt] -\dfrac{\Delta_{12}}{\Delta_{1122}} & \dfrac{\Delta_{11}}{\Delta_{1122}} \end{matrix}$	$\begin{matrix} \dfrac{\Delta_{11}}{\Delta} & \dfrac{\Delta_{21}}{\Delta} \\[4pt] \dfrac{\Delta_{12}}{\Delta} & \dfrac{\Delta_{22}}{\Delta} \end{matrix}$	$\begin{matrix} z_{11} & z_{12} \\[4pt] z_{21} & z_{22} \end{matrix}$	$\begin{matrix} \dfrac{y_{22}}{\lvert y\rvert} & -\dfrac{y_{12}}{\lvert y\rvert} \\[4pt] -\dfrac{y_{21}}{\lvert y\rvert} & \dfrac{y_{11}}{\lvert y\rvert} \end{matrix}$	$\begin{matrix} \dfrac{1}{g_{11}} & -\dfrac{g_{12}}{g_{11}} \\[4pt] \dfrac{g_{21}}{g_{11}} & \dfrac{\lvert g\rvert}{g_{11}} \end{matrix}$	$\begin{matrix} \dfrac{\lvert h\rvert}{h_{22}} & \dfrac{h_{12}}{h_{22}} \\[4pt] -\dfrac{h_{21}}{h_{22}} & \dfrac{1}{h_{22}} \end{matrix}$	$\begin{matrix} \dfrac{A}{C} & \dfrac{1}{C} \\[4pt] \dfrac{1}{C} & \dfrac{D}{C} \end{matrix}$
y	$\begin{matrix} \dfrac{\Delta_{11}}{\Delta} & \dfrac{\Delta_{21}}{\Delta} \\[4pt] \dfrac{\Delta_{12}}{\Delta} & \dfrac{\Delta_{22}}{\Delta} \end{matrix}$	$\begin{matrix} \dfrac{\Delta_{22}}{\Delta_{1122}} & -\dfrac{\Delta_{21}}{\Delta_{1122}} \\[4pt] -\dfrac{\Delta_{12}}{\Delta_{1122}} & \dfrac{\Delta_{11}}{\Delta_{1122}} \end{matrix}$	$\begin{matrix} \dfrac{z_{22}}{\lvert z\rvert} & -\dfrac{z_{12}}{\lvert z\rvert} \\[4pt] -\dfrac{z_{21}}{\lvert z\rvert} & \dfrac{z_{11}}{\lvert z\rvert} \end{matrix}$	$\begin{matrix} y_{11} & y_{12} \\[4pt] y_{21} & y_{22} \end{matrix}$	$\begin{matrix} \dfrac{\lvert g\rvert}{g_{22}} & \dfrac{g_{12}}{g_{22}} \\[4pt] -\dfrac{g_{21}}{g_{22}} & \dfrac{1}{g_{22}} \end{matrix}$	$\begin{matrix} \dfrac{1}{h_{11}} & -\dfrac{h_{12}}{h_{11}} \\[4pt] \dfrac{h_{21}}{h_{11}} & \dfrac{\lvert h\rvert}{h_{11}} \end{matrix}$	$\begin{matrix} \dfrac{D}{B} & -\dfrac{1}{B} \\[4pt] -\dfrac{1}{B} & \dfrac{A}{B} \end{matrix}$
g	$\begin{matrix} \dfrac{\Delta_{1122}}{\Delta_{22}} & \dfrac{\Delta_{21}}{\Delta_{22}} \\[4pt] -\dfrac{\Delta_{12}}{\Delta_{22}} & \dfrac{\Delta}{\Delta_{22}} \end{matrix}$	$\begin{matrix} \dfrac{\Delta}{\Delta_{11}} & -\dfrac{\Delta_{21}}{\Delta_{11}} \\[4pt] \dfrac{\Delta_{12}}{\Delta_{11}} & \dfrac{\Delta_{1122}}{\Delta_{11}} \end{matrix}$	$\begin{matrix} \dfrac{1}{z_{11}} & -\dfrac{z_{12}}{z_{11}} \\[4pt] \dfrac{z_{21}}{z_{11}} & \dfrac{\lvert z\rvert}{z_{11}} \end{matrix}$	$\begin{matrix} \dfrac{\lvert y\rvert}{y_{22}} & \dfrac{y_{12}}{y_{22}} \\[4pt] -\dfrac{y_{21}}{y_{22}} & \dfrac{1}{y_{22}} \end{matrix}$	$\begin{matrix} g_{11} & g_{12} \\[4pt] g_{21} & g_{22} \end{matrix}$	$\begin{matrix} \dfrac{h_{22}}{\lvert h\rvert} & -\dfrac{h_{12}}{\lvert h\rvert} \\[4pt] -\dfrac{h_{21}}{\lvert h\rvert} & \dfrac{h_{11}}{\lvert h\rvert} \end{matrix}$	$\begin{matrix} \dfrac{C}{A} & -\dfrac{1}{A} \\[4pt] \dfrac{1}{A} & \dfrac{B}{A} \end{matrix}$
h	$\begin{matrix} \dfrac{\Delta}{\Delta_{11}} & -\dfrac{\Delta_{21}}{\Delta_{11}} \\[4pt] \dfrac{\Delta_{12}}{\Delta_{11}} & \dfrac{\Delta_{1122}}{\Delta_{11}} \end{matrix}$	$\begin{matrix} \dfrac{\Delta_{1122}}{\Delta_{22}} & \dfrac{\Delta_{21}}{\Delta_{22}} \\[4pt] -\dfrac{\Delta_{12}}{\Delta_{22}} & \dfrac{\Delta}{\Delta_{22}} \end{matrix}$	$\begin{matrix} \dfrac{\lvert z\rvert}{z_{22}} & \dfrac{z_{12}}{z_{22}} \\[4pt] -\dfrac{z_{21}}{z_{22}} & \dfrac{1}{z_{22}} \end{matrix}$	$\begin{matrix} \dfrac{1}{y_{11}} & -\dfrac{y_{12}}{y_{11}} \\[4pt] \dfrac{y_{21}}{y_{11}} & \dfrac{\lvert y\rvert}{y_{11}} \end{matrix}$	$\begin{matrix} \dfrac{g_{22}}{\lvert g\rvert} & -\dfrac{g_{12}}{\lvert g\rvert} \\[4pt] -\dfrac{g_{21}}{\lvert g\rvert} & \dfrac{g_{11}}{\lvert g\rvert} \end{matrix}$	$\begin{matrix} h_{11} & h_{12} \\[4pt] h_{21} & h_{22} \end{matrix}$	$\begin{matrix} \dfrac{B}{D} & \dfrac{1}{D} \\[4pt] -\dfrac{1}{D} & \dfrac{C}{D} \end{matrix}$
$A\ \ B$ $C\ \ D$	$\begin{matrix} -\dfrac{\Delta_{22}}{\Delta_{12}} & -\dfrac{\Delta}{\Delta_{12}} \\[4pt] -\dfrac{\Delta_{1122}}{\Delta_{12}} & -\dfrac{\Delta_{11}}{\Delta_{12}} \end{matrix}$	$\begin{matrix} \dfrac{\Delta_{11}}{\Delta_{12}} & \dfrac{\Delta_{1122}}{\Delta_{12}} \\[4pt] \dfrac{\Delta}{\Delta_{12}} & \dfrac{\Delta_{22}}{\Delta_{12}} \end{matrix}$	$\begin{matrix} \dfrac{z_{11}}{z_{21}} & \dfrac{\lvert z\rvert}{z_{21}} \\[4pt] \dfrac{1}{z_{21}} & \dfrac{z_{22}}{z_{21}} \end{matrix}$	$\begin{matrix} -\dfrac{y_{22}}{y_{21}} & -\dfrac{1}{y_{21}} \\[4pt] -\dfrac{\lvert y\rvert}{y_{21}} & -\dfrac{y_{11}}{y_{21}} \end{matrix}$	$\begin{matrix} \dfrac{1}{g_{21}} & \dfrac{g_{22}}{g_{21}} \\[4pt] \dfrac{g_{11}}{g_{21}} & \dfrac{\lvert g\rvert}{g_{21}} \end{matrix}$	$\begin{matrix} -\dfrac{\lvert h\rvert}{h_{21}} & -\dfrac{h_{11}}{h_{21}} \\[4pt] -\dfrac{h_{22}}{h_{21}} & -\dfrac{1}{h_{21}} \end{matrix}$	$\begin{matrix} A & B \\[4pt] C & D \end{matrix}$

Expressions for h_{12} and h_{22} can be determined in a similar manner; they are given in Table 1-2. The derivation is left to the student as an exercise.

The set of equations inverse to Eqs. 1.3-8 and 1.3-9 are found by solving these equations for I_1 and V_2 in terms of V_1 and I_2. The result is as follows:

$$I_1 = \left(\frac{h_{22}}{|h|}\right) V_1 - \left(\frac{h_{12}}{|h|}\right) I_2$$

$$V_2 = -\left(\frac{h_{21}}{|h|}\right) V_1 + \left(\frac{h_{11}}{|h|}\right) I_2$$

[1.3-14]

where

$$|h| = \begin{vmatrix} h_{11} & h_{12} \\ h_{21} & h_{22} \end{vmatrix}$$

[1.3-15]

Table 1-2 gives the interrelation between the various network parameters for reciprocal and nonreciprocal networks.

1.4 IMAGE AND CHARACTERISTIC IMPEDANCES

Consider an infinite number of identical unsymmetrical two-terminal pair networks connected in the special manner shown in Fig. 1-12, where each pair of terminals designated as 1 is connected to another pair of 1 terminals, and each pair of terminals designated as 2 is connected to another pair of 2 terminals. If the network cascade is cut at ab (in the figure), then the input impedance measured at the 1 terminals adjacent to ab is the same in either direction and is known as the *image impedance* Z_{I_1} measured at terminals 1. Similarly, the impedance measured at a cut, cd, is the same in either direction, and is known as the image impedance Z_{I_2} measured at terminals 2. In the case of a finite number of cascaded networks,

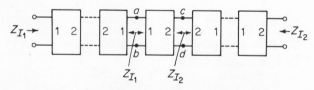

Figure 1-12 Infinite number of identical networks cascaded on an image basis.

the same impedances are measured at the terminals adjacent to the cuts ab and cd as in the infinite cascade, provided that the two sets of end terminals are terminated in the image impedances corresponding to the number of the end terminal, as indicated in Fig. 1-12.

For a single two-terminal pair network, the two image impedances Z_{I_1} and Z_{I_2} are the two values of impedance such that when the 1 terminals are terminated in Z_{I_1}, the input impedance at the 2 terminals is Z_{I_2}; and when the 2 terminals are terminated in Z_{I_2}, the input impedance at the 1 terminals is Z_{I_1}. In general, Z_{I_1} and Z_{I_2} are unequal. The image impedances for a single two-terminal pair network, N, are illustrated in Fig. 1-13.

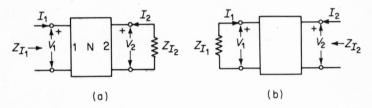

Figure 1-13   Networks terminated by image impedances.

The networks in Figs. 1-13(a) and 1-13(b) are said to be terminated on an image basis. Using the $ABCD$ equations (Eqs. 1.2-3) and referring to Fig. 1-13(a) we have

$$V_1 = AV_2 - BI_2$$
$$I_1 = CV_2 - DI_2$$

$$[1.4\text{-}1]$$

Since $V_2 = -I_2 Z_{I_2}$, Eqs. 1.4-1 can be written as

$$V_1 = -I_2(AZ_{I_2} + B)$$
$$I_1 = -I_2(CZ_{I_2} + D)$$

$$[1.4\text{-}2]$$

When the network is terminated in Z_{I_2}, its input impedance is Z_{I_1}. Hence

$$\frac{V_1}{I_1} = Z_{I_1} = \frac{AZ_{I_2} + B}{CZ_{I_2} + D}$$

$$[1.4\text{-}3]$$

When Eq. 1.2-9 is applied to the network shown in (b) of Fig. 1-13, the following results are obtained:

$$V_2 = DV_1 - BI_1$$
$$I_2 = CV_1 - AI_1$$

$$[1.4\text{-}4]$$

Since $V_1 = -I_1 Z_{I_1}$, Eqs. 1.4-4 become

$$V_2 = -I_1(DZ_{I_1} + B)$$
$$I_2 = -I_1(CZ_{I_1} + A)$$

$$[1.4\text{-}5]$$

Since $V_2/I_2 = Z_{I_2}$ it follows from Eqs. 1.4-5 that:

$$Z_{I_2} = \frac{DZ_{I_1} + B}{CZ_{I_1} + A} \qquad [1.4\text{-}6]$$

Equations 1.4-3 and 1.4-6 can now be written as follows:

$$CZ_{I_1}Z_{I_2} + DZ_{I_1} - AZ_{I_2} - B = 0 \qquad [1.4\text{-}7]$$

$$CZ_{I_1}Z_{I_2} - DZ_{I_1} + AZ_{I_2} - B = 0 \qquad [1.4\text{-}8]$$

Addition and subtraction of Eqs. 1.4-7 and 1.4-8 yield

$$Z_{I_1}Z_{I_2} = \frac{B}{C} \qquad [1.4\text{-}9]$$

$$\frac{Z_{I_1}}{Z_{I_2}} = \frac{A}{D} \qquad [1.4\text{-}10]$$

Multiplication and division of Eqs. 1.4-9 and 1.4-10 give the following results:

$$Z_{I_1} = \sqrt{\frac{AB}{CD}} \qquad [1.4\text{-}11]$$

$$Z_{I_2} = \sqrt{\frac{DB}{AC}} \qquad [1.4\text{-}12]$$

If the network is symmetrical, $A = D$, and $Z_{I_1} = Z_{I_2}$. In the case of a symmetrical network

$$Z_{I_1} = Z_{I_2} = Z_0 = \sqrt{\frac{B}{C}} \qquad [1.4\text{-}13]$$

where Z_0 is termed the *characteristic impedance* of a symmetrical network.

Equations 1.4-11, 1.4-12, and 1.4-13 can be expressed in terms of the two-terminal pair impedances and admittances by the use of Eqs. 1.2-4 through 1.2-7. When expressed in these terms, the impedances are:

$$Z_{I_1} = \sqrt{\frac{AB}{CD}} = \sqrt{\frac{(z_{11}/z_{12})(|z|/z_{12})}{(1/z_{12})(z_{22}/z_{12})}} = \sqrt{\left(\frac{z_{11}}{z_{22}}\right)|z|} = \sqrt{\frac{z_{11}}{y_{11}}} \qquad [1.4\text{-}14]$$

$$Z_{I_2} = \sqrt{\frac{DB}{AC}} = \sqrt{\frac{(z_{22}/z_{12})(|z|/z_{12})}{(z_{11}/z_{12})(1/z_{12})}} = \sqrt{\left(\frac{z_{22}}{z_{11}}\right)|z|} = \sqrt{\frac{z_{22}}{y_{22}}} \qquad [1.4\text{-}15]$$

where $|z| = z_{11}z_{22} - z_{12}^2$ in the case of a reciprocal network. Since z_{11} is the input open-circuit impedance, and since y_{11} is the input short-circuit admittance, the image impedance at the 1 terminals can be expressed as

$$Z_{I_1} = \sqrt{Z_{oc_1} Z_{sc_1}} \qquad [1.4\text{-}16]$$

where $Z_{oc_1} = z_{11}$ is the input impedance measured at the 1 terminals with the 2 terminals open-circuited, and $Z_{sc_1} = 1/y_{11}$ is the input impedance when these two terminals are short-circuited. It can be shown in a similar manner that

$$Z_{I_2} = \sqrt{Z_{oc_2} Z_{sc_2}} \qquad [1.4\text{-}17]$$

If the network is symmetrical, $A = D$, $z_{11} = z_{22}$, and

$$Z_{I_1} = Z_{I_2} = Z_0 = \sqrt{\frac{B}{C}} = \sqrt{\frac{|z|/z_{12}}{1/z_{12}}} = \sqrt{|z|} = \sqrt{\frac{z_{11}}{y_{11}}} \qquad [1.4\text{-}18]$$

where Z_0 is the characteristic impedance of the network and

$$|z| = z_{11}^2 - z_{12}^2 = (z_{11} + z_{12})(z_{11} - z_{12})$$

for the special case of a symmetrical network. It follows directly from Eqs. 1.4-16 and 1.4-17 that, for a symmetrical network,

$$Z_0 = \sqrt{Z_{oc} Z_{sc}} \qquad [1.4\text{-}19]$$

where the open-circuit and short-circuit impedances may be measured at either set of terminals.

The characteristic admittance of a symmetrical network is given by

$$Y_0 = \frac{1}{Z_0} = \sqrt{\frac{C}{B}} = \sqrt{|y|} = \sqrt{\frac{y_{11}}{z_{11}}} = \sqrt{Y_{oc} Y_{sc}} \qquad [1.4\text{-}20]$$

where $|y| = y_{11}^2 - y_{12}^2 = (y_{11} + y_{12})(y_{11} - y_{12})$.

Networks can also be connected on an iterative basis as shown in Fig.

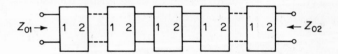

Figure 1-14 Infinite number of identical networks cascaded on an iterative basis.

1-14, where the pair of terminals 2 of one network is connected to the pair of terminals 1 of the following network. The infinite cascade shown in Fig. 1-14 is characterized by two impedances, Z_{01} and Z_{02}, depending upon the terminals at which the impedance is measured. It can be shown, in a manner similar to that used in deriving Eqs. 1.4-11 and 1.4-12, that

$$Z_{01} = \frac{(A - D) + \sqrt{(A + D)^2 - 4}}{2C} \qquad [1.4\text{-}21]$$

$$Z_{02} = \frac{(D - A) + \sqrt{(A + D)^2 - 4}}{2C} \qquad [1.4\text{-}22]$$

When the network is symmetrical, $A = D$, and with the aid of Eqs. 1.2-8, the expressions for Z_{01} and Z_{02} reduce to

$$Z_{01} = Z_{02} = \frac{\sqrt{A^2 - 1}}{C} = \frac{\sqrt{BC}}{C} = \sqrt{\frac{B}{C}} = Z_0 \qquad [1.4\text{-}23]$$

The iterative connection is not commonly used and will not be further considered in this text. The important point to be stressed is that a general two-terminal pair network is characterized by several impedances: two image impedances and two iterative impedances. In the case of symmetrical networks, all these impedances become identical and reduce to a single impedance, Z_0, commonly known as the characteristic impedance of a symmetrical network. This definition of characteristic impedance is entirely consistent with the definition of characteristic impedance as that impedance in which a network must be terminated so that the input and terminating impedances are identical. A network is not completely described by these impedances; the propagation function from input to output must also be specified. This feature is discussed in Section 1.5.

1.5 IMAGE PROPAGATION FUNCTIONS

The transmission characteristics of general two-terminal pair networks will now be considered. It will be assumed that these networks are cascaded as shown in Fig. 1-12, or terminated by their image impedances as shown in (a) of Fig. 1-13. Using Fig. 1-13(a), the ratio of current or voltage between the input terminals and the output terminals will be determined.

It is seen from Fig. 1-13 that

$$V_2 = -I_2 Z_{I_2}$$
$$I_2 = -\frac{V_2}{Z_{I_2}} \qquad [1.5\text{-}1]$$

If we substitute I_2 from Eqs. 1.5-1 into the first of Eqs. 1.2-3, we have

$$V_1 = AV_2 + B\left(\frac{V_2}{Z_{I_2}}\right)$$

$$\frac{V_1}{V_2} = A + \frac{B}{Z_{I_2}} \qquad [1.5\text{-}2]$$

Equations 1.5-2 give the ratio of the voltages at the input and output terminals of the network. Likewise, substituting for V_2 from Eqs. 1.5-1 into the second of Eqs. 1.2-3, we have

$$I_1 = -CZ_{I_2}I_2 - DI_2$$

$$\frac{I_1}{-I_2} = CZ_{I_2} + D \qquad [1.5\text{-}3]$$

Equations 1.5-3 give the ratio of the currents at the input and output terminals of the network.

The voltage and current ratios given by Eqs. 1.5-2 and 1.5-3 can be expressed in terms of the $ABCD$ coefficients by substituting for Z_{I_2} from Eq. 1.4-12 into Eqs. 1.5-2 and 1.5-3. This gives the following result:

$$\frac{V_1}{V_2} = A + B\sqrt{AC/BD} = \sqrt{A/D}\,(\sqrt{AD} + \sqrt{BC}) \qquad [1.5\text{-}4]$$

$$\frac{I_1}{-I_2} = C\sqrt{BD/AC} + D = \sqrt{D/A}\,(\sqrt{AD} + \sqrt{BC}) \qquad [1.5\text{-}5]$$

When the network is symmetrical, $A = D$, $BC = A^2 - 1$, and Eqs. 1.5-4 and 1.5-5 become

$$\frac{V_1}{V_2} = -\frac{I_1}{I_2} = \epsilon^\gamma = A + \sqrt{A^2 - 1} \qquad [1.5\text{-}6]$$

where

$$\gamma = \alpha + j\beta \qquad [1.5\text{-}7]$$

is defined as the *propagation function* of a symmetrical network. The real part, α, measures the change in magnitude of the voltage or current, and the imaginary part, β, measures the change in phase caused by the network. The real part of γ is termed the *attenuation function*, and the imaginary part is termed the *phase function*. When the network contains resistance, α is positive. Expression of the voltage and current ratios in exponential form is useful in determining the net response of several networks connected in cascade. Consider $n - 1$ networks with propagation functions, $\gamma_1, \gamma_2, \ldots \gamma_{n-1}$, connected in cascade. Since the output voltage of any intermediate network is the input voltage to the following network, it follows from Eq. 1.5-6 that the ratio between the voltage input to the first network and the voltage output of the last network is given by

$$\frac{V_1}{V_n} = \epsilon^{(\gamma_1 + \gamma_2 + \dots + \gamma_{n-1})} = \epsilon^{\gamma} \qquad [1.5\text{-}8]$$

Equation 1.5-8 shows that the propagation function of a cascade of a number of networks is the sum of the individual propagation functions. This is a very useful relation, and results from the exponential expression for the voltage ratios.

It follows from Eq. 1.5-6 that

$$\epsilon^{\gamma} = A + \sqrt{A^2 - 1} \qquad [1.5\text{-}9]$$

Also,

$$\epsilon^{-\gamma} = \frac{1}{A + \sqrt{A^2 - 1}} = \left(\frac{1}{A + \sqrt{A^2 - 1}}\right)\left(\frac{A - \sqrt{A^2 - 1}}{A - \sqrt{A^2 - 1}}\right)$$

$$= A - \sqrt{A^2 - 1} \qquad [1.5\text{-}10]$$

The hyperbolic cosine, $\cosh \gamma$, is defined as

$$\cosh \gamma = \frac{\epsilon^{\gamma} + \epsilon^{-\gamma}}{2} \qquad [1.5\text{-}11]$$

It follows from Eqs. 1.5-9, 1.5-10, 1.5-11, and 1.2-4 that the propagation function of a symmetrical network is given by

$$\cosh \gamma = A = \frac{z_{11}}{z_{12}} = -\frac{y_{22}}{y_{12}} \qquad [1.5\text{-}12]$$

Hence,

$$\gamma = \cosh^{-1} A \qquad [1.5\text{-}13]$$

where $\cosh^{-1} A$ denotes the inverse hyperbolic cosine.

A summary of hyperbolic functions is given in Appendix B. From Eqs. B-37, B-38, and B-39 in Appendix B, it follows that:

$$\sinh \frac{\gamma}{2} = \sqrt{\frac{A - 1}{2}} \qquad [1.5\text{-}14]$$

$$\cosh \frac{\gamma}{2} = \sqrt{\frac{A + 1}{2}} \qquad [1.5\text{-}15]$$

$$\tanh \frac{\gamma}{2} = \sqrt{\frac{A - 1}{A + 1}} \qquad [1.5\text{-}16]$$

where $A = \cosh \gamma$. Since, in a symmetrical network, $A = z_{11}/z_{12} = -y_{11}/y_{12}$ (Eq. 1.2-4), Eq. 1.5-16 can also be written as

$$\tanh \frac{\gamma}{2} = \sqrt{\frac{z_{11} - z_{12}}{z_{11} + z_{12}}} = \sqrt{\frac{y_{11} + y_{12}}{y_{11} - y_{12}}} \qquad [1.5\text{-}17]$$

It follows from Eq. B-14 of Appendix B that γ in Eq. 1.5-13 can be expressed as

$$\gamma = \ln \left[A + \sqrt{A^2 - 1} \right] \qquad [1.5\text{-}18]$$

Equation 1.5-18 can also be written as

$$\gamma = \ln \left[(A + \sqrt{A + 1} \sqrt{A - 1}) \left(\frac{\sqrt{A + 1} - \sqrt{A - 1}}{\sqrt{A + 1} - \sqrt{A - 1}} \right) \right]$$

$$= \ln \left[\frac{\sqrt{A + 1} + \sqrt{A - 1}}{\sqrt{A + 1} - \sqrt{A - 1}} \right] \qquad [1.5\text{-}19]$$

Since $A = z_{11}/z_{12}$ in symmetrical networks, Eq. 1.5-19 can be expressed as

$$\gamma = \ln \left(\frac{1 + \sqrt{(A - 1)/(A + 1)}}{1 - \sqrt{(A - 1)/(A + 1)}} \right)$$

$$= \ln \left(\frac{1 + \sqrt{(z_{11} - z_{12})/(z_{11} + z_{12})}}{1 - \sqrt{(z_{11} - z_{12})/(z_{11} + z_{12})}} \right) \qquad [1.5\text{-}20]$$

For unsymmetrical networks terminated in their image impedances, the image propagation function, θ, is defined in terms of the volt-ampere ratio as follows:

$$\frac{V_1 I_1}{-V_2 I_2} = \epsilon^{2\theta} \qquad [1.5\text{-}21]$$

where θ is in general complex, and is usually a function of the frequency. The real part of θ denotes a change in amplitude, and the imaginary part denotes a change in phase. Equation 1.5-21 can be expressed as

$$\frac{V_1^2/Z_{I_1}}{V_2^2/Z_{I_2}} = \frac{I_1^2/Z_{I_1}}{I_2^2/Z_{I_2}} = \epsilon^{2\theta} \qquad [1.5\text{-}22]$$

where Z_{I_1} and Z_{I_2} are the image impedances. It follows from Eq. 1.5-22 that:

$$\frac{V_1}{V_2} \sqrt{\frac{Z_{I_2}}{Z_{I_1}}} = \epsilon^{\theta} \qquad [1.5\text{-}23]$$

and

$$\frac{I_1}{I_2}\sqrt{\frac{Z_{I_1}}{Z_{I_2}}} = \epsilon^\theta \qquad [1.5\text{-}24]$$

Inspection of Eqs. 1.5-23 and 1.5-24 shows that the voltage and current ratios are equal only when $Z_{I_1} = Z_{I_2}$ as in symmetrical networks.

It follows from Eq. 1.5-21 that:

$$\epsilon^\theta = \sqrt{\frac{V_1 I_1}{-V_2 I_2}} \qquad [1.5\text{-}25]$$

The voltage and current ratios in Eq. 1.5-25 are given in Eqs. 1.5-4 and 1.5-5. Substitution of Eqs. 1.5-4 and 1.5-5 into Eq. 1.5-25 yields

$$\epsilon^\theta = \sqrt{\left[\sqrt{\frac{A}{D}}\left(\sqrt{AD}+\sqrt{BC}\right)\right]\left[\sqrt{\frac{D}{A}}\left(\sqrt{AD}+\sqrt{BC}\right)\right]}$$
$$\epsilon^\theta = \sqrt{AD}+\sqrt{BC} \qquad [1.5\text{-}26]$$

It follows from Eq. 1.5-26 that

$$\epsilon^{-\theta} = \frac{1}{\sqrt{AD}+\sqrt{BC}} \qquad [1.5\text{-}27]$$

Multiplying the numerator and denominator of the right side of Eq. 1.5-27 by $\sqrt{AD} - \sqrt{BC}$, and making use of the relation $AD - BC = 1$ (Eq. 1.2-8), yields

$$\epsilon^{-\theta} = \frac{\sqrt{AD}-\sqrt{BC}}{AD-BC} = \sqrt{AD}-\sqrt{BC} \qquad [1.5\text{-}28]$$

Division of Eq. 1.5-26 by Eq. 1.5-28 gives the following result:

$$\frac{\epsilon^\theta}{\epsilon^{-\theta}} = \epsilon^{2\theta} = \frac{\sqrt{AD}+\sqrt{BC}}{\sqrt{AD}-\sqrt{BC}} \qquad [1.5\text{-}29]$$

Hence,

$$\theta = \frac{1}{2}\ln\left[\frac{\sqrt{AD}+\sqrt{BC}}{\sqrt{AD}-\sqrt{BC}}\right] \qquad [1.5\text{-}30]$$

It follows from Eqs. 1.5-26 and 1.5-28 that

$$\frac{\epsilon^\theta + \epsilon^{-\theta}}{2} = \cosh\theta = \sqrt{AD} \qquad\qquad [1.5\text{-}31]$$

$$\frac{\epsilon^\theta - \epsilon^{-\theta}}{2} = \sinh\theta = \sqrt{BC} \qquad\qquad [1.5\text{-}32]$$

When $A = D$, Eq. 1.5-31 reduces to Eq. 1.5-12 that was derived for symmetrical networks.

1.6 SPECIAL NETWORKS

A point should be made here in regard to certain definitions used in connection with networks. We have already stated that a network is symmetrical if z_{11} equals z_{22} or if A equals D. This statement means that impedances at the input and output terminals are equal. A network may also be classified as being *balanced* or *unbalanced*. An unbalanced symmetrical network is shown in (a) of Fig. 1-15, where the impedance between one input terminal and one output terminal is zero, while the impedance between the other (top) input terminal and output terminal is Z_1. This is a completely unbalanced network; and when an unbalanced network is specified, it means that there is zero impedance between one input terminal and one output terminal, and that these terminals are usually at ground potential. A balanced symmetrical network is shown in (b) of Fig. 1-15. Here the impedance is divided equally between the upper and the lower terminals.

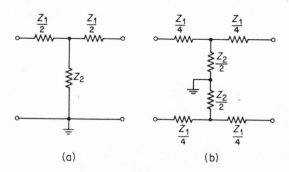

(a)   (b)

Figure 1-15   Symmetrical networks. (a) T network (unbalanced). (b) H network (balanced).

The characteristic impedance and the propagation function are the same for both networks in Fig. 1-15. There is an infinite number of networks that lie between the two cases shown in the figure, but these intermediate networks will not be considered as they have little practical use as transmission networks. As used in this text, an unbalanced network is completely unbalanced.

The formulas developed in Sections 1.1 through 1.5 show that the characteristic impedance and the propagation function of a network can be expressed in terms of various circuit parameters. The physical definitions of those quantities are given in Table 1-2.

Consider now the symmetrical T network shown in Fig. 1-15. It can be seen by inspection that $z_{11} = (Z_1/2 + Z_2)$, and that $z_{12} = Z_2$. It follows from Eq. 1.4-18 that:

$$Z_{0T} = \sqrt{|z|} = \sqrt{(z_{11} + z_{12})(z_{11} - z_{12})}$$
$$= \sqrt{Z_1 Z_2 + Z_1^2/4} = \sqrt{Z_1 Z_2}\sqrt{1 + Z_1/4Z_2} \qquad [1.6\text{-}1]$$

where Z_{0T} is the characteristic impedance of the symmetrical T network. The propagation function is given by Eq. 1.5-12 as

$$\cosh \gamma = \frac{z_{11}}{z_{12}} = 1 + \frac{Z_1}{2Z_2} \qquad [1.6\text{-}2]$$

It follows from B-45 of Appendix B that:

$$\gamma = 2 \ln \left(\sqrt{\frac{z_{11} + z_{12}}{2z_{12}}} + \sqrt{\frac{z_{11} - z_{12}}{2z_{12}}} \right) \qquad [1.6\text{-}3]$$
$$= 2 \ln \left(\sqrt{1 + Z_1/4Z_2} + \sqrt{Z_1/4Z_2} \right)$$

Equation 1.6-3 can also be derived by adding Eqs. 1.5-14 and 1.5-15.

It is interesting to note that if the symmetrical network in Fig. 1-15(a) is "bisected", or divided into two identical half-sections, as shown in Fig. 1-16, the characteristic impedance is given by the square root of the open-circuited

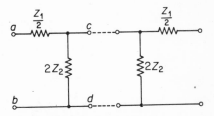

Figure 1-16 Bisected T network.

and short-circuited impedances of the bisected section. Thus,

$$Z_{0T} = \sqrt{\left(\frac{Z_1}{2} + 2Z_2 \right) Z_1/2} = \sqrt{Z_1 Z_2 + Z_1^2/4}$$
$$= \sqrt{Z_1 Z_2}\sqrt{1 + Z_1/4Z_2} = \sqrt{Z_{och} Z_{sch}} \qquad [1.6\text{-}4]$$

Referring to the left-hand part of Fig. 1-16, Z_{och} and Z_{sch} are the impedances of the half-section measured at ab with the output terminals,

cd, of the bisected section open-circuited and short-circuited respectively. The theory of bisection will be more fully developed in Section 1.7 where the bisection theorem is derived.

A symmetrical π section is shown in Fig. 1-17(a). Inasmuch as this network has three meshes and two nodes, the Y determinant resulting from

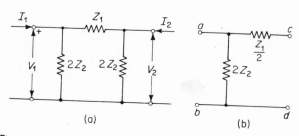

Figure 1-17 (a) Symmetrical π network. (b) Bisected π network.

the node voltage equations will be used. It can be seen by inspection that $y_{11} = 1/Z_1 + 1/2Z_2$, and that $y_{12} = 1/Z_1$. The characteristic admittance is found from Eq. 1.4-20 to be

$$Y_{0\pi} = \sqrt{|y|} = \sqrt{(y_{11} + y_{12})(y_{11} - y_{12})} = \sqrt{\frac{1}{2Z_2}\left(\frac{2}{Z_1} + \frac{1}{2Z_2}\right)}$$

and

$$Z_{0\pi} = \frac{1}{Y_{0\pi}} = \frac{1}{\sqrt{\frac{1}{2Z_2}\left(\frac{2}{Z_1} + \frac{1}{2Z_2}\right)}} = \frac{1}{\sqrt{\frac{1}{Z_1 Z_2} + \frac{1}{4Z_2^2}}}$$

$$= \frac{\sqrt{Z_1 Z_2}}{\sqrt{1 + \frac{Z_1}{4Z_2}}} = \frac{Z_1 Z_2}{\sqrt{Z_1 Z_2}\sqrt{1 + \frac{Z_1}{4Z_2}}} \qquad [1.6\text{-}5]$$

Comparison of Eqs. 1.6-4 and 1.6-5 shows that

$$Z_{0\pi} = \frac{Z_1 Z_2}{Z_{0T}} \qquad [1.6\text{-}6]$$

Equation 1.6-6 can also be derived by the application of Eq. 1.6-4, which assumes the validity of the bisection theorem. Figure 1.17(b) shows a bisected π section. It can be seen that the open-circuit impedance of the half-section at terminals ab is $2Z_2$ and the short-circuit impedance is

$\dfrac{Z_1 Z_2}{\dfrac{Z_1}{2} + 2Z_2}$. It follows from Eq. 1.6-4 that

$$Z_{0\pi} = \sqrt{Z_{och} Z_{sch}} = \sqrt{\dfrac{Z_1 Z_2}{Z_1/4Z_2 + 1}} = \dfrac{Z_1 Z_2}{Z_{0T}} \qquad [1.6\text{-}7]$$

An infinite cascade of bisected π sections is shown in Fig. 1-18. Inspection of Fig. 1-18 shows that $Z_{0\pi}$ and Z_{0T} are the image impedances measured respectively at terminals 1,1′ and 2,2′ of the bisected section. Reference to Eqs. 1.4-16 and 1.4-17 shows that Z_{0T} and $Z_{0\pi}$ have been determined in Eqs. 1.6-4 and 1.6-7 as the image impedances of the bisected section. It is for this reason that the open and short circuited impedances of the bisected section may be used to determine the characteristic impedances. The image impedances can also be calculated from the y and z parameters.

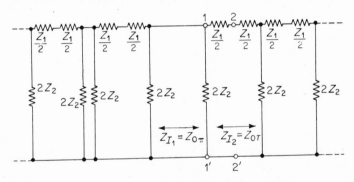

Figure 1-18   Infinite cascade of bisected π sections.

The image impedance at terminals 1,1′ of the half-section in Fig. 1-18 is

$$Z_{I_1} = \sqrt{\dfrac{z_{11}}{y_{11}}} = \sqrt{\dfrac{2Z_2}{\dfrac{Z_1/2 + 2Z_2}{Z_1 Z_2}}} = \sqrt{\dfrac{2Z_1 Z_2^2}{Z_1/2 + 2Z_2}} \qquad [1.6\text{-}8]$$

$$Z_{I_1} = \dfrac{Z_1 Z_2}{\sqrt{Z_1 Z_2 + Z_1^2/4}} = \dfrac{Z_1 Z_2}{Z_{0T}} = Z_{0\pi}$$

The image impedance at 2,2′ is given by

$$Z_{I_2} = \sqrt{z_{22}/y_{22}} = \sqrt{\dfrac{Z_1}{2}\left(Z_1/2 + 2Z_2\right)}$$

$$= \sqrt{Z_1 Z_2 + Z_1^2/4} = Z_{0T} \qquad [1.6\text{-}9]$$

A network of considerable importance is the lattice structure shown in Fig. 1-19. This is essentially a special case of a bridge where the opposite arms are of the same type, as is shown in (a) of Fig. 1-19. Z_a in Fig. 1-19 is called the series arm, and Z_b is known as the diagonal arm. In the case

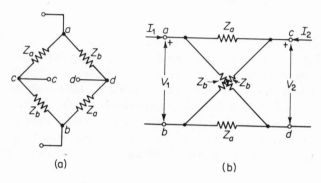

(a)   (b)

Figure 1-19 Lattice network.

of a lattice, the impedances z_{11} and z_{12} may not be immediately obvious. Reference to Table 1-1 shows that z_{11} is the input impedance with the output terminals open-circuited, and z_{12} is the ratio of output voltage to input current under the same condition. Inspection of Fig. 1-19 shows that $z_{11} = (Z_a + Z_b)/2$. This follows from the fact that two equal paths of impedance $(Z_a + Z_b)$ are present. If a current, I_1, is introduced at a, one half, or $I_1/2$, will flow through acb, and the other half through adb. The voltage, $V_{cd} = V_2$, is given by the following equation:

$$\left(\frac{I_1}{2}\right) Z_a + V_{cd} - \left(\frac{I_1}{2}\right) Z_b = 0$$

Hence

$$V_{cd} = V_2 = \frac{I_1 (Z_b - Z_a)}{2}$$

and

$$z_{12} = \frac{V_2}{I_1} = \frac{Z_b - Z_a}{2}$$

It follows that $z_{11} + z_{12} = Z_b$, and that $z_{11} - z_{12} = Z_a$. Hence

$$Z_{0L} = \sqrt{Z_a Z_b} \qquad [1.6\text{-}10]$$

where Z_{0L} is the characteristic impedance of the lattice. The propagation function is found in a convenient form from Eq. 1.5-20 to be

$$\gamma = \ln\left(\frac{1 + \sqrt{\dfrac{z_{11} - z_{12}}{z_{11} + z_{12}}}}{1 - \sqrt{\dfrac{z_{11} - z_{12}}{z_{11} + z_{12}}}}\right) = \ln\left(\frac{1 + \sqrt{Z_a/Z_b}}{1 - \sqrt{Z_a/Z_b}}\right) \qquad [1.6\text{-}11]$$

Since $Z_{0L} = \sqrt{Z_a Z_b}$

$$\gamma = \ln \left(\frac{1 + Z_a/Z_{0L}}{1 - Z_a/Z_{0L}} \right) \qquad [1.6\text{-}12]$$

It also follows from Eq. 1.5-17 that

$$\tanh \frac{\gamma}{2} = \sqrt{\frac{z_{11} - z_{12}}{z_{11} + z_{12}}} = \sqrt{\frac{Z_a}{Z_b}} = \frac{Z_{0L}}{Z_b} = \frac{Z_a}{Z_{0L}} \qquad [1.6\text{-}13]$$

Hence

$$Z_a = Z_{0L} \tanh \frac{\gamma}{2} \qquad [1.6\text{-}14]$$

$$Z_b = Z_{0L} \coth \frac{\gamma}{2} \qquad [1.6\text{-}15]$$

1.7 THE BISECTION THEOREM*

The bisection theorem is useful in determining equivalent networks and for the calculation of the characteristic impedance of symmetrical networks. This theorem states that networks having mirror-image symmetry can be reduced to an equivalent lattice structure. The series arm of the equivalent lattice is found by cutting or "bisecting" the given network into two parts, short-circuiting all the cut wires, and equating the series impedance of the lattice to the input impedance of the bisected network when the cut wires are short-circuited; the diagonal arm is equal to the input impedance to the bisected section formed by open-circuiting the cut wires.

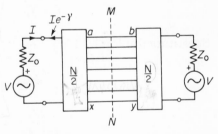

Figure 1-20 Network to illustrate bisection theorem.

For proof of this theorem, consider the symmetrical network shown in Fig. 1-20. The horizontal lines, ab-xy, represent the wires which are cut when the network is bisected. When this network is terminated by its characteristic impedance with the generator on the right-hand side short-circuited, the input current is

---

* This theorem is discussed in: (a), *Theory of Artificial Lines and Filters*, by A. C. Bartlett (John Wiley & Sons, Inc., New York, 1930), page 28; and (b), "Note on Bartlett's Bisection Theorem," by O. Brune (*Philosophical Magazine and Journal of Science*, Section 7, Volume 14, 1932), page 806.

$$I = \frac{V}{2Z_0} \qquad [1.7\text{-}1]$$

An open circuit along the line of bisection, MN, can be simulated electrically by introducing an opposing generator of voltage V, with the polarity shown, on the right-hand side of Fig. 1-20. Because of symmetry, the introduction of this voltage will cause equal and opposite currents in the connecting wires, $ab\text{-}xy$, and the conditions of open-circuit input impedance, Z_{och}, will prevail. The current flowing into the network can be calculated by means of the superposition theorem. If the current flowing into the left-hand terminals and delivered by the left-hand generator is I, the current delivered by the right-hand generator will be $I\epsilon^{-\gamma}$, where γ is the propagation function of the symmetrical network terminated by its characteristic impedance.

Since this corresponds to an open-circuited bisected network,

$$\frac{V}{I - I\epsilon^{-\gamma}} = Z_0 + Z_{och} \qquad [1.7\text{-}2]$$

The short-circuited condition can be simulated by reversing the polarity of the right-hand generator. This causes the voltages between the cut wires to vanish. Under this condition, the following relation holds:

$$\frac{V}{I + I\epsilon^{-\gamma}} = Z_0 + Z_{sch} \qquad [1.7\text{-}3]$$

Substitution of Eq. 1.7-1 into Eqs. 1.7-2 and 1.7-3 yields

$$\frac{2Z_0}{1 - \epsilon^{-\gamma}} = Z_0 + Z_{och} \qquad [1.7\text{-}4]$$

$$\frac{2Z_0}{1 + \epsilon^{-\gamma}} = Z_0 + Z_{sch} \qquad [1.7\text{-}5]$$

$$Z_{sch} = \frac{2Z_0}{1 + \epsilon^{-\gamma}} - Z_0 = Z_0 \left(\frac{1 - \epsilon^{-\gamma}}{1 + \epsilon^{-\gamma}}\right)$$

$$Z_{sch} = Z_0 \left(\frac{\epsilon^{\gamma/2} - \epsilon^{-\gamma/2}}{\epsilon^{\gamma/2} + \epsilon^{-\gamma/2}}\right) = Z_0 \tanh \frac{\gamma}{2} \qquad [1.7\text{-}6]$$

$$Z_{och} = \frac{2Z_0}{1 - \epsilon^{-\gamma}} - Z_0 = Z_0 \left(\frac{1 + \epsilon^{-\gamma}}{1 - \epsilon^{-\gamma}}\right) = Z_0 \coth \frac{\gamma}{2} \qquad [1.7\text{-}7]$$

Comparison of Eq. 1.6-14 with 1.7-6, and of Eq. 1.6-15 with 1.7-7, shows that the series arm of the equivalent lattice is the short-circuited input impedance of the bisected network, and the diagonal arm is the open-circuited impedance. The propagation function of the entire network is given by Eqs. 1.6-11 and 1.6-12.

The utility of this theorem is derived from the basic theorem that things equal to the same thing are equal to each other. It follows that bisected networks having the same open-circuited and short-circuited input impedances are equivalent. Furthermore, the square root of the product of these impedances is the characteristic impedance of the whole network, as shown by Eq. 1.6-10. It should be noted that although the lattice network plays such an important part in the theory of network bisection, it cannot be bisected in the Bartlett sense. This is because the lattice structure makes it impossible to cancel all the currents in the electrically bisected network. It should always be remembered that geometrical bisection is not sufficient for the application of Bartlett's bisection theorem. The necessary condition is that it should be possible to make the currents through and the voltages between the connecting wires zero by the introduction of a voltage generator as described in the derivation of the theorem.

The lattice is the general type of symmetrical network, and any symmetrical balanced or unbalanced network can be transformed into an equivalent lattice, but the inverse of the statement is not true. The lattice, in addition to being symmetrical, is also a balanced network, and many applications require an unbalanced network structure.

It follows directly from the bisection theorem that any symmetrical two-terminal pair network that can be bisected in the sense considered in the derivation of the theorem can be transformed into a lattice that is equivalent at all frequencies. Illustrations of this transformation for T, π, and bridged-T networks, and for a transformer, are shown in Figs. 1-21 through 1-24. The series arm, Z_a, of the lattice is equal to the short-

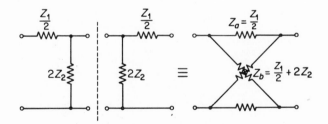

Figure 1-21   Transformation of T network into lattice.

circuited input impedance of the bisected network, and the diagonal arm, Z_b, is the open-circuited impedance of the bisected network. A similar relation holds for the admittances.

The conversion of the lattice to unbalanced networks is usually more

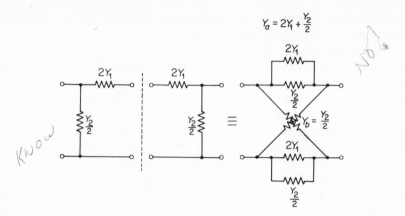

Figure 1-22 Transformation of π network into lattice.

difficult and not always possible if a realizable network is to be attained. The conversion from a lattice into equivalent T and π networks is shown in Figs. 1-25 and 1-26. The transformation is always possible when all the elements of the given lattice are of the same kind (all resistors, all inductors, etc.); otherwise the transformation may not be physically realizable because of the need for negative resistance, etc.

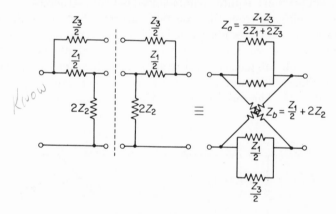

Figure 1-23 Transformation of bridged-T network into lattice.

The quantity $Z_b - Z_a$, or $Y_a - Y_b$, can sometimes be made positive by interchanging the Z_a and Z_b arms in the lattice. This does not change the value of the characteristic impedance or the magnitude of the propagation function, but produces a change in phase of π radians. This statement can be proved by referring to Eq. 1.6-11 where the propagation function can be expressed as

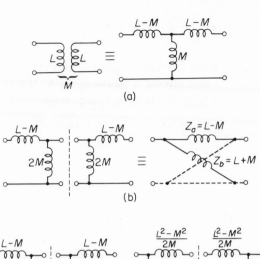

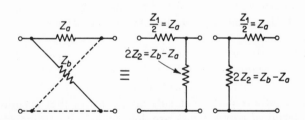

Figure 1-24 Equivalent circuits for lossless transformer with unity turns ratio. (a) Equivalent T network. (b) Conversion of T network into lattice. (c) Conversion of T network into π network.

Figure 1-25 Conversion of lattice network into T network.

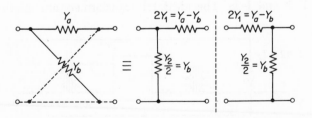

Figure 1-26 Conversion of lattice network into π network.

$$\gamma = \ln\left(\frac{1+x}{1-x}\right) = \ln\left(|r|\epsilon^{j\theta}\right) = \ln|r| + j\theta \qquad [1.7\text{-}8]$$

where $x = \sqrt{Z_a/Z_b}$ and γ may be a complex number having an absolute value denoted by $|r|$, and having a phase angle, θ. When Z_a and Z_b are interchanged, the propagation function, γ', is given by

$$\gamma' = \ln\left(\frac{1+1/x}{1-1/x}\right) = \ln\left(\frac{x+1}{x-1}\right) = \ln\left(-|r|\epsilon^{j\theta}\right) \qquad [1.7\text{-}9]$$

Since

$$\epsilon^{\pm j\pi} = \cos\pi \pm j\sin\pi = -1 \qquad [1.7\text{-}10]$$

It follows that

$$\gamma' = \ln\left(|r|\,\epsilon^{j(\theta\pm\pi)}\right) = \ln|r| + j(\theta\pm\pi) \qquad [1.7\text{-}11]$$

1.8 A GENERAL METHOD FOR DETERMINING NETWORK EQUIVALENCE

It has been shown that Bartlett's bisection principle is an efficient method for determining the equivalence of symmetrical networks that can be bisected in the Bartlett sense. Unfortunately, not all networks, even though symmetrical, can be bisected in this manner. The lattice structure has been mentioned as a network that cannot be bisected. In general, networks having cross-over elements like Z_b in the lattice structure of Fig. 1-19 cannot be bisected. A more general method for determining network equivalence will be established in this section. The chief advantage of this method is that it is applicable to symmetrical networks having cross-over elements.

Referring to the lattice network of Fig. 1-19, it is clear that when a is connected to c, and b is connected to d, the input impedance at terminals, ab, is $Z_b/2$. Also, when a is connected to d, and b to c, the input impedance is $Z_a/2$. It follows that the elements of the lattice that is equivalent to a given two-terminal pair network are determined by two impedance measurements made when corresponding and diagonal input and output terminals of the network are connected. The connections for these impedance measurements on a symmetrical two-terminal pair network, N, are shown in Figs. 1-27 and 1-28. The ideal 1:1 transformers are inserted to take

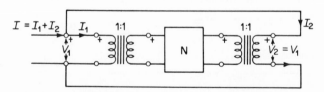

Figure 1-27   Connections for determining network equivalence.

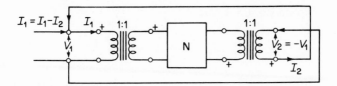

Figure 1-28 Connections for determining network equivalence.

care of cases where the network under consideration is unbalanced, as in Fig. 1-15(a). The transformers in no way affect the circuit impedances, but prevent short-circuiting of the input voltage, V, when the network is unbalanced. When the network is balanced, the transformers are not required.

The general mesh equations for the symmetrical network N, where $z_{11} = z_{22}$, and $z_{12} = z_{21}$, are the following:

$$z_{11}I_1 + z_{12}I_2 = V_1$$
$$z_{12}I_1 + z_{11}I_2 = V_2$$
[1.8-1]

Hence,
$$I_1 = \left(\frac{z_{11}}{|z|}\right) V_1 - \left(\frac{z_{12}}{|z|}\right) V_2$$
$$I_2 = \left(\frac{z_{11}}{|z|}\right) V_2 - \left(\frac{z_{12}}{|z|}\right) V_1$$
[1.8-2]

where
$$|z| = \begin{vmatrix} z_{11} & z_{12} \\ z_{12} & z_{11} \end{vmatrix} = z_{11}^2 - z_{12}^2 = (z_{11} - z_{12})(z_{11} + z_{12})$$
[1.8-3]

It follows that, for a symmetrical network connected as in Fig. 1-27 where $V_1 = V_2$,

$$I_1 = \left(\frac{z_{11} - z_{12}}{|z|}\right) V_1$$
$$I_2 = \left(\frac{z_{11} - z_{12}}{|z|}\right) V_1$$
[1.8-4]

Hence, $I_1 = I_2$, and the input current, I, is given by

$$I = I_1 + I_1 = 2I_1$$
[1.8-5]

The input impedance is

$$Z_{\text{in}} = \frac{V_1}{2I_1} = \frac{|z|}{2(z_{11} - z_{12})} = \frac{Z_b}{2}$$
[1.8-6]

It follows from Eq. 1.8-6 that:

$$Z_b = \frac{|z|}{z_{11} - z_{12}} = z_{11} + z_{12} \qquad [1.8\text{-}7]$$

where Z_b is the diagonal arm of the equivalent lattice structure, and is twice the input impedance when the network is connected as in Fig. 1-27.

The mesh equations for the symmetrical network shown in Fig. 1-28, where $V_2 = -V_1$, are the following:

$$\begin{aligned} z_{11}I_1 + z_{12}I_2 &= V_1 \\ z_{12}I_1 + z_{11}I_2 &= -V_1 \end{aligned} \qquad [1.8\text{-}8]$$

The currents are given by

$$\begin{aligned} I_1 &= \left(\frac{z_{11} + z_{12}}{|z|}\right) V_1 \\ I_2 &= -\left(\frac{z_{11} + z_{12}}{|z|}\right) V_1 \end{aligned} \qquad [1.8\text{-}9]$$

Hence, $I_1 = -I_2$, and the input current is given by

$$I = I_1 - (-I_1) = 2I_1 \qquad [1.8\text{-}10]$$

The input impedance is

$$Z_{\text{in}} = \frac{V_1}{2I_1} = \frac{|z|}{2(z_{11} + z_{12})} = \frac{Z_a}{2} \qquad [1.8\text{-}11]$$

It now follows from Eq. 1.8-11 that

$$Z_a = \frac{|z|}{z_{11} + z_{12}} = z_{11} - z_{12} \qquad [1.8\text{-}12]$$

where Z_a is the series arm of the equivalent lattice, and is twice the input impedance when the network is connected as in Fig. 1-28.

It follows directly from Eqs. 1.8-7 and 1.8-12 that

$$z_{11} = \frac{Z_b + Z_a}{2} \qquad [1.8\text{-}13]$$

$$z_{12} = \frac{Z_b - Z_a}{2} \qquad [1.8\text{-}14]$$

Equations 1.8-13 and 1.8-14 show that Z_a and Z_b completely determine the network. It also follows from Eq. 1.4-18 that:

$$Z_0 = \sqrt{(z_{11} + z_{12})(z_{11} - z_{12})} = \sqrt{Z_a Z_b} \qquad [1.8\text{-}15]$$

It should also be noted that if the network can be bisected, the connections shown in Figs. 1-27 and 1-28 are identical to those discussed in connection with Fig. 1-20, which was used in the derivation of the bisection theorem. From this point of view, the bisected impedances, Z_{och} and Z_{sch}, can be considered as special values of Z_a and Z_b. The method here developed lends itself directly to the determination of network equivalence by measurement, and holds for networks having cross-over elements.

The following examples will illustrate the use of the bisection principle for transforming from the lattice network into unbalanced ladder networks.

In Fig. 1-29, the lattice arms, Z_a and Z_b, are shown in (a), and the

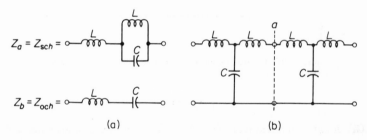

(a)   (b)

Figure 1-29 Transformation of lattice into unbalanced ladder network.

developed ladder is shown in (b). It is noticed that the bisection line is a-b, and if a and b are short-circuited, Z_a is obtained; and if the network is bisected at a-b and left open, Z_b is obtained.

Figure 1-30 shows the lattice arms, Z_a and Z_b, composed of resistors and capacitors, and two possible half-sections of an unbalanced network. If the output terminals on the right are all short-circuited at the same time, Z_a is obtained; whereas, if they are all left open, Z_b is obtained. The full section is obtained by constructing the other mirror-half of the network and combining the impedances to form a bridged-T network.

The network in (a) of Fig. 1-30 is realizable if $R_3 > (R_1 + R_2)$; otherwise, a negative resistance is required. In Fig. 1-30(b), C_1 must be greater than C_2, and R_3 must be greater than R_1. Other equivalent networks can be constructed by inspection.

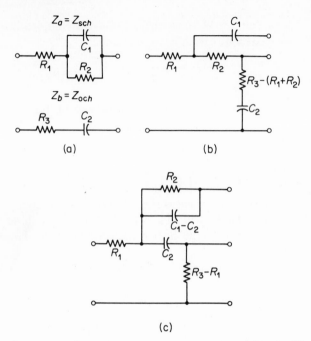

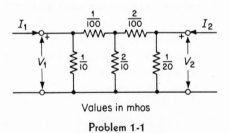

Figure 1-30   Transformation of lattice into unbalanced bridged-T network.

PROBLEMS

1-1 Given a two-terminal pair network as shown in the accompanying sketch.

Values in mhos

Problem 1-1

(a) Write the nodal determinant for this network, and calculate z_{11}, z_{12}, and z_{22}. Determine the equivalent T network.

(b) From the z's given in (a), write the mesh determinant and solve it for y_{11}, y_{12}, and y_{22} for the equivalent π network.

(c) Determine y_{11}, y_{12}, and y_{22} from the original nodal determinant, and compare the results with those obtained in (b).

(d) Write the mesh determinant for the original network. Calculate y_{11}, y_{12}, and y_{22}, and compare the results with (b) and (c).

1-2 Given the network shown below.

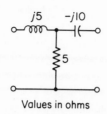

Values in ohms

Problem 1-2

(a) Write the mesh determinant; determine y_{11}, y_{12}, and y_{22}, and construct the π network.

(b) Is the network physically realizable?

1-3 Consider the T network shown in the accompanying sketch.

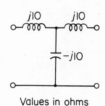

Values in ohms

Problem 1-3

(a) Write the mesh determinant; determine y_{11}, y_{12}, and y_{22}, and construct the π network.

(b) Find the ratio V_1/I_2 when the network is terminated by a load R_L.

(c) Does I_2 depend upon the value of R_L?

1-4 Consider the network in the accompanying sketch and find a single T section or π section which represents the network when (a) $\omega = 10^4$, and when (b) $\omega = 10^2$. Are the networks physically realizable?

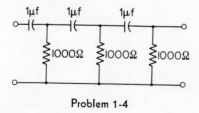

Problem 1-4

1-5 A T network has series arms equal to Z_1 and Z_3, and a shunt arm equal to Z_2.

(a) Find the $ABCD$ coefficients.

(b) Show that $A = V_1/V_2$ when $I_2 = 0$.

(c) When the network is terminated into a load Z_L, find the ratio V_1/V_2.

(d) Determine A/C, $1/C$, D/C in terms of the impedances.

1-6 Consider a transformer with $L_1 = 1.0$, $L_2 = 2.0$, and $M = 1.1$ henrys.

(a) What is the coefficient of coupling?

(b) Find a T-section equivalent. Is it physically realizable? If not, what is the maximum coefficient of coupling that can be used for a physically realizable T section?

(c) Find an equivalent π section, and state the conditions for it to be physically realizable.

1-7 Given the bridged-T network with the values shown in the sketch.

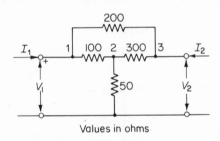

Values in ohms

Problem 1-7

(a) Write the mesh determinant, and find the equivalent π network.

(b) Find the equivalent T network directly from the mesh determinant.

(c) Write the nodal determinant, and find the equivalent π network directly.

1-8 Using the diagram shown below for a symmetrical T network, compute the characteristic resistance in the following ways:

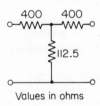

Values in ohms

Problem 1-8

(a) Terminate the network by R_0, and solve for the input impedance.

(b) Compute R_{11}, R_{12}, and R_0 equal to $\sqrt{(R_{11} - R_{12})(R_{11} + R_{12})}$.

(c) Bisect the network and determine $R_0 = \sqrt{R_{sch}R_{och}}$.

(d) Find R_{oc} and R_{sc} for the entire network, and determine $R_0 = \sqrt{R_{sc}R_{oc}}$. Find the network loss in nepers and db when terminated by R_0. Assuming that the resistance network shown is already a bisected network, and that another identical section follows the one given, find the lattice equivalent and develop an equivalent T network, for the two cascaded sections; also, determine the loss in decibels.

1-9 A symmetrical network N (sketched here) is terminated by its characteristic impedance, Z_0. Solve for Z_0 in terms of the z parameters.

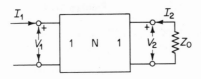

Problem 1-9

1-10 A symmetrical network N is terminated by its characteristic admittance Y_0. Solve for Y_0 in terms of the y parameters.

1-11 An unsymmetrical network N is terminated in the image impedances given in Figs. 1-13 and 1-14. Using Eqs. 1.1-33, develop Z_{I_1} and Z_{I_2}, as given by Eqs. 1.4-14 and 1.4-15, directly in terms of the z parameters.

1-12 Use the sketch given in Prob. 1-9 for a symmetrical network terminated by Z_0. Solve for the current ratio I_1/I_2 and denote this ratio by ϵ^γ. After substituting for Z_0, derive an expression for γ in terms of the z parameters.

1-13 Using the diagram shown here for the reactive T network, compute the characteristic impedance as follows:

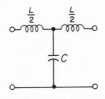

Problem 1-13

(a) Terminate by Z_0, and solve for the input impedance.

(b) Determine z_{11} and z_{12}, and calculate $Z_0 = \sqrt{(z_{11} - z_{12})(z_{11} + z_{12})}$.

(c) Find Z_{sc} and Z_{oc} for the entire network, and determine $Z_0 = \sqrt{Z_{oc}Z_{sc}}$.

(d) Bisect the network, and determine $Z_0 = \sqrt{Z_{och}Z_{sch}}$. Plot Z_0 as a function of ω, and determine the range where Z_0 is real and the range where Z_0 is imaginary.

1-14 Repeat Prob. 1-13 for the following circuit.

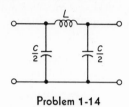

Problem 1-14

1-15 Repeat Prob. 1-13 for the following circuit.

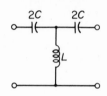

Problem 1-15

1-16 Repeat Prob. 1-13 for the following circuit.

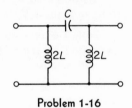

Problem 1-16

1-17 Repeat Prob. 1-13 for the following circuit, assuming that $L_1C_1 = L_2C_2$.

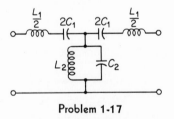

Problem 1-17

1-18 Repeat Prob. 1-13 for the following circuit, assuming that $L_1C_1 = L_2C_2$.

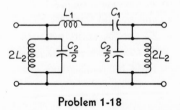

Problem 1-18

1-19 Determine cosh γ for the configurations in Probs. 1-13 to 1-18 inclusive.

1-20 (a) Using Bartlett's bisection principle on the networks in Probs. 1-13 to 1-18, determine the lattice equivalents of these networks.

(b) For each network, write the characteristic impedance $Z_0 = \sqrt{Z_a Z_b}$ and the propagation constant

$$\gamma = \ln \frac{1 + \sqrt{Z_a/Z_b}}{1 - \sqrt{Z_a/Z_b}}$$

1-21 Use the bisection principle to determine the lattice equivalent of the two networks shown here.

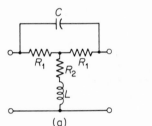 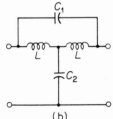

Problem 1-21

1-22 Transform the lattice network shown below into an equivalent T network. Consider the three cases where $L_1 = L_2$; $L_1 < L_2$; and $L_1 > L_2$.

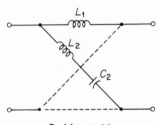

Problem 1-22

1-23 Transform the lattice network shown below into an equivalent π network. Consider the three cases where $C_1 = C_2$; $C_1 < C_2$, and $C_1 > C_2$.

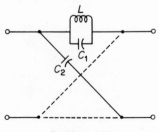

Problem 1-23

1-24 Transform the lattice network shown into an equivalent bridged-T network.

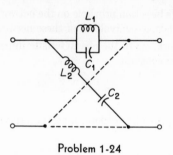

Problem 1-24

Consider three cases:

where $L_1 = L_2,$ $C_1 = C_2$ (two solutions)
$L_1 < L_2,$ $C_1 > C_2$ (two solutions)
$L_1 > L_2,$ $C_1 < C_2$ (two solutions)

design of resistance attenuators

2.0 INTRODUCTION

This chapter is devoted to the application of the relations developed in Chap. 1 to the design of resistance attenuators. A resistance attenuator is a network, composed of resistors, that is designed to reduce, by known amounts, the voltage, current, or power between the input and output terminals, when the network is properly terminated by a resistance. When the attenuator network is symmetrical, the design specifications are the attenuation and the characteristic resistance. Resistance attenuators are also used to match impedances between two networks when the insertion loss can be tolerated. In such cases, the attenuator network is unsymmetrical and the image impedances must be specified. Symmetrical attenuators are considered in this chapter. The unsymmetrical case is treated in Chap. 6.

A purely resistive attenuator has a loss characteristic that is independent of frequency. Inasmuch as all resistors contain residuals of inductance and capacitance, these residuals affect the loss characteristic, especially at high frequencies. The effect of the residuals can be minimized, but must be taken into account in the final design. An attenuator may also be designed as a capacitance network. Such attenuators have some application at high frequencies.

Resistance attenuators are used as volume and mixing controls in broadcasting stations. Attenuators are also used in the laboratory when it is necessary to obtain small values of voltage or current for test purposes.

The lattice structure will be used for the basis of design, and will then be converted into other types of equivalent networks that are more desirable.

51

2.1 DESIGN EQUATIONS

The resistance lattice network terminated by its characteristic resistance, R_0, as shown in Fig. 2-1, will be used as the basis of design for the attenuator. The lattice may then be converted into other equivalent networks.

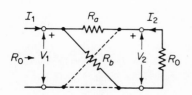

It follows from Eq. 1.6-10 that the characteristic resistance is given by

$$R_0 = \sqrt{R_a R_b} \qquad [2.1\text{-}1]$$

Figure 2-1 Resistance lattice network.

Inasmuch as the network contains no reactive elements, the propagation function is real, and signifies only attenuation without any phase shift. It follows from Eq. 1.6-11 that the propagation (attenuation) function is

$$\gamma = \alpha = \ln\left(\frac{1 + \sqrt{R_a/R_b}}{1 - \sqrt{R_a/R_b}}\right) \qquad [2.1\text{-}2]$$

The ratios of input and output voltage and current are given by

$$\frac{V_1}{V_2} = \frac{I_1}{-I_2} = a = \epsilon^\alpha = \frac{1 + \sqrt{R_a/R_b}}{1 - \sqrt{R_a/R_b}} \qquad [2.1\text{-}3]$$

where α is expressed in nepers.

It follows from Eq. 2.1-3 that

$$\alpha = \ln\left(\frac{V_1}{V_2}\right) = \ln\left(\frac{I_1}{-I_2}\right) = 2.30 \log_{10}\left(\frac{V_1}{V_2}\right)$$
$$= 2.30 \log_{10}\left(\frac{I_1}{-I_2}\right) \qquad [2.1\text{-}4]$$

Since

$$db = 20 \log_{10}\left(\frac{V_1}{V_2}\right) = 20 \log_{10}\left(\frac{I_1}{-I_2}\right) \qquad [2.1\text{-}5]$$

it follows from Eqs. 2.1-4 and 2.1-5 that

$$db = 8.69\alpha = 8.69 \times 2.30 \log_{10} a = 20.0 \log_{10} a \qquad [2.1\text{-}6]$$

and

$$a = \text{antilog}_{10}\, db/20 \qquad [2.1\text{-}7]$$

where db denotes the number of decibels, α denotes the number of nepers, and a is given by Eq. 2.1-3. Equation 2.1-6 shows that one neper is equivalent in magnitude to 8.69 decibels, or one decibel equals 0.115 neper.

It can be seen from Eq. 2.1-1 that $R_b = R_0^2/R_a$. Therefore, Eq. 2.1-3 can be written as follows:

$$a = \frac{1 + R_a/R_0}{1 - R_a/R_0} \tag{2.1-8}$$

where a and R_0 are design specifications. Equations 2.1-3 and 2.1-8 will be solved for R_a and R_b in terms of a and R_0. This yields

$$R_a = R_0 \left(\frac{a - 1}{a + 1}\right) \tag{2.1-9}$$

$$R_b = R_0 \left(\frac{a + 1}{a - 1}\right) \tag{2.1-10}$$

where a is given by Eq. 2.1-7. Equations 2.1-9 and 2.1-10 can also be written as

$$\frac{R_a}{R_0} = r_a = \frac{a - 1}{a + 1} \tag{2.1-11}$$

$$\frac{R_b}{R_0} = r_b = \frac{a + 1}{a - 1} \tag{2.1-12}$$

where r_a and r_b are the per-unit or normalized resistances. The network may first be designed on a normalized basis for a given attenuation, and the resistances then multiplied by the specified characteristic resistance.

2.2 ILLUSTRATIVE DESIGN

As a numerical illustration of the above relations, consider the design of a 500-ohm resistance attenuator to have an attenuation of 20 decibels. It follows from Eq. 2.1-7 that

$$a = \text{antilog}_{10} \left(\frac{20}{20}\right) = \text{antilog}_{10} 1 = 10$$

Substitution of $a = 10$ into Eqs. 2.1-9 and 2.1-10 yields

$$R_a = 500 \left(\frac{10 - 1}{10 + 1}\right) = 500 \left(\frac{9}{11}\right) = 409.09 \text{ ohms}$$

$$R_b = 500 \left(\frac{11}{9}\right) = 611.11 \text{ ohms}$$

The resulting lattice structure is shown in Fig. 2-2.

The equivalent T network can be found from the lattice by making use of the bisection principle of Sec. 1.7. The short-circuited resistance of the bisected T network is equal to R_a, and the open-circuited resistance of the bisected T network is equal to R_b.

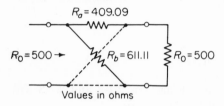

$R_a = 409.09$

$R_0 = 500 \rightarrow$ $R_b = 611.11$ $R_0 = 500$

Values in ohms

Figure 2-2 Lattice attenuator with 20-db loss.

If the bisected T section is composed of resistors, as shown in (b) of Fig. 2-3, the relation between the lattice components in Fig. 2-3(a) and the T-section components in Fig. 2-3(b) is the following:

$$R_a = \frac{R_1}{2} = R_{sch} \qquad [2.2\text{-}1]$$

$$R_b = \frac{R_1}{2} + 2R_2 = R_{och} \qquad [2.2\text{-}2]$$

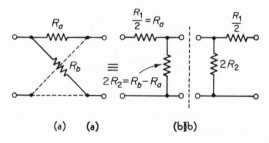

(a)   (a)   (b)(b)

Figure 2-3 Bisected T section derived from lattice network.

or the T network components in terms of the lattice arms are the following:

$$R_1 = 2R_a \qquad [2.2\text{-}3]$$

$$R_2 = \frac{R_b - R_a}{2} \qquad [2.2\text{-}4]$$

Using Eqs. 2.1-9 and 2.1-10, the T network can be found directly in terms of the voltage ratio and the characteristic resistance. Thus,

$$R_1 = 2R_0 \left(\frac{a-1}{a+1} \right) \qquad [2.2\text{-}5]$$

$$R_2 = \frac{R_0}{2} \left(\frac{a+1}{a-1} - \frac{a-1}{a+1} \right) = R_0 \left(\frac{2a}{a^2-1} \right) \qquad [2.2\text{-}6]$$

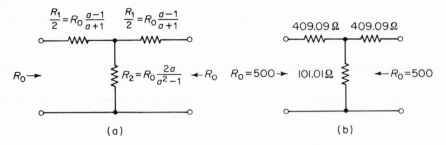

Figure 2-4 T network in terms of design specifications.

Equations 2.2-5 and 2.2-6 give a direct design of a T network in terms of the attenuation function and the characteristic resistance, as shown in (a) of Fig. 2-4. The equivalent T network of the attenuator in Fig. 2-2 is shown in Fig. 2-4(b).

The equivalent π network is readily found by applying the bisection theorem in terms of conductance. Referring to Fig. 2-5,

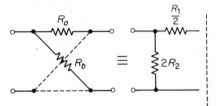

$$G_a = \frac{1}{R_a} = \frac{1}{2R_2} + \frac{2}{R_1} = G_{sch} \quad [2.2\text{-}7]$$

Figure 2-5 Conversion of lattice into π network.

$$G_b = \frac{1}{R_b} = \frac{1}{2R_2} = G_{och} \quad [2.2\text{-}8]$$

where R_a and R_b are given by Eqs. 2.1-9 and 2.1-10. It follows from Eqs. 2.2-7 and 2.2-8 that

$$R_2 = \frac{R_b}{2} = \frac{R_0}{2}\left(\frac{a+1}{a-1}\right) \quad [2.2\text{-}9]$$

$$R_1 = \frac{2R_aR_b}{R_b - R_a} = R_0\left(\frac{a^2-1}{2a}\right) \quad [2.2\text{-}10]$$

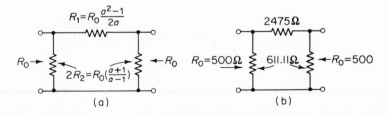

Figure 2-6 π network in terms of design specifications.

The general π network attenuator is shown in Fig. 2-6(a), and the equivalent π network of the attenuator in Fig. 2-2 is shown in Fig. 2-6(b).

2.3 SPECIAL NETWORKS

If either the T-section or π-section attenuator is to be made variable, all three resistors must be varied simultaneously. A more desirable form of a variable attenuator, requiring only two variable elements, is the special type of a bridged-T network shown in (a) of Fig. 2-7. It will be noted

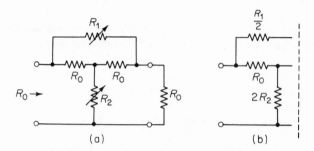

Figure 2-7 Special type of bridged-T network.

that only R_1 and R_2 are variable in this circuit. The bisected section is shown in Fig. 2-7(b).

The characteristic resistance of the network in Fig. 2-7(b) is given by

$$R_0 = \sqrt{R_{och}R_{sch}} = \sqrt{\frac{(R_0 + 2R_2)\,(R_0R_1/2)}{R_0 + R_1/2}} \qquad [2.3\text{-}1]$$

$$R_0^2\left(R_0 + \frac{R_1}{2}\right) = (R_0 + 2R_2)\left(\frac{R_0R_1}{2}\right)$$

$$R_0^2 = R_1R_2$$

$$R_0 = \sqrt{R_1R_2} \qquad [2.3\text{-}2]$$

It follows from the bisection principle that

$$R_{och} = R_0 + 2R_2 = R_b = R_0\left(\frac{a+1}{a-1}\right)$$

$$R_2 = \frac{R_0}{a-1} \qquad [2.3\text{-}3]$$

Then from Eqs. 2.3-2 and 2.3-3, it follows that

$$R_1 = \frac{R_0^2}{R_2} = R_0(a - 1) \qquad [2.3\text{-}4]$$

When $R_0 = 500$ ohms, and $a = 10$, as in Fig. 2-2, the elements of the equivalent special bridged-T network are given by

$$R_1 = 500(10 - 1) = 4,500 \text{ ohms}$$

$$R_2 = \frac{500}{10 - 1} = 55.55 \text{ ohms}$$

The special bridged-T network designed to give an attenuation of 20 decibels at an impedance level of 500 ohms is shown in Fig. 2-8.

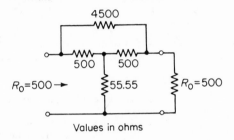

Figure 2-8 Bridged-T attenuator with 20-db loss.

Another special network is the L section shown in Fig. 2-9. This attenuator requires only two variable resistors, but maintains a constant resistance in only one direction. The two values of resistance are denoted by R_{k_1} and R_{k_2} in Fig. 2-9.

Considering the network to the right of terminals ab in (a) of Fig. 2-9, the mesh-current equations are

$$(R_1 + R_2)I_1 + R_2I_2 = V_1 \qquad [2.3\text{-}5]$$

$$R_2I_2 + (R_2 + R_L)I_2 = 0 \qquad [2.3\text{-}6]$$

where V_1 is the voltage existing at terminals ab. It follows from Eqs. 2.3-5 and 2.3-6 that the current ratio is

$$a = -\frac{I_1}{I_2} = -\frac{\Delta_{11}}{\Delta_{12}} = \frac{R_2 + R_L}{R_2} \qquad [2.3\text{-}7]$$

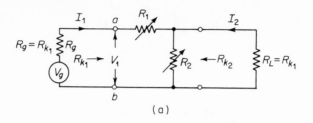

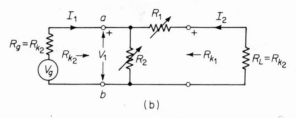

Figure 2-9 L-section attenuators.

Solution of Eq. 2.3-7 for R_2 yields

$$R_2 = \frac{R_L}{a - 1} \qquad\qquad [2.3\text{-}8]$$

Inasmuch as the network in Fig. 2-9(a) is terminated in R_{k_1}, $R_L = R_{k_1}$, and thus

$$R_2 = \frac{R_{k_1}}{a - 1} \qquad\qquad [2.3\text{-}9]$$

The input resistance at terminals ab is

$$R_{k_1} = R_1 + \frac{R_2 R_L}{R_2 + R_L} \qquad\qquad [2.3\text{-}10]$$

It follows from Eq. 2.3-7 that

$$\frac{R_2}{R_2 + R_L} = \frac{1}{a} \qquad\qquad [2.3\text{-}11]$$

The substitution of Eq. 2.3-11 into Eq. 2.3-10 yields

$$R_{k_1} = R_1 + \frac{R_L}{a} \qquad\qquad [2.3\text{-}12]$$

It follows from Eq. 2.3-8 that

$$R_L = (a - 1)R_2 \qquad\qquad [2.3\text{-}13]$$

The substitution of Eq. 2.3-13 into Eq. 2.3-12 yields

$$R_{k_1} = R_1 + \left(\frac{a-1}{a}\right) R_2 \qquad [2.3\text{-}14]$$

The substitution of R_2 as given by Eq. 2.3-9 into Eq. 2.3-14 gives the following results:

$$R_{k_1} = R_1 + \left(\frac{1}{a}\right) R_{k_1} \qquad [2.3\text{-}15]$$

and finally

$$R_1 = \left(\frac{a-1}{a}\right) R_{k_1} \qquad [2.3\text{-}16]$$

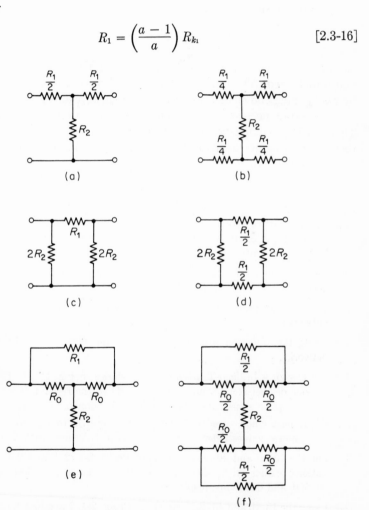

Figure 2-10 Unbalanced and balanced networks.

It can be shown in a similar manner that the resistors in Fig. 2-9(b) are given by

$$R_1 = (a - 1)R_{k_2} \qquad [2.3\text{-}17]$$

$$R_2 = \left(\frac{a}{a - 1}\right) R_{k_2} \qquad [2.3\text{-}18]$$

The derivation of Eqs. 2.3-17 and 2.3-18 is left as an exercise for the student.

2.4 ATTENUATOR CONFIGURATIONS

The lattice network was used as a design artifice for attenuators and then transformed to other networks. The lattice in itself is a symmetrical and balanced network, while the T, π, and bridged-T networks are symmetrical and unbalanced. These networks can be converted to balanced networks by rearranging the elements in the configurations shown in Fig. 2-10.

It is often necessary to design attenuators that are unsymmetrical. This can be accomplished by first designing a symmetrical network, and then converting it to an unsymmetrical network. Such conversions are considered in Chap. 6.

PROBLEMS

2-1 Use the lattice structure to design attenuator networks with losses of, respectively, 2, 5, 10, 20, 40, and 60 db. The characteristic resistance R_0 is to be taken as unity.

2-2 Plot Z_{oc} and Z_{sc} for the networks of Prob. 2-1 as a function of the loss in decibels.

2-3 Using the bisection principle, transform the networks of Prob. 2-1 to T-section networks.

2-4 Using the bisection principle, transform the networks of Prob. 2-1 to π networks.

2-5 (a) Design a bridged-T attenuator, as shown in Fig. 2-7, to be variable in one-decibel steps from 0 to 10 db. (Give the resistance values between successive steps). Assume that $R_0 = 500$ ohms.

(b) Repeat when variable in ten-db steps from 0 to 100 db. (Give the resistance values between successive steps.) Assume that $R_0 = 500$ ohms.

2-6 For the 10-db and 40-db networks of Probs. 2-1, 2-3, and 2-4, find the resistance values when the characteristic resistance R_0 takes on values of 10, 500, and 600 ohms, respectively.

2-7 Using the 10-db and 40-db networks of Probs. 2-1, 2-3, and 2-4, determine the error in db when the following changes are made in the network:

(a) Assume that the terminating resistor, R_0, is changed by ± 2 per cent.

(b) Assume that the R_a arm of the lattice is changed by ± 2 per cent.

(c) Assume that the R_1 branch of the T and π networks is changed by ± 2 per cent.

(d) Assume that the R_2 branch of the T and π networks is changed by ± 2 per cent.

Note: The current and voltage ratios can be determined by network analysis, and the db loss calculated and compared with the nominal values.

2-8 In Prob. 2-1, assume that the R_b resistance of the 40-db attenuator has a residual series inductance of 0.1 μh. Find the db loss at $\omega = 10^3$, and at $\omega = 10^7$.

2-9 A decimal attenuator is shown in the accompanying sketch. Design the attenuator for $R_0 = 20$ ohms.

(a) What resistance is presented to the source at each step?

(b) What change can be made in the circuit to make this resistance constant in value?

2-10 The arms for a lattice network are given by

$$Z_a = Z_0 \tanh \frac{\gamma}{2} \quad \text{and} \quad Z_b = Z_0 \coth \frac{\gamma}{2}$$

For a resistance network they may be modified as follows:

$$R_a = R_0 \tanh \frac{\alpha}{2} \quad \text{and} \quad R_b = R_0 \coth \frac{\alpha}{2}$$

where α is expressed in nepers.

Use the bisection principle to obtain the design equations for T-section and π-section attenuators in terms of hyperbolic functions.

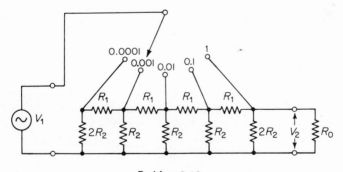

Problem 2-10

2-11 Derive Eqs. 2.3-17 and 2.3-18 for the L-section attenuator.

synthesis of one-terminal pair
reactive networks

3.0 INTRODUCTION

A one-terminal pair network or a one-port network has only a single pair of terminals available for external connection. Such networks are characterized by the driving-point impedance or admittance at this pair of terminals.

The material in this chapter is devoted to the formulation of the steady-state characteristics of driving-point impedances and admittances of purely reactive networks and the elementary procedures for the synthesis of such networks. Such networks are composed only of inductive and capacitive elements. The networks are dissipationless since they contain no resistive elements. Hence, the impedance is a reactance. Networks of these types were first treated by R. M. Foster in a paper containing a formulation that is known as *Foster's reactance theorem.**

3.1 DRIVING-POINT IMPEDANCE (FIRST FOSTER FORM)

Consider an m-mesh network consisting of purely reactive elements. Assume that each self and mutual impedance contains at least one inductor in series with at least one capacitor. The generalized impedance determinant of such a network is given by

---

* Foster, R. M., "A Reactance Theorem," *Bell System Technical Journal*, volume 3 (1924), pages 250–267.

$$\Delta_z(s) = \begin{vmatrix} \left(sL_{11} + \dfrac{1}{sC_{11}}\right) & \left(sL_{12} + \dfrac{1}{sC_{12}}\right) & \cdots & \left(sL_{1k} + \dfrac{1}{sC_{1k}}\right) & \cdots & \left(sL_{1m} + \dfrac{1}{sC_{1m}}\right) \\[2mm] \left(sL_{21} + \dfrac{1}{sC_{21}}\right) & \left(sL_{22} + \dfrac{1}{sC_{22}}\right) & \cdots & \left(sL_{2k} + \dfrac{1}{sC_{2k}}\right) & \cdots & \left(sL_{2m} + \dfrac{1}{sC_{2m}}\right) \\[2mm] \cdots & \cdots & \cdots & \cdots & \cdots & \cdots \\[1mm] \left(sL_{m1} + \dfrac{1}{sC_{m1}}\right) & \left(sL_{m2} + \dfrac{1}{sC_{m2}}\right) & \cdots & \left(sL_{mk} + \dfrac{1}{sC_{mk}}\right) & \cdots & \left(sL_{mm} + \dfrac{1}{sC_{mm}}\right) \end{vmatrix}$$

[3.1-1]

where s is the complex angular frequency.

The driving-point impedance is

$$Z(s) = \frac{\Delta_z(s)}{\Delta_{11}(s)}$$

[3.1-2]

where the input terminals are designated by the subscripts, 1,1. Multiplying each term of both $\Delta_z(s)$ and $\Delta_{11}(s)$ by s, it can be shown that

$$Z(s) = \frac{P_m(s^2)}{sQ_{m-1}(s^2)}$$

[3.1-3]

where $P_m(s^2)$ is a polynomial of order m in s^2, and Q_{m-1} is another polynomial of order $m - 1$ in s^2. Both polynomials are functions of s^2 because, after each term of $\Delta_z(s)$ and $\Delta_{11}(s)$ has been multiplied by s, the expansion of both the determinant and its cofactor contains only quadratic factors. Equation 3.1-3 can also be written as

$$Z(s) = \frac{P_n(s)}{M_{n-1}(s)} = \frac{a_n s^n + a_{n-2}s^{n-2} + \ldots + a_0}{b_{n-1}s^{n-1} + b_{n-3}s^{n-3} + \ldots + b_1 s}$$

[3.1-4]

where $n = 2m$. Equation 3.1-4 is the polynomial form of the driving-point impedance.

Another form of the impedance is obtained by applying the factor theorem to Eq. 3.1-3. This result is

$$Z(s) = H\left[\frac{(s^2 - s_1^2)(s^2 - s_3^2) \ldots}{s(s^2 - s_2^2) \ldots}\right]$$

[3.1-5]

where s_1 and s_3 are zeros of $P_m(s^2)$, and s_2 is a zero of $Q_{m-1}(s^2)$, and H in Eq. 3.1-5 equals a_n/b_{n-1} in Eq. 3.1-4.

The first Foster form of the driving-point impedance is obtained by expanding the right-hand side of Eq. 3.1-5 into a series of partial fractions, and identifying each component of the expansion as the reactance of an inductor, a capacitor, or a parallel L-C circuit. Since the order of the numerator is one degree higher than the denominator, the numerator must be divided by the denominator before $Z(s)$ can be resolved into partial fractions. Division of the numerator by the denominator yields

$$Z(s) = sH + \frac{HM_{m-1}(s^2)}{sQ_{m-1}(s^2)} \qquad [3.1\text{-}6]$$

where M_{m-1} is a polynomial of order $m - 1$, in s^2. Since the second term on the right side of Eq. 3.1-6 is a fraction in which the order of the denominator is one greater than that of the numerator, it can be resolved into partial fractions as follows

$$\frac{HM_{m-1}(s^2)}{sQ_{m-1}(s^2)} = \frac{A_0}{s} + \sum \frac{sA_k}{s^2 - s_k^2} \qquad [3.1\text{-}7]$$

where s_k is a zero of $Q_{m-1}(s^2)$, and the summation is taken over *all* the zeros of $Q_{m-1}(s^2)$. It should be noted that, in each term of the partial-fraction expansion, the order of the numerator is one less than that of the denominator.

It follows from Eqs. 3.1-6 and 3.1-7 that the driving-point impedance can be expressed as

$$Z(s) = \frac{A_0}{s} + \sum \frac{sA_k}{s^2 - s_k^2} + sH \qquad [3.1\text{-}8]$$

Equation 3.1-8 is the partial-fraction expansion of the driving-point impedance and is known as the first Foster form.

Before identifying the components of the expansion in Eq. 3.1-8, expressions for the generalized or operational impedance will be reviewed. The generalized impedance of an inductor is given by

$$Z(s) = sL \quad \text{(inductor)} \qquad [3.1\text{-}9]$$

where

$$s = \sigma + j\omega \qquad [3.1\text{-}10]$$

and σ and ω are the real and quadrature components of the complex frequency. The impedance of a capacitor is

$$Z(s) = \frac{1}{sC} \quad \text{(capacitor)} \qquad [3.1\text{-}11]$$

The corresponding steady-state impedances are found by letting $s = j\omega$ in Eqs. 3.1-9 and 3.1-11, giving

$$Z(j\omega) = j\omega L \quad \text{(inductor)} \qquad [3.1\text{-}12]$$

$$Z(j\omega) = \frac{1}{j\omega C} \quad \text{(capacitor)} \qquad [3.1\text{-}13]$$

In the analysis of this chapter, it will be found convenient to use Eqs. 3.1-9 and 3.1-11 in certain applications, and Eqs. 3.1-12 and 3.1-13 in other cases.

The generalized impedance of a circuit consisting of an inductance L_k in parallel with a capacitance C_k is given by

$$Z(s) = \frac{sL_k(1/sC_k)}{sL_k + 1/sC_k} = \frac{s/C_k}{s^2 + 1/L_kC_k} = \frac{s/C_k}{s^2 - s_k^2} \qquad [3.1\text{-}14]$$

where

$$s_k^2 = -\frac{1}{L_kC_k} \qquad [3.1\text{-}15]$$

The reason for using the negative sign in Eq. 3.1-15 will become clear when the equation for the steady-state impedance is written. The corresponding steady-state impedance is

$$Z(j\omega) = \frac{j\omega/C_k}{-\omega^2 + 1/L_kC_k} = \frac{-j\omega/C_k}{\omega^2 - 1/L_kC_k} = \frac{-j\omega/C_k}{\omega^2 - \omega_k^2} \qquad [3.1\text{-}16]$$

where

$$\omega_k^2 = \frac{1}{L_kC_k} \qquad [3.1\text{-}17]$$

and ω_k is the steady-state resonant frequency.

Referring to Eq. 3.1-8, it is seen that the first term represents the reactance of a capacitor of capacitance $1/A_0$ and the last term is the reactance of an inductor of magnitude H. Also, each term in the summation is the impedance of a parallel L-C circuit having a resonant frequency s_k. The first term approaches infinity as $s \to 0$, and the last term approaches infinity as $s \to \infty$. Furthermore, each term in the summation approaches infinity as $s \to s_k$. Equation 3.1-8 can be written as

$$Z(s) = \frac{A_0}{s} + \sum \frac{sA_k}{s^2 - s_k^2} + sA_\infty \qquad [3.1\text{-}18]$$

where $A_0 = 1/C_0$, $A_k = 1/C_k$, and $A_\infty = H = L_\infty$. The subscripts in Eq. 3.1-18 correspond to frequencies at which the poles of the impedance function occur. Equation 3.1-18 gives the impedance of a circuit consisting of a capacitor C_0 and an inductor L_∞ connected in series with a set of parallel L-C circuits. The driving-point impedance, $Z(s)$, in Eqs. 3.1-8 and 3.1-18 is said to have external poles at zero and infinity, and p internal poles where $p = m - 1$. The internal poles are designated by s_k, and correspond to the resonant frequencies of the parallel L-C circuits indicated in the summation which is taken over *all* of the p internal poles. It follows from Eq. 3.1-18 that the driving-point impedance of a reactive network can be represented by a series-parallel combination of reactive elements as shown in Fig. 3-1, which is derived from Eq. 3.1-18 by using only *even* values of k.

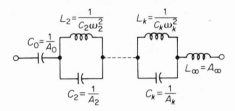

Figure 3-1 Partial fraction representation of driving-point impedance (first Foster form).

It will be seen later that in other cases only *odd* values of k are used. This notation is necessary to distinguish between succeeding poles and zeros.* In either case the summation is taken over the total number of internal poles.

Assuming that the network of Fig. 3-1 is composed simply of a capacitor in series with one parallel L-C circuit and an inductor, the driving-point impedance is

$$Z(s) = \frac{A_0}{s} + \frac{sA_2}{s^2 - s_2^2} + sA_\infty \qquad [3.1\text{-}19]$$

This circuit is composed of four elements, namely two capacitors and two inductors. Expressing the right-hand side of Eq. 3.1-19 under a common denominator yields

$$Z(s) = \frac{A_\infty s^4 + (A_0 + A_2 - A_\infty s_2^2)s^2 - A_0 s_2^2}{s^3 - s_2^2 s} = \frac{a_4 s^4 + a_2 s^2 + a_0}{b_3 s^3 + b_1 s} \qquad [3.1\text{-}20]$$

where $b_1 = -s_2^2$ and $b_3 = 1$. It follows from the factor theorem in algebra that the polynomials in s^2 in both numerator and denominator of Eq. 3.1-20 can be expressed in factors containing s^2. Hence $Z(s)$ can be expressed in the following two forms:

$$Z(s) = H\left[\frac{(s^2 - s_1^2)(s^2 - s_3^2)}{s(s^2 - s_2^2)}\right] \qquad [3.1\text{-}21]$$

---

* It is shown in Sec. 3.4 that the poles and zeros of a reactance function alternate in position. Hence the first (odd) subscript occurs *either* in the numerator or denominator, depending upon whether a pole or zero exists at $s = 0$.

$$Z(s) = sH \left[\frac{(s^2 - s_1^2)(s^2 - s_3^2)}{s^2(s^2 - s_2^2)} \right] \qquad [3.1\text{-}22]$$

where $H = a_4/b_3$.

In the above example a network composed of four elements was used for illustration. It should be noted that the maximum power of the polynomial (in this case the numerator) is four, which is equal to the number of elements in the network. If the degree of the polynomial of highest power in the partial-fraction expansion is n, there must be at least n elements in the network. No other network representation is possible with fewer than n elements. The partial-fraction network is composed of the minimum number of elements. A network without superfluous elements is defined as a canonical network. A partial-fraction network is therefore a canonical network.

In Eq. 3.1-21, the function $Z(s) \to 0$ when $s \to s_1$ or $s \to s_3$. Hence s_1 and s_3 are known as the *internal zeros* of the network. The function $Z(s) \to \infty$ when $s \to s_2$, and s_2 is known as an *internal pole* of the network because the impedance becomes infinite when $s = s_2$. It is also seen that when $s \to 0$, $Z(s) \to \infty$, and there is said to be an *external pole* at zero. Also, when $s \to \infty$, $Z(s) \to \infty$, and there is an *external pole* at infinity. This particular network has two external poles. It is shown in Sec. 3.2 that this condition does not always hold.

The term containing the parallel L-C elements in Eq. 3.1-19 can be separated into two partial fractions as follows:

$$\frac{sA_2}{s^2 - s_2^2} = \frac{1}{2} \left(\frac{A_2}{s + s_2} + \frac{A_2}{s - s_2} \right) \qquad [3.1\text{-}23]$$

Equation 3.1-23 clearly shows the poles at $s = s_2$ and $s = -s_2$. The zero-pole representation in the complex s plane is shown in (a) of Fig. 3-2 for the example used above, with the zeros and poles on the j or quadrature axis, since $\sigma = 0$ for this case. Poles are represented by crosses, and zeros by circles. If $s = j\omega$ and $s_k = j\omega_k$ is substituted in Eq. 3.1-22, the following result is obtained:

$$Z(j\omega) = j\omega H \frac{(-\omega^2 + \omega_1^2)(-\omega^2 + \omega_3^2)}{-\omega^2(-\omega^2 + \omega_2^2)} \qquad [3.1\text{-}24]$$

$$Z(j\omega) = j\omega H \frac{(\omega^2 - \omega_1^2)(\omega^2 - \omega_3^2)}{\omega^2(\omega^2 - \omega_2^2)} \qquad [3.1\text{-}25]$$

where ω_1 and ω_3 are internal zeros, and ω_2 is an internal pole. External poles exist at both $\omega = 0$ and $\omega = \infty$ for this particular network. Figure 3-2(b) illustrates the reactance plot with ω as the variable. The reactance variation will be plotted as in Fig. 3-2(b) hereafter regardless of whether σ or ω

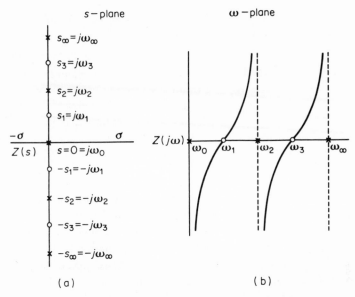

s – plane   ω – plane

Figure 3-2 Poles and zeros of a reactance function.

is used as the independent variable in the expression for the impedance.*
It is seen from Fig. 3-2(b) that the slope of the reactance curve is always
positive, and the zeros and poles alternate. It is proved later and discussed
in more detail that this is a general result and follows from the separation
property.

3.2 TYPES OF REACTANCE FUNCTIONS

Returning to the general partial-fraction expansion, we can discuss the
general form that this equation may have. The driving-point impedance
is given by

$$Z(s) = \frac{A_0}{s} + \Sigma \frac{sA_k}{s^2 - s_k^2} + sA_\infty \qquad [3.2\text{-}1]$$

where the summation is taken over all the p internal poles, and either or
both A_0 and A_∞ may vanish. Equation 3.2-1 can be written in the polynomial form as

$$Z(s) = \frac{a_n s^n + a_{n-2} s^{n-2} + \ldots + a_0}{b_{n-1} s^{n-1} + b_{n-3} s^{n-3} + \ldots + b_1 s} \qquad [3.2\text{-}2]$$

where n is the total number of elements in the canonical network.

*In other words, the frequency axis will always be horizontal.

If a comparison is made between Eqs. 3.2-1 and 3.2-2, keeping in mind that the pole at zero is represented by the A_0/s term, while the pole at infinity is the sA_∞ term, it is seen from the partial-fraction form that:

(1) If poles exist at both zero and infinity, $n = 2p + 2$, and n is even.

(2) If a pole exists at zero, and there is a zero at infinity, the sA_∞ term is missing, and $n = 2p + 1$, where n is odd.

(3) If a zero exists at zero, the A_0/s term is missing, and there is a pole at infinity, $n = 2p + 1$, and n is odd.

(4) If a zero exists at zero, and there is also a zero at infinity, $n = 2p$, and n is even.

This gives four possible forms of the reactance function. These four forms are considered separately as four cases with $Z(s)$ expressed in: (a), the partial-fraction form; (b), the polynomial form; and (c), the factored polynomial form, as follows:

Case (1). A pole of $Z(s)$ exists at $s = j\omega = 0$, and there is a pole at $s = j\omega = \infty$. In this case the partial-fraction form is

$$Z(s) = \frac{A_0}{s} + \sum_{k=2}^{k=2p} \frac{sA_k}{s^2 - s_k^2} + sA_\infty \qquad [k \text{ even}] \qquad [3.2\text{-}3]$$

and in the polynomial form the driving-point impedance is given by

$$Z(s) = \frac{a_n s^n + a_{n-2} s^{n-2} + \ldots + a_0}{b_{n-1} s^{n-1} + b_{n-3} s^{n-3} + \ldots + b_1 s} \qquad [3.2\text{-}4]$$

where $n = 2p + 2$. Since the order of the numerator is one greater than that of the denominator, the factored polynomial form can be written

$$Z(s) = H \left[\frac{(s^2 - s_1^2)(s^2 - s_3^2) \ldots (s^2 - s_{2p+1}^2)}{s(s^2 - s_2^2) \ldots (s^2 - s_{2p}^2)} \right] \qquad [3.2\text{-}5]$$

where $H = a_n/b_{n-1}$. The poles and zeros are shown in Fig. 3-3.

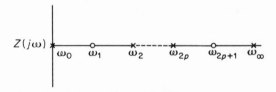

Figure 3-3 Pole-zero distribution with poles at $\omega = 0$ and $\omega = \infty$.

Case (2). A pole of $Z(s)$ exists at $s = j\omega = 0$, and there is a zero at $s = j\omega = \infty$. Here

$$Z(s) = \frac{A_0}{s} + \sum_{k=2}^{k=2p} \frac{sA_k}{s^2 - s_k^2} \qquad [k \text{ even}] \qquad [3.2\text{-}6]$$

and in the polynominal form, the driving-point impedance is given by

$$Z(s) = \frac{a_{n-1}s^{n-1} + a_{n-3}s^{n-3} + \ldots + a_0}{b_n s^n + b_{n-2}s^{n-2} + \ldots + b_1 s} \qquad [3.2\text{-}7]$$

where $n = 2p + 1$. In this case the order of the denominator is one greater than that of the numerator, and the factored polynomial form is

$$Z(s) = H\left[\frac{(s^2 - s_1^2)(s^2 - s_3^2) \ldots (s^2 - s_{2p-1}^2)}{s(s^2 - s_2^2)(s^2 - s_4^2) \ldots (s_2 - s_{2p}^2)}\right] \qquad [3.2\text{-}8]$$

where $H = a_{n-1}/b_n$. The poles and zeros are shown in Fig. 3-4.

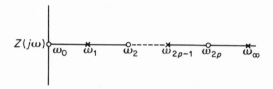

Figure 3-4 Pole-zero distribution with pole at $\omega = 0$ and zero at $\omega = \infty$.

Case (3). A zero of $Z(s)$ exists at $s = j\omega = 0$, and there is a pole at $s = j\omega = \infty$. In this case the partial-fraction form is

$$Z(s) = \sum_{k=1}^{k=2p-1} \frac{sA_k}{s^2 - s_k^2} + sA_\infty \qquad [k \text{ odd}] \qquad [3.2\text{-}9]$$

and in the polynomial form the driving-point impedance is given by

$$Z(s) = \frac{a_n s^n + a_{n-2}s^{n-2} + \ldots + a_1 s}{b_{n-1}s^{n-1} + b_{n-3}s^{n-3} + \ldots + b_0} \qquad [3.2\text{-}10]$$

where $n = 2p + 1$. Since the order of the numerator is one greater than that of the denominator, the factored polynomial form is

$$Z(s) = H\left[\frac{s(s^2 - s_2^2)(s^2 - s_4^2) \ldots (s^2 - s_{2p}^2)}{(s^2 - s_1^2)(s^2 - s_3^2) \ldots (s^2 - s_{2p-1}^2)}\right] \qquad [3.2\text{-}11]$$

where $H = a_n/b_{n-1}$. The poles and zeros are shown in Fig. 3-5.

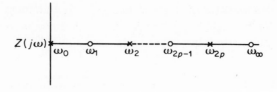

Figure 3-5 Pole-zero distribution with zero at $\omega = 0$
and pole at $\omega = \infty$.

Case (4). A zero of $Z(s)$ exists at $s = j\omega = 0$, and there is a zero at $s = j\omega = \infty$. Inasmuch as the poles at both zero and infinity are missing, the partial-fraction form is the summation term only, and

$$Z(s) = \sum_{k=1}^{2p=1} \frac{sA_k}{s^2 - s_k^2} \qquad [k \text{ odd}] \qquad [3.2\text{-}12]$$

In the polynomial form the driving-point impedance is given by

$$Z(s) = \frac{a_{n-1}s^{n-1} + a_{n-3}s^{n-3} + \ldots + a_1 s}{b_n s^n + b_{n-2}s^{n-2} + \ldots + b_0} \qquad [3.2\text{-}13]$$

where $n = 2p$. Since the order of the numerator is one less than that of the denominator, the factored polynomial form is

$$Z(s) = H\left[\frac{s(s^2 - s_2^2)(s^2 - s_4^2) \ldots (s^2 - s_{2p-2}^2)}{(s^2 - s_1^2)(s^2 - s_3^2) \ldots (s^2 - s_{4p-1}^2)}\right] \qquad [3.2\text{-}14]$$

where $H = a_{n-1}/b_n$. The poles and zeros are shown in Fig. 3-6.

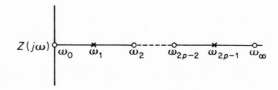

Figure 3-6 Pole-zero distribution with zero at $\omega = 0$
and zero at $\omega = \infty$.

The above are the four possible expressions for a function that expresses the driving-point impedance of a one-terminal pair reactive network. At this point the student is urged to realize that it is unnecessary to commit the various forms of the reactance function to memory, and that these forms can always be written by simply placing the factors corresponding to the *internal* zeros in the numerator and the factors corresponding to the *internal* poles in the denominator of $Z(s)$, noting that s appears as a factor of the denominator only when a pole exists at $s = 0$, and that s appears as a factor of the numerator only when a zero exists at $s = 0$.

3.3 DRIVING-POINT ADMITTANCE (SECOND FOSTER FORM)

When there is no dissipation, the driving-point admittance is a susceptance and can be simulated by a parallel arrangement of inductors and capacitors connected in series as shown in Fig. 3-7. Since for an inductor,

$$Y(s) = \frac{1}{sL}, \qquad Y(j\omega) = \frac{1}{j\omega L}$$

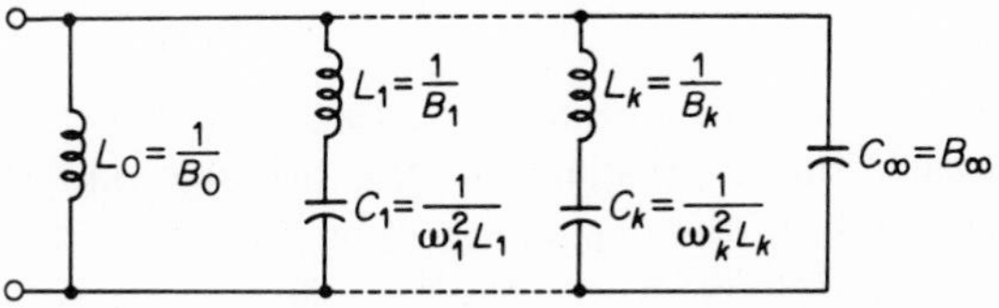

Figure 3-7 Partial fraction representation of driving-point admittance (second Foster form).

and for a capacitor,

$$Y(s) = sC, \qquad Y(j\omega) = j\omega C$$

the admittance of a series circuit component in Fig. 3-7 is given by

$$Y(s) = \frac{1}{sL_k + 1/sC_k} = \frac{s(1/L_k)}{s^2 + 1/L_kC_k} = \frac{sB_k}{s^2 - s_k^2} \qquad [3.3\text{-}1]$$

where $B_k = 1/L_k$ and

$$s_k^2 = -\frac{1}{L_kC_k} \qquad [3.3\text{-}2]$$

Addition of the admittances of the elements in Fig. 3-7 yields

$$Y(s) = \frac{B_0}{s} + \sum \frac{sB_k}{s^2 - s_k^2} + sB_\infty \qquad [3.3\text{-}3]$$

where $$B_0 = \frac{1}{L_0}, \quad B_k = \frac{1}{L_k}, \quad B_\infty = C_\infty$$

Equation 3.3-5 has the same form as Eq. 3.1-8, which was derived for the driving-point impedance. The polynomial form of the driving-point admittance in Fig. 3-7 is

$$Y(s) = \frac{a^n s^n + a^{n-2} s^{n-2} + \ldots + a_0}{b^{n-1} s^{n-1} + b^{n-3} s + \ldots + b_1 s}$$ [3.3-4]

and the factored polynomial form is given by

$$Y(s) = H \left[\frac{(s^2 - s_1^2)(s^2 - s_3^2) \ldots (s^2 - s_{2p+1}^2)}{s(s^2 - s_2^2) \ldots (s^2 - s_{2p}^2)} \right]$$ [3.3-5]

where $H = a_n/b_{n-1}$.

Inspection of Fig. 3-7 shows that since L_0 is a short circuit when $s = 0$, and C_∞ becomes a short circuit as $s \to \infty$, the driving-point admittance has poles at zero and infinity. Hence Eqs. 3.3-3 through 3.3-5 have exactly the same form as Eqs. 3.2-3 through 3.2-5 for a driving-point impedance with poles at zero and infinity. Just as in the case of the driving-point impedance, the expression for the driving-point admittance can assume four possible forms depending upon the *external* zeros and poles. The admittance equations for a pole at $s = 0$ and a zero at infinity have the same form as Eqs. 3.2-6 through 3.2-8. The admittance equations for a zero at $s = 0$ and a pole at infinity are analogous to Eqs. 3.2-9 through 3.2-11, while those for zeros at $s = 0$ and infinity have the same form as Eqs. 3.2-12 through 3.2-14.

3.4 THE SEPARATION PROPERTY AND OTHER CHARACTERISTICS

It was noted in connection with Fig. 3-2 that the slope of the reactance curve as a function of ω is always positive, and that the zeros and poles of the reactance function alternate. The same statement can be made concerning the susceptance curve and the susceptance function. The alternation of zeros and poles is known as the *separation property*, which will now be proved.

It follows directly from Eqs. 3.1-18 and 3.3-3 that both the driving-point impedance (reactance) and admittance (susceptance) have the following general form:

$$F(s) = \frac{P_0}{s} + \sum \frac{s P_k}{s^2 - s_k^2} + s P_\infty$$ [3.4-1]

where all the coefficients are *positive*. Differentiation of Eq. 3.4-1 with respect to s gives

$$\frac{d}{ds} F(s) = -\frac{P_0}{s^2} + \sum -\frac{(s^2 + s_k^2) P_k}{..(s^2 - s_k^2)^2} + P_\infty$$ [3.4-2]

When $\sigma = 0$, then $s = j\omega$, $s^2 = -\omega^2$, $s_k^2 = -\omega_k^2$. Under this condition,

$$\frac{d}{j\,d\omega} F(j\omega) = \frac{P_0}{\omega^2} + \sum \frac{(\omega^2 + \omega_k^2)P_k}{(\omega_k^2 - \omega^2)^2} + P_\infty \qquad [3.4\text{-}3]$$

Each term on the right-hand side of Eq. 3.4-3 is either a positive coefficient or the square of a real number. Hence the right-hand side of Eq. 3.4-3 is positive for all values of ω, and the slopes of both the reactance and susceptance curves are always positive. Inasmuch as the function must change in sign between consecutive zeros, and since it cannot change signs in a continuous manner because the slope is always positive, the function must change signs in a discontinuous manner at the poles. Hence the zeros and poles must *alternate*, and the separation property follows directly as a consequence of the positive slope of the reactance and susceptance curves.

The following general characteristics of both the reactance and susceptance functions should be noted:

(1) Since only positive values of L and C are admissible for realizable networks, the a's and b's of the polynomial form are positive real numbers. The constant H is also positive and real.

(2) The zeros and poles alternate, and the difference between the number of internal zeros and poles may never exceed unity.

(3) The power n of the polynomial is equal to the number of elements in the canonical network.

(4) The number of internal zeros and poles is one less than the number of elements in the canonical network.

(5) The orders of the numerator and denominator always differ by unity and only unity.

(6) Only even or odd powers of s appear in the individual polynomials, never both.

3.5 SYNTHESIS OF LOSSLESS NETWORKS

The material presented so far has been used to analyze reactance and susceptance networks. The equations will now be used to synthesize functions with prescribed characteristics. The factored form of the reactance or susceptance function places the zeros and poles in evidence. These equations show that a two-terminal (driving-point) reactance function is specified by the location of its zeros and poles plus the determination of the multiplying constant H. The constant H can be determined in a number of ways depending on what is required of the network. For example,

(1) H may be specified.

(2) The value of the reactance or susceptance at a certain frequency may be specified at a point other than the zeros or poles.

(3) The value of the slope of the reactance or susceptance curve at a specified frequency other than the poles of the network may be given.

The actual network for the reactance case can be determined in the following manner. The factored polynomial form can be written directly from the location of the zeros and poles, and H can be determined by methods 1 through 3. This equation is written in the general partial-fraction form, and the two expressions for Z must be equal. For example, using Case 1, Eq. 3.2-3.

$$Z(s) = \frac{A_0}{s} + \sum_{k=2}^{k=2p} \frac{sA_k}{s^2 - s_k^2} + sA_\infty = H\left[\frac{(s^2 - s_1^2)(s^2 - s_3^2)\ldots(s^2 - s_{2p+1}^2)}{s\ldots(s^2 - s_k^2)\ldots(s^2 - s_{2p}^2)}\right]$$

[3.5-1]

Assume that H and all zeros and poles are specified. Hence the right-hand side of Eq. 3.5-1 is completely determined. The problem then is to evaluate the coefficients on the left-hand side of Eq. 3.5-1. These coefficients can be determined in the following manner. To evaluate A_0, multiply through both sides by s, and let $s \to 0$ in the limit. Then A_0 is the only term that does not vanish, and

$$A_0 = H\left[\frac{(-s_1^2)(-s_3^2)\ldots(-s_{p+1}^2)}{\ldots(-s_k^2)\ldots(-s_{2p}^2)}\right]$$

[3.5-2]

For the A_k term, multiply both sides by $(s^2 - s_k^2)/s$ and let $s = s_k$. Then A_k is the only coefficient that does not vanish, and

$$A_k = H\left[\frac{(s_k^2 - s_1^2)(s_k^2 - s_3^2)\ldots(s_k^2 - s_{p+1}^2)}{s_k^2\ldots(s_k^2 - s_{k-2}^2)(s_k^2 - s_{k+2}^2)\ldots(s_k^2 - s_{2p}^2)}\right]$$

[3.5-3]

A_∞ is determined by multiplying both sides of the equation by $1/s$, and letting $s \to \infty$. Hence in the limit,

$$A_\infty = H$$

[3.5-4]

These results can be expressed in more compact form as follows:

$$A_0 = \lim_{s \to 0}\left[s \cdot Z(s)\right]$$

[3.5-5]

$$A_k = \lim_{s \to s_k}\left[\frac{s^2 - s_k^2}{s} Z(s)\right]$$

[3.5-6]

$$A_\infty = \operatorname*{Lim}_{s\to\infty} \left[\frac{Z(s)}{s}\right]$$ [3.5-7]

The circuit parameters are given by

$$C_0 = \frac{1}{A_0}$$ [3.5-8]

$$C_k = \frac{1}{A_k}$$ [3.5-9]

$$L_\infty = A_\infty$$ [3.5-10]

and L_k is determined from the following relations:

$$s_k^2 = -\frac{1}{L_k C_k}, \qquad \omega_k^2 = \frac{1}{L_k C_k}$$

$$L_k = \frac{1}{C_k \omega_k^2} = \frac{A_k}{\omega_k^2}$$ [3.5-11]

Equations 3.5-8 through 3.5-11 completely specify the network in Fig. 3-1 as a partial-fraction network.

The procedure for the synthesis of a susceptance network is the same as for a reactance network. Referring to Eq. 3.3-3 applied to Fig. 3-7, the coefficients for the admittance form are

$$B_0 = \operatorname*{Lim}_{s\to 0} [s \cdot Y(s)]$$ [3.5-12]

$$B_k = \operatorname*{Lim}_{s\to s_k} \left[\frac{s^2 - s_k^2}{s} Y(s)\right]$$ [3.5-13]

$$B_\infty = \operatorname*{Lim}_{s\to\infty} \left[\frac{Y(s)}{s}\right]$$ [3.5-14]

Equations 3.5-12 through 3.4-14 completely specify the network in Fig. 3-7 as a partial-fraction network.

3.6 EXAMPLES OF LOSSLESS NETWORK SYNTHESIS BY PARTIAL FRACTIONS

Assume that a reactance network as shown in Fig. 3-8 is to be synthesized. The zeros and poles are given in simple arithmetic form, but can be related to the actual frequencies. The frequencies given in this form are known as *normalized* frequencies. The angular frequency, specified as $\omega_1 = 1$, might correspond to an actual frequency of 10^6 radians per second. The impedance is also specified in normalized form. The relation between normalized and actual frequencies and impedances is developed in Sec. 3.9.

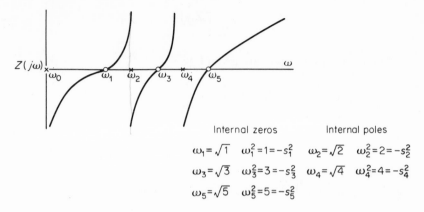

Internal zeros   Internal poles

$\omega_1 = \sqrt{1}$ $\omega_1^2 = 1 = -s_1^2$ $\omega_2 = \sqrt{2}$ $\omega_2^2 = 2 = -s_2^2$

$\omega_3 = \sqrt{3}$ $\omega_3^2 = 3 = -s_3^2$ $\omega_4 = \sqrt{4}$ $\omega_4^2 = 4 = -s_4^2$

$\omega_5 = \sqrt{5}$ $\omega_5^2 = 5 = -s_5^2$

Figure 3-8   Reactance function specified by poles and zeros.

From the information concerning zeros and poles given in Fig. 3-8, the following reactance function can be written

$$Z(s) = H\left[\frac{(s^2 + 1)(s^2 + 3)(s^2 + 5)}{s(s^2 + 2)(s^2 + 4)}\right]$$ [3.6-1]

It follows from Fig. 3-8 that an external pole exists as $s \to 0$, and that there is another external pole as $s \to \infty$. These external poles are shown in Fig. 3-8.

After the factors containing the internal poles are written into Eq. 3.6-1, the additional factor s is supplied to the denominator to provide for the external pole at zero, and to make the orders of the numerator and denominator differ by unity. The constant H must be specified. In order to obtain a simple value of H, assume that a normalized reactance of $-j3.03$ ohms at $\omega = 0.707$ radian is specified. Then, when a value of $s = j0.707$ and $s^2 = -0.5$ is substituted in Eq. 3.6-1, the following result is obtained:

$$-j3.03 = H\left[\frac{(\frac{1}{2})(\frac{5}{2})(\frac{9}{2})}{j0.707(\frac{3}{2})(\frac{7}{2})}\right] = -j1.515H$$ [3.6-2]

Hence $H = 2.0$. Inspection of Fig. 3-8 shows that between ω_0 and ω_1 the reactance is negative. Therefore a negative reactance was specified to determine H. If a value of ω is chosen between ω_1 and ω_2, a positive reactance must be chosen, etc. Thus the final expression for the reactance is

$$Z(s) = 2\left[\frac{(s^2 + 1)(s^2 + 3)(s^2 + 5)}{s(s^2 + 2)(s^2 + 4)}\right]$$ [3.6-3]

Since poles exist at $s = 0$ and $s = \infty$, all partial fractions are present in

Eq. 3.1-18. The coefficients are evaluated by Eqs. 3.5-5 through 3.5-7 as follows:

$$A_0 = [s \cdot Z(s)]_{s=0} = \left[2 \cdot \frac{1 \cdot 3 \cdot 5}{2 \cdot 4} \right] = \frac{15}{4} \qquad [3.6\text{-}4]$$

$$C_0 = \frac{1}{A_0} = \frac{4}{15} \quad \text{farad}$$

$$A_2 = \left[\frac{s^2 + 2}{s} Z(s) \right]_{s^2 = -2} = \left[2 \cdot \frac{-1 \cdot 1 \cdot 3}{-2 \cdot 2} \right] = \frac{3}{2}$$

$$C_2 = \frac{1}{A_2} = \frac{2}{3} \quad \text{farad}$$

$$L_2 = \frac{1}{\omega_2^2 C_2} = \frac{1}{2 \cdot \frac{2}{3}} = \frac{3}{4} \quad \text{henry}$$

$$A_4 = \left[\frac{s^2 + 4}{s} Z(s) \right]_{s^2 = -4} = \left[2 \cdot \frac{-3 \cdot -1 \cdot 1}{-4 \cdot -2} \right] = \frac{3}{4} \qquad [3.6\text{-}5]$$

$$C_4 = \frac{1}{A_4} = \frac{4}{3} \quad \text{farads}$$

$$L_4 = \frac{1}{\omega_4^2 C_4} = \frac{1}{4 \cdot \frac{4}{3}} = \frac{3}{16} \quad \text{henry}$$

$$A_\infty = L_\infty = \lim_{s \to \infty} \left[\frac{Z(s)}{s} \right] = 2.0 \quad \text{henrys} \qquad [3.6\text{-}6]$$

The network can now be constructed to meet the specified requirements. This network is shown in Fig. 3-9.

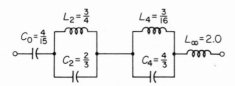

Values in farads and henrys

Figure 3-9 Partial fraction impedance network corresponding to Eq. 3.6-3.

The distribution of zeros and poles for the admittance form is given in Fig. 3-10. The positions of the zeros and poles have been interchanged, and now zeros appear at both $\omega = 0$ and $\omega = \infty$. In order to obtain the identical network, $H = \frac{1}{2}$, and the susceptance function is given by

$$\frac{1}{Z(s)} = Y(s) = \frac{1}{2} \left[\frac{s(s^2 + 2)(s^2 + 4)}{(s^2 + 1)(s^2 + 3)(s^2 + 5)} \right] \qquad [3.6\text{-}7]$$

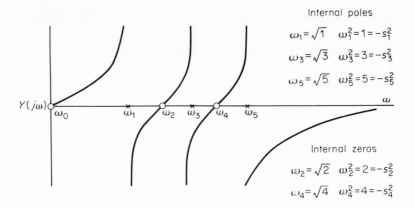

Figure 3-10 Susceptance function specified by poles and zeros.

Since poles do not exist at $\omega = 0$ or $\omega = \infty$,

$$B_0 = B_\infty = 0 \qquad [3.6\text{-}8]$$

The other coefficients are given by

$$B_1 = \left[\frac{s^2 + 1}{s} Y(s) \right]_{s^2 = -1} = \left[\frac{1}{2} \cdot \frac{1 \cdot 3}{2 \cdot 4} \right] = \frac{3}{16}$$

$$L_1 = \frac{1}{B_1} = \frac{16}{3} \quad \text{henrys}$$

$$C_1 = \frac{1}{\omega_1^2 L_1} = \frac{1}{1 \cdot \frac{16}{3}} = \frac{3}{16} \quad \text{farad}$$

$$B_3 = \left[\frac{s^2 + 3}{s} Y(s) \right]_{s^2 = -3} = \left[\frac{1}{2} \cdot \frac{-1 \cdot 1}{-2 \cdot 2} \right] = \frac{1}{8}$$

$$L_3 = \frac{1}{B_3} = 8 \quad \text{henrys} \qquad [3.6\text{-}9]$$

$$C_3 = \frac{1}{\omega_3^2 L_3} = \frac{1}{3 \times 8} = \frac{1}{24} \quad \text{farad}$$

$$B_5 = \left[\frac{s^2 + 5}{s} Y(s) \right]_{s^2 = -5} = \left[\frac{1}{2} \cdot \frac{-3 \cdot -1}{-4 \cdot -2} \right] = \frac{3}{16}$$

$$L_5 = \frac{1}{B_5} = \frac{16}{3} \quad \text{henrys}$$

$$C_5 = \frac{1}{\omega_5^2 L_5} = \frac{1}{5 \cdot \frac{16}{3}} = \frac{3}{80} \quad \text{farad}$$

The admittance network is shown in Fig. 3-11. This network is identical in characteristics to the network of Fig. 3-9. In Fig. 3-11, the sum of the three capacitances in parallel, $C_1 + C_3 + C_5$, is $\frac{4}{15}$ farad, which is the capacitance C_0 of Fig. 3-9. Likewise, the sum of the three inductors in parallel, $L_1 + L_3 + L_5$, is 2.0 henrys, which is the value of L_∞ in Fig. 3-9. The selection of either the impedance or admittance

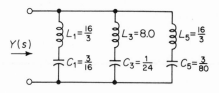

Values in farads and henrys

Figure 3-11   Partial fraction admittance network corresponding to Eq. 3.6-7.

form of synthesis depends upon the availability and economy of the circuit components and other factors.

3.7 CONTINUED-FRACTION NETWORKS

The reactance networks discussed above can be developed into two more fundamental forms. These methods were presented by W. Cauer.* The Cauer or continued-fraction form of network is a ladder network as shown in Fig. 3-12. If we start with admittance Y_6, we can add impedances in series and parallel until the total impedance $Z(s)$ is obtained. Thus when the impedance $1/Y_6$ is added in series with impedance Z_5, the impedance in parallel with Y_4 in Fig. 3-12 is

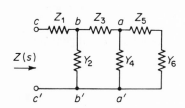

Figure 3-12   Illustration of a ladder network.

$$Z_a = Z_5 + \frac{1}{Y_6} \qquad [3.7\text{-}1]$$

Hence the admittance at terminals aa' is

$$Y_{aa'} = Y_4 + \cfrac{1}{Z_5 + \cfrac{1}{Y_6}} \qquad [3.7\text{-}2]$$

Similarly the impedance in parallel with Y_2 is

$$Z_b = Z_3 + \cfrac{1}{Y_4 + \cfrac{1}{Z_5 + \cfrac{1}{Y_6}}} \qquad [3.7\text{-}3]$$

* Cauer, W. "Die Verwirklichung von Wechslestromwiderstände Vorgeschriebener Frequenzabhängigkeit," *Arch. Elektrotech.*, Vol. 17 (1927), pp. 355–388.

Therefore

$$Y_{bb'} = Y_2 + \cfrac{1}{Z_3 + \cfrac{1}{Y_4 + \cfrac{1}{Z_5 + \cfrac{1}{Y_6}}}} \qquad [3.7\text{-}4]$$

It follows from Eqs. 3.7-1 through 3.7-4 that

$$Z(s) = Z_{cc'} = Z_1 + \cfrac{1}{Y_2 + \cfrac{1}{Z_3 + \cfrac{1}{Y_4 + \cfrac{1}{Z_5 + \cfrac{1}{Y_6}}}}} \qquad [3.7\text{-}5]$$

The form of $Z(s)$ as given in Eq. 3.7-5 is termed a *continued fraction*. This term is derived from the fact that the expression is formed by continued inversion and addition.

Assume that the polynomial form for the driving-point impedance is as given by Eq. 3.2-4, where

$$Z(s) = \frac{a_n s^n + a_{n-2} s^{n-2} + \ldots + a_0}{b_{n-1} s^{n-1} + b_{n-3} s^{n-3} + \ldots + b_1 s} \qquad [3.7\text{-}6]$$

Equation 3.7-6 can be expressed in abbreviated form as

$$Z(s) = \frac{P_n(s)}{P_{n-1}(s)} \qquad [3.7\text{-}7]$$

where P_n is a polynomial of degree n, and P_{n-1} is of degree $n - 1$. The continued-fraction development similar to Eq. 3.7-5 is formed by breaking off one term by dividing P_n by P_{n-1} as in long division, and then inverting the remainder and extracting another term. Thus

$$Z(s) = \frac{P_n(s)}{P_{n-1}(s)} = c_1 s + \frac{P_{n-2}(s)}{P_{n-1}(s)} = c_1 s + \cfrac{1}{\cfrac{P_{n-1}(s)}{P_{n-2}(s)}} \qquad [3.7\text{-}8]$$

where $c_1 = a_n/b_{n-1}$. It follows in a similar manner that

$$\left.\begin{array}{l}
\dfrac{P_{n-1}(s)}{P_{n-2}(s)} = c_2 s + \dfrac{P_{n-3}(s)}{P_{n-2}(s)} = c_2 s + \dfrac{1}{\dfrac{P_{n-2}(s)}{P_{n-3}(s)}} \\[4ex]
\dfrac{P_{n-2}(s)}{P_{n-3}(s)} = c_3 s + \dfrac{P_{n-4}(s)}{P_{n-3}(s)} \\[3ex]
\cdots\cdots\cdots\cdots\cdots\cdots\cdots\cdots\cdots\cdots\cdots\cdots \\[1ex]
\dfrac{P_2(s)}{P_1(s)} = c_{n-1} s + \dfrac{P_0(s)}{P_1(s)} \\[3ex]
\dfrac{P_1(s)}{P_0(s)} = c_n s + 0
\end{array}\right\} \qquad [3.7\text{-}9]$$

where $P_0(s)$ is a constant.

The continued-fraction process can be carried out by two different methods. The one shown in Eq. 3.7-9 is the development about infinity. The term that is first divided out is the limiting value of the original function as $s \to \infty$. If we start with the lowest power of s, then the continued-fraction development is about the origin. The term that is divided out in this process is the limiting value of the original function as $s \to 0$.

As a specific example, let

$$Z(s) = \frac{s^4 + 4s^2 + 3}{s^3 + 2s} \qquad [3.7\text{-}10]$$

where both the numerator and denominator are expressed in *descending* powers of s. The development about infinity is

$$Z(s) = \frac{s^4 + 4s^2 + 3}{s^3 + 2s} = \underline{s} + \frac{2s^2 + 3}{s^3 + 2s}$$

and $\underline{s}$ is the continued-fraction component. Note that s is the value of $Z(s)$ as $s \to \infty$ in the limit. Inverting the remainder and continuing the process yields

$$\frac{s^3 + 2s}{2s^2 + 3} = \underline{\frac{1}{2}} s + \frac{\frac{1}{2}s}{2s^2 + 3}$$

where the underlined term is again a component of the continued fraction. Continuation of the division process gives

$$\frac{2s^2 + 3}{\frac{1}{2}s} = \underline{4s} + \frac{3}{\frac{1}{2}s}, \qquad \frac{\frac{1}{2}s}{3} = \underline{\tfrac{1}{6}s} + 0$$

Using the underlined terms as the continued-fraction components gives

$$Z(s) = s + \cfrac{1}{\frac{1}{2}s + \cfrac{1}{4s + \cfrac{1}{\frac{1}{6}s}}} \qquad [3.7\text{-}11]$$

Since this is an impedance function, the first term is an impedance. The ladder network corresponding to the continued fraction development in Eq. 3.7-11 is shown in Fig. 3-13.

If the same function is designated as an admittance function, then the first term is an admittance and the second an impedance, etc. The resultant network is shown in Fig. 3-14. The shorting connection at the

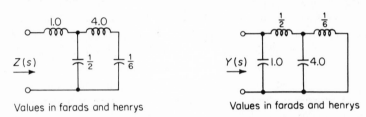

Values in farads and henrys   Values in farads and henrys

Figure 3-13 Ladder network corresponding to Eq. 3.7-11.

Figure 3-14 Ladder network corresponding to an admittance in Eq. 3.7-10.

end of the network in Fig. 3-14 is required because $4s + 1/\frac{1}{6}s$ in Eq. 3.7-11 would in this case represent the admittance of a capacitor in parallel with an inductor. The network in Fig. 3-14 is the inverse of the network in Fig. 3-13.

If the same function is developed about the origin, $Z(s)$ is expressed as a quotient of two polynomials in *ascending* powers of s as follows:

$$Z(s) = \frac{3 + 4s^2 + s^4}{2s + s^3} = \underline{\frac{\frac{3}{2}}{s}} + \frac{\frac{5}{2}s^2 + s^4}{2s + s^3} \qquad [3.7\text{-}12]$$

Note that division gives $\frac{3}{2}/s$ as the first term plus the remainder, and that $\frac{3}{2}/s$ is the value $Z(s)$ approaches as $s \to 0$. Also, the underlined term is the first component of the continued fraction. Inverting the remainder and continuing the process, yields

$$\frac{2s + s^3}{\frac{5}{2}s^2 + s^4} = \underline{\frac{\frac{4}{5}}{s}} + \frac{\frac{1}{5}s^3}{\frac{5}{2}s^2 + s^4}$$

$$\frac{\frac{5}{2}s^2 + s^4}{\frac{1}{5}s^3} = \underline{\frac{\frac{25}{2}}{s}} + \frac{s^4}{\frac{1}{5}s^3}$$

$$\frac{\frac{1}{5}s^3}{s^4} = \underline{\frac{\frac{1}{5}}{s}} + 0$$

Since the underlined terms are the continued-fraction components, $Z(s)$ can be expressed as

$$Z(s) = \frac{\frac{3}{2}}{s} + \cfrac{1}{\frac{\frac{4}{5}}{s} + \cfrac{1}{\frac{\frac{25}{2}}{s} + \cfrac{1}{\frac{\frac{1}{5}}{s}}}} \qquad [3.7\text{-}13]$$

The ladder network corresponding to Eq. 3.7-13 is shown in Fig. 3-15. This is the second type of continued-fraction network, and is equivalent to Fig. 3-13.

If the function in Eq. 3.7-12 is designated an admittance, the first term of the continued fraction is an admittance, the second an impedance, etc. The corresponding network is shown in Fig. 3-16. The network of Fig. 3-16 is the inverse of Fig. 3-15, but is equivalent to Fig. 3-14.

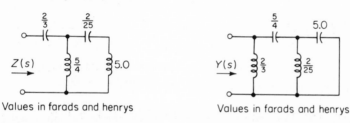

Values in farads and henrys   Values in farads and henrys

Figure 3-15 Ladder network corresponding to Eq. 3.7-13.   Figure 3-16 Ladder network corresponding to an admittance in Eq. 3.7-12.

Illustrations of the application of continued fractions have been confined to the case when $Z(s) = P_n(s)/P_{n-1}(s)$. When $Z(s) = P_{n-1}(s)/P_n(s)$, a zero impedance term or short circuit is first removed, and the remainder $Z(s)$ is inverted. Long division then yields a shunt admittance, and the inversion process is continued to determine the equivalent ladder network.

3.8 EXAMPLES OF LOSSLESS NETWORK SYNTHESIS BY CONTINUED FRACTIONS

Using the same example as for the partial-fraction network (Eq. 3.6-3), we can develop two continued-fraction networks. The first will be the development about infinity, or starting with the highest powers of s. When the factors in the numerator and denominator of Eq. 3.6-3 are multiplied out, and both numerator and denominator are expressed in descending powers of s, the following result is obtained:

$$Z(s) = \frac{2(s^2 + 1)(s^2 + 3)(s^2 + 5)}{s(s^2 + 2)(s^2 + 4)} = \frac{2s^6 + 18s^4 + 46s^2 + 30}{s^5 + 6s^3 + 8s} \qquad [3.8\text{-}1]$$

Carrying out the continued fraction calculations yields

$$\frac{2s^6 + 18s^4 + 46s^2 + 30}{s^5 + 6s^3 + 8s} = \underline{2s} + \frac{6s^4 + 30s^2 + 30}{s^5 + 6s^3 + 8s}$$

$$\frac{s^5 + 6s^3 + 8s}{6s^4 + 30s^2 + 30} = \underline{\tfrac{1}{6}s} + \frac{s^3 + 3s}{6s^4 + 30s^2 + 30}$$

$$\frac{6s^4 + 30s^2 + 30}{s^3 + 3s} = \underline{6s} + \frac{12s^2 + 30}{s^3 + 3s}$$

$$\frac{s^3 + 3s}{12s^2 + 30} = \underline{\tfrac{1}{12}s} + \frac{\tfrac{1}{2}s}{12s^2 + 30}$$

$$\frac{12s^2 + 30}{\tfrac{1}{2}s} = \underline{24s} + \frac{30}{\tfrac{1}{2}s}$$

$$\frac{\tfrac{1}{2}s}{30} = \underline{\tfrac{1}{60}s} + 0$$

Hence
$$Z(s) = 2s + \cfrac{1}{\tfrac{1}{6}s + \cfrac{1}{\tfrac{1}{12}s + \cfrac{1}{24s + \cfrac{1}{\tfrac{1}{60}s}}}} \qquad [3.8\text{-}2]$$

Since this is an impedance function and the denominator is divided into the numerator, the first term is an impedance, the second term an admittance, etc. The ladder network corresponding to the continued-fraction expression of Eq. 3.8-2 is shown in Fig. 3-17. The network of Fig. 3-17 again is equivalent to both the partial-fraction networks previously developed in Figs. 3-9 and 3-11.

Developing the network about the origin gives the second continued-fraction network. Expressing $Z(s)$ as a quotient of polynomials in ascending powers of s, and applying continued fractions, yields

$$Z(s) = \frac{30 + 46s^2 + 18s^4 + 2s^6}{8s + 6s^3 + s^5} = \frac{15}{4s} + \frac{23.5s^2 + 14.25s^4 + 2s^6}{8s + 6s^3 + s^5} \qquad [3.8\text{-}3]$$

$$\frac{8s + 6s^3 + s^5}{23.5s^2 + 14.25s^4 + 2s^6} = \frac{0.34}{s} + \frac{1.16s^3 + 0.36s^5}{23.5s^2 + 14.25s^4 + 2s^6}$$

$$\frac{23.5s^2 + 14.25s^4 + 2s^6}{1.16s^3 + 0.36s^5} = \frac{20.2}{s} + \frac{6.98s^4 + 2s^6}{1.16s^3 + 0.36s^5}$$

$$\frac{1.16s^3 + 0.36s^5}{6.98s^4 + 2s^6} = \frac{0.166}{s} + \frac{0.03s^5}{6.98s^4 + 2s^6}$$

$$\frac{6.98s^4 + 2s^6}{0.03s^5} = \frac{233}{s} + \frac{2s^6}{0.03s^5}$$

$$\frac{0.03s^5}{2s^6} = \frac{0.015}{s} + 0$$

Hence $$Z(s) = \dfrac{15}{4s} + \cfrac{1}{\dfrac{0.34}{s} + \cfrac{1}{\dfrac{20.2}{s} + \cfrac{1}{\dfrac{0.166}{s} + \cfrac{1}{\dfrac{233}{s} + \cfrac{1}{\dfrac{0.015}{s}}}}}}$$ [3.8-4]

The ladder network corresponding to the continued-fraction expansion in Eq. 3.8-4 is shown in Fig. 3-18.

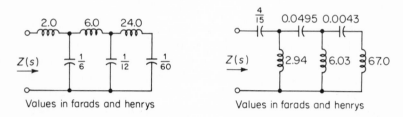

Figure 3-17 Ladder network corresponding to Eq. 3.8-2.

Figure 3-18 Ladder network corresponding to Eq. 3.8-4.

The two partial-fraction networks and the two continued-fraction networks determined in the examples are basic networks. Numerous other equivalent networks can be obtained, depending on the number of elements in the network. For example, a few terms can be extracted by continued fractions and the remainder developed by partial fractions. This can be accomplished in several ways.

3.9 NORMALIZED FREQUENCY AND IMPEDANCE

In the illustrative problem of Sec. 3.6, the zeros and poles were specified in simple arithmetic form in order to facilitate the computations. Also, the reactance was specified in order to obtain a simple value of constant H. In actual synthesis, the zeros, poles, and impedance are determined by circuit requirements. However, they may be normalized in order to simplify calculations, and then the circuit can by synthesized with proper circuit elements that are obtained from the normalized parameters. It is the purpose of this section to investigate the relation between normalized and actual circuit parameters.

The subscript a will be used to denote the actual value of a parameter, and the subscript n will be used to denote its normalized value. When the impedance level is maintained constant while the frequency is normalized, the following relations hold:

$$L_a = \left(\frac{\omega_n}{\omega_a}\right) L_n \qquad\qquad [3.9\text{-}1]$$

$$C_a = \left(\frac{\omega_n}{\omega_a}\right) C_n \qquad\qquad [3.9\text{-}2]$$

Equations 3.9-1 and 3.9-2 follow from the fact that the products ωL and ωC must remain constant if the impedance level remains constant. Multiplication of Eqs. 3.9-1 and 3.9-2 yields

$$L_a C_a = \left(\frac{\omega_n^2}{\omega_a^2}\right) L_n C_n \qquad\qquad [3.9\text{-}3]$$

Equation 3.9-3 is an identity that holds for all values of the variables.

When the frequency is unaltered but the impedance level is normalized, the inductance is directly proportional to the impedance ratio whereas the capacitance is inversely proportional to the impedance ratio. This follows from the fact that inductive reactance is directly proportional to frequency whereas capacitative reactance is inversely proportional to frequency. Therefore, when the frequency is unaltered while the impedance is normalized, the actual values of inductance and capacitance are given by:

$$L_a = \left(\frac{Z_a}{Z_n}\right) L_n \qquad\qquad [3.9\text{-}4]$$

$$C_a = \left(\frac{Z_n}{Z_a}\right) C_n \qquad\qquad [3.9\text{-}5]$$

Multiplication of Eqs. 3.9-4 and 3.9-5 yields

$$L_a C_a = L_n C_n \qquad\qquad [3.9\text{-}6]$$

It follows from Eq. 3.9-6 that $\omega_a = \omega_n$, showing that the frequency remains unchanged.

When both the frequency and the impedance are normalized in order to simplify the calculation, it follows from Eqs. 3.9-1, 3.9-2, 3.9-4, and 3.9-5 that the actual parameters are given in terms of the normalized parameters by the following equations:

$$L_a = \left(\frac{\omega_n}{\omega_a}\right)\left(\frac{Z_a}{Z_n}\right) L_n \qquad\qquad [3.9\text{-}7]$$

$$C_a = \left(\frac{\omega_n}{\omega_a}\right)\left(\frac{Z_n}{Z_a}\right) C_n \qquad\qquad [3.9\text{-}8]$$

To illustrate the application of normalization, assume that in the illustrative problem in Sec. 3.6 the frequency ratio, ω_n/ω_a, is 10^{-6}, and the impedance ratio, Z_n/Z_a, is 10^{-3}. In other words, the frequency is reduced by a factor of 10^6, and the impedance level is reduced by a factor of 10^3. It follows from Eqs. 3.9-7 and 3.9-8 that

$$L_a = 10^{-6} \times \left(\frac{1}{10^{-3}}\right) L_n = 10^{-3}L_n = \frac{L_n}{10^3} \qquad [3.9\text{-}9]$$

$$C_a = 10^{-6} \times 10^{-3}C_n = 10^{-9}C_n = \frac{C_n}{10^9} \qquad [3.9\text{-}10]$$

Hence, the actual impedance is found by dividing the normalized impedance by 10^3, and the actual capacitance is found by dividing the normalized capacitance by 10^9. Figure 3-19(a) shows the synthesis on a

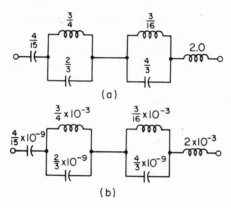

Figure 3-19 (a) Normalized circuit components. (b) Actual circuit components.

normalized basis, and Fig. 3-19(b) is the actual network required by the specifications.

PROBLEMS

3-1 A reactance function has zeros at $\omega = 8$, 25, and 50 radians per sec. It has poles at $\omega = 0$, 10, 30, and infinity. The driving-point impedance is $-j1.0$ ohm when $\omega = 15$ radians per sec. Sketch the reactance curve, and determine the first equivalent partial-fraction (impedance) network.

3-2 A reactance function has an internal zero at $\omega = 2$, and an internal pole at $\omega = 10$ radians per sec. The driving-point impedance is $j2.0$ ohms at $\omega = 8$ radians per sec. Sketch the reactance curve and determine the first equivalent partial-fraction network.

3-3 A reactance function has an internal zero at $\omega = 30,000$ and an internal pole at $\omega = 20,000$ radians per sec. The driving-point impedance is $j1000$ ohms at $\omega = 40,000$ radians per sec. Sketch the reactance curve and determine the first equivalent partial-fraction network.

3-4 A reactance function has an internal zero at $\omega = 40,000$ and internal poles at $\omega = 20,000$ and $\omega = 50,000$ radians per sec. The driving-point impedance is $-j5000$ ohms when $\omega = 60,000$ radians per sec. Sketch the reactance curve, and determine the first equivalent partial-fraction network.

3-5 For the data given in Prob. 3-1, determine the second equivalent partial-fraction (admittance) network.

3-6 For the data given in Prob. 3-2, determine the second equivalent partial-fraction network.

3-7 For the data given in Prob. 3-3, determine the second equivalent partial-fraction network.

3-8 For the data given in Prob. 3-4, determine the second equivalent partial-fraction network.

3-9 Determine the poles and zeros of the driving-point reactance function of the accompanying network.

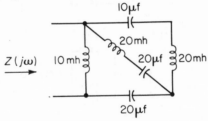

Problem 3-9

3-10 Determine the first equivalent partial-fraction network for the circuit in Prob. 3-9.

3-11 Determine the second equivalent partial-fraction network for the circuit in Prob. 3-9.

3-12 The driving-point impedance $Z(j\omega)$ in the accompanying figure is to be $70 + j0$ when $\omega = 10^7$, and zero when $\omega = 2 \times 10^7$, 3×10^7, and 4×10^7 radians per sec. Determine L; and, assuming that the poles of Z_f are located midway between the zeros and that a pole exists at infinity, design a first equivalent partial-fraction network Z_f to be connected across ab that meets the above specifications.

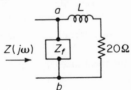

Problem 3-12

3-13 A reactance function has zeros at $\omega_1 = 10^6$ radians per sec and infinity. It has poles at $\omega = 0$ and at $\omega_2 = 1.1 \times 10^6$ radians per sec. It is required that the slope of the reactance curve at $\omega = 10^6$ radians per sec be 0.1 ohm per radian per sec. Find a network meeting this requirement.

3-14 Use the data in Prob. 3-13, and let $H = 2.0 \times 10^9$. Assume that ω_2 is adjusted to such a value that the slope of the reactance curve at $\omega = 10^6$ radians per sec is 0.1 ohm per radian per sec. Find a network meeting this requirement.

3-15 Use the data in Prob. 3-13, and let the slope of the susceptance curve be specified as 10 mhos per radian at $\omega_2 = 1.1 \times 10^6$ radians. Find a network meeting this requirement.

3-16 Develop the first continued-fraction network (about infinity) for the reactance function specified in Prob. 3-1.

3-17 Develop the first continued-fraction network for the reactance function specified in Prob. 3-2.

3-18 Develop the first continued-fraction network for the reactance function specified in Prob. 3-3.

3-19 Develop the first continued-fraction network for the reactance function specified in Prob. 3-4.

3-20 Develop the first continued-fraction network for the data given in Prob. 3-12.

3-21 Develop the second continued-fraction network (about zero) for the reactance function specified in Prob. 3-1.

3-22 Develop the second continued-fraction network for the reactance function specified in Prob. 3-2.

3-23 Develop the second continued-fraction network for the reactance function specified in Prob. 3-3.

3-24 Develop the second continued-fraction network for the reactance function specified in Prob. 3-4.

3-25 Develop the second continued-fraction network for the data given in Prob. 3-12.

3-26 Two generators with frequencies indicated in the accompanying sketch are to feed a common load of one-ohm resistance with maximum power and without interaction between the generators. Design lossless one-terminal pair networks N_1 and N_2 so that this is accomplished. (Use normalized impedances.)

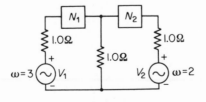

Problem 3-26

design of electric wave filters

4.0 INTRODUCTION

An electric wave filter is a two-terminal pair network designed to transmit a certain range of frequencies and attenuate other ranges. The electric wave filter probably has its greatest application in carrier-current telephony, but it has also numerous other applications in instrumentation, telemetering equipment, etc., where it is necessary to transmit or attenuate a limited range of frequencies.

In any electric wave filter, there is always some loss of energy in the pass-band or transmitting range, and never complete attenuation in the non-pass or rejection range of the filter.

Attenuator networks usually contain only one type of element, namely a resistor. For electric wave filters, however, the networks are generally designed with reactive elements, and two types of elements are involved, namely, inductors and capacitors. It is impossible to obtain elements that are entirely reactive, but the residual loss caused by resistance in the components can be taken into consideration in the final design of the filter.

4.1 GENERAL THEORY OF ELECTRIC WAVE FILTERS

Electric wave filters may be classified as follows:

(a) Low-pass filters that transmit all frequencies from zero to a cut-off frequency, and attenuate all higher frequencies.

(b) High-pass filters that transmit all frequencies above a certain cut-off frequency, and attenuate all frequencies below the cut-off frequency.

(c) Band-pass filters that transmit only those frequencies above a fixed minimum, f_1, and below a fixed maximum, f_2, the band being bounded by f_2 and f_1.

(d) Band-elimination filters that transmit all frequencies from 0 to f_1

93

and from f_2 to infinity, and attenuate all the frequencies in the band between f_1 and f_2.

The ideal wave filter is one that transmits a certain band of frequencies without attenuation, causes infinite attenuation for all other frequencies, and has constant impedance in the transmission band. The attenuation characteristics of an ideal band-pass filter are shown in Fig. 4-1. Such a filter is not realizable in practice. Losses in coils and capacitors cause attenuation in the pass-band, and finite rather than infinite attenuation characterizes the rejection band. The characteristics of the ideal filter can be approached by the use of several specially designed sections in cascade. Economy demands that the filter be constructed as simply as possible to meet given specifications.

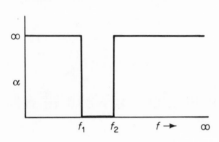

Figure 4-1   Attenuation characteristic of an ideal band-pass filter.

There is a limitless number of possible types of filter networks. The arms of these networks can assume any degree of complexity, but engineering considerations and economy in manufacture are usually the controlling factors. Only the simpler and more commonly used networks will be discussed here. These include the T, π, bridged-T, and lattice structures, all of which are symmetrical networks. In addition to the above, the bisected T and π sections, often referred to as L sections, find application as terminating networks. These will be considered after the impedance characteristics of the symmetrical structures have been investigated.

As in the case of attenuators, the symmetrical lattice structure will be taken as the basis of design. The characteristic impedance and the propagation function of the lattice network are

$$Z_0 = \sqrt{Z_a Z_b} \qquad [4.1\text{-}1]$$

$$\gamma = \alpha + j\beta = \ln\left(\frac{1 + \sqrt{Z_a/Z_b}}{1 - \sqrt{Z_a/Z_b}}\right) \qquad [4.1\text{-}2]$$

where Z_a and Z_b are the impedances of the series and lattice arms, and α and β are respectively the attenuation and phase functions. It will be assumed that Z_a and Z_b are impedances of pure reactors, and that they have the form of $\pm jX_a$ and $\pm jX_b$. Under this assumption the following relations hold:

When X_a and X_b have like signs, it follows from Eq. 4.1-2 that:

TGS

$$\gamma = \alpha + j\beta = \ln\left(\frac{1 + \sqrt{\pm jX_a/\pm jX_b}}{1 - \sqrt{\pm jX_a/\pm jX_b}}\right) = \ln\left(\frac{1+y}{1-y}\right) \qquad [4.1\text{-}3]$$

where $y = \sqrt{X_a/X_b}$. Equation 4.1-3 can be written as

$$\gamma = 2\tanh^{-1} y \qquad [4.1\text{-}4]$$

Equation 4.1-4 follows from Eq. B-51 in Appendix B.

It follows from Eq. 4.1-3 that when X_a and X_b have like signs, y is real and

$$\gamma = \ln N/\underline{\pm\pi} = \ln(N\,\epsilon^{j\pm\pi}) \qquad \text{when } y > 1$$
$$\gamma = \ln N/\underline{0} = \ln(N\,\epsilon^{j0}) \qquad \text{when } y < 1 \qquad [4.1\text{-}5]$$

where $N = \left|\dfrac{1+y}{1-y}\right|$

When X_a and X_b have opposite signs, it follows from Eq. 4.1-2 that:

$$\gamma = \alpha + j\beta = \ln\left(\frac{1 + \sqrt{\pm jX_a/\mp jX_b}}{1 - \sqrt{\pm jX_a/\mp jX_b}}\right) = \ln\left(\frac{1+jy}{1-jy}\right) \qquad [4.1\text{-}6]$$

$$= \ln[1/\underline{2\tan^{-1}y}] = \ln(1\,\epsilon^{j\,2\tan^{-1}y}) = 0 + j\,2\tan y$$

Equation 4.1-6 follows from the fact that $|1 + jy| = |1 - jy|$, and $\ln 1 = 0$.

It follows directly from Eqs. 4.1-5 and 4.1-6 that when X_a and X_b have like signs

$$\alpha = \ln N; \qquad \beta = \pm\pi \text{ or } \beta = 0$$

and when X_a and X_b have opposite signs

$$\alpha = 0; \qquad \beta = 2\tan^{-1} y$$

Equation 4.1-3 shows that the attenuation is infinite when X_a and X_b are equal and of like sign. The condition for transmission without attenuation is that the frequency range should be such that X_a and X_b have opposite signs. This relation is of fundamental importance in filter design.

Equation 4.1-1 shows that when X_a and X_b have opposite signs

$$Z_0 = \sqrt{\pm jX_a(\mp jX_b)} = \sqrt{-j^2 X_a X_b} = \sqrt{X_a X_b} \qquad [4.1\text{-}7]$$

$$\text{and } Z_0 \text{ is real;}$$

peally we like no attenuation

where $e^{\alpha + j\beta} = \dfrac{U_1}{U_2}$

and when X_a and X_b are of like sign

$$Z_0 = \sqrt{\pm jX_a(\pm jX_b)} = \sqrt{j^2 X_a X_b} = j\sqrt{X_a X_b} \qquad [4.1\text{-}8]$$

and Z_0 is imaginary.

Equations 4.1-7 and 4.1-8 show that the characteristic impedance is a pure resistance in the pass range, and a pure reactance in the rejection range, when losses (resistance) in the network components are neglected. When the characteristic impedance is purely resistive, the network absorbs real power from the source, and since the network is assumed to be lossless, all of this power is transmitted to the load without attenuation.

When a network is terminated by its characteristic impedance, and the characteristic impedance is reactive, the network does not absorb real power from the source.* This condition does not result in infinite attenuation, as might at first be expected. It should be remembered that attenuation is proportional to the ratio of output voltage to input voltage, and to the ratio of output current to input current, regardless of the phase relation between the voltage and the current. When the characteristic impedance Z_0 is reactive, and the filter is terminated by Z_0, the output voltage and current may have any values and still satisfy the condition that the real power is zero. Hence, the ratio of input to output voltage and the ratio of input to output current may vary in the attenuation range. This accounts for the variable attenuation in this range.

Equations 4.1-7 and 4.1-8 show that the characteristic impedance, whether real or imaginary, is a function of the frequency. It follows that a single network with a fixed termination cannot be matched to a generator at all frequencies. An attempt to do so causes reflection that decreases the received power in the pass range and changes the propagation characteristic of the filter when terminated by a constant resistance.

A lattice network is a low-pass filter if the reactances of the series and diagonal arms have opposite signs in a frequency range between $\omega = 0$ to $\omega = \omega_c$, where ω_c is the cut-off frequency (the frequency at which attenuation begins), and if they have the same signs from $\omega = \omega_c$ to $\omega = \infty$. The network is a high-pass filter if the signs of the reactances are the same from $\omega = 0$ to $\omega = \omega_c$, and are opposite from $\omega = \omega_c$ to $\omega = \infty$.

Possible reactance curves for Z_a and Z_b for low-pass and high-pass lattice filters are shown in Figs. 4-2 and 4-3, which illustrate the zero-pole

---

*If the network is not terminated by its characteristic impedance, the effects of reflection must be considered. The analysis that follows here assumes that the network is always terminated by Z_0.

configurations studied in Chap. 3. It can be seen that cut-off occurs at a frequency, ω_c, where one of the reactances changes sign in passing through a zero or a pole. The task of designing a filter consists of calculating the values of the network parameters for a given value of ω_c, and for a specified impedance. The design of simple filter sections will be presented in Sec. 4.2, which follows.

4.2 DESIGN OF PROTOTYPE LOW-PASS AND HIGH-PASS FILTERS

It follows from the bisection principle that π and T sections having open-circuited and short-circuited impedances given by Z_{och} and Z_{sch} in Figs. 4-2 and 4-3 will constitute either low-pass or high-pass filters. These

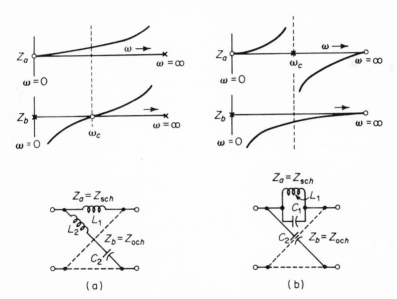

Figure 4-2 Low-pass filters (lattice).

basic structures are known as prototypes from which more complicated networks can be derived.

Consider the T and π sections shown in Fig. 4-4. The corresponding bisected sections are shown in Fig. 4-5. A comparison of Figs. 4-2 and 4-5 shows that the open-circuited impedance of Fig. 4-5(a) corresponds to Z_b in Fig. 4-2(a), and that the short-circuited impedance corresponds to Z_a. In this case, the inductance in Z_b equals the inductance of Z_a. Likewise, the open-circuited impedance of the bisected section in Fig. 4-5(b) corresponds to Z_b. In this case, the capacitance in Z_a equals

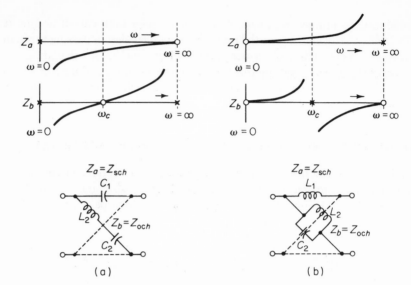

Figure 4-3 High-pass filters (lattice).

the capacitance of Z_b. Inasmuch as cutoff occurs when the reactance changes in sign, the cut-off frequency corresponds to series resonance, or an impedance zero, in Fig. 4-5(a), and to parallel resonance, or an impedance pole, in Fig. 4-5(b). In either case the cut-off frequency is given by

$$\omega_c \left(\frac{L_1}{2}\right) = \frac{1}{\omega_c \, (C_2/2)}$$

$$\omega_c = \frac{2}{\sqrt{L_1 C_2}}$$

[4.2-1]

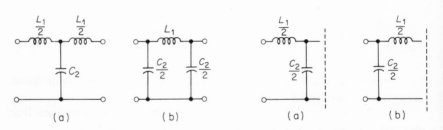

Figure 4-4 T and π sections of prototype low-pass filter.

Figure 4-5 Bisected T and π sections of prototype low-pass filter.

The characteristic impedances of the T and π sections are given by Eqs. 1.6-4 and 1.6-7 as

$$Z_{0T} = \sqrt{Z_1 Z_2} \sqrt{1 + Z_1/4Z_2} \qquad [4.2\text{-}2]$$

$$Z_{0\pi} = \frac{\sqrt{Z_1 Z_2}}{\sqrt{1 + Z_1/4Z_2}} = \frac{Z_1 Z_2}{Z_{0T}} \qquad [4.2\text{-}3]$$

If Z_1 and Z_2 are reactances of opposite sign, $\sqrt{Z_1 Z_2}$ is a real number, and $\sqrt{1 + Z_1/4Z_2}$ is imaginary when $|Z_1/4Z_2| > 1$. It follows from the analysis of the previous section that cutoff occurs when the characteristic impedance becomes reactive. Hence, the transition between the pass band and the attenuation band occurs when $Z_1/4Z_2 = -1$.

The radical $\sqrt{Z_1 Z_2}$ appears in both Eqs. 4.2-2 and 4.2-3. This term is called the nominal characteristic impedance of the filter and will be denoted by R_k.

If

$$\sqrt{Z_1 Z_2} = R_k = \sqrt{L_1/C_2} = K \qquad [4.2\text{-}4]$$

where K is a constant, Z_1 and Z_2 are the impedances of inverse networks, and the entire network is termed a constant-k network.

Cutoff occurs when

$$\frac{Z_1}{4Z_2} = \frac{Z_1^2}{4R_k^2} = \frac{R_k^2}{4Z_2^2} = -1 \qquad [4.2\text{-}5]$$

It follows from Eq. 4.2-5 that cutoff occurs when

$$Z_1 = \pm j2R_k \qquad [4.2\text{-}6]$$

In a low-pass filter $Z_1 = j\omega L_1$. Hence, the cut-off angular frequency is found by using the positive sign in Eq. 4.2-6, and is given by

$$\omega_c L_1 = 2R_k$$
$$\omega_c = \frac{2R_k}{L_1} \qquad [4.2\text{-}7]$$

and

$$L_1 = \frac{2R_k}{\omega_c} = \frac{R_k}{\pi f_c} \qquad [4.2\text{-}8]$$

where ω_c is the cut-off frequency.

It also follows from Eq. 4.2-5 that cutoff also occurs when

$$Z_2 = \pm \frac{jR_k}{2} \qquad [4.2\text{-}9]$$

Since $Z_2 = -j/\omega C_2$ in a low-pass filter, the cut-off relation is also found by using the minus sign in Eq. 4.2-4. Thus,

$$\frac{1}{\omega_c C_2} = \frac{R_k}{2}$$

$$C_2 = \frac{2}{\omega_c R_k} = \frac{1}{\pi f_c R_k}$$

[4.2-10]

Equations 4.2-7, 4.2-8, and 4.2-10 are the design equations for a prototype low-pass constant-k filter.

Application of Eqs. 4.2-2 and 4.2-3 to T-section and π-section filters gives the following expressions for the characteristic impedance of the prototype low-pass constant-k filters:

$$Z_{0T} = \sqrt{L_1/C_2}\,\sqrt{1 + (j\omega L_1)(j\omega C_2/4)} = \sqrt{L_1/C_2}\,\sqrt{1 - (\omega/\omega_c)^2}$$
$$= R_k\,\sqrt{1 - (f/f_c)^2}$$

[4.2-11]

$$Z_{0\pi} = \frac{Z_1 Z_2}{Z_{0T}} = \frac{L_1/C_2}{\sqrt{L_1/C_2}\,\sqrt{1 - (\omega/\omega_c)^2}}$$

$$= \frac{\sqrt{L_1/C_2}}{\sqrt{1 - (\omega/\omega_c)^2}} = \frac{R_k}{\sqrt{1 - (f/f_c)^2}}$$

[4.2-12]

Figures 4-6 and 4-7 show complete and bisected T and π sections of high-pass filters. The bisected T section in Fig. 4-7(a) has the same reactance characteristics as the lattice in Fig. 4-3(a), and the bisected π section

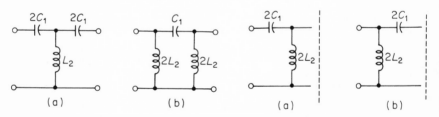

| Figure 4-6   T and π sections of prototype high-pass filter. | Figure 4-7   Bisected T and π sections of prototype high-pass filter. |

of Fig. 4-7(b) corresponds to the lattice in Fig. 4-3(b). It follows that the cut-off frequency for Fig. 4-7(a) is defined by series resonance, or an impedance zero, and the cut-off frequency for Fig. 4-7(b) is determined by parallel resonance, or an impedance pole. Hence, for the T section of the high-pass filter, the cut-off angular frequency is given by

$$\frac{1}{\omega_c(2C_1)} = \omega_c(2L_2)$$

[4.2-13]

$$\omega_c = \frac{1}{2\sqrt{L_2 C_1}}$$

$$\omega_c = \frac{1}{2R_k C_1} = \frac{R_k}{2L_2}$$

[4.2-14]

where R_k is defined as $R_k = \sqrt{Z_1 Z_2} = \sqrt{L_2/C_1}$.

The elements of a high-pass T-section filter are given by:

$$L_2 = \frac{R_k}{2\omega_c}$$

[4.2-15]

$$C_1 = \frac{1}{2\omega_c R_k}$$

[4.2-16]

A consideration of parallel resonance for the π section gives the same results as in Eqs. 4.2-15 and 4.2-16.

The characteristic impedance of the high-pass T-section filter is given by

$$Z_{0T} = \sqrt{Z_1 Z_2} \sqrt{1 + Z_1/4Z_2} = \sqrt{(1/\omega C_1)(\omega L_2)} \left(\sqrt{1 - 1/4\omega^2 L_1 C_2} \right)$$

Equation 4.2-13 shows that for a high-pass filter

$$\omega_c^2 = \frac{1}{4L_2 C_1}$$

Hence,

$$Z_{0T} = \sqrt{L_2/C_1} \sqrt{1 - (\omega_c/\omega)^2} = R_k \sqrt{1 - (\omega_c/\omega)^2}$$
$$= R_k \sqrt{1 - f_c^2/f^2}$$

[4.2-17]

The characteristic impedance of the corresponding π section is

$$Z_{0\pi} = \frac{Z_1 Z_2}{Z_{0T}} = \frac{R_k}{\sqrt{1 - f_c^2/f^2}}$$

[4.2-18]

Equations 4.2-17 and 4.2-18 show that the characteristic impedance of a high-pass filter approaches R_k as f approaches infinity. Note that Eqs. 4.2-17 and 4.2-18 can be obtained from Eq. 4.2-11 and 4.2-12 by interchanging f and f_c.

It follows from Eqs. 4.2-5 and 4.2-9 that cutoff occurs when

$$Z_1 = \pm 2jR_k, \quad \text{or} \quad Z_2 = \pm \frac{jR_k}{2}$$

For a high-pass filter, $Z_1 = -j/\omega C_1$. Hence, the cut-off angular frequency is given by

$$\frac{1}{\omega_c C_1} = 2R_k$$

$$\omega_c = \frac{1}{2R_k C_1}$$

[4.2-19]

Equation 4.2-19 agrees with Eq. 4.2-14. The solution of Eq. 4.2-19 for C_1 yields

$$C_1 = \frac{1}{2\omega_c R_k} = \frac{1}{4\pi f_c R_k}$$

[4.2-20]

Since $Z_2 = j\omega L_2$ in a high-pass filter, it follows that

$$\omega_c L_2 = \frac{R_k}{2}$$

$$L_2 = \frac{R_k}{2\omega_c} = \frac{R_k}{4\pi f_c}$$

[4.2-21]

Equations 4.2-19, 4.2-20, and 4.2-21 are the design equations for a prototype high-pass constant-k filter.

The normalized characteristic impedance, Z_0/R_k, found from Eqs. 4.2-11 and 4.2-12 for prototype low-pass and Eqs. 4.2-17 and 4.2-18 for high-pass filters is shown as a function of f/f_c in Figs. 4-8 and 4-9. It will be noted that the characteristic impedance is always real in the pass range and always reactive in the attenuation range. The reactive impedances are multiplied by $\pm j$ in order to plot them conveniently as real variables. The wide variations of characteristic impedance in the pass region make it impossible to terminate the prototype sections in a satisfactory manner. This is an inherent deficiency of the prototype constant-k section that must be remedied to obtain satisfactory filter performance. The m-derived filter, to be discussed in Sec. 4.3, improves the performance in this respect.

Another deficiency of the prototype constant-k filter is that the attenuation is not great in the vicinity of cutoff. In other words, this filter does not provide sharp cutoff. The attenuation and phase characteristics can be determined by analyzing the equation for the propagation function as derived from the equivalent lattice structure. Inasmuch as the prop-

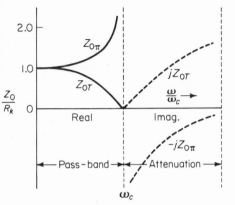

Figure 4-8 Normalized characteristic impedance of prototype low-pass filter.

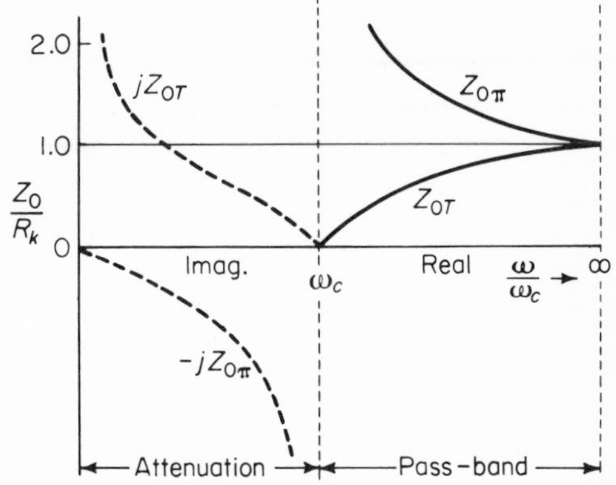

Figure 4-9 Normalized characteristic impedance of prototype high-pass filter.

agation function is identical for T and π structures derived from the same lattice, only the T structure will be analyzed. For a T structure

$$\gamma = \alpha + j\beta = \ln\left(\frac{1 + \sqrt{Z_a/Z_b}}{1 - \sqrt{Z_a/Z_b}}\right)$$

$$= \ln\left(\frac{1 + \sqrt{\dfrac{Z_1}{2} \Big/ \left(\dfrac{Z_1}{2} + 2Z_2\right)}}{1 - \sqrt{\dfrac{Z_1}{2} \Big/ \left(\dfrac{Z_1}{2} + 2Z_2\right)}}\right) \qquad [4.2\text{-}22]$$

Equation 4.2-22 shows that the attenuation is infinite when $Z_a = Z_b$, since under this condition the denominator vanishes. For a prototype low-pass filter,

$$Z_a = \frac{Z_1}{2} = \frac{j\omega L_1}{2}; \qquad Z_b = \frac{Z_1}{2} + 2Z_2 = \frac{j\omega L_1}{2} + \frac{2}{j\omega C_2}$$

As ω approaches infinity, Z_a and Z_b approach equality, and the attenuation becomes infinite. Hence, the prototype low-pass filter does not produce infinite attenuation in the finite frequency range, and cannot give sharp cutoff. Equation 4.2-22 can be expressed in terms of the cut-off frequency of a prototype low-pass filter as follows:

$$\gamma = \alpha + j\beta = \ln \left[\frac{1 + \sqrt{\dfrac{j\omega L_1}{2(j\omega L_1/2 + 2/j\omega C_2)}}}{1 - \sqrt{\dfrac{j\omega L_1}{2(j\omega L_1/2 + 2/j\omega C_2)}}} \right]$$

$$= \ln \left[\frac{1 + \sqrt{\dfrac{1}{1 - 4/\omega^2 L_1 C_2}}}{1 - \sqrt{\dfrac{1}{1 - 4/\omega^2 L_1 C_2}}} \right] \qquad [4.2\text{-}23]$$

Since, for a prototype low-pass filter, $\omega_c^2 = 4/L_1 C_2$, Eq. 4.2-23 can be written as

$$\gamma = \alpha + j\beta = \ln \left[\frac{1 + \sqrt{\dfrac{1}{1 - f_c^2/f^2}}}{1 - \sqrt{\dfrac{1}{1 - f_c^2/f^2}}} \right]$$

$$= \ln \left[\frac{\sqrt{1 - f_c^2/f^2} + 1}{\sqrt{1 - f_c^2/f^2} - 1} \right] \text{ (low-pass)} \qquad [4.2\text{-}24]$$

Inspection of Eq. 4.2-24 shows that, when $f < f_c$, $\alpha = 0$ and β is a function of f; whereas, when $f > f_c$, $\beta = \pi$ and α is variable, as shown in Fig. 4-10.

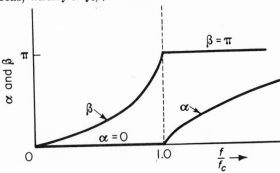

Figure 4-10   Variation of attenuation and phase functions of a prototype low-pass filter with frequency.

It can be shown in a similar manner that the propagation function of a prototype high-pass filter is given by

$$\gamma = \alpha + j\beta = \ln \left[\frac{\sqrt{1 - f^2/f_c^2} + 1}{\sqrt{1 - f^2/f_c^2} - 1} \right] \text{ (high-pass)} \qquad [4.2\text{-}25]$$

The variation of attenuation and phase shift is shown in Fig. 4-11 for a prototype high-pass filter.

The attenuation and impedance characteristics of electric wave filters can be improved by modifying the prototype sections without changing the impedance. A particularly effective modification is the m-derived section to be discussed in Sec. 4.3.

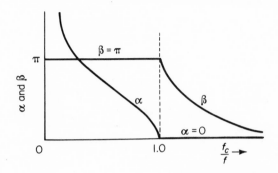

Figure 4-11   Variation of attenuation and phase functions of a prototype high-pass filter with frequency.

4.3 THE m-DERIVED SECTION

If the impedance of the series arm of a lattice is multiplied by a constant, m, and the impedance of the diagonal arm is divided by m, the characteristic impedance, Z_0', of the resulting m-derived lattice is unchanged since

$$Z_0' = \sqrt{mZ_a(Z_b/m)} = \sqrt{Z_aZ_b} = Z_0 \qquad [4.3\text{-}1]$$

The propagation function, γ', of the m-derived lattice is given by

$$\gamma' = \alpha' + j\beta' = \ln\left[\frac{1 + m\sqrt{Z_a/Z_b}}{1 - m\sqrt{Z_a/Z_b}}\right] \qquad [4.3\text{-}2]$$

It follows from Eq. 4.3-2 that the attenuation is infinite when $m\sqrt{Z_a/Z_b} = 1$. This makes it possible to achieve infinite attenuation at any specific frequency by adjusting the value of m without changing the characteristic impedance.

A T section is equivalent to a lattice if $Z_a = Z_1/2$ and $Z_b = Z_1/2 + 2Z_2$. Figure 4-12 shows an m-derived T section with

$$\frac{Z_1'}{2} = \frac{mZ_1}{2} \qquad [4.3\text{-}3]$$

$$Z_1' + 2Z_2' = \frac{Z_1/2 + 2Z_2}{m} \qquad [4.3\text{-}4]$$

Since $Z_1' = mZ_1$,

$$Z_2' = \frac{1}{2}\left(\frac{Z_1}{2m} + \frac{2Z_2}{m} - \frac{mZ_1}{2}\right) = Z_1\left(\frac{1-m^2}{4m}\right) + \frac{Z_2}{m} \qquad [4.3\text{-}5]$$

The point of infinite attenuation is determined by

$$m\sqrt{\frac{Z_a}{Z_b}} = m\sqrt{\frac{Z_1/2}{Z_1/2 + 2Z_2}} = 1 \qquad [4.3\text{-}6]$$

In the case of a low-pass T section, shown with its equivalent lattice in Fig. 4-13, $Z_1 = j\omega L_1$, and $Z_2 = 1/j\omega C_2$.

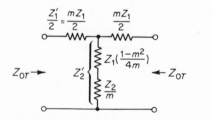
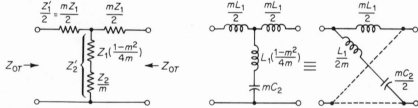

Figure 4-12   m-derived T section.

Figure 4-13   m-derived T section of low-pass filter and equivalent lattice.

The angular frequency ω_∞, at which infinite attenuation occurs, is given by

$$m\sqrt{\frac{j\omega_\infty L_1/2}{j\omega_\infty L_1/2 + 2/j\omega_\infty C_2}} = 1 \qquad [4.3\text{-}7]$$

Squaring both sides of Eq. 4.3-7 yields

$$\frac{jm^2\omega_\infty L_1}{2} = \frac{j\omega_\infty L_1}{2} + \frac{2}{j\omega_\infty C_2}$$

$$(1 - m^2)\left(\frac{\omega_\infty L_1}{2}\right) = \frac{2}{\omega_\infty C_2} \qquad [4.3\text{-}8]$$

$$\omega_\infty^2 = \frac{4}{(1 - m^2)L_1C_2}$$

Since the cut-off frequency, ω_c, equals $2/\sqrt{L_1C_2}$, Eq. 4.3-8 can be written as

$$\omega_\infty = \frac{\omega_c}{\sqrt{1 - m^2}} \qquad\qquad [4.3\text{-}9]$$

In a design problem, ω_∞ is usually specified; in those instances, m is given by

$$m = \sqrt{1 - \frac{\omega_c^2}{\omega_\infty^2}} \quad \text{(low-pass filter)} \qquad [4.3\text{-}10]$$

In a similar manner, the value of m for a high-pass filter can be shown to be

$$m = \sqrt{1 - \frac{\omega_\infty^2}{\omega_c^2}} \quad \text{(high-pass filter)} \qquad [4.3\text{-}11]$$

Note that Eq. 4.3-11 can be obtained from Eq. 4.3-10 by interchanging ω_c and ω_∞.

The attenuation function can be made to rise as sharply as desired in the vicinity of cutoff by specifying ω_∞ in Eqs. 4.3-10 and 4.3-11 as close to the cut-off frequency as necessary. This produces very sharp cutoff, but the attenuation falls off beyond ω_∞. The decrease in attenuation is a disadvantage that can be overcome by cascading the *m*-derived section with a constant-*k* prototype having a rising attenuation characteristic beyond cutoff, as shown in Figs. 4.10 and 4.11. No reflection occurs because both sections have the same characteristic impedance. Figure 4-14 shows

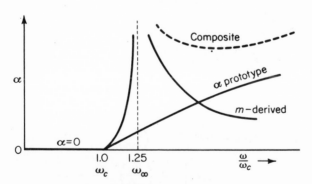

Figure 4-14 Attenuation characteristic of prototype low-pass filter cascaded with m-derived section (m = 0.6).

the attenuation characteristic of a prototype low-pass filter cascaded with an *m*-derived section. Note the sharp cutoff and the rising attenuation characteristic of the composite filter following a decrease just after the point of infinite attenuation occurring at $f_\infty/f_c = 1.25$. The attenuation of the low-pass *m*-derived filter section is given by

$$\lim_{\omega \to \infty} \alpha = \ln\left[(1 + m)/(1 - m)\right]$$

as the frequency approaches infinity, as can be seen by referring to Eq. 4.3-2 and by realizing that Z_a/Z_b approaches unity in this case.

If the m-derived T section is rearranged as a π section as shown in Fig. 4-15, the resulting bisected or half-section makes a rather satisfactory

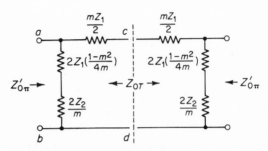

Figure 4-15 m-derived T section rearranged as a π section.

impedance-matching element. It follows directly from Eq. 1.6-8 that the image impedances at the terminals, ab and cd, of Fig. 4-15 are related as follows:

$$Z'_{0\pi} = \frac{Z'_1 Z'_2}{Z'_{0T}} \qquad [4.3\text{-}12]$$

where $Z'_1 = mZ_1$

$Z'_2 = Z_2/m + Z_1(1 - m^2)/4m$

$Z'_{0T} = Z_{0T}$

It follows that

$$Z'_1 Z'_2 = mZ_1\left[\frac{Z_2}{m} + \left(\frac{Z_1}{4m}\right)(1 - m^2)\right]$$

$$= Z_1 Z_2\left[1 + \left(\frac{Z_1}{4Z_2}\right)(1 - m^2)\right]$$

Hence,

$$Z'_{0\pi} = \frac{Z'_1 Z'_2}{Z_{0T}} = \frac{Z_1 Z_2}{Z_{0T}}\left[1 + \left(\frac{Z_1}{4Z_2}\right)(1 - m^2)\right]$$

$$= \left[1 + \left(\frac{Z_1}{4Z_2}\right)(1 - m^2)\right]Z_{0\pi} \qquad [4.3\text{-}13]$$

It follows from Eq. 4.3-13 that:

$$Z'_{0\pi} = \frac{[1 - (f/f_c)^2 (1 - m^2)]R_k}{\sqrt{1 - (f/f_c)^2}} \qquad [4.3\text{-}14]$$

When the substitution

$$x = -\left(\frac{f}{f_c}\right)^2 \qquad [4.3\text{-}15]$$

is made, Eq. 4.3-14 becomes

$$Z'_{0\pi} = \frac{[1 + x(1 - m^2)]R_k}{\sqrt{1 + x}} \qquad [4.3\text{-}16]$$

where x is given by Eq. 4.3-15.

Differentiation of Eq. 4.3-16 with respect to x yields

$$\frac{dZ'_{0\pi}}{dx} = \frac{R_k}{1 + x}\left[(1 - m^2)\sqrt{1 + x} - \frac{1}{2\sqrt{1 + x}}[1 + x(1 - m^2)]\right]$$

$$[4.3\text{-}17]$$

Setting the derivative equal to zero determines the equation for the minimum value of x, namely x_{min}, as follows:

$$2(1 - m^2)(1 + x_{min}) - [1 + (1 - m^2)x_{min}] = 0 \qquad [4.3\text{-}18]$$

It follows from Eq. 4.3-18 that:

$$x_{min} = -\frac{1 - 2m^2}{1 - m^2} \qquad [4.3\text{-}19]$$

As shown by Eq. 4.3-15, x is always negative. Hence, it follows from Eq. 4.3-19 that if x_{min} is to remain negative,

$$m < 0.707 \qquad [4.3\text{-}20]$$

Substitution of x_{min} from Eq. 4.3-19 into the general expression for $Z'_{0\pi}$ in Eq. 4.3-16 gives the following value of $[Z'_{0\pi}]_{min}$, the minimum value of $Z'_{0\pi}$:

$$[Z'_{0\pi}]_{min} = R_k\left(\frac{1 - (1 - 2m^2)}{m/\sqrt{1 - m^2}}\right) = 2mR_k\sqrt{1 - m^2} \qquad [4.3\text{-}21]$$

Assume that

$$[Z'_{0\pi}]_{min} = 0.95R_k \qquad [4.3\text{-}22]$$

This is equivalent to a deviation of 5 per cent from the nominal characteristic impedance. Under this assumption, it follows from Eq. 4.3-21 that:

$$2m\sqrt{1 - m^2} = 0.95$$

$$4m^2(1 - m^2) = 0.90 \qquad [4.3\text{-}23]$$

$$m^2(1 - m^2) = 0.225$$

and

$$m^4 - m^2 + 0.225 = 0 \qquad [4.3\text{-}24]$$

The solution of Eq. 4.3-24 gives the value of m required for five-percent deviation in the impedance at the minimum point. The corresponding value of m^2 is given by

$$m^2 = \frac{1 - \sqrt{1 - 0.90}}{2} = \frac{1 - 0.32}{2} = \frac{0.68}{2} = 0.33 \qquad [4.3\text{-}25]$$

Hence

$$m = 0.58 \qquad [4.3\text{-}26]$$

In practice, a value of $m = 0.6$ is used. This gives a minimum of $0.96R_k$.

The variation of $Z'_{0\pi}$ with f/f_c for $m = 0.6$ is shown in Fig. 4-16. Substitution of $m = 0.6$ in Eq. 4.3-19 yields

$$x_{\min} = -\left(\frac{f}{f_c}\right)^2 = -\frac{1 - 0.72}{1 - 0.36} = -\frac{0.28}{0.64} = -0.44 \qquad [4.3\text{-}27]$$

Hence

$$f_{\min} = 0.67f_c \qquad [Z'_{0\pi} = 0.96R_k] \qquad [4.3\text{-}28]$$

where $f_{\min}$ is the frequency corresponding to $[Z'_{0\pi}]_{\min}$. It follows from Eq. 4.3-16 that the frequency corresponding to an impedance equal to $1.04R_k$ satisfies the following relations:

$$\frac{1 + (1 - 0.36)x}{\sqrt{1 + x}} = 1.04 \qquad [4.3\text{-}29]$$

$$1 + 1.28x + 0.41x^2 = 1.08 + 1.08x \qquad [4.3\text{-}30]$$

$$0.41x^2 + 0.2x - 0.08 = 0$$

$$x = -\left(\frac{f}{f_c}\right)^2 = \frac{-0.2 - \sqrt{0.04 + 0.13}}{0.82} = -0.76 \qquad [4.3\text{-}31]$$

Hence

$$f = 0.87f_c \qquad [Z'_{0\pi} = 1.04R_k] \qquad [4.3\text{-}32]$$

It follows from Eqs. 4.3-28 and 4.3-32 that, when $m = 0.6$, there is a maximum net deviation in impedance of only 4 per cent in 87 per cent of the pass range. These variations are shown in Fig. 4-16, which illustrates the utility of the m-derived half-section with $m = 0.6$ as an impedance matching device.

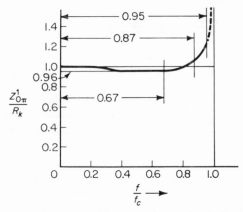

Figure 4-16 Variation of normalized characteristic impedance with frequency of m-derived filter (m = 0.6).

4.4 DESIGN OF COMPOSITE FILTERS

A composite filter consists of at least the following three components:

(a) A prototype constant-k section to produce cutoff or transition between the pass-band and the attenuation band at a specified frequency, f_c.

(b) An m-derived section to give infinite attenuation at a frequency, f_∞, in the vicinity of the cut-off frequency.

(c) Two terminating m-derived half-sections, with $m = 0.6$, to give reasonably constant input and output impedances.

In order to clarify the design of a composite filter, the following example will be used. Assume that a low-pass filter is to be designed to meet these specifications: $f_c = 2000$ cycles; $f_\infty = 2050$ cycles; $R_k = 500$ ohms. The elements of the constant-k prototype are the following:

$$L_1 = \frac{R_k}{\pi f_c} = \frac{500}{2000\pi} = \frac{1}{4\pi} = 0.0795 \text{ henry}$$

$$C_2 = \frac{1}{\pi f_c R_k} = \frac{10^6}{2000\pi \times 500} = 0.318 \text{ microfarad}$$

The constant-k prototype is shown as a T section in Fig. 4-17.

The value of m to give infinite attenuation at 2050 cycles in a section derived from a prototype with cutoff at 2000 cycles is given by

$$m = \sqrt{1 - \frac{f_c^2}{f_\infty^2}} = \sqrt{1 - \left(\frac{2000}{2050}\right)^2} = 0.227$$

The components of this m-derived section are

$$\frac{mL_1}{2} = \frac{0.227 \times 0.0795}{2} = 0.00901 \text{ henry}$$

$$\left(\frac{1 - m^2}{4m}\right) L_1 = \left(\frac{1 - (0.227)^2}{4 \times 0.227}\right) \times 0.0795 = 0.0831 \text{ henry}$$

$$mC_2 = 0.227 \times 0.318 = 0.0721 \text{ microfarad}$$

The m-derived T section that gives infinite attenuation at 2050 cycles with $R_k = 500$ ohms is shown in Fig. 4-18.

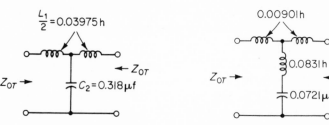

Figure 4-17 Constant-k prototype T section filter.

Figure 4-18 m-derived T section filter ($m = 0.227$).

In the terminating half-sections, the value of m is 0.6. Therefore the elements of this section are

$$\frac{mL_1}{2} = \frac{0.6 \times 0.0795}{2} = 0.0238 \text{ henry}$$

$$\left(\frac{1 - m^2}{4m}\right) L_1 = \left(\frac{1 - (0.6)^2}{4 \times 0.6}\right) \times 0.0795 = 0.0212 \text{ henry}$$

$$mC_2 = 0.6 \times 0.318 = 0.1908 \text{ microfarad}$$

The complete section derived from the prototype with $m = 0.6$, and the half-section used for termination, are shown in Figs. 4-19 and 4-20.

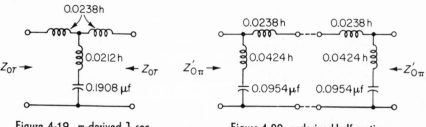

Figure 4-19 m-derived 1 section filter ($m = 0.6$).

Figure 4-20 m-derived half-sections used for terminations ($m = 0.6$).

The composite filter is constructed by using the constant-k prototype in cascade with the sharp-cutoff m-derived section ($m = 0.227$) and the terminating half-sections ($m = 0.6$) as shown in Fig. 4-21. Almost matched

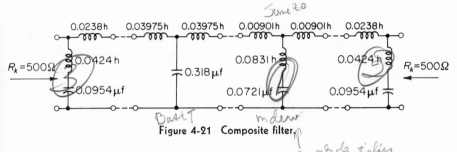

Figure 4-21   Composite filter.

impedances are maintained at all the junctions in Fig. 4-21. Therefore, these junctions can be connected without introducing reflections, and the individual sections can be combined. In this process the individual T sections lose their identity as T sections, as can be seen from Fig. 4-22 which

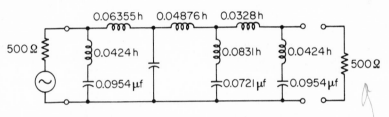

Figure 4-22   Composite filter with elements combined.

shows the composite design to meet the specifications set forth in the statement of the problem. The T section has been used to develop a composite filter. A π section also may be used as the basis of the design to develop a composite filter. The results are outlined in Figs. 4-23 and 4-24 for a general π section filter.*

The material presented so far has been based on the use of a constant-k filter and the m-derived sections. Further improvement can be made in both the characteristic impedance and the sharpness of cutoff by continued modification of the m-derived sections through the use of additional values of m or by other designs derived from the lattice section. These modifications will not be treated here.

In the design illustrated in this section, the filter was specified in terms of its characteristic impedance, its cut-off frequency, and the frequency at which infinite attenuation theoretically occurs. In practice, the filter

*When $m = 0.6$, Z'_{0T} in Fig. 4-23(c) is nearly constant in most of the pass-band.

is generally specified on a somewhat different basis. For example, a nominal characteristic impedance of, say, 500 ohms is specified, and it is required that this value should not deviate from the nominal value by more than

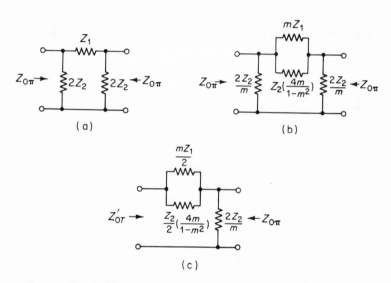

Figure 4-23 Component sections developed from π section. (a) Prototype π section. (b) m-derived π section. (c) Half-section with modified characteristic impedance.

± 5 per cent over 90 per cent of the transmission band. The cut-off frequency is specified, and a sharpness of cutoff is specified such that the attenuation shall be not less than a certain number of decibels in the attenuation range.

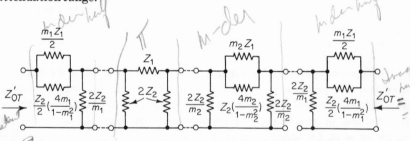

Figure 4-24 Cascading of π sections to form a composite filter.

A maximum loss may be specified in the pass-band. Hence, the coils and capacitor losses must be considered in the final analysis. The filter design can be greatly aided by use of loss charts for sections of the various types, and from these charts one can fairly well determine the type and number of sections required for a given specification. In the final analysis, the filter can be checked by assuming a unit current through the load impedance, and then calculating the input voltage and current. The losses in the inductors and capacitors can thus be included. This computation must be carried out for a large number of frequencies, and it requires considerable time and effort unless a special network analyzer is used.

4.5 THE BAND-PASS FILTER

The principles developed for low-pass and high-pass filters apply also to band-pass filters. Such a filter is characterized by a transmission band between two specified frequencies, ω_1 and ω_2, and the attenuation of all other frequencies. One set of reactance curves that satisfies the requirements of a band-pass filter is shown in Fig. 4-25, which gives the zeros and poles of the equivalent lattice arms.

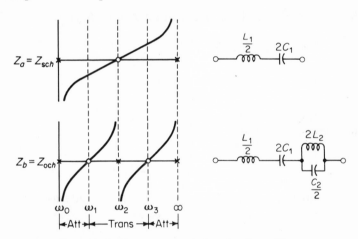

Figure 4-25 Reactance curves for a band-pass filter.

Unless the internal zero of Z_a coincides with the internal pole of Z_b, the network will have two transmission bands. If the equivalent T network is constructed, the series and shunt arms are given by

$$Z_a = \frac{Z_1}{2} = Z_{sch} \qquad [4.5\text{-}1]$$

$$Z_b = \frac{Z_1}{2} + 2Z_2 = Z_{och} \qquad [4.5\text{-}2]$$

$$Z_a = \frac{Z_1}{2} = \frac{j\omega L_1}{2} + \frac{1}{j2\omega C_1} \qquad [4.5\text{-}3]$$

$$Z_b = \frac{Z_1}{2} + 2Z_2 = \frac{j\omega L_1}{2} + \frac{1}{j2\omega C_1} + \frac{(j2\omega L_2)(2/j\omega C_2)}{j2\omega L_2 + 2/j\omega C_2} \qquad [4.5\text{-}4]$$

The bisected T network, as well as the entire T network, is shown in Fig. 4-26.

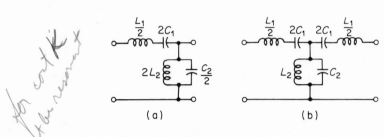

(a)   (b)

Figure 4-26 T section of band-pass filter and bisected T section.

The solution of Eqs. 4.5-3 and 4.5-4 for Z_1 and Z_2 yields

$$Z_1 = j\omega L_1 \left(1 - \frac{1}{\omega^2 L_1 C_1}\right) \qquad [4.5\text{-}5]$$

$$Z_1 = j\omega L_1 \left(\frac{\omega^2 - \omega_0^2}{\omega^2}\right) \qquad [4.5\text{-}6]$$

where $\omega_0^2 = 1/L_1 C_1$.

The expression for Z_2 is

$$Z_2 = \frac{1}{j\omega C_2} \left(\frac{1}{1 - 1/\omega^2 L_2 C_2}\right) \qquad [4.5\text{-}7]$$

When the internal zero of Z_a coincides with the internal pole of Z_b, $L_1 C_1 = L_2 C_2$, and Eq. 4.5-7 can be written as

$$Z_2 = \left(\frac{1}{j\omega C_2}\right)\left(\frac{\omega^2}{\omega^2 - \omega_0^2}\right) \qquad [4.5\text{-}8]$$

Setting

$$Z_1 Z_2 = R_k^2 = \frac{L_1}{C_2} = \frac{L_2}{C_1} \qquad [4.5\text{-}9]$$

and since, at cutoff,

$$Z_1 = \pm j2R_k \qquad [4.5\text{-}10]$$

it follows that

$$\omega_1 L_1 \left(\frac{\omega_1^2 - \omega_0^2}{\omega_1^2}\right) = -2R_k \qquad [4.5\text{-}11]$$

$$\omega_2 L_1 \left(\frac{\omega_2^2 - \omega_0^2}{\omega_2^2}\right) = 2R_k \qquad [4.5\text{-}12]$$

where ω_1 is the lower cut-off frequency and ω_2 is the upper cut-off frequency. Division of Eq. 4.5-11 by Eq. 4.5-12 yields the following relations:

$$\frac{\omega_1^2 - \omega_0^2}{\omega_1} = -\frac{\omega_2^2 - \omega_0^2}{\omega_2} \qquad [4.5\text{-}13]$$

$$\omega_0^2 = \omega_1\omega_2 \qquad [4.5\text{-}14]$$

It is thus seen that ω_0 is the geometric mean of the two cut-off frequencies, ω_1 and ω_2.

The substitution of Eq. 4.5-14 into Eq. 4.5-11 yields the following expression for L_1:

$$L_1 = \frac{2R_k}{\omega_2 - \omega_1} = \frac{R_k}{\pi(f_2 - f_1)} \qquad [4.5\text{-}15]$$

The other design equations are:

$$C_1 = \frac{1}{\omega_0^2 L_1} = \frac{\omega_2 - \omega_1}{2R_k\omega_1\omega_2} = \frac{f_2 - f_1}{4\pi f_1 f_2 R_k} \qquad [4.5\text{-}16]$$

$$L_2 = R_k^2 C_1 = \frac{R_k(\omega_2 - \omega_1)}{2\omega_1\omega_2} = \frac{R_k(f_2 - f_1)}{4\pi f_2 f_1} \qquad [4.5\text{-}17]$$

$$C_2 = \frac{L_1}{R_k^2} = \frac{2}{R_k(\omega_2 - \omega_1)} = \frac{1}{\pi R_k(f_2 - f_1)} \qquad [4.5\text{-}18]$$

These are the design equations for the prototype constant-k band-pass filter section. The m-derived filters are obtained in the same manner as for the low-pass and high-pass filters previously discussed. The band-elimination filter can be obtained in the same manner as the band-pass filter by interchanging the Z_1 and Z_2 impedances of the T network.

4.6 APPLICATION OF LATTICE SECTIONS TO NETWORK ANALYSIS

In order to illustrate the use of the lattice structure in analyzing a network, a doubly-tuned circuit, used as a coupling network in intermediate-frequency amplifiers, will be analyzed. This network is a type of band-pass filter. The structure is shown in (a) of Fig. 4-27, and it cannot be considered as either a T or a π network. The network is symmetrical. The transformer that is shown in (a) of Fig. 4-27 can be converted to an equivalent T network as shown in Fig. 4-27(b), and also in bisected form in Fig. 4-27(c).

The open-circuited and short-circuited impedances in Fig. 4-27 are:

$$Z_{sch} = Z_a = \frac{j\omega(L-M)(1/j\omega C)}{j\omega(L-M) + 1/j\omega C} = \frac{j\omega(-1/C)}{\omega^2 - \omega_2^2} \qquad [4.6\text{-}1]$$

$$Z_{och} = Z_b = \frac{j\omega(L+M)(1/j\omega C)}{j\omega(L+M) + 1/j\omega C} = \frac{j\omega(-1/C)}{\omega^2 - \omega_1^2} \qquad [4.6\text{-}2]$$

where $\omega_1^2 = \dfrac{1}{(L+M)C}$ and $\omega_2^2 = \dfrac{1}{(L-M)C}$

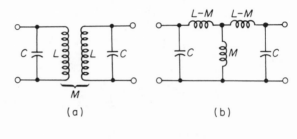

(a)   (b)

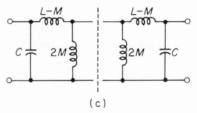

(c)

Figure 4-27 Doubly-tuned transformer with equivalent and bisected circuits.

The lattice equivalent is shown in Fig. 4-28.

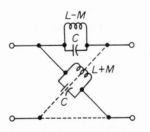

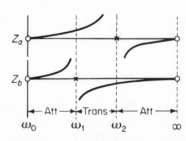

Figure 4-28 Lattice equivalent of doubly-tuned transformer.

Figure 4-29 Reactance curves of lattice arms equivalent to doubly-tuned transformer.

A plot of the reactance curves of Z_a and Z_b is shown in Fig. 4-29. Let ω_0 represent the frequency at which the primary and secondary are in resonance when uncoupled. Then

$$\omega_0 = \frac{1}{\sqrt{LC}} \qquad [M = 0] \qquad\qquad [4.6\text{-}3]$$

The equations for the cut-off frequencies are as follows:

$$\omega_1 = \frac{1}{\sqrt{(L + M)C}} = \frac{1}{\sqrt{LC}\,\sqrt{1 + M/L}} = \frac{\omega_0}{\sqrt{1 + M/L}} \qquad [4.6\text{-}4]$$

$$\omega_2 = \frac{1}{\sqrt{(L - M)C}} = \frac{1}{\sqrt{LC}\,\sqrt{1 - M/L}} = \frac{\omega_0}{\sqrt{1 - M/L}} \qquad [4.6\text{-}5]$$

The coefficient of coupling of a transformer is defined as $k = M/\sqrt{L_1 L_2}$. Since $L_1 = L_2$ in this case, $k = M/L$, and

$$\omega_1 = \frac{\omega_0}{\sqrt{1 + k}} \qquad\qquad [4.6\text{-}6]$$

$$\omega_2 = \frac{\omega_0}{\sqrt{1 - k}} \qquad\qquad [4.6\text{-}7]$$

The coefficient of coupling, k, can now be expressed in terms of ω_1 and ω_2. It follows from Eqs. 4.6-6 and 4.6-7 that:

$$k = \frac{\omega_2^2 - \omega_1^2}{\omega_2^2 + \omega_1^2} \qquad\qquad [4.6\text{-}8]$$

The characteristic impedance is given by

$$Z_0 = \sqrt{Z_a Z_b} = \frac{1}{C}\sqrt{\frac{-\omega^2}{(\omega^2 - \omega_2^2)(\omega^2 - \omega_1^2)}} \qquad [4.6\text{-}9]$$

It is seen from Eq. 4.6-9 that

Z_0 is real if $\omega_1 < \omega < \omega_2$ (transmission band)

Z_0 is imaginary if $\omega < \omega_1$ or if $\omega > \omega_2$ (attenuation bands)

The geometric mean frequency, ω_m, is defined as

$$\omega_m = \sqrt{\omega_1 \omega_2} \qquad\qquad [4.6\text{-}10]$$

When Eqs. 4.6-6 and 4.6-7 are substituted into Eq. 4.6-10, the following expression for the geometric mean frequency is obtained:

$$\omega_m^2 = \omega_1 \omega_2 = \frac{\omega_0^2}{\sqrt{1 - k^2}} \qquad\qquad [4.6\text{-}11]$$

When $k \ll 1$, $\omega_m = \omega_0$.

The nominal characteristic impedance, Z_0', is defined at the geometric mean frequency. It follows from Eq. 4.6-9 and 4.6-10 that

$$Z_0' = R = \frac{1}{C} \sqrt{\frac{-\omega_m^2}{(\omega_m^2 - \omega_2^2)(\omega_m^2 - \omega_1^2)}} \qquad [4.6\text{-}12]$$

where R is a nominal resistance. Since $\omega_m^2 = \omega_1\omega_2$, Eq. 4.6-12 can be written as

$$Z_0' = R = \frac{1}{C} \sqrt{\frac{-1}{(\omega_1 - \omega_2)(\omega_2 - \omega_1)}} \qquad [4.6\text{-}13]$$

or

$$Z_0' = R = \frac{1}{C(\omega_2 - \omega_1)} \qquad [4.6\text{-}14]$$

This value of $Z_0' = R$ can be used for design purposes to determine the impedance level at the geometric mean frequency. It should be noted that this is not a filter network of the constant-k type.

The propagation function is given by

$$\gamma = \alpha + j\beta = \ln \left[\frac{1 + \sqrt{\dfrac{\omega^2 - \omega_1^2}{\omega^2 - \omega_2^2}}}{1 - \sqrt{\dfrac{\omega^2 - \omega_1^2}{\omega^2 - \omega_2^2}}} \right]$$

$$= 2 \tanh^{-1} \sqrt{\frac{\omega^2 - \omega_1^2}{\omega^2 - \omega_2^2}} \qquad [4.6\text{-}15]$$

The second form of Eq. 4.6-15 follows from Eq. B-51 in Appendix B. This result is not of much value as such, however, when the network is terminated by a constant resistance, and reflection losses change the propagation function considerably for a single section. By using the $ABCD$ coefficients, the network can be analyzed for any given load condition.

Numerous other types of filter networks can be analyzed and designed on a lattice basis, but space does not permit discussion of these other types.

PROBLEMS

4-1 The propagation function for a lattice network is

$$\gamma = \ln \left(\frac{1 + \sqrt{Z_a/Z_b}}{1 - \sqrt{Z_a/Z_b}} \right)$$

Show that the propagation function for the T and π sections may be expressed as $\cosh \gamma = 1 + Z_1/2Z_2$.

4-2 Design a low-pass constant-k T-section filter with $f_c = 3000$ cycles and $R_0 = 500$ ohms.

4-3 Compute α and β for the filter of Prob. 4-2 from 0 to 12,000 cycles.

4-4 Design the terminating half-sections for the filter of Prob. 4-2 with $m = 0.6$.

4-5 Compute α and β for the filter of Prob. 4-4 from 0 to 12,000 cycles. Determine the frequency of infinite attenuation.

4-6 Design a sharp-cutoff T-section filter for Prob. 4-5, with $f_\infty = 3060$ cycles.

4-7 Compute α and β for the filter of Prob. 4-6 from 0 to 12,000 cycles.

4-8 Plot the characteristic impedance of each filter section in Probs. 4-2, 4-4, and 4-6.

4-9 Plot α and β for the three combined filter sections of Probs. 4-2, 4-4, and 4-6.

4-10 Assuming that coils with a $Q = 50$ are used in constructing the filters of Probs. 4-2 and 4-4, compute α and β from 0 to 12,000 cycles. Determine α and β at the f_∞ points.

4-11 Apply the results of Prob. 4-1 to determine the relation between the signs of Z_1 and Z_2 in the pass and attenuation ranges. Prove that the phase shift in the attenuation range is π.

4-12 Starting with the elements of Prob. 4-2, rearrange as a π-section filter, and repeat Probs. 4-3 to 4-9 inclusive.

4-13 Design a high-pass filter as follows: one constant-k T section with $R_0 = 500$ ohms and $f_c = 400$ cycles; one sharp-cutoff section with $f_\infty = 380$ cycles; and terminating half-sections with $m = 0.6$. Combine the elements to form the composite filter.

4-14 Design a band-pass filter as follows: one constant-k section with $R_0 = 500$ ohms, $f_{c1} = 2000$ cycles, and $f_{c2} = 3000$ cycles; one sharp-cutoff section with $m = 0.2$; and terminating half-sections with $m = 0.6$. Combine the elements to form the composite filter.

4-15 The zeros and poles of the Z_a and Z_b arms of a lattice are specified in the accompanying figure.

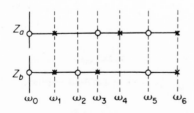

Problem 4-15

(a) Define the cut-off frequencies and the type of filter.
(b) Sketch the characteristic impedance variation in the transmission region of the filter.

(c) Sketch two types of reactance networks for each of the one-terminal pair reactances Z_a and Z_b.

4-16 Using the bisection principle, determine the following information in regard to the network in the accompanying figure.

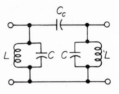

Problem 4-16

(a) The cut-off frequencies.

(b) The expression for the characteristic impedance; plot Z_0 versus ω.

(c) The value of Z_0 at the geometric mean frequency.

(d) The expression for the propagation function; plot α and β as a function of ω. Note especially the values of α and β as $\omega \to 0$ and $\omega \to \infty$.

(e) Is this a constant-k filter? Explain.

4-17 Repeat Prob. 4-16 for the network shown.

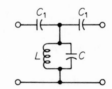

Problem 4-17

4-18 Repeat Prob. 4-16 for the network shown.

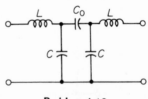

Problem 4-18

4-19 Repeat Prob. 4-16 for the network shown (consider three possible cases).

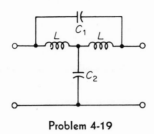

Problem 4-19

4-20 Using the filter shown, determine, by mesh-current analysis, α and β as a function of ω; compare with the results obtained by Eq. 4.2-24.

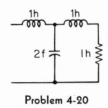

Problem 4-20

synthesis of R-L and R-C networks

5.0 INTRODUCTION

In the networks studied thus far, we have confined ourselves to either purely resistive networks in the case of attenuators or purely reactive networks in the case of electric wave filters. The purpose now is to introduce, in an elementary way, networks that contain both resistance and reactance.

Such networks may be utilized as equalizers and perform various other functions in a system. An *attenuation equalizer* is a network that exhibits a prescribed amplitude change between input and output as a function of frequency, generally without regard to phase. A *phase equalizer* is one that exhibits a prescribed phase change between input and output as a function of frequency, generally without regard to amplitude. Such a network may be constructed solely of reactive elements. Attenuation equalizers are used largely in the transmission, recording, and reproduction of speech and music to give the desired characteristics, or to correct for the frequency characteristics of various transducers, transmission lines, amplifiers, etc.

Another important application of equalizers is in the design of feedback control systems or servomechanisms. They are used as lag networks and as lead networks to improve the stability, response, and performance of a system. Because of the fact that a servomechanism generally operates at low frequencies, the transfer function is generally designed using only R-C networks, as this gives a network with less weight and lower cost.

Equalizers may be of several different types, such as series, shunt, L, T, π, bridged-T, or lattice structures. The lattice is a balanced network, and therefore is not very useful for practical applications, but it is used as a design artifice and converted into an unbalanced network when possible.

Both one-terminal pair networks with one pair of terminals available for external connection, and two-terminal pairs with two pairs of terminals, will be considered. The former are completely characterized by the driving-point impedance or driving-point admittance, and the latter are characterized by the two-terminal pair parameters developed in Chap. 1. One-terminal pair networks will be considered first.

5.1 R-C DRIVING POINT IMPEDANCE AND R-L DRIVING POINT ADMITTANCE

A one-terminal pair network containing parallel R-C branches connected in series is shown in Fig. 5-1. The impedance of an R-C branch in the network at the complex frequency, s, is given by

$$Z_{\text{R-C}}(s) = \frac{1}{sC_k + 1/R_k} = \frac{1/C_k}{s + 1/R_kC_k} \qquad [5.1\text{-}1]$$

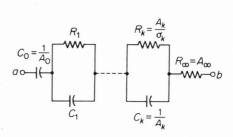

Figure 5-1   One-terminal pair R-C network.

The driving-point impedance at terminals ab in Fig. 5-1 can be expressed as follows:

$$Z(s) = \frac{1}{sC_0} + \sum_{k=1}^{k=n} \frac{1/C_k}{s + 1/R_kC_k} + R_\infty \qquad [5.1\text{-}2]$$

where it is assumed that there are n parallel R-C branches in series, and that R_∞ is the value of the driving-point impedance at infinite frequency, where the impedance of the capacitors is zero. Equation 5.1-2 can be written in the standard partial-fraction form as

$$Z(s) = \frac{A_0}{s} + \sum_{k=1}^{k=n} \frac{A_k}{s - s_k} + R_\infty \qquad [5.1\text{-}3]$$

In Eq. 5.1-3, $A_0 = 1/C_0$, $A_k = 1/C_k$, and $s_k = -1/R_kC_k = -\sigma_k$. Since s_k is real, it may be denoted by σ_k, the real part of the complex frequency, $s_k = \sigma_k + j\omega_k$. A_k is defined as the *residue* at the pole, s_k.

Inspection of Eq. 5.1-3 shows that the poles of $Z(s)$ are located on the negative real axis of the s-plane. When $A_0 \neq 0$, a pole exists at $s = 0$. Since the poles are real, the analysis and synthesis of R-C networks is concerned with the variation of the driving-point impedance with σ, the real part of the complex frequency, s. This is in contrast to the synthesis of L-C networks, which depends upon the variation of the driving-point impedance with ω, the imaginary part of the complex frequency.

The slope of the impedance curve is found by differentiating Eq. 5.1-3. Thus

$$\frac{dZ(s)}{ds} = -\frac{A_0}{s^2} - \sum_{k=1}^{k=n} \frac{A_k}{(s - s_k)^2}$$ [5.1-4]

If only variations with respect to σ are considered,

$$\frac{dZ(\sigma)}{d\sigma} = -\frac{A_0}{\sigma^2} - \sum_{k=1}^{k=n} \frac{A_k}{(\sigma - \sigma_k)^2}$$ [5.1-5]

It follows from Eq. 5.1-5 that, when σ is the variable, the slope of the impedance curve is always negative. Throughout this chapter s will be used to represent the angular frequency, but it will be understood that only the real part, σ, of s is considered, just as only the imaginary part was considered in Chap. 3.

Inspection of Fig. 5-1 or Eq. 5.1-3 shows that $Z(0)$ is finite when $A_0 = 0$. When $A_0 = 0$,

$$Z(0) = R_\infty + \sum_{k=1}^{k=n} R_k$$ [5.1-6]

Also

$$Z(\infty) = R_\infty$$ [5.1-7]

where $Z(0)$ and $Z(\infty)$ are the driving-point impedances when s (actually σ) is respectively zero or infinite. It follows from Eqs. 5.1-6 and 5.1-7 that $Z(0) > Z(\infty)$.

The facts that (1), the slope of the impedance curve is always negative; that (2), $Z(0)$ is either infinite or a finite positive quantity given by Eq. 5.1-6; and that (3), $Z(0) > Z(\infty)$ lead to the two types of impedance curves shown in Fig. 5-2.* When $R_\infty = 0$, the last critical frequency is a zero, and occurs at infinity. It is assumed in (a) of Fig. 5-2 that $A_0 = 0$, whereas A_0 is assumed to be different from zero in (b) of the figure. Inspection of Fig. 5-2 shows that the poles and zeros alternate; they are said to be interlaced. This follows from the requirement of a negative slope. The poles and zeros of R-C networks vary as a function of σ in the same manner as the poles and zeros of L-C networks vary as a function of ω.

The properties of R-C driving-point impedance functions are summarized here:

---

*The variation of $Z(s)$ is shown only in the left-hand part of the s plane, because all of the internal poles and zeros of $Z(s)$ are located in that part of the plane.

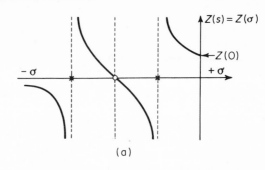

(a)

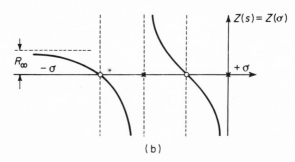

(b)

Figure 5-2 Impedance of R-C network as a function of σ.

(1) All internal poles and zeros are located on the negative real axis of the s-plane.

(2) The slope of the impedance curve as a function of σ is negative at all points.

(3) The poles and zeros alternate, and are said to be interlaced.

(4) The critical frequency nearest to the origin is a pole. When $A_0 \neq 0$, a pole is located at the origin.

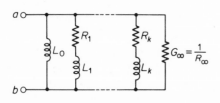

Figure 5-3 One-terminal pair R-L network.

(5) The critical frequency at the greatest distance from the origin is a zero. It follows from Eq. 5.1-3 that this critical frequency occurs at infinity when $R_\infty = 0$.

(6) The impedance at infinity is always less than the impedance at zero, and, as noted in (5), may be zero.

A one-terminal pair network containing series R-L branches connected in parallel is shown in Fig. 5-3. The admittance of a series branch is given by

$$Y_{R-L}(s) = \frac{1}{R_k + sL_k} = \frac{1/L_k}{s + R_k/L_k} \qquad [5.1\text{-}8]$$

The driving-point admittance at terminals ab is given by

$$Y(s) = \frac{1}{sL_0} + \sum_{k=1}^{k=n} \frac{1/L_k}{s + R_k/L_k} + G_\infty \qquad [5.1\text{-}9]$$

where it is assumed that there are n series R-L branches in parallel, and that G_∞ is the driving-point admittance at infinite frequency where the admittance of the R-L branches is zero. Equation 5.1-9 can also be written in partial-fraction form as

$$Y(s) = \frac{B_0}{s} + \sum_{k=1}^{k=n} \frac{B_k}{s - s_k} + B_\infty \qquad [5.1\text{-}10]$$

where $B_0 = 1/L_0$, $B_k = 1/L_k$, and $s_k = -R_k/L_k = -\sigma_k$.

The form of Eq. 5.1-10 is exactly the same as that of Eq. 5.1-3. Therefore, the properties of R-L admittance functions are the same as the properties of R-C impedance functions. It should be noted that the admittance functions are those of series R-L branches, while the impedance functions correspond to parallel R-C branches. This is consistent with the concept of *duality*. Curves for $Y(s)$ in Eq. 5.1-10 as a function of σ are the same as those given for $Z(s)$ in Fig. 5-2.

Both the driving-point impedance of R-C networks and the driving-point admittance of R-L networks can be expressed as the ratio of two polynomials. The theoretical basis of the polynomial form is the expression for the driving-point impedance or admittance as the ratio of a network determinant to its cofactor. The polynomial form of $Z(s)$ can also be obtained by placing the right-hand side of Eq. 5.1-3 under a common denominator. This yields

$$Z(s) = \frac{P(s)}{sQ(s)} = H\left[\frac{(s + s_1)(s + s_3) \cdots}{s(s + s_2)(s + s_4) \cdots}\right] \qquad [5.1\text{-}11]$$

where H is the ratio of the leading terms in $P(s)$ and $Q(s)$; $s = s_1, s_3 \cdots$ are the zeros of $Z(s)$; and $s = 0$, $s = s_2, s_4 \cdots$ are the poles of $Z(s)$. All the poles and zeros are real and negative.

A similar expression can be formed for $Y(s)$ by placing the right-hand side of Eq. 5.1-10 under a common denominator. As in the case of L-C networks, the factored polynomial form is very useful for synthesis when the poles and zeros are specified. Examples of synthesis are given in Sec. 5.2, following.

5.2 PARTIAL-FRACTION SYNTHESIS OF R-C IMPEDANCE AND R-L ADMITTANCE

For the first example, consider the pole-zero distribution shown in Fig. 5-4. The factored form of $Z(s)$ is

$$Z(s) = H\left[\frac{(s+2)(s+4)}{(s+1)(s+3)}\right] \tag{5.2-1}$$

The factor, H, is determined by specifying $Z(s)$ at some value of s other than the given poles and zeros, or by specifying a derivative of $Z(s)$ at some

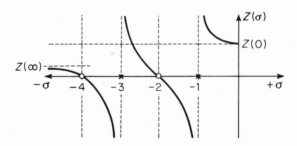

Figure 5-4 Pole-zero distribution of Z(s) in Eq. 5.2-1.

value of s. It should again be noted that only σ, the real part of s, is being considered.

For simplicity it will be assumed that $H = 1$ in Eq. 5.2-1. Then

$$Z(s) = \frac{(s+2)(s+4)}{(s+1)(s+3)} \tag{5.2-2}$$

The first critical frequency is a pole that identifies $Z(s)$ as an R-C impedance. Synthesis is accomplished by resolving the right-hand side of Eq. 5.2-2 into partial fractions, and associating the terms with those in Eq. 5.1-3 and the network components in Fig. 5-1. Since the order of the numerator is the same as that of the denominator in Eq. 5.2-2, the denominator must be divided into the numerator before resolution into partial fractions is attempted. Division of the denominator into the numerator of the right-hand side of Eq. 5.2-2 yields

$$Z(s) = 1 + \frac{2s+5}{(s+1)(s+3)} = 1 + Z_1(s) \tag{5.2-3}$$

where

$$Z_1(s) = \frac{2s+5}{(s+1)(s+3)} = \frac{A_1}{s+1} + \frac{A_2}{s+3} \tag{5.2-4}$$

The constant, A_1, in Eq. 5.2-4 is determined by multiplying both sides of the equation by the factor $(s + 1)$, and evaluating the result when $s = -1$. Thus

$$(s + 1)Z_1(s) = \frac{2s + 5}{s + 3} = A_1 + A_2\left(\frac{s + 1}{s + 3}\right)$$ [5.2-5]

When $s = -1$, the last term on the right-hand side of Eq. 5.2-5 vanishes, and A_1 is given by

$$A_1 = [(s + 1)Z_1(s)]_{s=-1} = \left[\frac{2s + 5}{s + 3}\right]_{s=-1} = \frac{3}{2}$$ [5.2-6]

Similarly, A_2 is found by multiplying both sides of Eq. 5.2-4 by the factor $(s + 3)$, and evaluating the result when $s = -3$. Thus,

$$A_2 = [(s + 3)Z_1(s)]_{s=-3} = \left[\frac{2s + 5}{s + 1}\right]_{s=-3} = \frac{1}{2}$$ [5.2-7]

It follows from Eqs. 5.2-3, 5.2-4, 5.2-6, and 5.2-7 that

$$Z(s) = 1 + \frac{3/2}{s + 1} + \frac{1/2}{s + 3}$$ [5.2-8]

A comparison of Eqs. 5.1-3 and 5.2-8 shows immediately that $R_\infty = 1.0$ ohm, $C_1 = 1/A_1 = 2/3$ farad, and $C_2 = 1/A_2 = 2$ farads.

The resistors for the parallel R-C circuits are found from the relation

$$R_k = -\frac{1}{s_k C_k}$$ [5.2-9]

where the values of s_k for R_1 and R_2 are respectively $s_k = -1$, and $s_k = -3$. Hence,

$$R_1 = -\frac{1}{s_1 C_1} = \frac{1}{2/3} = \frac{3}{2} \text{ ohms}$$

$$R_2 = -\frac{1}{s_2 C_1} = \frac{1}{3 \times 2} = \frac{1}{6} \text{ ohm}$$ [5.2-10]

The synthesized network is shown in Fig. 5.5.

An alternative way for determining the components of the network in Fig. 5-5 from Eq. 5.2-8 is to write Eq. 5.2-8 so that the numerators of all the fractions are unity. Thus Eq. 5.2-8 can be written as

$$Z(s) = 1 + \frac{1}{2s/3 + 2/3} + \frac{1}{2s + 6}$$ [5.2-11]

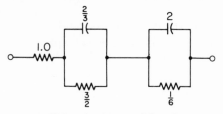

Values in ohms and farads

Figure 5-5   R-C network having $Z(s)$ in Eq.
5.2-8.

Since the right-hand side of Eq. 5.2-11 represents an impedance, the denominators of the last two terms must be admittances of the form

$$Y_k = G_k + sC_k \qquad [5.2\text{-}12]$$

It follows directly from Eqs. 5.2-11 and 5.2-12 that:

$$G_1 = \frac{2}{3}\text{ mho}, \quad R_1 = \frac{3}{2}\text{ ohm}, \quad C_1 = \frac{2}{3}\text{ farad}$$

$$G_2 = 6\text{ mhos}, \quad R_2 = \frac{1}{6}\text{ ohm}, \quad C_2 = 2\text{ farads}$$

These results are the same as those obtained from Eqs. 5.2-8 and 5.2-9.

As a second example, consider the pole-zero distribution shown in Fig. 5-6, where the first pole occurs at the origin. The factored polynomial

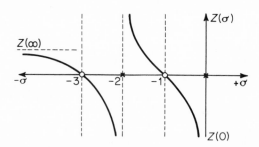

Figure 5-6   Pole-zero distribution of $Z(s)$ in Eq. 5.2-13.

form of the driving-point impedance of an R-C network having the impedance variation shown in the figure is

$$Z(s) = H\left[\frac{(s+1)(s+3)}{s(s+2)}\right] \qquad [5.2\text{-}13]$$

The factor s appears in the denominator because a pole exists at $s = 0$. A series capacitor $(A_0 \neq 0)$ yields such a pole. Assuming that $H = 1$,

$$Z(s) = \frac{(s + 1)(s + 3)}{s(s + 2)} \qquad [5.2\text{-}14]$$

Division of the denominator into the numerator yields

$$Z(s) = 1 + \frac{2s + 3}{s(s + 2)} = 1 + Z_1(s) \qquad [5.2\text{-}15]$$

where

$$Z_1(s) = \frac{A_0}{s} + \frac{A_1}{s + 2} \qquad [5.2\text{-}16]$$

Application of the same technique as used in the previous example to evaluate A_0 and A_1 gives the following results:

$$A_0 = [sZ_1(s)]_{s=0} = \frac{3}{2} \qquad [5.2\text{-}17]$$

$$A_1 = [(s + 2)Z_1(s)]_{s=-2} = \frac{1}{2} \qquad [5.2\text{-}18]$$

Therefore, the partial-fraction expansion is

$$Z(s) = 1 + \frac{3/2}{s} + \frac{1/2}{s + 2} = 1 + \frac{1}{2s/3} + \frac{1}{2s + 4} \qquad [5.2\text{-}19]$$

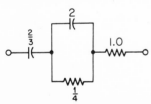

Values in ohms and farads

Figure 5-7   R-C network having $Z(s)$ in Eq. 5.2-19.

The network is shown in Fig. 5-7. It should be noted that $R_\infty = 1.0$ ohm in both illustrative examples because it was assumed that $H = 1$. This is not a general result.

As an illustration of R-L network synthesis, substitute $Y(s)$ for $Z(s)$ in Eq. 5.2-2. Then,

$$Y(s) = \frac{(s + 2)(s + 4)}{(s + 1)(s + 3)} \qquad [5.2\text{-}20]$$

It follows from Eq. 5.2-8 that $Y(s)$ in Eq. 5.2-20 can be expressed as

$$Y(s) = 1 + \frac{3/2}{s + 1} + \frac{1/2}{s + 3} \qquad [5.2\text{-}21]$$

Eq. 5.2-21 can also be written as

$$Y(s) = 1 + \frac{1}{2s/3 + 2/3} + \frac{1}{2s + 6} \qquad [5.2\text{-}22]$$

The denominator of the last two terms on the right-hand side of Eq. 5.2-22 are impedances of the form $R_k + sL_k$. Hence,

$$R_1 = 2/3 \text{ ohm} \qquad L_1 = 2/3 \text{ henry}$$
$$R_2 = 6 \text{ ohms} \qquad L_2 = 2 \text{ henrys}$$

The network is shown in Fig. 5-8. Inasmuch as the product of $Z(s)$ in Eq. 5.2-2 and $Y(s)$ in Eq. 5.2-20 is unity, the network in Fig. 5-8 is the inverse of the network in Fig. 5-5.

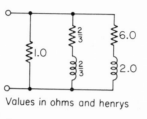

Values in ohms and henrys

Figure 5-8 R-L network having Y(s) in Eq. 5.2-22.

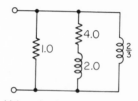

Values in ohms and henrys

Figure 5-9 R-L network having Y(s) in Eq. 5.2-24.

As a second illustration of R-L network synthesis, substitute $Y(s)$ for $Z(s)$ in Eq. 5.2-14. This yields

$$Y(s) = \frac{(s+1)(s+3)}{s(s+2)} \qquad [5.2\text{-}23]$$

The partial-fraction expansion of $Y(s)$ in Eq. 5.2-23 is

$$Y(s) = 1 + \frac{3/2}{s} + \frac{1/2}{s+2} = 1 + \frac{1}{2s/3} + \frac{1}{2s+4} \qquad [5.2\text{-}24]$$

The R-L network that yields $Y(s)$ in Eq. 5.2-24 is shown in Fig. 5-9. The network in Fig. 5-9 is the inverse of the network in Fig. 5-7.

As in the synthesis of L-C networks, the use of normalized impedance and frequency simplifies the calculations. Following the procedure of Sec. 3.9, the subscript a denotes the actual value, and the subscript n denotes the normalized value. If only the impedance level is normalized, the relation between the actual and normalized parameters is

$$R_a = \left(\frac{Z_a}{Z_n}\right) R_n \qquad [5.2\text{-}25]$$

$$L_a = \left(\frac{Z_a}{Z_n}\right) L_n \qquad [5.2\text{-}26]$$

$$C_a = \left(\frac{Z_n}{Z_a}\right) C_n \qquad\qquad [5.2\text{-}27]$$

Equations 5.2-26 and 5.2-27 follow from the fact that, for a given frequency, the inductive reactance is directly proportional to the inductance, but the capacitive reactance is inversely proportional to the capacitance. If only the frequency is normalized, the following relations hold:

$$R_a = R_n \qquad\qquad [5.2\text{-}28]$$

$$L_a = \left(\frac{\omega_n}{\omega_a}\right) L_n \qquad\qquad [5.2\text{-}29]$$

$$C_a = \left(\frac{\omega_n}{\omega_a}\right) C_n \qquad\qquad [5.2\text{-}30]$$

Equations 5.2-29 and 5.2-30 follow from the fact that, for a given impedance level, the products ωL and ωC must remain constant. When both impedance and frequency are normalized, the relation between the actual and normalized parameters is

$$R_a = \left(\frac{Z_a}{Z_n}\right) R_n \qquad\qquad [5.2\text{-}31]$$

$$L_a = \left(\frac{Z_a}{Z_n}\right)\left(\frac{\omega_n}{\omega_a}\right) L_n \qquad\qquad [5.2\text{-}32]$$

$$C_a = \left(\frac{Z_n}{Z_a}\right)\left(\frac{\omega_n}{\omega_a}\right) C_n \qquad\qquad [5.2\text{-}33]$$

5.3 R-C DRIVING-POINT ADMITTANCE AND R-L DRIVING-POINT IMPEDANCE

A network containing series R-C branches connected in parallel is shown in Fig. 5-10. The admittance of an R-C branch is

$$Y_{\text{R-C}}(s) = \frac{1}{R_k + 1/sC_k}$$

$$= \frac{s/R_k}{s + 1/R_kC_k} = \frac{s/R_k}{s - s_k} \quad [5.3\text{-}1]$$

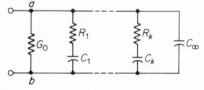

Figure 5-10 One-terminal pair R-C network.

where $s_k = -1/R_kC_k$. Hence, the poles are located on the negative real axis. The driving-point admittance at terminals ab is

$$Y(s) = G_0 + \sum_{k=1}^{k=n} \frac{s/R_k}{s - s_k} + sC_\infty \qquad\qquad [5.3\text{-}2]$$

where it is assumed that the network contains n parallel branches. Equation 5.3-2 can be expressed in partial-fraction form as

$$Y(s) = B_0 + \sum_{k=1}^{k=n} \frac{sB_k}{s - s_k} + sB_\infty \qquad [5.3\text{-}3]$$

where $B_0 = G_0$, $B_k = 1/R_k$, and $B_\infty = G_\infty$.

The slope of the admittance curve is found by differentiating Eq. 5.3-3 with respect to s. Thus

$$\frac{dY(s)}{ds} = \sum_{k=1}^{k=n} \frac{B_k(s - s_k - s)}{(s - s_k)^2} + B_\infty = B_\infty - \sum_{k=1}^{k=n} \frac{s_k B_k}{(s - s_k)^2} \quad [5.3\text{-}4]$$

Since s_k is real and negative, the slope is positive at all points.

It follows from Eq. 5.3-2 that:

$$Y(0) = G_0 \qquad [5.3\text{-}5]$$

Also, when $C_\infty = 0$,

$$Y(\infty) = G_0 + \sum_{k=1}^{k=n} \frac{1}{R_k} \qquad [5.3\text{-}6]$$

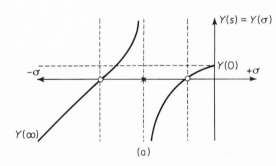

(a)

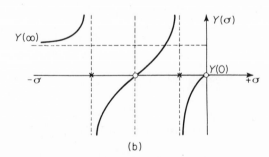

(b)

Figure 5-11   Admittance of R-C network as a function of σ.

When $C_\infty \neq 0$, $Y(\infty)$ is infinite. Therefore $Y(\infty)$ is always greater than $Y(0)$. Typical admittance variations as a function of σ are shown in Fig. 5-11. The function is only shown in the left-hand part of the s-plane, as in Figure 5-2.

The properties of R-C driving-point admittance functions are summarized here:

(1) All internal poles and zeros are located on the negative real axis of the s-plane.

(2) The slope of the admittance curve as a function of σ is positive at all points.

(3) The poles and zeros alternate, and are said to be interlaced.

(4) The critical frequency nearest the origin is a zero. When $B_0 = 0$, a zero exists at the origin.

(5) The critical frequency at the greatest distance from the origin is a pole. It follows from Eq. 5.3-2 that this critical frequency occurs at infinity when $C_\infty \neq 0$.

(6) The admittance at infinity is always greater than the admittance at zero, and, as noted in (5), may be infinite.

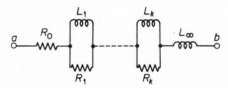

Figure 5-12 One-terminal pair R-L network.

A network containing parallel R-L branches connected in series is shown in Fig. 5-12. The impedance of an R-L branch is

$$Z_{\text{R}-\text{L}}(s) = \frac{sL_kR_k}{R_k + sL_k} = \frac{s/R_k}{s + R_k/L_k} = \frac{s/R_k}{s - s_k} \qquad [5.3\text{-}7]$$

where $s_k = -R_k/L_k$, and is real and negative.

The driving-point impedance at terminals ab is

$$Z(s) = R_0 + \sum_{k=1}^{k=n} \frac{s/R_k}{s - s_k} + sL_\infty \qquad [5.3\text{-}8]$$

Equation 5.3-8 for the driving-point impedance of the R-L network has exactly the same form as Eq. 5.3-2 for the driving-point admittance of the

R-C network. Hence, the driving-point impedance of R-L networks has the same properties as the driving-point admittance of R-C networks.

Both Eqs. 5.3-2 and 5.3-8 can be expressed in factored polynomial form as

$$Y(s) = \frac{P(s)}{Q(s)} = H\left[\frac{(s - s_1)(s - s_3)(s - s_5) \cdots}{(s - s_2)(s - s_4)(s - s_6) \cdots}\right] \qquad [5.3\text{-}9]$$

where $s_1, s_3, s_5, \ldots$ are the zeros, and $s_2, s_4, s_6 \ldots$ are the poles of the function. The factored polynomial form is useful in synthesis when the poles and zeros are specified. Examples of admittance synthesis of R-C networks and impedance synthesis of R-L networks are given in Sec. 5-4, following.

5.4 PARTIAL-FRACTION SYNTHESIS OF R-C ADMITTANCE AND R-L IMPEDANCE

Partial-fraction synthesis consists of resolving the admittance or impedance having the form given in Eq. 5.3-9, and associating the partial fractions with the network components in Fig. 5-10 or Fig. 5-12. Inspection of the right-hand sides of Eqs. 5.3-3 and 5.3-8 shows that the terms in the summations are not in standard partial-fraction form because the order of the numerator is the same as that of the denominator. In order to apply partial fractions, it is necessary to divide each side of the equation by s. In the case of the admittance function in Eq. 5.3-3, the resulting expression is

$$\frac{Y(s)}{s} = \frac{B_0}{s} + \sum_{k=1}^{k=n} \frac{B_k}{s - s_k} + B_\infty \qquad [5.4\text{-}1]$$

and for the impedance function in Eq. 5.3-8,

$$\frac{Z(s)}{s} = \frac{A_0}{s} + \sum_{k=1}^{k=n} \frac{A_k}{s - s_k} + A_\infty \qquad [5.4\text{-}2]$$

where $A_0 = R_0$, $A_k = 1/R_k$, $A_\infty = L_\infty$, and $B_0 = G_0$, $B_k = 1/R_k$, $B_\infty = G_\infty$.

Equations 5.4-1 and 5.4-2 can be resolved into partial fractions by standard methods.

As the first example, consider the admittance function

$$Y(s) = \frac{(s + 1)(s + 3)}{(s + 2)(s + 4)} \qquad [5.4\text{-}3]$$

The first critical frequency is a zero, which identifies $Y(s)$ as an R-C admittance. Y_s in Eq. 5.4-3 is the reciprocal of the impedance function in

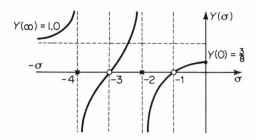

Figure 5-13   Pole-zero distribution of $Y(s)$ in Eq. 5.4-3.

Eq. 5.2-2. The admittance function is shown in Fig. 5-13. Following the form of Eq. 5.4-1, Eq. 5.4-3 is written as

$$\frac{Y(s)}{s} = \frac{(s+1)(s+3)}{s(s+2)(s+4)} = \frac{A_0}{s} + \frac{A_1}{s+2} + \frac{A_2}{s+4} \qquad [5.4\text{-}4]$$

The constants on the right-hand side of Eq. 5.4-4 are determined as follows:

$$A_0 = \left[\frac{sY(s)}{s}\right]_{s=0} = \frac{3}{8} \qquad [5.4\text{-}5]$$

$$A_1 = \left[\frac{(s+2)Y(s)}{s}\right]_{s=-2} = \frac{1}{4} \qquad [5.4\text{-}6]$$

$$A_2 = \left[\frac{(s+4)Y(s)}{s}\right]_{s=-4} = \frac{3}{8} \qquad [5.4\text{-}7]$$

The substitution of Eqs. 5.4-5, 5.4-6, and 5.4-7 into Eq. 5.4-4 yields

$$\frac{Y(s)}{s} = \frac{3/8}{s} + \frac{1/4}{s+2} + \frac{3/8}{s+4} \qquad [5.4\text{-}8]$$

Hence,

$$Y(s) = \frac{3}{8} + \frac{s/4}{s+2} + \frac{3s/8}{s+4} \qquad [5.4\text{-}9]$$

A comparison of Eq. 5.4-9 with Eq. 5.3-2 shows that

$$G_0 = \frac{3}{8} \, \text{mho} \qquad [5.4\text{-}10]$$

$$R_1 = 4 \, \text{ohms} \qquad [5.4\text{-}11]$$

$$C_1 = \frac{1}{2R_1} = \frac{1}{8} \, \text{farad} \qquad [5.4\text{-}12]$$

$$R_2 = \frac{8}{3} \text{ ohm} \qquad [5.4\text{-}13]$$

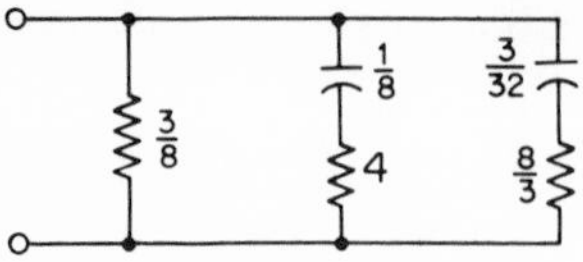

$$C_2 = \frac{1}{4 \times 8/3} = \frac{3}{32} \text{ farad} \qquad [5.4\text{-}14]$$

Values in ohms and farads

Figure 5-14 R-C network having $Y(s)$ in Eq. 5.4-9.

The network is shown in Fig. 5-14; it is equivalent to the network in Fig. 5-5.

An alternative way to obtain the network in Fig. 5-14 is to write Eq. 5.4-9 as

$$Y(s) = \frac{3}{8} + \frac{1}{4 + 8/s} + \frac{1}{8/3 + 32/3s}$$

$$= \frac{3}{8} + \frac{1}{4 + \dfrac{1}{s/8}} + \frac{1}{\dfrac{8}{3} + \dfrac{1}{3s/32}} \qquad [5.4\text{-}15]$$

where the denominators on the right-hand side of Eq. 5.4-15 are impedances.

The inverse of the impedance function given by Eq. 5.2-14 will be used for the second example of R-C admittance synthesis. In this case

$$Y(s) = \frac{s(s+2)}{(s+1)(s+3)} \qquad [5.4\text{-}16]$$

The admittance function is shown in Fig. 5-15.

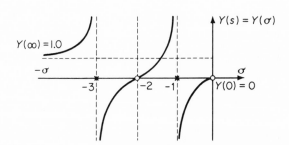

Figure 5-15 Pole-zero distribution of $Y(s)$ in Eq. 5.4-16.

Equation 5.4-16 can be written as

$$\frac{Y(s)}{s} = \frac{s+2}{(s+1)(s+3)} = \frac{A_1}{s+1} + \frac{A_2}{s+3} \qquad [5.4\text{-}17]$$

where

$$A_1 = \left[(s + 1) \frac{Y(s)}{s} \right]_{s=-1} = \frac{1}{2} \qquad [5.4\text{-}18]$$

$$A_1 = \left[(s + 3) \frac{Y(s)}{s} \right]_{s=-3} = \frac{1}{2} \qquad [5.4\text{-}19]$$

The substitution of Eqs. 5.4-18 and 5.4-19 into Eq. 5.4-17 yields

$$\frac{Y(s)}{s} = \frac{1/2}{s+1} + \frac{1/2}{s+3} \qquad [5.4\text{-}20]$$

$$Y(s) = \frac{s/2}{s+1} + \frac{s/2}{s+3} = \frac{1}{2 + 2/s} + \frac{1}{2 + 6/s}$$

$$= \frac{1}{2 + \dfrac{1}{s/2}} + \frac{1}{2 + \dfrac{1}{s/6}} \qquad [5.4\text{-}21]$$

The network is shown in Fig. 5-16. Figure 5-16 is equivalent to Fig. 5-7.

The substitution of $Z(s)$ for $Y(s)$ in Eq. 5.4-15 yields

$$Z(s) = \frac{3}{8} + \frac{1}{4 + \dfrac{1}{s/8}} + \frac{1}{\dfrac{8}{3} + \dfrac{1}{3s/32}} \qquad [5.4\text{-}22]$$

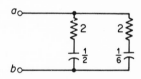

Values in ohms and farads

Figure 5-16 R-C network having $Y(s)$ in Eq. 5.4-21.

The R-L impedance network that yields $Z(s)$ as given by Eq. 5.4-22 is shown in (a) of Fig. 5-17. The network in Fig. 5-17(a) is equivalent to the network in Fig. 5-8, and is the inverse of the network in Fig. 5-14.

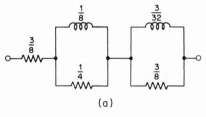

(a)

Values in ohms and henrys

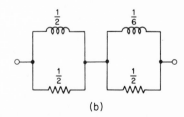

(b)

Values in ohms and henrys

Figure 5-17 R-L impedance networks. (a) Network having $Z(s)$ in Eq. 5.4-22. (b) Network having $Z(s)$ in Eq. 5.4-23.

The substitution of $Z(s)$ for $Y(s)$ in Eq. 5.4-21 yields

$$Z(s) = \frac{1}{2 + 1/\frac{1}{2}s} + \frac{1}{2 + 1/\frac{1}{6}s}$$ [5.4-23]

The R-L impedance network is shown in (b) of Fig. 5-17. The network in Fig. 5-17(b) is equivalent to Fig. 5-9, and is the inverse of the network in Fig. 5-16.

5.5 CONTINUED-FRACTION NETWORKS (CAUER-TYPE NETWORKS)

We have developed two types of networks of the partial-fraction form or Foster type. One is based on the impedance function, and the other is based on the admittance function. These networks contain the minimum number of elements, and are called *canonic* forms.

Two other canonic forms can be obtained by the Cauer continued-fraction expansion. The general method is given in Sec. 3.7. Using Eq. 5.2-2, we have

$$Z(s) = \frac{(s + 2)(s + 4)}{(s + 1)(s + 3)} = \frac{s^2 + 6s + 8}{s^2 + 4s + 3}$$ [5.5-1]

This is an R-C impedance network, since the first critical frequency is a pole. Developing $Z(s)$ in Eq. 5.5-1 by continued fractions about $s = \infty$ we have

$$Z(s) = \frac{s^2 + 6s + 8}{s^2 + 4s + 3} = 1 + \cfrac{1}{\frac{1}{2}s + \cfrac{1}{\frac{4}{3} + \cfrac{1}{\frac{3}{2}s + \cfrac{1}{1/3}}}}$$ [5.5-2]

where the first term is the limit of $Z(s)$ as s approaches infinity. In Eq. 5.5-2, the first term is an impedance that was obtained by dividing the denominator into the numerator, the term, $s/2$, is an admittance, etc. The network is shown in Fig. 5-18, which is equivalent to Fig. 5-5.

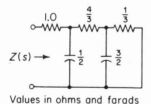

Values in ohms and farads

Figure 5-18 Continued-fraction network for $Z(s)$ in Eq. 5.5-1 developed about infinity.

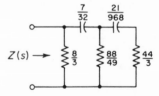

Values in ohms and farads

Figure 5-19 Continued-fraction network for $Z(s)$ in Eq. 5.5-1 developed about zero.

If we carry out the continued-fraction development about $s = 0$ for the same $Z(s)$ function, another canonic form is developed as shown in Fig. 5-19; this is equivalent to Fig. 5-18 as to driving-point impedance.

$$Z(s) = \frac{8 + 6s + s^2}{3 + 4s + s^2} = 0 + \cfrac{1}{\dfrac{3}{8} + \cfrac{1}{\dfrac{32}{7s} + \cfrac{1}{\dfrac{49}{88} + \cfrac{1}{\dfrac{968}{21s} + \cfrac{1}{3/44}}}}} \qquad [5.5\text{-}3]$$

Since the initial division of the denominator into the numerator yields a negative remainder, a zero impedance is first taken out; the term, $\frac{3}{8}$, is an admittance; etc.

Returning to Eq. 5.5-2, and calling this an admittance function, we have an R-L admittance network. Thus,

$$Y(s) = \frac{s^2 + 6s + 8}{s^2 + 4s + 3} = 1 + \cfrac{1}{\dfrac{1}{2}s + \cfrac{1}{\dfrac{4}{3} + \cfrac{1}{\dfrac{3}{2}s + \cfrac{1}{1/3}}}} \qquad [5.5\text{-}4]$$

The first term is now an admittance, the term, $s/2$, is an impedance, etc. The network is shown in Fig. 5-20, which is the inverse of Fig. 5-18.

The other networks discussed can be treated in a similar manner, and their continued-fraction networks can be obtained similarly. It should be mentioned that network functions that can be realized in one canonic form may not be realizable in all forms. In some cases negative circuit elements would be required.

Besides the forms mentioned above, other mixed forms of realization may be used. For example, a Foster form may be used for a portion of the

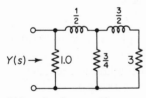

Values in ohms and henrys

Figure 5-20 Continued-fraction R-L network having $Y(s)$ in Eq. 5.5-4.

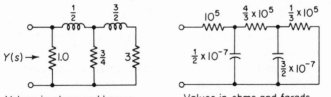

Values in ohms and farads

Figure 5-21 Network of Fig. 5-18 with impedance and frequency levels increased respectively by 10^5 and 10^2.

network and the remainder realized as a Cauer network, or vice versa. Another possible procedure is to remove a finite impedance pole as an impedance, invert the remainder, remove a finite admittance pole, and so on.

The network functions considered so far in this discussion have been developed from realizable networks, but it should be emphasized here that not all polynomial functions are realizable. It requires a considerable amount of mathematical work to determine functions that are realizable, and in what form they are realizable. Such determinations are left for more advanced textbooks on network synthesis.*

Before leaving the subject, however, we shall give here an example of determining the actual values of a network from the normalized values. For this example, refer to Fig. 5-18, and assume that the impedance is to be increased by a factor of 10^5 $(Z_a/Z_n = 10^5)$, and that ω is to be increased by 10^2. It follows from Eqs. 5.2-31 and 5.2-33 that all R values are increased by 10^5 and that all C values are decreased by $(10^5 \times 10^2) = 10^7$. The network with its actual values is shown in Fig. 5-21.

5.6 THE R-L-C NETWORK

In the preceding sections of this chapter, as well as in Chap. 3, only two-element networks have been considered. The poles and zeros for the L-C networks are restricted to purely imaginary values of s, and are situated on the $j\omega$ axis; whereas for the R-C and R-L networks, the poles and zeros are restricted to the negative σ-axis.

In R-L-C networks, the poles and zeros are in general complex, and they may lie anywhere in the left-hand portion of the s-plane. This is a necessary but not a sufficient condition for an R-L-C network to be physically realizable. The conditions listed below must all be satisfied if an R-L-C function is to be realizable:

(1) $Z(s)$ is real for real values of s.

(2) The polynomial in the denominator of $Z(s)$ must have poles restricted to the left-hand portion of the s-plane.

(3) When $s = j\omega$, the real part of $Z(j\omega)$ must be zero or greater than zero for all real values of ω (that is, the real part of a driving-point impedance cannot be negative for real frequencies, as such a condition would require one or more negative resistances).

---

* For example: Guellemin, E. A., *Synthesis of Passive Networks* (John Wiley & Sons, Inc., New York, 1957); or Tuttle, D. F., Jr., *Network Synthesis* (John Wiley & Sons, Inc., New York, 1958); or Balabanian, Norman, *Network Synthesis* (Prentice-Hall, Inc., Englewood Cliffs, N.J., 1958).

The complete discussion of the R-L-C function cannot be treated adequately here. One basic equation can, however, be given. The driving-point impedance of an R-L-C network has the general form of

$$Z(s) = H\left[\frac{(s - s_1)(s - s_3) \ldots}{(s - s_2)(s - s_4) \ldots}\right] \qquad [5.6\text{-}1]$$

where the poles and zeros are in general complex.

5.7 TWO-TERMINAL PAIR SYNTHESIS OF R-C AND R-L NETWORKS

Network synthesis and design can take a wide variety of forms. The purpose here, however, will be to limit the discussion to a rather simple method of approach based on the lattice network. The transfer impedance will be used to characterize the two-terminal pair network.

Any realizable transfer function can be obtained from a lattice network. The lattice is generally not a desirable structure from a practical standpoint, but it is used here as a design artifice and will be converted into an unbalanced structure whenever possible. In general, there is no way of knowing in advance whether the lattice can be reduced to an unbalanced structure. This places it at a disadvantage over methods that determine unbalanced structures directly. The latter methods are varied, and are a subject that is a course of study in itself.

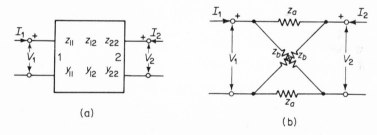

(a)

(b)

Figure 5-22 Two-terminal pair networks.

In a two-terminal pair network, as shown in Fig. 5-22(a), the internal network is defined in terms of z_{11}, z_{22}, and z_{12}, or in terms of y_{11}, y_{22}, and y_{12}. The equations for the network in terms of the z parameters are:

$$V_1 = z_{11}I_1 + z_{12}I_2$$
$$V_2 = z_{21}I_1 + z_{22}I_2 \qquad [5.7\text{-}1]$$

or in terms of the y parameters:

$$I_1 = y_{11}V_1 + y_{12}V_2$$
$$I_2 = y_{21}V_1 + y_{22}V_2 \qquad \text{[5.7-2]}$$

During the following discussion, it should be kept in mind that z_{11} and z_{22} are open-circuit driving-point impedances; their realizability has been treated in the preceding sections. Also, for a reciprocal network, $z_{12} = z_{21}$, and represents the open-circuit transfer impedance.

For the lattice network in (b) of Fig. 5-22, we have

$$z_{11} = z_{22} = \frac{z_b + z_a}{2} \qquad \text{[5.7-3]}$$

$$z_{12} = \frac{z_b - z_a}{2} \qquad \text{[5.7-4]}$$

Hence the arms of the lattice are

$$z_a = z_{11} - z_{12}$$
$$z_b = z_{11} + z_{12} \qquad \text{[5.7-5]}$$

If z_{11} is an R-C driving-point impedance, the residues at its poles are real and positive. If z_{11} is an R-L driving-point impedance, then z_{11}/s has residues at its poles that are real and positive. Likewise, z_a and z_b are driving-point impedances, and the residues at their poles must be real and positive for R-C and R-L impedances, as indicated for z_{11}. The transfer impedance, z_{12}, must be such that, when it is added to or subtracted from z_{11}, the resulting impedance, z_a or z_b, is physically realizable.

The necessary and sufficient conditions that z_{12} must satisfy when it is an R-C impedance are these:

(1) The poles of the transfer impedance must be simple, and they must lie on the negative real axis.

(2) The zeros of the transfer impedance may lie anywhere in the complex plane, and they may be of any multiplicity. Complex zeros must occur in conjugate pairs.

(3) The residues of z_{12} must be real, but they may be either positive or negative.

(4) The poles of z_{12} must be contained in the poles of z_{11} and z_{22}, and the residue condition must be satisfied in each of these poles. That is, if K_{11}, K_{12}, and K_{22} are the residues at the poles of z_{11}, z_{12}, and z_{22}, then at each pole $(K_{11}K_{22} - K_{12}^2) \geqq 0$. Since, in a lattice, $z_{11} = z_{22}$, then $K_{11} - |K_{12}| \geqq 0$.

(5) The self-impedance and mutual impedances must satisfy the following limiting condition: $|z_{11}(\infty)z_{22}(\infty)| - |z_{12}(\infty)|^2 \geqq 0$; or for a lattice, since $z_{11} = z_{22}$, $|z_{11}(\infty)| \geqq |z_{12}(\infty)|$.

The following examples will help to clarify the material given thus far.

A. Example of Transfer Impedance with a Zero at s = 0

Assume that an open-circuit transfer impedance is given as follows:

$$z_{12} = \frac{s}{s+2} = 1 - \frac{2}{s+2} \qquad [5.7\text{-}6]$$

This impedance has a pole on the negative real axis, and it has a zero at $s = 0$. The pole-zero plot is shown in Fig. 5-23. The transfer impedance, z_{12}, is also given in partial-fraction form, which yields a constant of 1.0 at $s = \infty$, and a residue of -2 for the pole at $s = -2$.

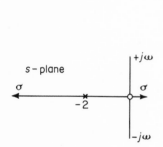

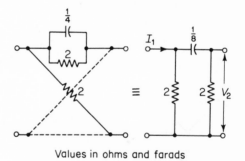

Values in ohms and farads

Figure 5-23 Pole-zero distribution of z_{12} in Eq. 5.7-6.

Figure 5-24 Lattice and equivalent ladder network having z_{12} in Eq. 5.7-6.

Since the residues at the poles of z_{11} are real and positive, the simplest network is obtained if the residues at the poles of z_{11} are taken equal in absolute value to those of z_{12}. The residues of z_{11} might be chosen larger than those of z_{12}, but nothing is gained except a different z_{11}. In addition, z_{11} may contain poles not in z_{12}.

Choosing a z_{11} with residues at the poles equal in absolute value to those of z_{12}, and meeting the condition at $s = \infty$, we have

$$z_{11} = 1 + \frac{2}{s+2} \qquad [5.7\text{-}7]$$

Using Eqs. 5.7-5, 5.7-6, and 5.7-7, we have

$$z_a = z_{11} - z_{12} = \frac{4}{s+2} = \frac{1}{1/2 + s/4} \qquad [5.7\text{-}8]$$

$$z_b = z_{11} + z_{12} = 2 \qquad [5.7\text{-}9]$$

The lattice network, with its equivalent ladder or unbalanced network, is shown in Fig. 5-24. If the network on the right is bisected, the open-circuited impedance gives the z_b arm of the lattice, and the short-circuited impedance gives the z_a arm.

The same network can be realized as an R-L network. In this case, the impedance is treated as $Z(s)/s$ and then the partial-fraction expansion is multiplied by s. Thus,

$$\frac{z_{12}}{s} = \frac{1}{s+2}$$

The partial-fraction expansion of z_{12} is given by

$$z_{12} = \frac{s}{s+2} \qquad [5.7\text{-}10]$$

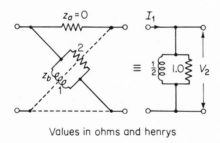

Values in ohms and henrys

Figure 5-25 Lattice and equivalent network having z_{12} in Eq. 5.7-10.

Then z_{11} is chosen as an R-L impedance such that

$$\frac{z_{11}}{s} = \frac{1}{s+2}$$

or

$$z_{11} = \frac{s}{s+2} \qquad [5.7\text{-}11]$$

which is an R-L impedance, since the first critical frequency is a zero.

Now we have

$$z_a = z_{11} - z_{12} = 0$$

$$z_b = z_{11} + z_{12} = \frac{2s}{s+2} = \frac{1}{1/2 + 1/s} \qquad [5.7\text{-}12]$$

where z_b is recognized as the impedance of a parallel R-L network. The lattice network with its equivalent ladder are shown in Fig. 5-25. Figures 5-24 and 5-25 have the same open-circuited transfer impedance.

B. *Example of Transfer Impedance with a Zero at $s = \infty$**

Let

$$z_{12} = \frac{1}{(s + 1)(s + 3)} = \frac{1/2}{s + 1} - \frac{1/2}{s + 3} \qquad [5.7\text{-}13]$$

The pole-zero distribution in the s-plane is given in Fig. 5-26.

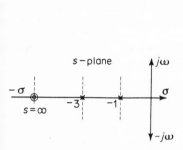

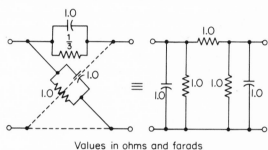

Values in ohms and farads

Figure 5-26 Pole-zero distribution of z_{12} in Eq. 5.7-13.

Figure 5-27 Lattice and equivalent ladder network having z_{12} in Eq. 5.7-13.

A form of z_{11} is chosen so that the residues at the poles are equal to those of z_{12}, but are positive for a realizable open-circuit driving-point impedance. Therefore,

$$z_{11} = \frac{1/2}{s + 1} + \frac{1/2}{s + 3} \qquad [5.7\text{-}14]$$

From Eqs. 5.7-5, 5.7-13, and 5.7-14, we have

$$z_a = z_{11} - z_{12} = \frac{1}{s + 3}$$

$$z_b = z_{11} + z_{12} = \frac{1}{s + 1}$$

The lattice with its equivalent unbalanced network is shown in Fig. 5-27.

C. *Example of Transfer Impedance with Zeros at Finite Frequencies on the Negative Real Axis*

Consider the transfer impedance

$$z_{12} = \frac{(s + 2)(s + 3)}{(s + 1)(s + 4)} = 1 + \frac{2/3}{s + 1} - \frac{2/3}{s + 4} \qquad [5.7\text{-}15]$$

*This transfer function has a second-order zero at $s = \infty$ because

$$\lim_{s=\infty} z_{12}(s) = \lim_{s=\infty} 1/s^2$$

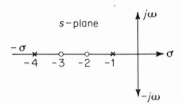

s-plane

Figure 5-28 Pole-zero distribution of z_{12} in Eq. 5.7-15.

with the pole-zero distribution in the s-plane shown in Fig. 5-28. Then, choosing

$$z_{11} = 1 + \frac{2/3}{s+1} + \frac{2/3}{s+4} \qquad [5.7\text{-}16]$$

the lattice arms are

$$z_a = z_{11} - z_{12} = \frac{4/3}{s+4} = \frac{1}{3 + 3s/4}$$

$$z_b = z_{11} + z_{12} = 2 + \frac{4/3}{s+1} = 2 + \frac{1}{3/4 + 3s/4} \qquad [5.7\text{-}17]$$

In order to find the unbalanced ladder form of the lattice, it is convenient to express the z_b arm in an admittance form. Thus

$$y_b = \frac{1}{z_b} = \frac{s+1}{2s + 10/3} = \frac{3}{10} + \frac{s/5}{s + 5/3}$$

$$= \frac{3}{10} + \frac{1}{5 + 25/3s} \qquad [5.7\text{-}18]$$

The arms are shown in Fig. 5-29. The conversion of the lattice network to an unbalanced ladder is shown in Fig. 5-30, with the ladder in bisected form. Note that, when the bisected network is open-circuited, the series resistors, with values of $10/27$ ohm and $125/27$ ohms respectively, give the 5 ohms of the z_b arm; and, when short-circuited, the resistor of $10/27$ ohm in parallel with the resistor of $10/3$ ohms yield the $1/3$ ohm of the z_a arm.

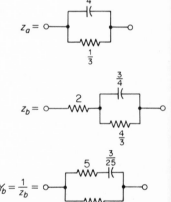

Values in ohms and farads

Figure 5-29 Arms of lattice network having z_{12} in Eq. 5.7-15.

D. Example of Transfer Impedance with j-Axis Zeros

Consider the following open-circuit transfer impedance:

$$z_{12} = \frac{s^2 + 1}{(s+1)(s+3)} = 1 + \frac{1}{s+1} - \frac{5}{s+3} \qquad [5.7\text{-}19]$$

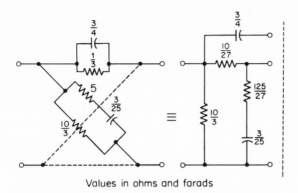

Values in ohms and farads

Figure 5-30 Lattice and equivalent unbalanced network having z_{12} in Eq. 5.7-15.

with the pole-zero plot in the s-plane shown in Fig. 5-31. The driving-point impedance is chosen as

$$z_{11} = 1 + \frac{1}{s+1} + \frac{5}{s+3} \qquad [5.7\text{-}20]$$

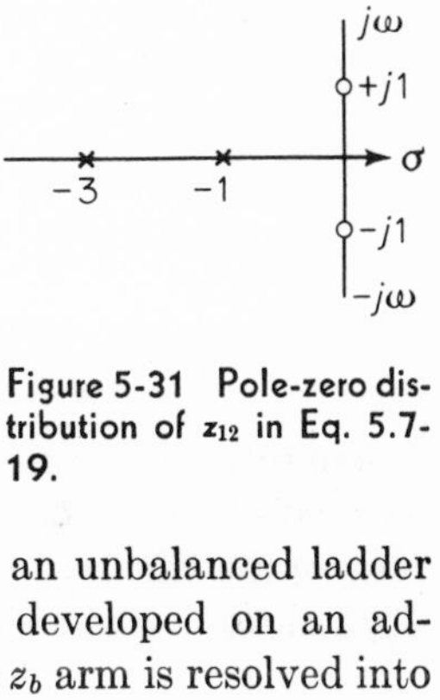

Then,

$$z_a = z_{11} - z_{12} = \frac{10}{s+3}$$

$$z_b = z_{11} + z_{12} = 2 + \frac{2}{s+1} \qquad [5.7\text{-}21]$$

Figure 5-31 Pole-zero distribution of z_{12} in Eq. 5.7-19.

Here again, the development of the lattice into an unbalanced ladder requires a special technique. First, the z_b arm is developed on an admittance basis as in the previous example; then, the z_b arm is resolved into parallel components. The admittance expression for the z_b arm is the following:

$$y_b = \frac{1}{z_b} = \frac{s+1}{2s+4} = \frac{1}{4} + \frac{s/4}{s+2} = \frac{1}{4} + \frac{1}{4+8/s} \qquad [5.7\text{-}22]$$

The arms of the lattice network are shown in Fig. 5-32. The development of the lattice into an unbalanced network is shown in Fig. 5-33, with the unbalanced network in Fig. 5-33(b) left in the bisected form to demonstrate that z_a corresponds to the short-circuited impedance and z_b to the open-circuited impedance.

The process can be described as follows. The y_b form is obtained from z_b, and yields the equivalent network for z_b shown in (c) of Fig. 5-32. The

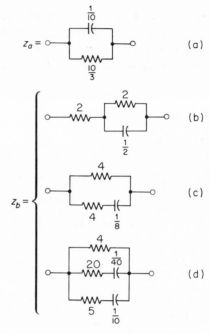

Values in ohms and farads

Figure 5-32 Arms of lattice network
having z_{12} in Eq. 5.7-19.

4-ohm resistor in series with the 1/8 farad capacitor branch is resolved into
two parallel branches, as shown in Fig. 5-32(d). The value of the 20-ohm
resistor is critical since the 20 ohms in parallel with 4 ohms must be equal to
10/3 ohms or the resistance in the z_a arm, as can be seen in Fig. 5-33(b).

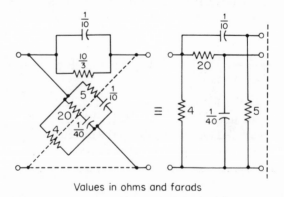

Values in ohms and farads

Figure 5-33 Lattice and equivalent unbalanced network having z_{12} in Eq. 5.7-19.

Since the RC product of 4 ohms and $1/8$ farad is equal to $1/2$, it follows that $20C = 1/2$, and $C = 1/40$ farad. The other branch consists of a 5-ohm resistor in series with a capacitor of $1/10$ farad. This follows from the method of combining resistors and capacitors in parallel.

E. Example of a Transfer Impedance with a Pair of Complex Zeros

Assume that

$$z_{12} = \frac{(s + 1 + j1)(s + 1 - j1)}{(s + 1/2)(s + 1)} = \frac{s^2 + 2s + 2}{(s + 1/2)(s + 1)}$$

$$= 1 + \frac{5/2}{s + 1/2} - \frac{2}{s + 1} \qquad [5.7\text{-}23]$$

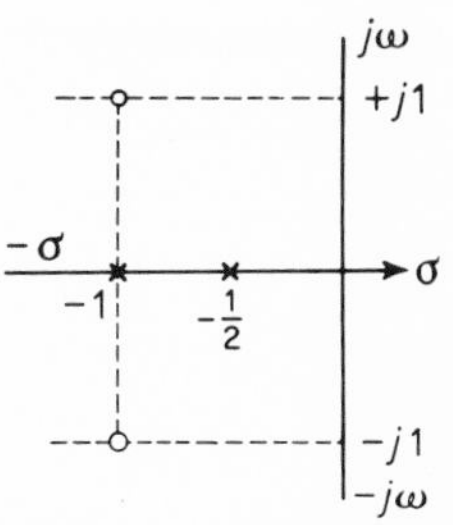

The pole-zero plot in the s-plane is given in Fig. 5-34. Choose

$$z_{11} = 1 + \frac{5/2}{s + 1/2} + \frac{2}{s + 1} \qquad [5.7\text{-}24]$$

Then

$$z_a = z_{11} - z_{12} = \frac{4}{s + 1}$$

$$[5.7\text{-}25]$$

$$z_b = z_{11} + z_{12} = 2 + \frac{5}{s + 1/2} = \frac{2s + 6}{s + 1/2}$$

Figure 5-34 Pole-zero distribution of z_{12} in Eq. 5.7-23.

or

$$y_b = \frac{s + 1/2}{2s + 6} = \frac{1}{12} + \frac{5s/12}{s + 3} = \frac{1}{12} + \frac{1}{12/5 + 36/5s} \qquad [5.7\text{-}26]$$

The lattice and the unbalanced bisected network are shown in Fig. 5-35. The process of development is the same as used in the preceding example

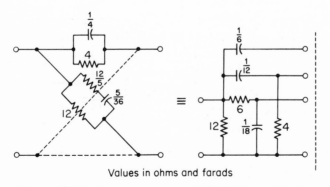

Values in ohms and farads

Figure 5-35 Lattice and equivalent unbalanced network having z_{12} in Eq. 5.7-23.

except that the 1/6 farad capacitor is added in parallel with the 1/12 farad capacitor to give the required capacitance for the short-circuited impedance.

F. Example of Transfer Impedance with a Zero on the Positive Real Axis

Let

+jω
−σ
−2
−1
+1
σ
−jω

Figure 5-36 Pole-zero distribution of z_{12} in Eq. 5.7-27.

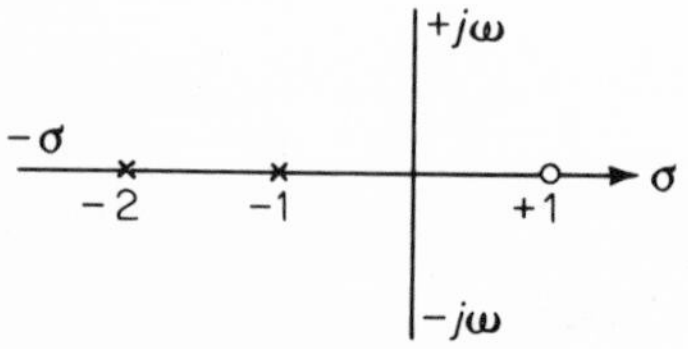

$$z_{12} = \frac{s-1}{(s+1)(s+2)} = \frac{-2}{s+1} + \frac{3}{s+2} \qquad [5.7\text{-}27]$$

with a pole-zero plot as shown in Fig. 5-36. Choose

$$z_{11} = \frac{2}{s+1} + \frac{3}{s+2} \qquad [5.7\text{-}28]$$

It follows that:

$$z_a = z_{11} - z_{12} = \frac{4}{s+1} = \frac{1}{1/4 + s/4}$$
$$z_b = z_{11} + z_{12} = \frac{6}{s+2} = \frac{1}{1/3 + s/6} \qquad [5.7\text{-}29]$$

The development of the lattice into an unbalanced network is shown in Fig. 5-37, and it should be noticed that a negative resistance of −1 ohm appears in the unbalanced form. Hence, the unbalanced form is not realizable. It should also be noticed that as $s \to 0$, z_{12} is negative. This indicates that an unbalanced form is not physically realizable.

As another illustration of impedance and frequency scaling, refer to Fig. 5-35, and increase the impedance by 10^5 and the frequency by 10. It

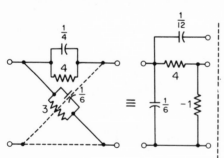

1/4
4
1/6
3
≡
1/12
4
1/6
−1
Values in ohms and farads

Figure 5-37 Lattice and equivalent unbalanced network having z_{12} in Eq. 5.7-27.

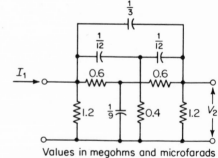

1/3
1/12
1/12
I_1
0.6
0.6
1.2
1/9
0.4
1.2
V_2
Values in megohms and microfarads

Figure 5-38 Network of Fig. 5-35 with impedance and frequency levels increased respectively by 10^5 and 10.

follows from Eqs. 5.2-31 and 5.2-33 that the R values are increased by 10^5, and the C values are decreased by 10^6. The result is shown as a complete network in Fig. 5-38.

It might be mentioned here that the current generator I_1 in conjunction with the 1.2-megohm input resistance can be converted into a voltage generator. The 1.2-megohm output resistance can be absorbed as part of the load.

5.8 THE CONSTANT-RESISTANCE LATTICE

If a two-terminal pair network is terminated by a resistance R_0 and if the driving-point impedance is equal to R_0, the two-terminal pair network is termed a *constant-resistance network*. In Fig. 5-39 is shown a two-terminal

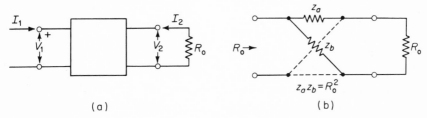

(a)   (b)

Figure 5-39 Two-terminal pair network and constant-resistance lattice.

pair network terminated by a resistance R_0, together with a constant-resistance lattice network, also terminated by R_0.

The characteristic impedance of a lattice network is given by

$$Z_0 = \sqrt{Z_a Z_b}\qquad\qquad [5.8\text{-}1]$$

Hence, for the lattice to be a constant-resistance network, it is required that Z_a and Z_b be inverse impedances about R_0^2. That is,

$$Z_b = \frac{R_0^2}{Z_a}\qquad\qquad [5.8\text{-}2]$$

Using the z parameters for (a) of Fig. 5-39, we have

$$V_1 = z_{11}I_1 + z_{12}I_2$$
$$V_2 = z_{21}I_1 + z_{22}I_2\qquad\qquad [5.8\text{-}3]$$

where $V_2 = -R_0 I_2$.
Hence,

$$V_1 = z_{11}I_1 + z_{12}I_2$$
$$0 = z_{21}I_1 + (R_0 + z_{22})I_2\qquad\qquad [5.8\text{-}4]$$

The z determinant of the terminated network is

$$\Delta_z = \begin{vmatrix} z_{11} & z_{12} \\ z_{21} & R_0 + z_{22} \end{vmatrix}$$ [5.8-5]

The driving-point impedance is given by

$$Z = \frac{V_1}{I_1} = \frac{\Delta}{\Delta_{11}} = \frac{|z| + z_{11}R_0}{R_0 + z_{22}}$$ [5.8-6]

Since, in a lattice,

$$|z| = Z_a Z_b; \qquad z_{11} = z_{22} = \frac{Z_b + Z_a}{2}$$

the driving-point impedance of the lattice network terminated by R_0 is given by

$$Z = \frac{V_1}{I_1} = \frac{Z_a Z_b + [(Z_b + Z_a)/2]R_0}{R_0 + (Z_b + Z_a)/2}$$ [5.8-7]

The substitution of R_0^2 for $Z_a Z_b$ in Eq. 5.8-7 gives the following result:

$$Z = \frac{V_1}{I_1} = R_0$$ [5.8-8]

It is now seen that the driving-point impedance is equal to the terminating resistance, R_0. Hence, the lattice in Fig. 5-39(b) is a constant-resistance network.

The solution of Eqs. 5.8-4 for the current ratio yields

$$\frac{I_2}{I_1} = \frac{\Delta_{12}}{\Delta_{11}} = \frac{-z_{12}}{R_0 + z_{22}}$$ [5.8-9]

Since $V_2 = - I_2 R_0$, it follows that:

$$\frac{V_2}{I_1} = \frac{z_{12}R_0}{R_0 + z_{22}}$$ [5.8-10]

Then, for the constant-resistance lattice, where

$$z_{12} = \frac{Z_b - Z_a}{2}; \qquad z_{11} = z_{22} = \frac{Z_b + Z_a}{2}$$

Eq. 5.8-10 can be written as

$$\frac{V_2}{I_1} = Z'_{12} = \frac{[(Z_b - Z_a)/2]R_0}{R_0 + (Z_b + Z_a)/2}$$

and since $Z_b = R_0^2/Z_a$ in a constant resistance lattice,

$$Z'_{12} = R_0 \left[\frac{R_0 - Z_a}{R_0 + Z_a} \right] = R_0 \left[\frac{1 - z_a}{1 + z_a} \right] \qquad [5.8\text{-}11]$$

where z_a is the normalized impedance of the series arm and Z'_{12} is the transfer impedance of the lattice terminated by R_0.

If $R_0 = 1.0$, it follows from Eq. 5.8-11 that

$$Z_{12} = \frac{1 - z_a}{1 + z_a} \qquad [5.8\text{-}12]$$

where Z_{12} is the transfer impedance of the lattice terminated by 1 ohm. The solution of Eq. 5.8-12 for z_a yields

$$z_a = \frac{1 - Z_{12}}{1 + Z_{12}} \qquad [5.8\text{-}13]$$

and the lattice arm z_b is given by

$$z_b = \frac{1}{z_a} = \frac{1 + Z_{12}}{1 - Z_{12}} \qquad [5.8\text{-}14]$$

When the network is terminated by a 1-ohm resistance, the transfer impedance of the terminated network is given by

$$Z_{12} = \frac{V_2}{I_1} = \frac{I_2 \times 1}{V_1} = \frac{V_2}{V_1} = \epsilon^{-\gamma} = T(s) \qquad [5.8\text{-}15]$$

where $T(s)$ is the transfer function of the network. It should be carefully noted that the relation between Z_{12} and $T(s)$ given by Eq. 5.8-15 holds only for the special case of a one-ohm resistive termination.

For the network terminated by its characteristic resistance, R_0, the power input is

$$P_1 = |I_1|^2 R_0 \qquad [5.8\text{-}16]$$

and the power output is

$$P_2 = |I_2|^2 R_0 \qquad [5.8\text{-}17]$$

In a network with loss, $P_2 \leqq P_1$. It follows from Eqs. 5.8-16 and 5.8-17 that

$$|I_2(j\omega)| \leqq |I_1(j\omega)| \qquad [5.8\text{-}18]$$

For a one-ohm termination,

$$V_2 = - I_2 \times 1 \qquad [5.8\text{-}19]$$

Hence, $|I_2(j\omega)| = |V_2(j\omega)|$, and

$$\frac{|I_2(j\omega)|}{|I_1(j\omega)|} = \frac{|V_2(j\omega)|}{|I_1(j\omega)|} = |Z_{12}(j\omega)| \leqq 1 \qquad [5.8\text{-}20]$$

It follows that $Z_{12}(j\omega)$ has an upper limit, and Z_{12} is therefore said to be *bounded*. As a consequence of it being bounded, $Z_{12}(j\omega)$ has no poles on the imaginary axis. Also, if Z_{12} is the transfer impedance of a network with loss, it has no poles in the right-hand half of the complex plane. If poles exist in the right-hand half of the complex plane, there is no finite steady-state response. The conditions on $Z_{12}(j\omega)$, outlined above, must be satisfied in order that a constant-resistance lattice be realizable.

Returning now to Eq. 5.8-12 and solving it for z_a, we obtain

$$z_a = \frac{1 - Z_{12}}{1 + Z_{12}} = \frac{1 - T(s)}{1 + T(s)} \qquad [5.8\text{-}21]$$

For a one-ohm constant-resistance lattice, the lattice arm z_b is given by

$$z_b = \frac{1}{z_a} = \frac{1 + T(s)}{1 - T(s)} \qquad [5.8\text{-}22]$$

When $T(s)$ is specified, the arms of the lattice are determined from Eqs. 5.8-21 and 5.8-22.

Examples will now be given in the synthesis of lattice networks to yield a specified transfer function, and in the conversion of the lattice network into an unbalanced structure. For the first example, assume that

$$Z_{12}(s) = \frac{k}{s + 1} \qquad [5.8\text{-}23]$$

From Eq. 5.8-21, z_a is determined as

$$z_a = \frac{1 - k/(s + 1)}{1 + k/(s + 1)} = \frac{s + (1 - k)}{s + (1 + k)} \qquad [5.8\text{-}24]$$

An inspection of Eq. 5.8-24 shows that z_a has a zero in the right-hand half of the complex plane when $k > 1$. Since $z_b = 1/z_a$, z_b has a pole in the right-hand half of the complex plane when $k > 1$. Hence, the maximum permissible value of k is 1.0.

If k is chosen so that $k \leqq 1$, z_a is realizable as an $R\text{-}L$ impedance. It follows from Eq. 5.8-23 that the maximum permissible value of k gives the maximum value of V_1/I_2 and the minimum loss.

For $k = 1$, the lattice arms are given by

$$z_a = \frac{s}{s+2} \qquad [5.8\text{-}25]$$

$$z_b = \frac{1}{z_a} = \frac{s+2}{s} \qquad [5.8\text{-}26]$$

A network with the z_a and z_b arms for $k = 1$ is shown in Fig. 5-40, together with the equivalent bridged-T network.

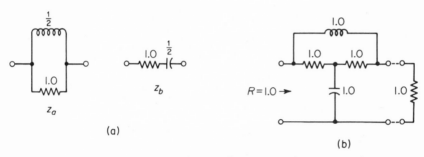

(a)

(b)

Values in ohms, farads, and henrys

Figure 5-40   Lattice arms and equivalent bridged-T network having $Z_{12}(s)$ in Eq. 5.8-23 ($k = 1$).

If k is taken as $1/2$, it follows from Eq. 5.8-24 that

$$z_a = \frac{s + 1/2}{s + 3/2} \qquad [5.8\text{-}27]$$

and, since $z_b = 1/z_a$,

$$z_b = \frac{s + 3/2}{s + 1/2} = 1 + \frac{1}{s + 1/2} \qquad [5.8\text{-}28]$$

It is convenient to convert z_a to an admittance form to obtain the lattice. Thus,

$$y_a = \frac{1}{z_a} = 1 + \frac{1}{s + 1/2} \qquad [5.8\text{-}29]$$

Note that the y_a admittance form is the same as the z_b impedance form, which is as it should be. The lattice arms and the bisected unbalanced network are shown in Fig. 5-41.

Next consider the transfer function

$$Z_{12}(s) = k \left[\frac{s + 1}{s + 10} \right] \qquad [5.8\text{-}30]$$

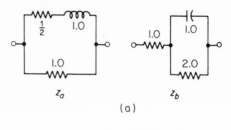

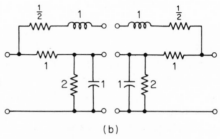

(b)

Values in ohms, farads, and henrys

Figure 5-41 Lattice arms and equivalent bridged-T network having $Z_{12}(s)$ in Eq. 5.8-23 ($k = \frac{1}{2}$).

From Eq. 5.8-21, it follows that

$$z_a = \frac{1 - \dfrac{k(s + 1)}{s + 10}}{1 + \dfrac{k(s + 1)}{s + 10}} = \frac{(1 - k)s + (10 - k)}{(1 + k)s + (10 + k)} \qquad [5.8\text{-}31]$$

For z_a to be realizable, $k \leq 1$. When $k = 1$, it follows from Eq. 5.8-31 that:

$$z_a = \frac{9}{2s + 11} \qquad [5.8\text{-}32]$$

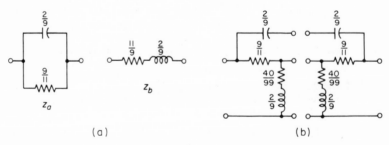

Values in ohms, farads, and henrys

Figure 5-42 Lattice arms and equivalent unbalanced network having $Z_{12}(s)$ in Eq. 5.8-30 ($k = 1$).

and, since $z_b = 1/z_a$,

$$z_b = \frac{2s + 11}{9} \qquad [5.8\text{-}33]$$

The lattice arms z_a and z_b are shown in Fig. 5-42, together with the unbalanced network.

5.9 DESIGN OF CONSTANT-RESISTANCE AMPLITUDE EQUALIZERS

An amplitude equalizer is a network in which the amplitude of the current or voltage varies with frequency in some prescribed manner, generally without regard to the phase variation. The design of the equalizer in this case is based on the constant-resistance lattice network presented in Sec. 5.8. The design will be considered on a normalized basis with a one-ohm termination. For such a termination, the transfer function is given in terms of the ratio of output to input voltages by Eq. 5.8-15.

Using Eqs. 5.8-12 and 5.8-15, we have

$$\epsilon^{-\gamma} = T(s) = \frac{V_2}{V_1} = \frac{1 - z_a}{1 + z_a} \qquad [5.9\text{-}1]$$

where

$$\gamma = \alpha + j\beta = -\ln\frac{1 - z_a}{1 + z_a} \qquad [5.9\text{-}2]$$

When the magnitude alone is to be considered

$$\alpha = -\ln\left|\frac{V_2}{V_1}\right| = -\ln\left|\frac{1 - z_a}{1 + z_a}\right| \qquad [5.9\text{-}3]$$

where α is in nepers. The negative sign indicates a loss in the circuit; that is, $V_2 < V_1$. In terms of decibels, the loss in the circuit is defined as

$$\text{db} = 20 \log\left|\frac{V_1}{V_2}\right| \qquad [5.9\text{-}4]$$

The impedance, z_a, is determined by solving Eq. 5.9-1. Thus

$$z_a = \frac{1 - T(s)}{1 + T(s)} \qquad [5.9\text{-}5]$$

and, since $R_0 = 1$,

$$z_b = \frac{1}{z_a} \qquad [5.9\text{-}6]$$

The absolute value of $T(s)$ must be equal to or less than unity for z_a to be physically realizable. The complexity of the transfer function, $T(s)$, is determined by the complexity of z_a. If z_a is a resistance, the design gives a loss independent of frequency, and becomes that of attenuators as given in Chap. 2. If z_a is a reactance, the network passes all frequencies without amplitude loss, but gives a change in phase, resulting in a phase-shift network or phase equalizer. When a combination of resistive and reactive elements is used, an amplitude equalizer is obtained. If a definite loss at n frequencies is specified, then in general z_a will contain at least n elements.

We can best illustrate the equalizer design by starting with an assumed transfer function. Assume the following transfer function:

$$T(j\omega) = \frac{V_2}{V_1} = \epsilon^{-\gamma} = k\left[\frac{a + j\omega}{b + j\omega}\right] \qquad [5.9\text{-}7]$$

where a, b, and k are constants to be determined. It is seen from Eq. 5.9-7 that

$$\operatorname*{Lim}_{\omega\to 0} T(j\omega) = \operatorname*{Lim}_{\omega\to 0} \frac{V_2}{V_1} = k\left(\frac{a}{b}\right) \qquad [5.9\text{-}8]$$

$$\operatorname*{Lim}_{\omega\to\infty} T(j\omega) = \operatorname*{Lim}_{\omega\to\infty} \frac{V_2}{V_1} = k \qquad [5.9\text{-}9]$$

It follows from Eq. 5.9-5 that, if z_a is to be physically realizable, $|T(j\omega)| \leqq 1$. It also follows from Eqs. 5.9-8 and 5.9-9 that $k(a/b) \leqq 1$ and $k \leqq 1$ if z_a is to be physically realizable.

Now assume that $a < b$, and that $k = 1.0$. It is seen from Eq. 5.9-7 that the loss is zero at $\omega = \infty$, and that the loss at $\omega = 0$ is given by

$$\alpha = \ln\frac{a}{b} \qquad [5.9\text{-}10]$$

Hence, Eq. 5.9-7 represents a transfer function that gives a definite loss at $\omega = 0$.

As a specific example in the design of an amplitude equalizer, suppose that the design specifications include a constant-resistance input of 500 ohms, with a 20-db amplitude attenuation when $\omega = 0$, and a loss of 10 db when $\omega = 10{,}000$ radians per second. Hence, when $\omega = 0$, the required voltage ratio for a 20-db loss is

$$20 = 20\log_{10}\frac{V_1}{V_2} \qquad [5.9\text{-}11]$$

$$\frac{V_1}{V_2} = 10 \qquad (\omega = 0) \qquad [5.9\text{-}12]$$

Then, assuming that $k = 1.0$ in Eq. 5.9-8,

$$\frac{V_2}{V_1} = \frac{1}{10} = \frac{a}{b} \qquad \text{[5.9-13]}$$

It follows from Eq. 5.9-13 that, for k equal to unity, $a/b = 1/10$ for the given specification. It is now possible to assume a transfer function of the following form:

$$T(j\omega) = \frac{1 + j\omega}{10 + j\omega} \qquad \text{[5.9-14]}$$

The db loss characteristic of the transfer function in Eq. 5.9-14 is shown

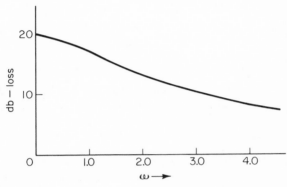

Figure 5-43   Loss characteristic of the transfer function in Eq. 5.9-14.

in Fig. 5-43. It follows from Eq. 5.9-14 that the absolute value of the transfer function is given by

$$|T(j\omega)| = \epsilon\alpha = \sqrt{\frac{1 + \omega^2}{100 + \omega^2}} \qquad \text{[5.9-15]}$$

Since a loss of 10 db is specified at an internal frequency, $\omega = \omega_1$, this corresponds to $V_2/V_1 = 1/\sqrt{10}$ when $\omega = \omega_1$. Then, using Eq. 5.9-15, we have for this internal frequency

$$\sqrt{\frac{1 + \omega_1^2}{100 + \omega_1^2}} = \frac{1}{\sqrt{10}} \qquad \text{[5.9-16]}$$

$$\omega_1 = \sqrt{10} = \omega_n$$

Since $\sqrt{10}$ is not the specified angular frequency, it may be considered as the normalized angular frequency, ω_n, at which the attenuation is 10 db for an assumed constant-resistance termination of one ohm.

Since Eq. 5.9-14 can be obtained from Eq. 5.8-30 by letting $s = j\omega$ and $k = 1.0$, Fig. 5-42 gives the required network for a one-ohm termination and a loss of 10 db at the normalized angular frequency, $\omega_n = \sqrt{10}$. To determine the actual network for the equalizer from Fig. 5-42, which shows the normalized circuit parameters, the L and R values must be calculated by the use of Eqs. 5.2-31 and 5.2-32. Then, referring to the bridged-T network in Fig. 5-42 where $R_n = 9/11$, it follows from Eq. 5.2-31 that

$$R_{a1} = R_0 R_{n1} = 500 \times \frac{9}{11} = 409.09 \text{ ohms}$$

$$R_{a2} = R_0 R_{n2} = 500 \times \frac{40}{99} = 202.02 \text{ ohms}$$

[5.9-17]

where the subscripts, a and n, are used to denote the actual and normalized values. Since the normalized angular frequency is $\sqrt{10}$, and since $C_n = 2/9$, it follows from Eqs. 5.2-32 and 5.2-33 that:

$$C_a = \frac{1}{500} \left(\frac{\sqrt{10}}{10,000} \right) \times \frac{2}{9} = 0.1406 \text{ microfarad}$$ [5.9-18]

$$L_a = 500 \left(\frac{\sqrt{10}}{10,000} \right) \times \frac{2}{9} = 35.12 \text{ millihenrys}$$ [5.9-19]

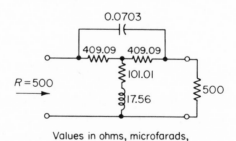

Values in ohms, microfarads, and millihenrys

Figure 5-44   Bridged-T constant resistance network designed to meet specifications.

The bridged-T network for the required specifications is given in Fig. 5-44, where the 0.0703-μf capacitor is actually $C_a/2$, the 17.56-m.h. inductor is $L_a/2$, and the 101.01-ohm resistor is $R_{a2}/2$.

If the transfer function given by Eq. 5.9-7 is used, and if $a > b$, then the constant k must be chosen such that $k(a/b) \leqq 1$ in order that $T(j\omega) \leqq 1$, and that z_a be physically realizable. If $a/b = 10$, then k must be equal to or less than 1/10. Assuming that $k = 1/10$, Eq. 5.9-7 becomes

$$T(j\omega) = \frac{1}{10}\left(\frac{10 + j\omega}{1 + j\omega}\right) \qquad [5.9\text{-}20]$$

$$\lim_{\omega \to 0} T(j\omega) = \lim_{\omega \to 0} \frac{V_2}{V_1} = 1.0 \qquad [5.9\text{-}21]$$

$$\lim_{\omega \to \infty} T(j\omega) = \lim_{\omega \to \infty} \frac{V_2}{V_1} = \frac{1}{10} \qquad [5.9\text{-}22]$$

The function given in Eq. 5.9-20 gives a 20-db loss at $\omega = \infty$, and zero loss at $\omega = 0$. The db loss characteristic of the transfer function in Eq. 5.9-20 is shown in Fig. 5-45.

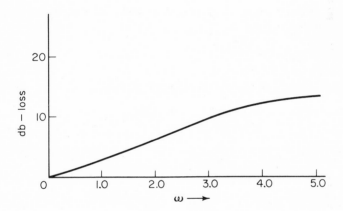

Figure 5-45   Loss characteristic of the transfer function in Eq. 5.9-20.

Assume now that the design specifications are a constant resistance of 500 ohms, a loss of 20 db when $\omega \to \infty$, and a loss of 10 db at $\omega = 10{,}000$ radians per second. The specified network will give the inverse type of attenuation as a function of frequency when compared with the function shown in Fig. 5-43. Solving Eq. 5.9-22 for the 10 db normalized frequency yields

$$\frac{1}{10}\sqrt{\frac{100 + \omega_1^2}{1 + \omega_1^2}} = \frac{1}{\sqrt{10}} \qquad [5.9\text{-}23]$$

Hence,

$$\omega_1 = \sqrt{10} = \omega_n$$

and

$$T(s) = \frac{1}{10}\left(\frac{s + 10}{s + 1}\right)$$

$$z_a = \frac{1 - T(s)}{1 + T(s)} = \frac{1 - \dfrac{1}{10}\left(\dfrac{s + 10}{s + 1}\right)}{1 + \dfrac{1}{10}\left(\dfrac{s + 10}{s + 1}\right)}$$

$$z_a = \frac{9s}{11s + 20} \qquad [5.9\text{-}24]$$

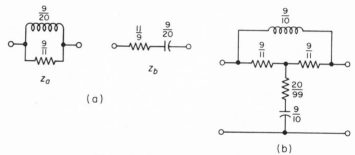

Values in ohms, farads, and henrys

Figure 5-46 Lattice arms and equivalent bridged-T network for $R_0 = 1$ and $\omega_n = \sqrt{10}$.

Also, assuming that R_0 is equal to unity,

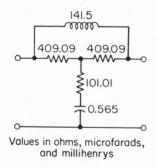

Values in ohms, microfarads, and millihenrys

Figure 5-47 Network of Figure 5-46 with resistance and frequency levels increased respectively by 500 and $10^4/\sqrt{10}$.

$$z_b = \frac{1}{z_a} = \frac{11s + 20}{9s} \qquad [5.9\text{-}25]$$

The z_a and z_b arms of the lattice, together with the equivalent unbalanced network, are shown in Fig. 5-46. Figure 5-47 shows the network with the impedance level changed to 500 ohms and the frequency changed by the ratio $10,000/\sqrt{10}$ as required by the specifications. The circuit can be changed to any impedance level and any frequency ratio by use of Eqs. 5.2-31, 5.2-32, and 5.2-33.

If the transfer functions in Eqs. 5.9-14 and 5.9-20 are multiplied together, corresponding to the lattices in cascade, the total transfer function is given by

$$T_0(j\omega) = \frac{1 + j\omega}{10 + j\omega} \times \frac{1}{10}\left(\frac{10 + j\omega}{1 + j\omega}\right) = \frac{1}{10} \qquad [5.9\text{-}26]$$

Thus $T_0(j\omega)$ reduces to $1/10$, and the two networks produce a 20-db loss at all frequencies from zero to infinity.

As another example of cascade synthesis, assume that the transfer function is given as

$$T(s) = \frac{k(s + 1)}{(s + 2)(s + 5)} \qquad [5.9\text{-}27]$$

The transfer function in Eq. 5.9-27 can be expressed as the product of two transfer functions as follows:

$$T(s) = T_1(s) \times T_2(s) = \frac{k_1}{s + 2} \times \frac{k_2(s + 1)}{s + 5} \qquad [5.9\text{-}28]$$

Equation 5.9-28 gives the transfer functions of two lattice networks that are to be connected in cascade to yield the transfer function in Eq. 5.9-27. It is assumed that the network is terminated by its characteristic resistance of one ohm. Expressing $T(s)$ in terms of its components in Eq. 5.9-28 simplifies the synthesis.

It follows from Eqs. 5.9-5 and 5.9-6 that the arms of the first lattice network are

$$z_{a1} = \frac{1 - k_1/(s + 2)}{1 + k_1/(s + 2)} = \frac{s + 2 - k_1}{s + 2 + k_1} \qquad [5.9\text{-}29]$$

$$z_{b1} = \frac{1}{z_{a1}} = \frac{s + 2 + k_1}{s + 2 - k_1} \qquad [5.9\text{-}30]$$

Similarly, for the second lattice

$$z_{a2} = \frac{1 - k_2(s + 1)/(s + 5)}{1 + k_2(s + 1)/(s + 5)} = \frac{(1 - k_2)\,s + 5 - k_2}{(1 + k_2)\,s + 5 + k_2} \qquad [5.9\text{-}31]$$

$$z_{b2} = \frac{1}{z_{a2}} = \frac{(1 + k_2)\,s + 5 + k_2}{(1 - k_2)\,s + 5 - k_2} \qquad [5.9\text{-}32]$$

An inspection of Eqs. 5.9-29 and 5.9-31 shows that z_{a1} has a zero in the right-hand half of the complex plane when $k_1 > 2$, and that z_{a2} has a zero in the right-hand half of the complex plane when $k_2 > 1$. Hence, the maximum value of k_1 is 2.0, and the maximum value of k_2 is 1.0.

Using the maximum value of k_1 in Eqs. 5.9-29 and 5.9-30, the arms of the first lattice are

$$z_{a1} = \frac{s}{s+4} \qquad\qquad [5.9\text{-}33]$$

$$z_{b1} = \frac{1}{z_{a1}} = \frac{s+4}{s} \qquad\qquad [5.9\text{-}34]$$

Using the maximum permissible value for k_2 in Eqs. 5.9-31 and 5.9-32, the arms of the second lattice are

$$z_{a2} = \frac{2}{s+3} \qquad\qquad [5.9\text{-}35]$$

$$z_{b2} = \frac{1}{z_{a2}} = \frac{s+3}{2} \qquad\qquad [5.9\text{-}36]$$

The unbalanced network is shown in Fig. 5-48.

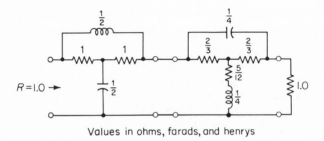

Values in ohms, farads, and henrys

Figure 5-48   Network for transfer function of Eq. 5.9-27.

The transfer function in Eq. 5.9-28 can be realized as a single lattice, but the conversion to an unbalanced form is more difficult and will not be treated in this text. In the conversion of lattice networks into unbalanced structures, only one type of unbalanced form was shown, but the unbalanced network may take on a number of different configurations that are equivalent.

PROBLEMS

5-1 Given the following functions, state which are realizable as R-C driving-point impedances (or R-L driving-point admittances). Also state which are realizable as R-C driving-point admittances (or R-L driving-point impedances). If any of them is not realizable as either, state why.

(a) $\dfrac{s+1}{s+2}$

(b) $\dfrac{s+3}{s+2}$

(c) $\dfrac{s+1}{s(s+3)}$

(d) $\dfrac{s(s+1)(s+3)}{(s+\frac{1}{2})(s+2)}$

(e) $\dfrac{(s+1)(s+4)}{s(s+2)(s+6)}$ (f) $\dfrac{s^2+6s+8}{s^2+4s+3}$

(g) $\dfrac{s^2+2s+2}{s^2+\frac{5}{2}s+1}$ (h) $\dfrac{s^2+5s+4}{s(s+2)(s+5)}$

(i) $\dfrac{(s+2)(s+3)}{(s+1)(s+4)}$ (j) $\dfrac{s^2+3s-4}{(s+1)(s+3)}$

5-2 Consider the functions in Prob. 5-1 that are realizable as R-C driving-point impedances. Realize them in two forms of partial-fraction networks, and in two forms of continued-fraction networks where possible. Also sketch the R-L admittance networks in each case.

5-3 Consider the functions in Prob. 5-1 that are realizable as R-C admittances. Realize them in two forms of partial-fraction networks and in two forms of continued-fraction networks. Sketch also the R-L impedance networks in each case.

5-4 (a) Develop the following R-C driving-point impedance function as a continued-fraction network about zero:

$$Z(s) = \frac{(s+1)(s+3)}{s(s+2)(s+4)}$$

(b) Plot the poles and zeros of the original function.

(c) Plot the poles and zeros of each successive function as each pole is removed at $s=0$.

(d) Repeat (a), (b), and (c) when the given function is developed about infinity.

5-5 Given the following impedance functions:

$$Z(s) = \frac{s+2}{(s+1)(s+3)} \qquad Z(s) = \frac{(s+1)(s+3)}{s+2} \qquad Z(s) = \frac{(s+1)(s+3)}{s(s+2)}$$

(a) For real frequencies ($s = j\omega$), compute $Z(j\omega)$ for ω equal to 0, 1, 2, 3, 5, and 10.

(b) Plot the real part of $Z(j\omega)$ as a function of ω.

(c) Plot the imaginary part of $Z(j\omega)$ as a function of ω.

(d) Discuss the results.

5-6 An impedance has poles at $s = -1$ and $s = -3$; the residues at all the poles are equal to unity. As $s \to \infty$, $Z(s) \to 4$. Determine a network for this impedance function.

5-7 The following open-circuited transfer impedance functions are to be realized as an open-circuited R-C lattice, and then converted into an unbalanced structure where possible. (Plot the poles and zeros for each transfer function.)

(a) $z_{12} = \dfrac{1}{s(s+2)}$ (b) $z_{12} = \dfrac{s}{(s+1)(s+3)}$

(c) $z_{12} = \dfrac{s^2}{(s+1)(s+3)}$ (d) $z_{12} = \dfrac{(s+3)(s+5)}{(s+1)(s+9)}$

(e) $z_{12} = \dfrac{s+5}{(s+1)(s+4)}$ (f) $z_{12} = \dfrac{s+2}{s(s+1)(s+4)}$

(g) $z_{12} = \dfrac{s^2+9}{(s+1)(s+3)}$ (h) $z_{12} = \dfrac{s^2-3s+2}{(s+1)(s+3)}$

(i) $z_{12} = \dfrac{s^2-2s+2}{(s+1)(s+3)}$ (j) $z_{12} = \dfrac{s^2+4s+8}{(s+1)(s+3)}$

(k) $z_{12} = \dfrac{s-4}{(s+1)(s+3)}$

5-8 The following open-circuited transfer impedance functions are to be realized as an open-circuited R-L lattice, and then converted into an unbalanced network. (Expand the given functions as z_{12}/s, and then multiply by s for the R-L networks.)

(a) $z_{12} = \dfrac{s^2}{(s+1)(s+3)}$ (b) $z_{12} = \dfrac{s^2+9}{(s+1)(s+3)}$

5-9 Using the network of Fig. 5-33, draw the complete unbalanced network. Instead of the network being driven by a constant-current generator and operating on an open-circuit, modify the network to meet the following conditions:

(a) Constant-voltage generator and a resistive load of 4 ohms.
(b) Constant-voltage generator with 2 ohms internal resistance and a resistive load of 2 ohms.
(c) Constant-voltage generator with 8 ohms internal resistance and a resistive load of 8 ohms.
(d) Increase the impedance level by a factor of 10^4, and increase the frequency factor by 60.

5-10 The following transfer impedance functions are to be realized as constant-resistance lattices, and converted into unbalanced structures when possible. Use the maximum possible value of k and then half the maximum value.

(a) $Z_{12} = \dfrac{k}{s+3}$ (b) $Z_{12} = \dfrac{k}{s+5}$

(c) $Z_{12} = \dfrac{ks}{s+2}$ (d) $Z_{12} = \dfrac{k(s+2)}{(s+4)}$

(e) $Z_{12} = \dfrac{k(s+3)}{(s+1)}$ (f) $Z_{12} = k\left(\dfrac{1-s}{s+1}\right)$

(g) $Z_{12} = k\left(\dfrac{s-2}{s+1}\right)$ (h) $Z_{12} = \dfrac{-\frac{1}{2}s}{s^2+s+1}$

(i) $Z_{12} = \dfrac{\frac{1}{2}s}{s^2+s+1}$

5-11 An amplitude equalizer is to have a 30-db loss at $\omega = 0$, and a 10-db loss at $\omega = 25,000$ rad/sec. Choose a suitable transfer impedance; realize the equalizer as a constant-resistance lattice, and convert it to an unbalanced equivalent network. Assume $R_0 = 1000$ ohms.

5-12 An amplitude equalizer is to have a 30-db loss at $\omega = \infty$, and a 10-db loss at $\omega = 25,000$ rad/sec. Choose a suitable transfer impedance; realize the equalizer as a constant-resistance lattice, and convert it to an equivalent unbalanced network. Assume $R_0 = 1000$ ohms.

5-13 For Probs. 5-11 and 5-12, plot the db loss versus ω for each network, and then for the two networks in cascade.

5-14 Realize the following transfer impedances as cascade lattices, and convert them to equivalent unbalanced networks:

$$Z_{12} = \frac{ks(s+1)}{(s+2)(s+4)}$$

$$Z_{12} = \frac{k}{(s+1)(s+3)(s+5)}$$

$$Z_{12} = \frac{k(s+1)(s+10)}{(s+2)(s+5)}$$

5-15 The following transfer impedance functions are all-pass functions at real frequencies and may therefore be used as phase equalizers:

$$Z_{12} = \frac{s^2 - s + 1}{s^2 + s + 1} \qquad\qquad Z_{12} = \frac{s^2 - \frac{1}{2}s + 1}{s^2 + \frac{1}{2}s + 1}$$

$$Z_{12} = \frac{s^2 - 2s + 1}{s^2 + 2s + 1} \qquad\qquad Z_{12} = \frac{s^2 - 4s + 1}{s^2 + 4s + 1}$$

(a) Show that $|Z_{12}(j\omega)|$ is a constant.
(b) Plot the phase angle as a function of ω.
(c) Realize the transfer function as a constant-resistance lattice, and convert it to an unbalanced form where possible. (Use a transformer if necessary.)

the application of matrix agebra to
two-terminal pair networks

6.0 INTRODUCTION

The algebra of determinants is used for the purpose of organizing and simplifying the solution of a single system of linear equations. A large part of network theory involves such equations, and the algebra of determinants often greatly facilitates working with them.

In this chapter, matrix algebra will be discussed as a means of organizing and simplifying the manipulation of *multiple* systems of linear equations. The intrinsic value of the matrix technique results from the fact that the general problem of the cascading of networks and their connection in series and parallel involves the cumulative effects of one system of equations (the $ABCD$ system, for example) upon others. No attempt will be made to give a complete treatment of matrix algebra. Only the basic theory required for the solution of networks in cascade, in parallel, and in series, will be considered. Some of the operations that can be performed with matrices are discussed in Sec. 6.1, and are applied to network theory in later sections of this chapter.

6.1 FUNDAMENTAL DEFINITIONS AND OPERATIONS

Matrix arrays look very much like determinant arrays; each is an arrangement of elements in rows and columns. The elements may be any designations of mathematical quantities: real numbers, imaginary numbers, complex numbers, letter symbols, and so forth. In a determinant, the number of rows must always be the same as the number of columns; that is, a determinant array must always be square in this sense. A matrix array, however, may be either square or rectangular. A determinant array is bounded at its sides by straight vertical lines, whereas a matrix is enclosed in brackets.

A matrix has no numerical value, but is merely a convenient way of arranging its elements or constituents. Two matrices are considered equal when, and only when, all their corresponding elements are equal.

Consider first the following system of linear equations:

$$x_1 = a_{11}y_1 + a_{12}y_2$$
$$x_2 = a_{21}y_1 + a_{22}y_2$$

[6.1-1]

These equations can be expressed in matrix form as

$$\begin{bmatrix} x_1 \\ x_2 \end{bmatrix} = \begin{bmatrix} a_{11} & a_{12} \\ a_{21} & a_{22} \end{bmatrix} \times \begin{bmatrix} y_1 \\ y_2 \end{bmatrix}$$

[6.1-2]

where the bracket symbols [ ] enclose the array and identify it as a matrix. Equation 6.1-2 can also be written in abbreviated form as

$$[X] = [A][Y]$$

[6.1-3]

where the capital letters in the brackets denote the corresponding matrices of Eq. 6.1-2.

Now assume that x_1' and x_2' are given in terms of the same y_1 and y_2 used in Eqs. 6.1-1, and assume further that

$$x_1' = a_{11}'y_1 + a_{12}'y_2$$
$$x_2' = a_{21}'y_1 + a_{22}'y_2$$

[6.1-4]

or, in abbreviated matrix notation,

$$[X'] = [A'][Y]$$

[6.1-5]

Equations 6.1-1 and 6.1-4 can be considered to be two sets of node-voltage equations giving the input and output currents for two networks connected in parallel between a given set of input and output terminals. Those two pairs of equations, 6.1-1 and 6.1-4, can be added in matrix algebra, resulting in

$$\begin{bmatrix} x_1' + x_1 \\ x_2' + x_2 \end{bmatrix} = \begin{bmatrix} a_{11}' + a_{11} & a_{12}' + a_{12} \\ a_{21}' + a_{21} & a_{22}' + a_{22} \end{bmatrix} \times \begin{bmatrix} y_1 \\ y_2 \end{bmatrix}$$

[6.1-6]

or, in abbreviated form,

$$[X' + X] = [A' + A] \times [Y]$$

[6.1-7]

which in turn can be further abbreviated to

$$[X''] = [A''][Y] \qquad [6.1\text{-}8]$$

where $[X'']$ represents the sum of the two matrices on the left-hand sides of Eqs. 6.1-3 and 6.1-5, and may be considered as the matrix of the total current in the two networks connected in parallel.* It follows that the sum of two matrices is formed by adding the corresponding elements of the two arrays. The difference between two matrices is formed in an analogous manner. It follows that one matrix may be added to another matrix having the same number of rows and columns.

Assume now that y_1 and y_2 in Eq. 6.1-1 can be expressed in terms of z_1 and z_2 as follows:

$$y_1 = b_{11}z_1 + b_{12}z_2$$
$$y_2 = b_{21}z_1 + b_{22}z_2 \qquad [6.1\text{-}9]$$

In the abbreviated matrix notation,

$$[Y] = [B][Z] \qquad [6.1\text{-}10]$$

When Eqs. 6.1-9 are substituted into Eqs. 6.1-1, the following result is obtained:

$$x_1 = a_{11}b_{11}z_1 + a_{11}b_{12}z_2 + a_{12}b_{21}z_1 + a_{12}b_{22}z_2$$
$$x_2 = a_{21}b_{11}z_1 + a_{21}b_{12}z_2 + a_{22}b_{21}z_1 + a_{22}b_{22}z_2 \qquad [6.1\text{-}11]$$

or

$$x_1 = (a_{11}b_{11} + a_{12}b_{21})z_1 + (a_{11}b_{12} + a_{12}b_{22})z_2$$
$$x_2 = (a_{21}b_{11} + a_{22}b_{21})z_1 + (a_{21}b_{12} + a_{22}b_{22})z_2 \qquad [6.1\text{-}12]$$

Equations 6.1-12 can be written in matrix form as follows:

$$\begin{bmatrix} x_1 \\ x_2 \end{bmatrix} = \begin{bmatrix} a_{11} & a_{12} \\ a_{21} & a_{22} \end{bmatrix} \times \begin{bmatrix} b_{11} & b_{12} \\ b_{21} & b_{22} \end{bmatrix} \times \begin{bmatrix} z_1 \\ z_2 \end{bmatrix} \qquad [6.1\text{-}13]$$

or

$$[X] = [A][Y] = [A][B][Z] \qquad [6.1\text{-}14]$$

where

$$[A][B] = \begin{bmatrix} a_{11} & a_{12} \\ a_{21} & a_{22} \end{bmatrix} \times \begin{bmatrix} b_{11} & b_{12} \\ b_{21} & b_{22} \end{bmatrix}$$

$$= \begin{bmatrix} a_{11}b_{11} + a_{12}b_{21} & a_{11}b_{12} + a_{12}b_{22} \\ a_{21}b_{11} + a_{22}b_{21} & a_{21}b_{12} + a_{22}b_{22} \end{bmatrix} \qquad [6.1\text{-}15]$$

---

* $[A'']$ would be the sum of the two admittance matrices in node-voltage equations.

Equation 6.1-15 illustrates the general rule for multiplying matrices, namely that the elements of the mth row and nth column of the product consists of the sum of the products formed by the corresponding elements of the mth row of the left-hand member and the nth column of the right-hand member of the product.

Two matrices can be multiplied only if the number of columns of the first matrix is the same as the number of rows of the second.

It follows from the above definition of multiplication that:

$$[B][A] = \begin{bmatrix} b_{11}a_{11} + b_{12}a_{21} & b_{11}a_{12} + b_{12}a_{22} \\ b_{21}a_{11} + b_{22}a_{21} & b_{21}a_{12} + b_{22}a_{22} \end{bmatrix} \qquad [6.1\text{-}16]$$

A comparison of Eqs. 6.1-15 and 6.1-16 shows that

$$[A][B] \neq [B][A] \qquad [6.1\text{-}17]$$

Hence, the multiplication of matrices is not in general commutative.

As numerical examples of matrix multiplication, consider the products of $[A]$ and $[B]$ where

$$[A] = \begin{bmatrix} 1 & -2 & 3 \\ 2 & 0 & 4 \end{bmatrix} \quad \text{and} \quad [B] = \begin{bmatrix} 2 & -3 \\ 5 & 0 \\ 1 & -2 \end{bmatrix}$$

The product of $[A] \times [B]$ is given by

$$[A][B] = \begin{bmatrix} 1 & -2 & 3 \\ 2 & 0 & 4 \end{bmatrix} \times \begin{bmatrix} 2 & -3 \\ 5 & 0 \\ 1 & -2 \end{bmatrix}$$

Following the rule for the multiplication of matrices,

$$[A][B] = \begin{bmatrix} [1(2) + (-2)5 + 3(1)] & [1(-3) + (-2)(0) + 3(-2)] \\ [2(2) + (0)5 + 4(1)] & [2(-3) + (0)(0) + 4(-2)] \end{bmatrix}$$

$$= \begin{bmatrix} -5 & -9 \\ 8 & -14 \end{bmatrix}$$

The product of $[B] \times [A]$, however, is given by

$$[B][A] = \begin{bmatrix} [2(1) + (-3)2] & [2(-2) + (-3)(0)] & [2(3) + (-3)4] \\ [5(1) + (0)2] & [5(-2) + (0)(0)] & [5(3) + (0)4] \\ [1(1) + (-2)2] & [1(-2) + (-2)(0)] & [1(3) + (-2)4] \end{bmatrix}$$

$$= \begin{bmatrix} -4 & -4 & -6 \\ 5 & -10 & 15 \\ -3 & -2 & -5 \end{bmatrix}$$

This numerical example illustrates the fact that multiplication of matrices is not commutative. Moreover, the example shows that the number of rows of the first matrix determines the number of rows of the product, whereas the number of columns of the second matrix determines the number of columns of the product.

Another important operation is the calculation of the inverse of a matrix. This corresponds to converting mesh-current equations that express voltage in terms of current into node-voltage equations giving current in terms of voltage. Let the equations expressing x in terms of y be

$$x_1 = a_{11}y_1 + a_{12}y_2 + a_{13}y_3 + \ldots + a_{1k}y_k + \ldots + a_{1n}y_n$$

$$x_2 = a_{21}y_1 + a_{22}y_2 + a_{23}y_3 + \ldots + a_{2k}y_k + \ldots + a_{2n}y_n$$

$$x_3 = a_{31}y_1 + a_{32}y_2 + a_{33}y_3 + \ldots + a_{3k}y_k + \ldots + a_{3n}y_n \qquad [6.1\text{-}18]$$

$$\cdot \quad \cdot \quad \cdot \quad \cdot \quad \cdot \quad \cdot \quad \cdot \quad \cdot \quad \cdot \quad \cdot \quad \cdot \quad \cdot \quad \cdot \quad \cdot \quad \cdot \quad \cdot \quad \cdot \quad \cdot \quad \cdot \quad \cdot$$

$$x_k = a_{k1}y_1 + a_{k2}y_2 + a_{k3}y_3 + \ldots + a_{kk}y_k + \ldots + a_{kn}y_n$$

$$\cdot \quad \cdot \quad \cdot \quad \cdot \quad \cdot \quad \cdot \quad \cdot \quad \cdot \quad \cdot \quad \cdot \quad \cdot \quad \cdot \quad \cdot \quad \cdot \quad \cdot \quad \cdot \quad \cdot \quad \cdot \quad \cdot \quad \cdot$$

$$x_n = a_{n1}y_1 + a_{n2}y_2 + a_{n3}y_3 + \ldots + a_{nk}y_k + \ldots + a_{nn}y_n$$

Then

$$X = [A][Y] \qquad\qquad [6.1\text{-}19]$$

where

$$[A] = \begin{bmatrix} a_{11} & a_{12} & a_{13} & \ldots & a_{1k} & \ldots & a_{1n} \\ a_{21} & a_{22} & a_{23} & \ldots & a_{2k} & \ldots & a_{2n} \\ a_{31} & a_{32} & a_{33} & \ldots & a_{3k} & \ldots & a_{3n} \\ \cdot & \cdot & \cdot & \cdot & \cdot & \cdot & \cdot \\ a_{k1} & a_{k2} & a_{k3} & \ldots & a_{kk} & \ldots & a_{kn} \\ \cdot & \cdot & \cdot & \cdot & \cdot & \cdot & \cdot \\ a_{n1} & a_{n2} & a_{n3} & \ldots & a_{nk} & \ldots & a_{nn} \end{bmatrix} \qquad [6.1\text{-}20]$$

The solution of Eqs. 6.1-18 for y in terms of x yields the following result:

$$y_1 = \frac{\Delta_{11}}{\Delta}x_1 + \frac{\Delta_{21}}{\Delta}x_2 + \frac{\Delta_{31}}{\Delta}x_3 + \ldots + \frac{\Delta_{k1}}{\Delta}x_k + \ldots + \frac{\Delta_{n1}}{\Delta}x_n$$

$$y_2 = \frac{\Delta_{12}}{\Delta}x_1 + \frac{\Delta_{22}}{\Delta}x_2 + \frac{\Delta_{32}}{\Delta}x_3 + \ldots + \frac{\Delta_{k2}}{\Delta}x_k + \ldots + \frac{\Delta_{n2}}{\Delta}x_n$$

$$y_3 = \frac{\Delta_{13}}{\Delta}x_1 + \frac{\Delta_{23}}{\Delta}x_2 + \frac{\Delta_{33}}{\Delta}x_3 + \ldots + \frac{\Delta_{k3}}{\Delta}x_k + \ldots + \frac{\Delta_{n3}}{\Delta}x_n \qquad [6.1\text{-}21]$$

$$\cdots \cdots \cdots \cdots \cdots \cdots \cdots \cdots \cdots \cdots \cdots$$

$$y_k = \frac{\Delta_{1k}}{\Delta}x_1 + \frac{\Delta_{2k}}{\Delta}x_2 + \frac{\Delta_{3k}}{\Delta}x_3 + \ldots + \frac{\Delta_{kk}}{\Delta}x_k + \ldots + \frac{\Delta_{nk}}{\Delta}x_n$$

$$\cdots \cdots \cdots \cdots \cdots \cdots \cdots \cdots \cdots \cdots \cdots$$

$$y_n = \frac{\Delta_{1n}}{\Delta}x_1 + \frac{\Delta_{2n}}{\Delta}x_2 + \frac{\Delta_{3n}}{\Delta}x_3 + \ldots + \frac{\Delta_{kn}}{\Delta}x_k + \ldots + \frac{\Delta_{nn}}{\Delta}x_n$$

where Δ_{kn} denotes the cofactor of the element in row k and column n, and Δ is the determinant of the system. Equation 6.1-21 can be expressed simply in matrice form as

$$[Y] = [A]^{-1}[X] \qquad [6.1\text{-}22]$$

where $[A]^{-1}$ denotes the *inverse* matrix of $[A]$, and is given by

$$[A]^{-1} = \frac{1}{\Delta} \times \begin{bmatrix} \Delta_{11} & \Delta_{21} & \Delta_{31} & \ldots & \Delta_{k1} & \ldots & \Delta_{n1} \\ \Delta_{12} & \Delta_{22} & \Delta_{32} & \ldots & \Delta_{k2} & \ldots & \Delta_{n2} \\ \Delta_{13} & \Delta_{23} & \Delta_{33} & \ldots & \Delta_{k3} & \ldots & \Delta_{n3} \\ \cdot & \cdot & \cdot & \cdot & \cdot & \cdot & \cdot \\ \Delta_{1k} & \Delta_{2k} & \Delta_{3k} & \ldots & \Delta_{kk} & \ldots & \Delta_{nk} \\ \cdot & \cdot & \cdot & \cdot & \cdot & \cdot & \cdot \\ \Delta_{1n} & \Delta_{2n} & \Delta_{3n} & \ldots & \Delta_{kn} & \ldots & \Delta_{nn} \end{bmatrix} \qquad [6.1\text{-}23]$$

The factor $1/\Delta$ multiplying the matrix denotes that each factor in the matrix is divided by the determinant of the coefficients in Eq. 6.1-20. Note that if Eq. 6.1-23 were to represent a determinant, this factor would be $(1/\Delta)^n$. A comparison of Eqs. 6.1-20 and 6.1-23 shows that the inverse matrix is formed by substituting for the element in row k and column m of the given matrix the cofactor of the element in row m and column k, divided by the numerical value of the determinant. Multiplication of Eq. 6.1-20 by Eq. 6.1-23, according to the rule for matrix multiplication, gives

$$[A][A]^{-1} = \begin{bmatrix} 1 & 0 & 0 & \dots & 0 & \dots & 0 \\ 0 & 1 & 0 & \dots & 0 & \dots & 0 \\ 0 & 0 & 1 & \dots & 0 & \dots & 0 \\ \multicolumn{7}{c}{\dots\dots\dots\dots\dots\dots} \\ 0 & 0 & 0 & \dots & 1 & \dots & 0 \\ \multicolumn{7}{c}{\dots\dots\dots\dots\dots\dots} \\ 0 & 0 & 0 & \dots & 0 & \dots & 1 \end{bmatrix} = [U] \qquad [6.1\text{-}24]$$

where the matrix having each term in its primary diagonal equal to unity, and all other terms zero, is known as the unit matrix, $[U]$. It follows that:

$$[U] = [A][A]^{-1} = [A]^{-1}[A] \qquad [6.1\text{-}25]$$

where Eq. 6.1-25 is a matrix equation.

6.2 TWO-TERMINAL PAIR NETWORKS IN CASCADE

The node and mesh equations of a two-terminal pair network can be written in matrix form as follows:

$$\begin{bmatrix} V_1 \\ V_2 \end{bmatrix} = \begin{bmatrix} z_{11} & z_{12} \\ z_{21} & z_{22} \end{bmatrix} \times \begin{bmatrix} I_1 \\ I_2 \end{bmatrix} \qquad [6.2\text{-}1]$$

$$\begin{bmatrix} I_1 \\ I_2 \end{bmatrix} = \begin{bmatrix} y_{11} & y_{12} \\ y_{21} & y_{22} \end{bmatrix} \times \begin{bmatrix} V_1 \\ V_2 \end{bmatrix} \qquad [6.2\text{-}2]$$

Equations 6.2-1 and 6.2-2 are an inverse set. It follows that the Y matrix is the inverse of the Z matrix. The corresponding $ABCD$ equations (see Eqs. 1.2-3 and 1.2-9) are

$$\begin{bmatrix} V_1 \\ I_1 \end{bmatrix} = \begin{bmatrix} A & B \\ C & D \end{bmatrix} \times \begin{bmatrix} V_2 \\ -I_2 \end{bmatrix} \qquad [6.2\text{-}3]$$

$$\begin{bmatrix} V_2 \\ I_2 \end{bmatrix} = \begin{bmatrix} D & B \\ C & A \end{bmatrix} \times \begin{bmatrix} V_1 \\ -I_1 \end{bmatrix} \qquad [6.2\text{-}4]$$

where

$$\begin{vmatrix} A & B \\ C & D \end{vmatrix} = 1 \qquad [6.2\text{-}5]$$

Equation 6.2-5 greatly simplifies the inversion procedure for the matrices of two-terminal pair networks, because the denominator required in the inversion of the $ABCD$ matrix is unity. It follows from Table 1-2, that:

$$y_{11} = \frac{z_{22}}{|z|} = \frac{D}{B} \qquad\qquad [6.2\text{-}6]$$

$$y_{12} = -\frac{z_{12}}{|z|} = -\frac{1}{B} \qquad\qquad [6.2\text{-}7]$$

$$y_{22} = \frac{z_{11}}{|z|} = \frac{A}{B} \qquad\qquad [6.2\text{-}8]$$

$$z_{11} = \frac{y_{22}}{|y|} = \frac{A}{C} \qquad\qquad [6.2\text{-}9]$$

$$z_{12} = z_{21} = -\frac{y_{21}}{|y|} = \frac{1}{C} \qquad\qquad [6.2\text{-}10]$$

$$z_{22} = \frac{y_{11}}{|y|} = \frac{D}{C} \qquad\qquad [6.2\text{-}11]$$

$$A = -\frac{y_{22}}{y_{12}} = \frac{z_{11}}{z_{12}} \qquad\qquad [6.2\text{-}12]$$

$$B = -\frac{1}{y_{12}} = \frac{|z|}{z_{12}} \qquad\qquad [6.2\text{-}13]$$

$$C = -\frac{|y|}{y_{12}} = \frac{1}{z_{12}} \qquad\qquad [6.2\text{-}14]$$

$$D = -\frac{y_{11}}{y_{12}} = \frac{z_{22}}{z_{12}} \qquad\qquad [6.2\text{-}15]$$

where $y_{12} = y_{21}$ and $z_{12} = z_{21}$ in reciprocal networks.

When two-terminal pair networks are connected in cascade, the output current of the first is the input current of the second. It will be recalled that in the derivation of the equations for two-terminal pair networks

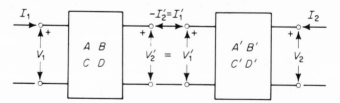

Figure 6-1 Two-terminal pair networks connected in cascade.

(Sec. 1.1), the input and output currents were assumed to be opposite in direction. Consider the two-terminal pair networks shown in Fig. 6-1.

The matrix equations in terms of the $ABCD$ coefficients for the cascaded networks in Fig. 6-1 are

$$\begin{bmatrix} V_1 \\ I_1 \end{bmatrix} = \begin{bmatrix} A & B \\ C & D \end{bmatrix} \times \begin{bmatrix} V_2 \\ -I_2 \end{bmatrix} \qquad [6.2\text{-}16]$$

and since $V_1' = V_2$ and $I_1' = -I_2$, it follows that:

$$\begin{bmatrix} V_2 \\ -I_2 \end{bmatrix} = \begin{bmatrix} A' & B' \\ C' & D' \end{bmatrix} \times \begin{bmatrix} V_2' \\ -I_2' \end{bmatrix} \qquad [6.2\text{-}17]$$

Substituting Eq. 6.2-17 into Eq. 6.2-16 yields

$$\begin{bmatrix} V_1 \\ I_1 \end{bmatrix} = \begin{bmatrix} A & B \\ C & D \end{bmatrix} \times \begin{bmatrix} A' & B' \\ C' & D' \end{bmatrix} \times \begin{bmatrix} V_2' \\ -I_2' \end{bmatrix} \qquad [6.2\text{-}18]$$

Multiplying the two network matrices gives the following relation between the input and output voltages and currents:

$$\begin{bmatrix} V_1 \\ I_1 \end{bmatrix} = \begin{bmatrix} AA' + BC' & AB' + BD' \\ CA' + DC' & CB' + DD' \end{bmatrix} \times \begin{bmatrix} V_2' \\ -I_2' \end{bmatrix} \qquad [6.2\text{-}19]$$

Equations 6.2-18 and 6.2-19 show that the resulting $ABCD$ matrix of two networks in cascade is the product of the individual $ABCD$ matrices.

6.3 TRANSFER OR CHAIN MATRICES

The $ABCD$ matrix of a network in a cascade is known as a chain or transfer matrix; it will be denoted by the symbol $[T]$. A simple network such as a T network can be considered to be the resultant of three components in a chain or cascade as shown in Fig. 6-2. The chain or transfer matrix of the T network in Fig. 6-2(a) is then found by taking the product of the matrices of the three components in Fig. 6-2(b) when these are ex-

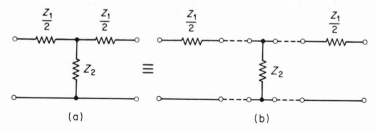

Figure 6-2 T network and its components.

pressed in $ABCD$ form. This form can be readily derived from the node or Y matrix, $[Y]$. Thus, for the component $Z_1/2$

$$[Y]_1 = \begin{bmatrix} \dfrac{2}{Z_1} & \dfrac{-2}{Z_1} \\ \dfrac{-2}{Z_1} & \dfrac{2}{Z_1} \end{bmatrix}$$

[6.3-1]

The $ABCD$ coefficients for the element $Z_1/2$ are found from Eqs. 6.2-12 through 6.2-15 to be

$$A = \frac{-y_{22}}{y_{12}} = \frac{-2/Z_1}{-2/Z_1} = 1$$

[6.3-2]

$$B = -\frac{1}{y_{12}} = \frac{Z_1}{2}$$

[6.3-3]

$$C = \frac{-|y|}{y_{12}} = \frac{0}{y_{12}} = 0$$

[6.3-4]

$$D = \frac{-y_{11}}{y_{12}} = \frac{-2/Z_1}{-2/Z_1} = 1$$

[6.3-5]

Hence,

$$[T]_1 = \begin{bmatrix} 1 & \dfrac{Z_1}{2} \\ 0 & 1 \end{bmatrix}$$

[6.3-6]

The transfer matrix for the shunt leg, Z_2, can be formed from its Z matrix. Thus,

$$[Z]_2 = \begin{bmatrix} Z_2 & Z_2 \\ Z_2 & Z_2 \end{bmatrix}$$

[6.3-7]

It follows from Eqs. 6.2-12 through 6.2-15 that, for Z_2,

$$A = \frac{z_{11}}{z_{12}} = \frac{Z_2}{Z_2} = 1$$

[6.3-8]

$$B = \frac{|z|}{z_{12}} = \frac{0}{Z_2} = 0$$

[6.3-9]

$$C = \frac{1}{z_{12}} = \frac{1}{Z_2}$$

[6.3-10]

$$D = \frac{z_{22}}{z_{12}} = \frac{Z_2}{Z_2} = 1$$

[6.3-11]

Therefore, $$[T]_2 = \begin{bmatrix} 1 & 0 \\ \dfrac{1}{Z_2} & 1 \end{bmatrix}$$ [6.3-12]

It follows from symmetry that:

$$[T]_3 = [T]_1 = \begin{bmatrix} 1 & \dfrac{Z_1}{2} \\ 0 & 1 \end{bmatrix}$$ [6.3-13]

Hence, the transfer matrice for a T network is given by

$$[T]_T = \begin{bmatrix} 1 & \dfrac{Z_1}{2} \\ 0 & 1 \end{bmatrix} \times \begin{bmatrix} 1 & 0 \\ \dfrac{1}{Z_2} & 1 \end{bmatrix} \times \begin{bmatrix} 1 & \dfrac{Z_1}{2} \\ 0 & 1 \end{bmatrix}$$ [6.3-14]

Multiplication of the first two matrices yields

$$[T]_{1,2} = \begin{bmatrix} 1 + \dfrac{Z_1}{2Z_2} & \dfrac{Z_1}{2} \\ \dfrac{1}{Z_2} & 1 \end{bmatrix}$$ [6.3-15]

Finally,

$$[T]_{1,2,3} = [T]_T = \begin{bmatrix} 1 + \dfrac{Z_1}{2Z_2} & Z_1\left(1 + \dfrac{Z_1}{4Z_2}\right) \\ \dfrac{1}{Z_2} & 1 + \dfrac{Z_1}{2Z_2} \end{bmatrix}$$ [6.3-16]

Note from Eq. 6.3-16 that in $[T]_T$, A equals D, indicating a symmetrical network; whereas, in $[T]_{1,2}$ of Eq. 6.3-15, A does not equal D, indicating that an unsymmetrical network results from the chain consisting of $Z_1/2$ and Z_2. The Z matrix of the T network is found from Eqs. 6.2-9, 6.2-10, and 6.2-11 to be:

$$[Z_T] = \begin{bmatrix} \dfrac{Z_1}{2} + Z_2 & Z_2 \\ Z_2 & \dfrac{Z_1}{2} + Z_2 \end{bmatrix}$$ [6.3-17]

The transfer matrix of a π network is formed by multiplying the transfer matrix of $2Z_2$ by the transfer matrix of Z_1 and then again by the transfer matrix of $2Z_2$. Thus

$$[T]_\pi = \begin{bmatrix} 1 & 0 \\ \dfrac{1}{2Z_2} & 1 \end{bmatrix} \times \begin{bmatrix} 1 & Z_1 \\ 0 & 1 \end{bmatrix} \times \begin{bmatrix} 1 & 0 \\ \dfrac{1}{2Z_2} & 1 \end{bmatrix}$$

$$[T]_\pi = \begin{bmatrix} 1 + \dfrac{Z_1}{2Z_2} & Z_1 \\ \dfrac{1}{Z_2}\left(1 + \dfrac{Z_1}{4Z_2}\right) & 1 + \dfrac{Z_1}{2Z_2} \end{bmatrix} \qquad [6.3\text{-}18]$$

The Y matrix is found from Eqs. 6.2-6, 6.2-7, and 6.2-8 to be

$$[Y_\pi] = \begin{bmatrix} \dfrac{1}{Z_1} + \dfrac{1}{2Z_2} & -\dfrac{1}{Z_1} \\ -\dfrac{1}{Z_1} & \dfrac{1}{Z_1} + \dfrac{1}{2Z_2} \end{bmatrix} \qquad [6.3\text{-}19]$$

When a load Z_r is connected across a network characterized by the matrix $\begin{bmatrix} A & B \\ C & D \end{bmatrix}$, the resulting transfer matrix is

$$[T] = \begin{bmatrix} A & B \\ C & D \end{bmatrix} \times \begin{bmatrix} 1 & 0 \\ \dfrac{1}{Z_r} & 1 \end{bmatrix} = \begin{bmatrix} A + \dfrac{B}{Z_r} & B \\ C + \dfrac{D}{Z_r} & D \end{bmatrix}$$

$$= \begin{bmatrix} A' & B' \\ C' & D' \end{bmatrix} \qquad [6.3\text{-}20]$$

where the primed coefficients refer to the terminated network. In the case of the terminated T network, it follows from Eqs. 6.3-16 and 6.3-20 that:

$$[T]_{T,Z_r} = \begin{bmatrix} 1 + \dfrac{Z_1}{2Z_2} + \dfrac{Z_1}{Z}\left(1 + \dfrac{Z_1}{4Z_2}\right) & Z_1\left(1 + \dfrac{Z_1}{4Z_2}\right) \\ \dfrac{1}{Z_2} + \dfrac{1}{Z_r}\left(1 + \dfrac{Z_1}{2Z_2}\right) & 1 + \dfrac{Z_1}{2Z_2} \end{bmatrix}$$

$$= \begin{bmatrix} A' & B' \\ C' & D' \end{bmatrix} \qquad [6.3\text{-}21]$$

where $[T]_{T,Z_r}$ is the transfer matrix of the terminated network.

Since $V_1 = AV_2 - BI_2$ for the combined network, the open-circuit output voltage ($I_2 = 0$) is given by*

* The output terminals are considered to include Z_r.

$$\frac{V_2}{V_1} = \frac{1}{A} = \frac{1}{1 + Z_1/2Z_2 + (Z_1/Z_r)(1 + Z_1/4Z_2)} \qquad [6.3\text{-}22]$$

6.4 THE IDEAL TRANSFORMER

The ideal transformer is a convenient device for theoretical analysis. An ideal transformer is defined as one that has infinite primary and secondary reactance, unity coupling, no losses, and a finite turns ratio. It is impossible to realize such a transformer physically. The requirement of infinite reactance is necessary if the transformer is to change the impedance level without drawing exciting current.

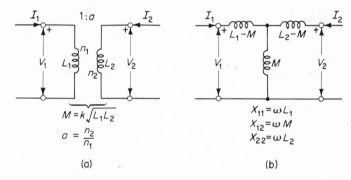

Figure 6-3   Lossless transformer and equivalent T network.

The transfer equations of the two-terminal pair network in Fig. 6-3(a) are the following:

$$V_1 = AV_2 - BI_2 \qquad [6.4\text{-}1]$$

$$I_1 = CV_2 - DI_2 \qquad [6.4\text{-}2]$$

The $ABCD$ coefficients are derived from the Z matrix of the transformer, which becomes an X matrix for the lossless case. Thus, in the equivalent T network shown in Fig. 6-3(b):

$$[Z] = [jX] = \begin{bmatrix} jX_{11} & jX_{12} \\ jX_{21} & jX_{22} \end{bmatrix} \qquad [6.4\text{-}3]$$

where X_{11}, X_{22}, and X_{12} denote the primary, secondary, and mutual reactances. Now let the turns ratio, a, of the lossless transformer be defined as follows:

$$a = \frac{n_2}{n_1} = \sqrt{\frac{L_2}{L_1}} = \sqrt{\frac{X_{22}}{X_{11}}} = \left[\frac{V_2}{V_1}\right]_{I_2=0} \qquad [6.4\text{-}4]$$

where n_2 and n_1 are respectively the number of turns in the secondary and primary. The mutual inductance, M, is given by

$$M = k\sqrt{L_1 L_2} \qquad [6.4\text{-}5]$$

where k is the coefficient of coupling. It follows from Eq. 6.4-5 that:

$$\omega^2 M^2 = k^2 \omega^2 \, L_1 L_2 \qquad [6.4\text{-}6]$$

Hence,

$$X_{12}^2 = k^2 X_{11} X_{22} \qquad [6.4\text{-}7]$$

The determinant of the X matrix in Eq. 6.4-3 is

$$|X| = X_{12} X_{21} - X_{11} X_{22} = X_{12}^2 - X_{11} X_{22} \qquad [6.4\text{-}8]$$

It is assumed that $k = 1$ in an ideal transformer. It follows from Eqs. 6.4-7 and 6.4-8 that in an ideal transformer

$$|X| = 0 \qquad [6.4\text{-}9]$$

The $ABCD$ coefficients for the ideal transformer are found as follows:

$$A = \left[\frac{V_1}{V_2}\right]_{I_2 = 0} = \frac{1}{a} \qquad [6.4\text{-}10]$$

Equation 6.4-10 follows from Eq. 6.4-4. Also, since $|X| = 0$,

$$B = \frac{|X|}{X_{12}} = 0 \qquad [6.4\text{-}11]$$

The coefficient, C, is given by

$$C = \frac{1}{X_{12}} = 0 \qquad [6.4\text{-}12]$$

Equation 6.4-12 results from the fact that the mutual reactance of an ideal transformer is, by definition, infinite. The coefficient, D, is found from the relation:

$$\begin{vmatrix} A & B \\ C & D \end{vmatrix} = AD - BC = 1 \qquad [6.4\text{-}13]$$

Since $B = C = 0$,

$$D = \frac{1}{A} = a \qquad [6.4\text{-}14]$$

It follows from Eqs. 6.4-10 through 6.4-14 that the transfer matrix, $[T]_t$, of an ideal transformer is given by

$$[T]_t = \begin{bmatrix} \dfrac{1}{a} & 0 \\ 0 & a \end{bmatrix} \qquad\qquad [6.4\text{-}15]$$

The transfer matrix of an ideal transformer followed by a load Z_r is given by

$$[T]_{t,z} = \begin{bmatrix} \dfrac{1}{a} & 0 \\ 0 & a \end{bmatrix} \times \begin{bmatrix} 1 & 0 \\ \dfrac{1}{Z_r} & 1 \end{bmatrix} = \begin{bmatrix} \dfrac{1}{a} & 0 \\ \dfrac{a}{Z_r} & a \end{bmatrix} \qquad\qquad [6.4\text{-}16]$$

The corresponding Z matrix is found from the relations $z_{11} = A/C$, $z_{22} = D/C$, and $z_{12} = z_{21} = 1/C$. Inspection of the right-hand side of Eq. 6.4-16 shows that $A = 1/a$; $B = 0$; $C = a/Z_r$; and $D = a$. Hence,

$$[Z]_{t,z} = \begin{bmatrix} \dfrac{Z_r}{a^2} & \dfrac{Z_r}{a} \\ \dfrac{Z_r}{a} & Z_r \end{bmatrix} = \begin{bmatrix} z_{11} & z_{12} \\ z_{21} & z_{22} \end{bmatrix} \qquad\qquad [6.4\text{-}17]$$

A network N, followed by an ideal transformer, is shown in Fig. 6-4. The impedance matrix of the network is

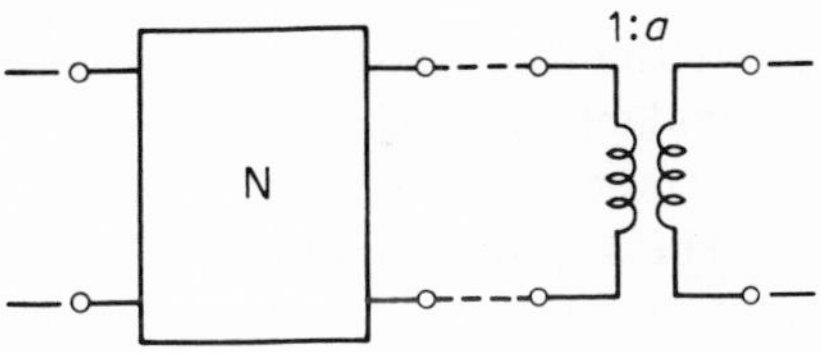

Figure 6-4 Network followed by ideal transformer.

$$[Z]_n = \begin{bmatrix} z_{11} & z_{12} \\ z_{21} & z_{22} \end{bmatrix} \qquad [6.4\text{-}18]$$

The transfer matrix of the network followed by an ideal transformer is given by

$$[T]_{n,t} = \begin{bmatrix} \dfrac{z_{11}}{z_{12}} & \dfrac{|z|}{z_{12}} \\ \dfrac{1}{z_{12}} & \dfrac{z_{22}}{z_{12}} \end{bmatrix} \times \begin{bmatrix} \dfrac{1}{a} & 0 \\ 0 & a \end{bmatrix} = \begin{bmatrix} \dfrac{z_{11}}{az_{12}} & \dfrac{a|z|}{z_{12}} \\ \dfrac{1}{az_{12}} & \dfrac{az_{12}}{z_{12}} \end{bmatrix} \qquad [6.4\text{-}19]$$

Since $z_{11} = A/C$, $z_{22} = D/C$, and $z_{12} = z_{21} = 1/C$, the Z matrix of the network followed by an ideal transformer is

$$[Z]_{n,t} = \begin{bmatrix} z_{11} & az_{12} \\ az_{21} & a^2z_{22} \end{bmatrix} \qquad [6.4\text{-}20]$$

The Z matrix of the network preceded by an ideal transformer is

$$[Z]_{t,n} = \begin{bmatrix} \dfrac{z_{11}}{a^2} & \dfrac{z_{12}}{a} \\ \dfrac{z_{21}}{a} & z_2 \end{bmatrix} \qquad [6.4\text{-}21]$$

Relations analogous to Eqs. 6.4-20 and 6.4-21 can be obtained for Y matrices. Thus, the Y matrix of a network followed by an ideal transformer is

$$[Y]_{n,t} = \begin{bmatrix} y_{11} & \dfrac{y_{12}}{a} \\ \dfrac{y_{21}}{a} & \dfrac{y_{22}}{a^2} \end{bmatrix} \qquad [6.4\text{-}22]$$

The Y matrix of a network preceded by an ideal transformer is given by

$$[Y]_{t,n} = \begin{bmatrix} a^2y_{11} & ay_{12} \\ ay_{21} & y_{22} \end{bmatrix} \qquad [6.4\text{-}23]$$

If the combination of a resistance network and transformer into one equivalent network is physically realizable, the self-impedance or self-admittance terms must be greater in magnitude than the mutual terms.

The transfer matrix of a network followed by an ideal transformer is given by Eq. 6.4-19, which was obtained by multiplying the transfer matrix of the generalized network by the transfer matrix of the transformer. The Z matrix is obtained by converting the final transfer matrix in Eq. 6.4-19 into Eq. 6.4-20. This procedure involves several steps. The process can be simplified by starting with Eq. 6.4-18 and multiplying the second row and second column by the turns ratio, a. This is indicated in Eq. 6.4-24, where the arrows denote the multiplication of the second row and the second column by the factor, a. Thus,

$$[Z]_{n,t} = \begin{bmatrix} z_{11} & z_{12} \\ z_{21} & z_{22} \end{bmatrix}_{\substack{\leftarrow a \\ a\uparrow}} \equiv \begin{bmatrix} z_{11} & az_{12} \\ az_{21} & a^2z_{22} \end{bmatrix} \qquad [6.4\text{-}24]$$

When the transformer precedes the network, the resultant Z matrix is formed by multiplying the first row and the first column by $1/a$, as shown in Eq. 6.4-25.

$$[Z]_{t,n} = \overset{\downarrow \frac{1}{a}}{\underset{1/a}{\overrightarrow{}}}\begin{bmatrix} z_{11} & z_{12} \\ & \\ z_{21} & z_{22} \end{bmatrix} \equiv \begin{bmatrix} \dfrac{z_{11}}{a^2} & \dfrac{z_{12}}{a} \\ \dfrac{z_{21}}{a} & z_{22} \end{bmatrix} \qquad [6.4\text{-}25]$$

When the transformer follows the network, the Y matrix is given by

$$[Y]_{n,t} = \begin{bmatrix} y_{11} & y_{12} \\ & \\ y_{21} & y_{22} \end{bmatrix}_{\underset{\underset{\frac{1}{a}\uparrow}{}}{\overset{1/a}{\leftarrow}}} \equiv \begin{bmatrix} y_{11} & \dfrac{y_{12}}{a} \\ \dfrac{y_{21}}{a} & \dfrac{y_{22}}{a^2} \end{bmatrix} \qquad [6.4\text{-}26]$$

When the transformer precedes the network, the resulting Y matrix is

$$[Y]_{t,n} = \overset{\downarrow a}{\underset{a}{\overrightarrow{}}}\begin{bmatrix} y_{11} & y_{12} \\ y_{21} & y_{22} \end{bmatrix} \equiv \begin{bmatrix} a^2 y_{11} & a y_{1_2} \\ a y_{12} & y_{22} \end{bmatrix} \qquad [6.4\text{-}27]$$

6.5 IMPEDANCE TRANSFORMATION

The ideal transformer is used in the synthesis of impedance transforming networks. In such applications, the ideal transformer is used in the process of synthesis, and its effect is absorbed in the transformation of the original network. This is accomplished by the use of transfer matrices.

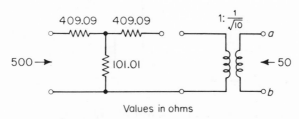

Values in ohms

Figure 6-5   Attenuator followed by ideal transformer.

Consider the attenuator that was designed in Sec. 2.1 to yield a 20-db loss and to operate between input and output impedance levels of 500 ohms. This attenuator, followed by an ideal transformer, is shown in Fig. 6-5.

Assume that it is required to reduce the output impedance level at terminals ab to 50 ohms by means of an ideal transformer, without changing the power loss. The Z matrix of the T attenuator is

$$[Z]_n = \begin{bmatrix} 510.10 & 101.01 \\ 101.01 & 510.10 \end{bmatrix}$$

The Z matrix of the network followed by an ideal transformer as given by Eq. 6.4-24 is

$$[Z]_{n,t} = \begin{bmatrix} 510.10 & 101.01 \\ 101.01 & 510.10 \end{bmatrix}_{\underset{a\uparrow}{\overset{a}{\leftarrow}}} \equiv \begin{bmatrix} 510.10 & a(101.01) \\ a(101.01) & a^2(510.10) \end{bmatrix} \qquad [6.5\text{-}1]$$

The output and input impedance levels, Z_2 and Z_1, are related to the turns ratio as follows:

$$\frac{Z_2}{Z_1} = \frac{V_2/(-I_2)}{V_1/I_1} = a^2$$

Hence,

$$a = \sqrt{Z_2/Z_1} \qquad [6.5\text{-}2]$$

Since the impedance level is to be reduced from 500 to 50 ohms,

$$a = \sqrt{\frac{50}{500}} = \frac{1}{\sqrt{10}} \qquad [6.5\text{-}3]$$

Substituting into Eq. 6.5-1, the value of the turns ratio given in Eq. 6.5-3, yields the following Z matrix:

$$[Z] = \begin{bmatrix} 510.10 & \dfrac{101.01}{\sqrt{10}} \\ \dfrac{101.01}{\sqrt{10}} & \dfrac{510.10}{10} \end{bmatrix} = \begin{bmatrix} 510.10 & 32 \\ 32 & 51.01 \end{bmatrix} \qquad [6.5\text{-}4]$$

It follows from Eq. 6.5-4 that

$$\begin{bmatrix} z_{11} & z_{12} \\ z_{12} & z_{22} \end{bmatrix} = \begin{bmatrix} 510.10 & 32 \\ 32 & 51.01 \end{bmatrix} \qquad [6.5\text{-}5]$$

Figure 6-6 shows the unsymmetrical T section corresponding to the matrix in Eq. 6.5-5. Figure 6-6 replaces the network and the ideal transformer of Fig. 6-5.

The transformation of a symmetrical section terminated by an ideal transformer into an unsymmetrical section is always possible, provided that the resulting network is physically realizable. Inspection of Eq. 6.4-24 shows that, since $a^2 z_{22}$ includes $a z_{21}$, the condition for physical realizability, when z_{22} and z_{12} are pure resistors, is the following:

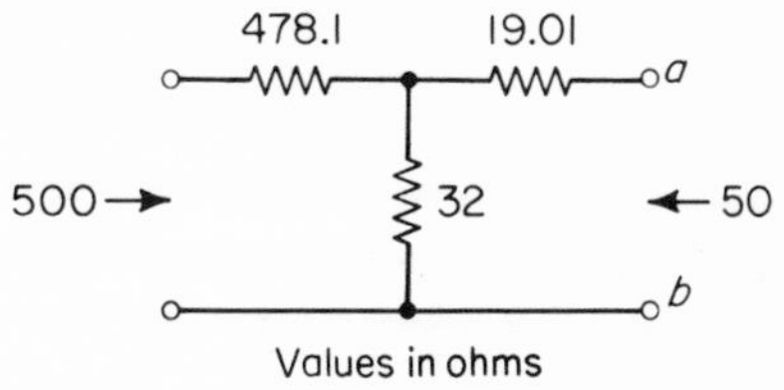

$$a^2 z_{22} \geqq a z_{21}$$

which can be simplified and re-written as

Figure 6-6   Attenuator with reduced output impedance.

$$a \geqq \frac{z_{21}}{z_{22}} \qquad [6.5\text{-}6]$$

It follows from Eq. 6.5-6 that, for the attenuator in Fig. 6-5, the minimum value of a for impedance step-down is

$$a_{\min} = \frac{z_{21}}{z_{22}} = \frac{101.01}{510.10} = 0.198 \qquad [6.5\text{-}7]$$

Also, since for pure resistors, $z_{11} \geqq a z_{12}$

or
$$a \leqq \frac{z_{11}}{z_{12}} \qquad [6.5\text{-}8]$$

it follows that the maximum value of a for impedance step-up is

$$a_{\max} = \frac{z_{11}}{z_{12}} = \frac{510.10}{101.01} = 5.05 \qquad [6.5\text{-}9]$$

Thus, the realizable range of a is given by

$$0.198 \ \leqq \ a \ \leqq \ 5.05 \qquad [6.5\text{-}10]$$

When the turns ratio, a, has its minimum value of 0.198, the Z matrix for the attenuator followed by the ideal transformer is given by

$$[Z]_{n,t} = \begin{bmatrix} z_{11} & z_{12} \\ z_{21} & z_{22} \end{bmatrix} = \begin{bmatrix} 510.10 & 0.198 \times 101.01 \\ 0.198 \times 101.01 & (0.198)^2 \times 510.10 \end{bmatrix}$$

$$= \begin{bmatrix} 510.10 & 20.1 \\ 20.1 & 20.1 \end{bmatrix} \qquad [6.5\text{-}11]$$

Note that z_{21} is equal to z_{22} in Eq. 6.5-11. The corresponding network is shown in Fig. 6-7(a), where the input impedance is 500 ohms and the output impedance equals $(0.198)^2 \times 500 = 19.6$ ohms.

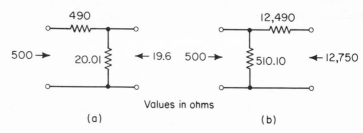

Values in ohms

(a)   (b)

Figure 6-7 Attenuator with minimum and maximum output impedance.

When the turns ratio, a, has its maximum value of 5.05, the Z matrix is given by

$$[Z]_{n,t} = \begin{bmatrix} z_{11} & z_{12} \\ z_{21} & z_{22} \end{bmatrix} = \begin{bmatrix} 510.10 & 5.05 \times 101.01 \\ 5.05 \times 101.01 & (5.05)^2 \times 510.10 \end{bmatrix}$$

$$= \begin{bmatrix} 510.10 & 510.10 \\ 510.10 & 13,000 \end{bmatrix} \qquad [6.5\text{-}12]$$

Note that z_{12} is equal to z_{11} in Eq. 6.5-12. The corresponding network is shown in Fig. 6-7(b), where the input impedance is 500 ohms and the output impedance equals $(5.05)^2 \times 500 = 12,750$ ohms.

Whenever the ideal transformer is used in the synthesis of an impedance transforming network, it is to be considered as a circuit artifice rather than a realizable circuit element.

As a second example, a band-pass filter is to be used as an impedance-transforming device. A symmetrical band-pass filter can be converted into an impedance-transforming network in unsymmetrical form by the use of an ideal transformer.

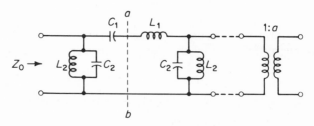

Figure 6-8 Band-pass filter followed by an ideal transformer.

In Fig. 6-8 is shown a symmetrical band-pass filter followed by an ideal transformer. It is not necessary to consider the whole network, as the elements to the left of ab will be unaffected by the transformer and they can be disregarded for the present. Only the circuit to the right of ab will be considered with the ideal transformer.

The Y matrix of the network to the right of ab without the transformer is given by

$$[Y]_n = \begin{bmatrix} \dfrac{1}{j\omega L_1} & -\dfrac{1}{j\omega L_1} \\[2ex] -\dfrac{1}{j\omega L_1} & \dfrac{1}{j\omega L_1} + \dfrac{1}{j\omega L_2} + j\omega C_2 \end{bmatrix} \qquad [6.5\text{-}13]$$

The matrix of the network followed by the ideal transformer is found from Eq. 6.4-26 to be

$$[Y]_{n,t} = \begin{bmatrix} \dfrac{1}{j\omega L_1} & -\dfrac{1}{aj\omega L_1} \\[2ex] \dfrac{-1}{aj\omega L_1} & \dfrac{1}{a^2}\left(\dfrac{1}{j\omega L_1} + \dfrac{1}{j\omega L_2} + j\omega C_2\right) \end{bmatrix} \qquad [6.5\text{-}14]$$

Equation 6.4-24 could have been used, but the admittance form is simpler in this case because of the parallel elements in the shunt branch.

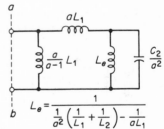

The reconstructed network, with the ideal transformer absorbed in the network, is shown in Fig. 6-9. For this network to be physically realizable, all the elements must be positive in value. It is evident that $[a/(a-1)]L_1$ is positive for all values of $a \geqq 1$. When $a = 1$, the original network is obtained, as would be expected. Also, aL_1 is positive when a is positive. For L_e in Fig. 6-9 to be positive, the following relation must hold:

$$L_e = \dfrac{1}{\dfrac{1}{a^2}\left(\dfrac{1}{L_1} + \dfrac{1}{L_2}\right) - \dfrac{1}{aL_1}}$$

Figure 6-9 Network equivalent to band-pass filter followed by ideal transformer.

$$\left(\dfrac{1}{a^2}\right)\left(\dfrac{1}{L_1} + \dfrac{1}{L_2}\right) \geqq \dfrac{1}{aL_1} \qquad [6.5\text{-}15]$$

Hence,

$$a \leqq \dfrac{L_1 + L_2}{L_2} \qquad [6.5\text{-}16]$$

Thus the realizable range of the turns ratio, a, is given by

$$1 \leqq a \leqq \dfrac{L_1 + L_2}{L_2} \qquad [6.5\text{-}17]$$

Figure 6-10 shows the complete network when a is equal to its maximum value of $(L_1 + L_2)/L_2$.

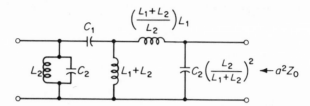

Figure 6-10 Band-pass filter transformed to have maximum output impedance.

Now refer again to Fig. 6-8. If the positions of L_1 and C_1 in Fig. 6.8 are interchanged, that portion of the network to the right of ab is changed. The capacitor C_1 will be to the right of ab, and C_1 in conjunction with C_2 can be used as an impedance-transforming circuit. The design of this circuit is left as an exercise for the student.

Only band-pass filters can be used as impedance-transforming filters. In low-pass and high-pass filters, the series and shunt arms of the T section do not contain like circuit elements.

In some cases it is desirable to use so-called impedance leveling in a network. This is illustrated in the band-pass filter shown in (a) of Fig. 6-11. Assume that it is desired to have all values of inductance equal to

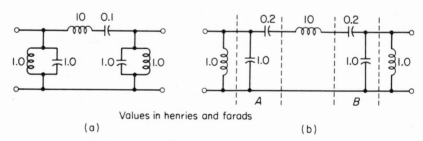

Values in henries and farads

(a)   (b)

Figure 6-11 Network illustrating impedance leveling.

one henry without changing the input or output impedance of the network.

The network is redrawn as shown in Fig. 6-11(b), where the 0.1-farad capacitor is resolved into two 0.2-farad capacitors in series. This does not alter the characteristics of the network. If the section designated as A is followed by an ideal transformer with $a = 1/\sqrt{10}$, and if the section designated as B is preceded by an ideal transformer with $a = \sqrt{10}$, the

10-henry inductor may be replaced by a 1-henry inductor. Then, by applying Eq. 6.4-26 to section A, we obtain

$$[Y]_{n,t} = \begin{bmatrix} j1.2\omega & -j0.2\omega \\ -j0.2\omega & j0.2\omega \end{bmatrix} \underset{\underset{\sqrt{10}\uparrow}{\overset{\sqrt{10}}{\leftarrow}}}{} \equiv \begin{bmatrix} j1.2\omega & -j0.632\omega \\ -j0.632\omega & j2.0\omega \end{bmatrix} \qquad [6.5\text{-}18]$$

By applying Eq. 6.4-27 to section B, we obtain

$$[Y]_{t,n} = \underset{\sqrt{10}\rightarrow}{\overset{\downarrow\sqrt{10}}{}} \begin{bmatrix} j0.2\omega & -j0.2\omega \\ -j0.2\omega & j1.2\omega \end{bmatrix} \equiv \begin{bmatrix} j2.0\omega & -j0.632\omega \\ -j0.632\omega & j1.2\omega \end{bmatrix} \qquad [6.5\text{-}19]$$

The complete network after impedance leveling is shown in Fig. 6-12. The input impedance and the output impedance, as well as the propagation

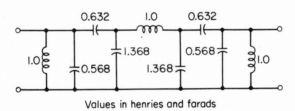

Values in henries and farads

Figure 6-12   Network of Fig. 6-11 after impedance leveling.

characteristics of the network, are unchanged. The inductors are all made equal to 1.0 henry. The number of capacitors, however, is twice the number in the original network.

6.6 PARALLEL CONNECTIONS

When two two-terminal pair networks are connected in parallel as shown in Fig. 6-13, the input voltage of one is the input voltage of the other, and the output voltage of one is the output voltage of the other. Under these conditions, the matrix equations have the following form:

$$\begin{bmatrix} I_1' \\ I_2' \end{bmatrix} = \begin{bmatrix} y_{11}' & y_{12}' \\ y_{21}' & y_{22}' \end{bmatrix} \times \begin{bmatrix} V_1 \\ V_2 \end{bmatrix} \qquad [6.6\text{-}1]$$

$$\begin{bmatrix} I_1'' \\ I_2'' \end{bmatrix} = \begin{bmatrix} y_{11}'' & y_{12}'' \\ y_{21}'' & y_{22}'' \end{bmatrix} \times \begin{bmatrix} V_1 \\ V_2 \end{bmatrix} \qquad [6.6\text{-}2]$$

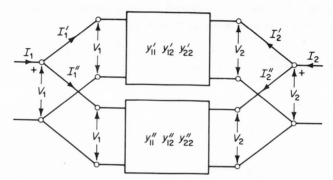

Figure 6-13   Networks connected in parallel.

The currents and admittances of the first network are indicated with a prime, and a double prime indicates those of the second network. Since V_1 and V_2 are common to the two networks in parallel, the two Y matrices can be added to obtain the resultant Y matrix for the combined network.*

The matrix expression for the total current is

$$\begin{bmatrix} I_1 \\ I_2 \end{bmatrix} = \begin{bmatrix} I_1' + I_1'' \\ I_2' + I_2'' \end{bmatrix} = \begin{bmatrix} y_{11}' + y_{11}'' & y_{12}' + y_{12}'' \\ y_{21}' + y_{21}'' & y_{22}' + y_{22}'' \end{bmatrix} \times \begin{bmatrix} V_1 \\ V_2 \end{bmatrix} \qquad [6.6\text{-}3]$$

Equations 6.6-3 correspond to the addition of admittances in parallel.

The conventional π network can be considered to result from the combi-

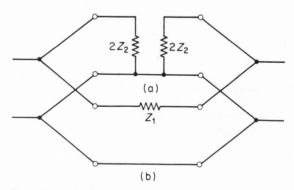

Figure 6-14   Connection of two networks in parallel to form π network.

nation in parallel of the two networks shown in Figs. 6-14(a) and (b). The Y matrices for these two networks separately are

* This method is valid only under certain conditions. The validity requirements for the interconnection of networks are discussed in Sec. 6.9.

$$[Y]_a = \begin{bmatrix} 1/2Z_2 & 0 \\ 0 & 1/2Z_2 \end{bmatrix} \qquad [6.6\text{-}4]$$

$$[Y]_b = \begin{bmatrix} 1/Z_1 & -1/Z_1 \\ -1/Z_1 & 1/Z_1 \end{bmatrix} \qquad [6.6\text{-}5]$$

Hence, the Y matrix for the π network is given by

$$[Y]_\pi = [Y]_a + [Y]_b = \begin{bmatrix} 1/2Z_2 + 1/Z_1 & -1/Z_1 \\ -1/Z_1 & 1/2Z_2 + 1/Z_1 \end{bmatrix} \qquad [6.6\text{-}6]$$

$$[Y]_\pi = \begin{bmatrix} Y_2/2 + Y_1 & -Y_1 \\ -Y_1 & Y_2/2 + Y_1 \end{bmatrix} \qquad [6.6\text{-}7]$$

where $Y_2 = 1/Z_2$ and $Y_1 = 1/Z_1$.

The Z matrix for the T network can be formed by inversion of the Y matrix.

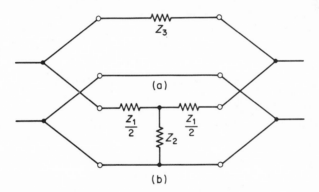

Figure 6-15 Connection of networks in parallel to form bridged-T network.

A bridged-T network can be formed by connecting in parallel the networks shown in (a) and (b) of Fig. 6-15. Since the T network consists of three nodes and two meshes, it is convenient first to write its Z matrix and then find its Y matrix by inversion. This gives the following results:

$$[Z]_a = \begin{bmatrix} Z_1/2 + Z_2 & Z_2 \\ Z_2 & Z_1/2 + Z_2 \end{bmatrix} \qquad [6.6\text{-}8]$$

$$[Y]_a = [Z]_a^{-1} = \begin{bmatrix} \dfrac{Z_1/2 + Z_2}{|Z|_a} & \dfrac{-Z_2}{|Z|_a} \\ \dfrac{-Z_2}{|Z|_a} & \dfrac{Z_1/2 + Z_2}{|Z|_a} \end{bmatrix} \qquad [6.6\text{-}9]$$

where $|Z|_a = Z_1^2/4 + Z_1 Z_2$.

The Y matrix for the network in Fig. 6-15(a) can be written directly as

$$[Y]_b = \begin{bmatrix} Y_3 & -Y_3 \\ -Y_3 & Y_3 \end{bmatrix} \qquad [6.6\text{-}10]$$

where $Y_3 = 1/Z_3$.

Hence the Y matrix of the bridged-T network is given by

$$[Y]_{bT} = [Y]_a + [Y]_b = \begin{bmatrix} \dfrac{Z_1/2 + \dot{Z}_2}{|Z|_a} + Y_3 & \dfrac{-Z_2}{|Z|_a} - Y_3 \\ \dfrac{-Z_2}{|Z|_a} - Y_3 & \dfrac{Z_1/2 + Z_2}{|Z|_a} + Y_3 \end{bmatrix} \qquad [6.6\text{-}11]$$

6.7 FURTHER APPLICATIONS OF MATRIX ANALYSIS

In this section, matrix methods will be applied to establish the transformation equations for equivalent T and π networks that were developed in Sec. 1.1. Matrix algebra will also be used in the analysis of the twin-T network.

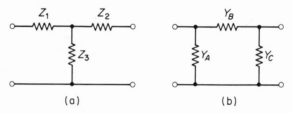

(a)   (b)

Figure 6-16 T and π networks.

Figure 6-16 shows T and π networks. The elements of the T network are denoted by impedances, whereas those of the π network are admittances. The Z matrix for the T network is

$$[Z]_T = \begin{bmatrix} Z_1 + Z_3 & Z_3 \\ Z_3 & Z_2 + Z_3 \end{bmatrix} \qquad [6.7\text{-}1]$$

The Y matrix of the π network is

$$[Y]_\pi = \begin{bmatrix} Y_A + Y_B & -Y_B \\ -Y_B & Y_B + Y_C \end{bmatrix} \qquad [6.7\text{-}2]$$

The Y matrix of the T network and the Z matrix of the π network can be found by the established methods of matrix inversion. Thus,

$$[Y]_T = [Z]_T^{-1} = \begin{bmatrix} \dfrac{Z_2 + Z_3}{|Z|_T} & -\dfrac{Z_3}{|Z|_T} \\ -\dfrac{Z_3}{|Z|_T} & \dfrac{Z_1 + Z_3}{|Z|_T} \end{bmatrix} \qquad [6.7\text{-}3]$$

where

$$|Z|_T = Z_1 Z_2 + Z_1 Z_3 + Z_2 Z_3 \qquad [6.7\text{-}4]$$

The Z matrix of the π network is given by

$$[Z]_\pi = [Y_1]_\pi^{-1} = \begin{bmatrix} \dfrac{Y_B + Y_C}{|Y|_\pi} & \dfrac{Y_B}{|Y|_\pi} \\ \dfrac{Y_B}{|Y|_\pi} & \dfrac{Y_A + Y_B}{|Y|_\pi} \end{bmatrix} \qquad [6.7\text{-}5]$$

where

$$|Y|_\pi = Y_A Y_B + Y_A Y_C + Y_B Y_C \qquad [6.7\text{-}6]$$

The conditions for network equivalence are found by equating corresponding terms of like matrices. Equating corresponding elements of the Z matrices in Eqs. 6.7-1 and 6.7-5 yields

$$Z_3 = \frac{Y_B}{|Y|_\pi} \qquad [6.7\text{-}7]$$

$$Z_1 + Z_3 = \frac{Y_B + Y_C}{|Y|_\pi} \qquad [6.7\text{-}8]$$

$$Z_2 + Z_3 = \frac{Y_A + Y_B}{|Y|_\pi} \qquad [6.7\text{-}9]$$

Equations 6.7-7, 6.7-8, and 6.7-9 can be solved to give the following relations between the impedances of the equivalent T and π networks. These are the following:

$$Z_3 = \frac{Y_B}{|Y|_\pi} = \frac{1/Z_B}{1/Z_A Z_B + 1/Z_A Z_C + 1/Z_B Z_C} = \frac{Z_A Z_C}{Z_A + Z_B + Z_C} \qquad [6.7\text{-}10]$$

It follows from Eqs. 6.7-8 and 6.7-10 that:

$$Z_1 = \frac{Y_C}{|Y|_\pi} = \frac{Z_A Z_B}{Z_A + Z_B + Z_C} \qquad [6.7\text{-}11]$$

It follows from Eqs. 6.7-9 and 6.7-10 that:

$$Z_2 = \frac{Z_B Z_C}{Z_A + Z_B + Z_C} \qquad [6.7\text{-}12]$$

Equating corresponding elements of the Y matrices, Eqs. 6.7-2 and 6.7-3, gives the following relations:

$$Y_B = \frac{Z_3}{|Z|_T} \qquad [6.7\text{-}13]$$

$$Y_A + Y_B = \frac{Z_2 + Z_3}{|Z|_T} \qquad [6.7\text{-}14]$$

$$Y_B + Y_C = \frac{Z_1 + Z_3}{|Z|_T} \qquad [6.7\text{-}15]$$

The solution of Eqs. 6.7-13, 6.7-14, and 6.7-15 gives the following relations between the impedances of π and T networks:

$$Z_B = \frac{Z_1Z_2 + Z_1Z_3 + Z_2Z_3}{Z_3} \qquad [6.7\text{-}16]$$

$$Z_A = \frac{Z_1Z_2 + Z_1Z_3 + Z_2Z_3}{Z_2} \qquad [6.7\text{-}17]$$

$$Z_C = \frac{Z_1Z_2 + Z_1Z_3 + Z_2Z_3}{Z_1} \qquad [6.7\text{-}18]$$

When the two T networks shown in Fig. 6-17 are connected in parallel, a twin-T network results. In order to find the matrix of the two networks,

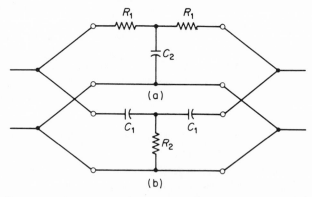

Figure 6-17 T networks connected in parallel to form twin-T network.

(a) and (b), connected in parallel, it is merely necessary to add their Y matrices. This gives the Y matrix of the resultant combination. The Y matrices of the T networks shown in Fig. 6-17 are found by writing their Z matrices and then inverting them. The Z matrices are given by

$$[Z]_a = \begin{bmatrix} R_1 + 1/j\omega C_2 & 1/j\omega C_2 \\ 1/j\omega C_2 & R_1 + 1/j\omega C_2 \end{bmatrix} \qquad [6.7\text{-}19]$$

$$[Z_b] = \begin{bmatrix} R_2 + 1/j\omega C_1 & R_2 \\ R_2 & R_2 + 1/j\omega C_1 \end{bmatrix} \qquad [6.7\text{-}20]$$

The Y matrices are

$$[Z]_a^{-1} = [Y]_a = \begin{bmatrix} \dfrac{R_1 + 1/j\omega C_2}{|Z|_a} & \dfrac{-1/j\omega C_2}{|Z|_a} \\ \dfrac{-1/j\omega C_2}{|Z|_a} & \dfrac{R_1 + 1/j\omega C_2}{|Z|_a} \end{bmatrix} \qquad [6.7\text{-}21]$$

$$[Z]_b^{-1} = [Y]_b = \begin{bmatrix} \dfrac{R_2 + 1/j\omega C_1}{|Z|_b} & -\dfrac{R_2}{|Z|_b} \\ -\dfrac{R_2}{|Z|_b} & \dfrac{R_2 + 1/j\omega C_1}{|Z|_b} \end{bmatrix} \qquad [6.7\text{-}22]$$

where $|Z|_a = R_1^2 + \dfrac{2R_1}{j\omega C_2}$

$$|Z|_b = \dfrac{2R_2}{j\omega C_1} - \dfrac{1}{\omega^2 C_1^2}$$

The resultant Y matrix is

$$[Y] = [Y]_a + [Y]_b$$

$$= \begin{bmatrix} \dfrac{R_1 + 1/j\omega C_2}{|Z|_a} + \dfrac{R_2 + 1/j\omega C_1}{|Z|_b} & -\left(\dfrac{1/j\omega C_2}{|Z|_a} + \dfrac{R_2}{|Z|_b} \right) \\ -\left(\dfrac{1/j\omega C_2}{|Z|_a} + \dfrac{R_2}{|Z|_b} \right) & \dfrac{R_1 + 1/j\omega C_2}{|Z|_a} + \dfrac{R_2 + 1/j\omega C_1}{|Z|_b} \end{bmatrix}$$

$$[6.7\text{-}23]$$

The twin-T network finds extensive application as a null network. The null conditions are obtained by setting equal to zero the transfer admittance term in the matrix of Eq. 6.7-23.* Thus, the condition for zero or null output, when networks (a) and (b) are connected in parallel, is the following:

$$\dfrac{1/j\omega C_2}{|Z|_a} + \dfrac{R_2}{|Z|_b} = \dfrac{1/j\omega C_2}{R_1^2 + 2R_1/j\omega C_2} + \dfrac{R_2}{2R_2/j\omega C_1 - 1/\omega^2 C_1^2} = 0 \qquad [6.7\text{-}24]$$

* This relation follows from the fact that the open-circuit output voltage, $V_2 = -y_{21}V_1/y_{22}$.

The solution of Eq. 6.7-24 yields

$$R_1^2 R_2 - \frac{2R_2}{\omega^2 C_1 C_2} + \frac{2R_1 R_2}{j\omega C_2} - \frac{1}{j\omega^3 C_1^2 C_2} = 0 \qquad [6.7\text{-}25]$$

Equating the real and imaginary parts of Eq. 6.7-25 gives the following relations:

$$R_1^2 = \frac{2}{\omega^2 C_1 C_2} \qquad [6.7\text{-}26]$$

$$\omega^2 = \frac{2}{R_1^2 C_1 C_2} \qquad [6.7\text{-}27]$$

$$2R_1 R_2 = \frac{1}{\omega^2 C_1^2} \qquad [6.7\text{-}28]$$

$$\omega^2 = \frac{1}{2R_1 R_2 C_1^2} \qquad [6.7\text{-}29]$$

Equations 6.7-27 and 6.7-29 give the frequencies for zero output. If $C_2 = 2C_1$, and $R_2 = R_1/2$, then

$$\omega^2 = \frac{1}{R_1^2 C_1^2} = \frac{1}{R_2^2 C_2^2} \qquad [6.7\text{-}30]$$

and

$$\omega = \frac{1}{R_1 C_1} = \frac{1}{R_2 C_2} \qquad [6.7\text{-}31]$$

Equation 6.7-31 gives the null frequency when $C_2 = 2C_1$, $R_2 = R_1/2$, and $R_1 C_1 = R_2 C_2$.

6.8 SERIES CONNECTION OF NETWORKS

Networks are said to be connected in series when they are connected in such a manner that their input currents I_1 are equal and their output currents I_2 are equal. The resultant Z matrix for a series connection is found by adding the component Z matrices. This assumes that the validity conditions for the interconnection of the networks are satisfied.

Two networks connected in series are shown in Fig. 6-18. The matrix equations for network N' are

$$\begin{bmatrix} V_1' \\ V_2' \end{bmatrix} = \begin{bmatrix} z_{11}' & z_{12}' \\ z_{21}' & z_{22}' \end{bmatrix} \times \begin{bmatrix} I_1 \\ I_2 \end{bmatrix} \qquad [6.8\text{-}1]$$

The matrix equations for network N'' are

$$\begin{bmatrix} V_1'' \\ V_2'' \end{bmatrix} = \begin{bmatrix} z_{11}'' & z_{12}'' \\ z_{21}'' & z_{22}'' \end{bmatrix} \times \begin{bmatrix} I_1 \\ I_2 \end{bmatrix} \qquad [6.8\text{-}2]$$

Note that the input currents are equal, and also the output currents are equal. Therefore it follows from Eqs. 6.8-1 and 6.8-2 that:

$$\begin{bmatrix} V_1' + V_1'' \\ V_2' + V_2'' \end{bmatrix} = \begin{bmatrix} V_1 \\ V_2 \end{bmatrix} = \begin{bmatrix} z_{11}' + z_{11}'' & z_{12}' + z_{12}'' \\ z_{21}' + z_{21}'' & z_{22}' + z_{22}'' \end{bmatrix} \times \begin{bmatrix} I_1 \\ I_2 \end{bmatrix} \qquad [6.8\text{-}3]$$

Equations 6.8-3 give the over-all characteristics of the networks connected in series.

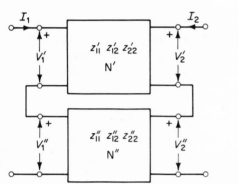

Figure 6-18 Networks connected in series.

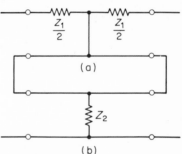

Figure 6-19 Connection of networks in series to form T network.

A T network can be formed by connecting in series the networks in (a) and (b) of Fig. 6-19, where the two elements, $Z_1/2$, in series constitute network (a), and the element Z_2 is the only component of network (b). Inspection of Fig. 6-19 shows that

$$[Z]_a = \begin{bmatrix} Z_1/2 & 0 \\ 0 & Z_1/2 \end{bmatrix} \qquad [6.8\text{-}4]$$

$$[Z]_b = \begin{bmatrix} Z_2 & Z_2 \\ Z_2 & Z_2 \end{bmatrix} \qquad [6.8\text{-}5]$$

The resultant Z matrix is given by

$$[Z]_a + [Z]_b = \begin{bmatrix} Z_1/2 + Z_2 & Z_2 \\ Z_2 & Z_1/2 + Z_2 \end{bmatrix} \qquad [6.8\text{-}6]$$

Equation 6.8-6 gives the Z matrix of a T network.

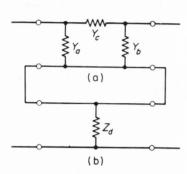

(a)

(b)

Figure 6-20 Connection of networks in series to form bridged-T network.

A bridged-T network can be formed by connecting in series the networks in (a) and (b) of Fig. 6-20. In this case Y_a, Y_b, and Y_c are the elements of network (a), and Z_d is the only component of network (b). The Y matrix for network (a) is

$$[Y]_a = \begin{bmatrix} Y_a + Y_c & -Y_c \\ -Y_c & Y_b + Y_c \end{bmatrix} \qquad [6.8\text{-}7]$$

Since the networks are to be connected in series, the Z matrices must be used. The Z matrix for network (a) is obtained by taking the inverse of the Y matrix. The sum of the Z matrices is given by

$$[Z]_a + [Z]_b = \begin{bmatrix} \dfrac{Y_b + Y_c}{|Y|} & \dfrac{Y_c}{|Y|} \\ \dfrac{Y_c}{|Y|} & \dfrac{Y_a + Y_c}{|Y|} \end{bmatrix} + \begin{bmatrix} Z_d & Z_d \\ Z_d & Z_d \end{bmatrix}$$

$$= \begin{bmatrix} \dfrac{Y_b + Y_c}{|Y|} + Z_d & \dfrac{Y_c}{|Y|}\ Z_d \\ \dfrac{Y_c}{|Y|} + Z_d & \dfrac{Y_a + Y_c}{|Y|} + Z_d \end{bmatrix} \qquad [6.8\text{-}8]$$

where

$$|Y| = Y_a Y_c + Y_a Y_b + Y_b Y_c \qquad [6.8\text{-}9]$$

Equation 6.8-8 gives the Z matrix of the bridged-T network.

6.9 VALIDITY REQUIREMENTS FOR THE INTERCONNECTION OF NETWORKS BY MATRIX METHODS

So far in the discussion of the application of matrix methods to the interconnection of networks, only brief reference has been made to the validity of the application of matrix methods to such interconnections. It is not always possible to make interconnections and still maintain the validity of matrix methods. The examples that have been treated thus far meet all the validity requirements to be developed in this section. The question of validity will now be investigated.

In the interconnection of networks, certain physical requirements must be met to make the over-all matrix a valid representation of the simple networks which are combined to produce more complex networks.

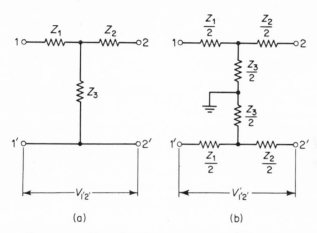

Figure 6-21 Example of interconnection where matrix methods are invalid.

Consider, for example, the two networks shown in Fig. 6-21. Each network has the same transfer matrix. However, the impedance between terminals $1'$ and $2'$ in Fig. 6.21(a) is zero; but the analogous impedance in Fig. 6-21(b) is finite. Hence, a series or parallel connection of the two networks would result in a short-circuiting of impedances in Fig. 6.21(b). This would alter the effective transfer matrix of the network in Fig. 6.21(b), and the use of its original matrix to determine the resultant matrix of the two interconnected networks would lead to an incorrect result. Hence, an application of the matrix methods previously developed would be invalid in this case. The reason for this is that these methods are based upon the use of the network matrices before interconnection.

In general, it may be stated that whenever an interconnection of networks does not alter the transfer matrices of the component networks, the methods developed in the previous sections of this chapter are valid. Whenever such an interconnection alters any component matrix, the application of these methods is invalid. The invalid conditions can often be determined by inspection of the networks.

Another way of considering the validity of the methods developed for

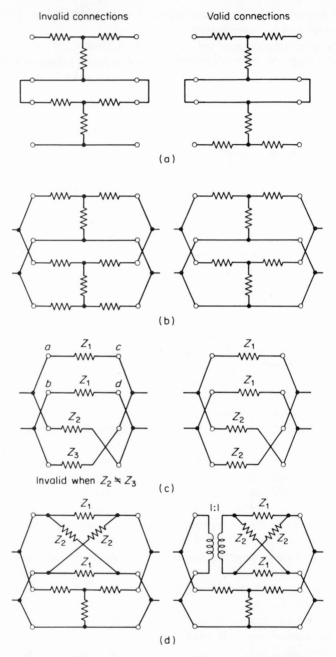

Figure 6-22 Examples of valid and invalid conditions for applying matrix methods.

interconnection is to examine the currents entering and leaving the input and output terminals. The validity of matrix methods for the interconnection networks is a matter of the condition of balance in the networks.

In each network in Fig. 6-21, all the current entering at terminal 1 leaves terminal $1'$. This is the current I_1 for the network. Likewise, for each network all the current entering at 2 leaves at $2'$. When the networks are interconnected, these conditions must still exist for each network. If they do not exist, the application of matrix methods is invalid.

When $V_{1'2'}$ in Fig. 6-21(a) is not equal to $V'_{1'2'}$ in Fig. 6-21(b), a current will circulate at these terminals when the networks are combined, and hence the current at 1 will not equal the current at $1'$ for each network as indicated above. When $V_{1'2'} = V'_{1'2'}$ at all loads and frequencies, these currents will be equal. In the examples given earlier, the analogous voltages, $V_{1'2'} = V'_{1'2'} = 0$. This satisfies the validity requirement.

Examples of invalid and valid conditions are given in (a), (b), (c), and (d) of Fig. 6-22. When matrix methods are involved, they can be made valid in some cases by changing the network. For example, in Fig. 6-22(a), the method can be made valid by inverting the lower portion of the network. In Fig. 6-22(b), the series impedances of the lower arms of one network can be transferred to the upper arms. This still gives the same matrix, and at the same time makes the method valid. In Fig. 6-22(c) the method is valid as soon as Z_3 is made equal to Z_2. The parallel combination is the familiar lattice network. Figure 6-22(d) illustrates the use of an ideal 1:1 ratio transformer in order to make the method valid. This requires one less transformer than the number of networks involved. The ideal transformer cannot be physically realized.

Certain practical tests have been developed for the validity of matrix methods in the interconnection of networks.* In (a) of Fig. 6-23, the networks are connected in parallel at the input terminals, and individually short-circuited at the output terminals. This makes the output voltages V_2 and V'_2 equal to zero. When the networks are energized, and the voltage V_p appearing between the short-circuited ends is zero, then $V_{1'2'} = V'_{1'2'}$. If the connections are reversed, that is, if the outputs are placed in parallel and energized, and if the inputs are individually short-circuited, and if again the voltage between the short-circuited ends is zero, then the parallel connection is valid. This must hold at all frequencies.

The validity test for the series connection is illustrated in (b) of Fig. 6-23. Here the networks are connected in series at the input terminals, and the output terminals are left open. Then, if the voltage V_s between the

---

* Descriptions of such tests are given in Guillemin, E. A., *Communications Networks* (John Wiley & Sons, Inc., New York, 1935), vol. 2, pp. 147–151; and in Kaufmann, A., "Conditions de Validité de la Méthode Matricielle pour les Associations de Quadripoles," *L'Onde Electrique*, October 1951, pp. 396–412, and November 1951, pp. 446–452.

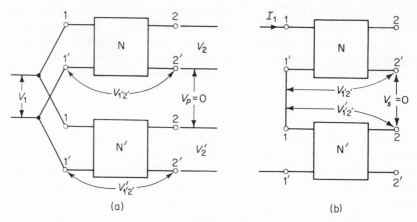

Figure 6-23   Connections to determine validity of matrix methods.

output terminals is zero, $V_{1'2'} = V'_{12}$, and if, when the connections are reversed, the corresponding voltage at the input terminals is zero, then matrix methods are valid.

PROBLEMS

6-1 Given the networks (a) and (b) in the accompanying sketch.

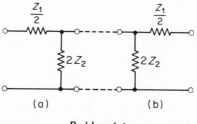

Problem 6-1

(a) Determine the transfer or chain matrix for networks (a) and (b).

(b) Multiply $[T]_a \times [T]_b$, and show that the result is a symmetrical **T** network.

(c) Multiply $[T]_b \times [T]_a$, and show that the result is a symmetrical π network.

6-2 A bridged-T network is composed of the following resistors: $R_1 = 1$ ohm;

$R_2 = 2$ ohms; $R_3 = 3$ ohms; and $R_4 = 11$ ohms. By matrix methods, find the following networks:

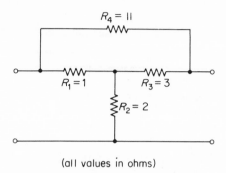

(all values in ohms)

Problem 6-2

(a) Unsymmetrical equivalent T and π networks.

(b) Symmetrical equivalent T and π networks when ideal transformers follow the networks.

(c) Symmetrical equivalent T and π networks when ideal transformers precede the networks.

(d) A lattice network formed from the symmetrical networks in parts (b) and (c).

6-3 A resistance network is to have the image resistances indicated in the drawing below.

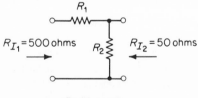

Problem 6-3

(a) Find the values of resistors R_1 and R_2 to satisfy the image resistances R_{I_1} and R_{I_2}.

(b) Convert to a symmetrical network, by using an ideal transformer, so that $R_0 = 500$ ohms.

(c) Determine the loss of the network in decibels.

6-4 Cascade the networks shown in (a) and (b) of the schematic diagram, using ideal transformers. Compare the results, and:

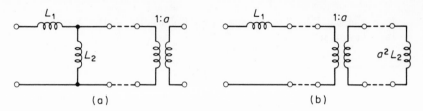

(a)   (b)

Problem 6-4

(a) Construct the T and π network representations from the final matrix so that the ideal transformer is eliminated.

(b) Determine the limits of the turns ratio, a, in terms of L_1 and L_2, for a network that is physically realizable.

(c) For the conditions $L_1 = 0.9$, $L_2 = 0.10$, and $a = 10$, show that the T and π networks reduce to the same network ($a = 1$ should give the original network).

(d) Using the circuit values given in part (c), determine the networks for $a = 8$ and for $a = 12$. Discuss the results.

(e) Determine the value of the turns ratio for a symmetrical network, and check this value.

(f) What is the coefficient of coupling for the network in part (e)?

6-5 Cascade the capacitance network in the figure with an ideal transformer.

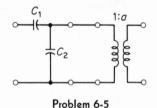

Problem 6-5

(a) Construct the equivalent T and π networks.

(b) Determine the limits of the turns ratio, a, in terms of C_1 and C_2 for the network to be physically realizable.

(c) Let $C_1 = 0.1\,\mu f$ and $C_2 = 0.9\,\mu f$; then find both the T and π networks for $a = 10$, $a = \sqrt{10}$, and $a = 12$. Discuss the results.

6-6 A symmetrical network is shown below. The impedance on the right-hand side is to be stepped up by the ratio of a^2.

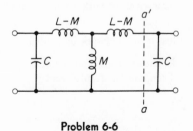

Problem 6-6

(a) Determine the network.

(b) Determine the maximum value of a in terms of the circuit parameters. *Hint:* The work is somewhat simplified if an ideal transformer is inserted at aa' and if the capacitor C is placed on its secondary as C/a^2.

6-7 Repeat Prob. 6-6 for the network sketched.

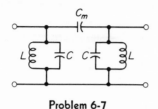

Problem 6-7

6-8 Repeat Prob. 6-6 for the network sketched.

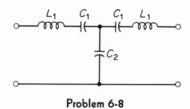

Problem 6-8

6-9 Connect in parallel the networks in (a) and (b) of the figure. Calculate the resulting matrix, and compare the results with that for the lattice structure. Also, invert the resulting Y matrix and find the Z matrix.

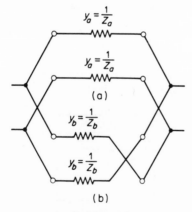

Problem 6-9

6-10 Connect in parallel the networks shown in (a) and (b) of the accompanying sketch, and solve for the condition that makes the transfer admittance equal to zero.

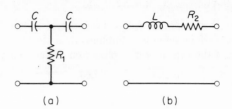

(a)   (b)

Problem 6-10

6-11 Repeat Prob. 6-10 for the networks shown.

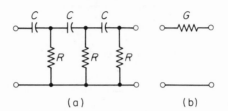

(a)   (b)

Problem 6-11

6-12 Repeat Prob. 6-10 for the networks shown.

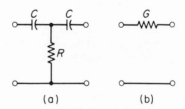

(a)   (b)

Problem 6-12

6-13 The networks in the accompanying diagram are to be connected in series. Apply matrix analysis to the following:

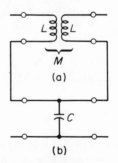

(a)

(b)

Problem 6-13

(a) Investigate the transfer impedance when M is both positive and negative.

(b) Find the $ABCD$ coefficients after the networks are placed in series.

(c) Find Z_0 from the transfer coefficients.

(d) Determine the attenuation factor, and note the points of infinite attenuation if any occur.

6-14 A band-pass filter is shown in the accompanying figure. Modify the network so that the 0.2-henry inductor is equal to 1.0 henry.

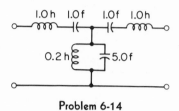

Problem 6-14

small-signal analysis of electron

tubes and transistors

7.0 INTRODUCTION

This chapter is devoted to an integrated circuit analysis of triode electron tubes and transistors considered as two-terminal pair networks. These devices actually have three terminals, but in operation one terminal is common to both the input and the output circuits. The common terminal is usually at ground potential, and the device is treated as a two-terminal pair network.

Electron tubes and transistors can be represented by equivalent circuits containing impedances that are linear over a limited range. This range determines the magnitude of the alternating signal that may be applied if linear circuit analysis is to be used in determining the response. Inasmuch as the range is small, this type of analysis is termed *small-signal analysis*.

The treatment in this chapter is based upon the hybrid or mixed set of equations developed in Sec. 1.3. The g parameters* are used for electron tubes, and the h parameters are used for transistors. The use of these parameters results in an integrated form of circuit analysis that is of pedagogic value. Formulas for the gain and input impedance of triodes and transistors are derived for the fundamental circuit configurations. The reader is referred to other textbooks and to articles in technical journals for more detailed treatments.†

* As pointed out in Sec. 1.3, the letter g in this context does not refer to conductance, but serves merely to distinguish this set of hybrid parameters from its inverse, the h parameters.

† For example, Zadeh, L. A., "A Note on the Analysis of Vacuum-Tube and Transistor Circuits," *Proceedings of the I.R.E.*, vol. 41 (August 1953), pp. 882–884; also Joyce, M. V., and K. K. Clarke, *Transistor Circuit Analysis* (Addison-Wesley Publishing Company, Inc., Reading, Mass., 1961).

7.1 THE ELECTRON-TUBE TRIODE

The triode shown in (a) of Fig. 7-1 as a "black box" is essentially a three-terminal device. The input terminal is labelled terminal 1, and the output is designated terminal 2. The third terminal, 3, is generally common to both the input and the output circuits. These terminals lead to the

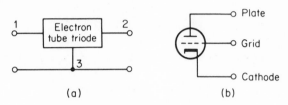

(a)   (b)

Figure 7-1 Electron tube triode and terminals.

plate, grid, and cathode shown in Fig. 7-1(b). It is to be stressed that any terminal in Fig. 7-1(a) may lead to any tube element in Fig. 7-1(b). This makes possible three circuit configurations, depending upon which tube element is common to both the input and the output circuits. These configurations are termed the *common-cathode circuit*, the *common-plate circuit*, and the *common-grid circuit*. The term "grounded" is often used in place of the term "common."

In formulating the behavior of the electron-tube triode as a circuit element, it is convenient to consider the input voltage and the output current as the *independent variables*, and the output voltage and the input current as the *dependent variables*. The equations expressing these relations have the following general form:

$$i_1 = F(v_1, i_2) \qquad [7.1\text{-}1]$$

$$v_2 = G(v_1, i_2) \qquad [7.1\text{-}2]$$

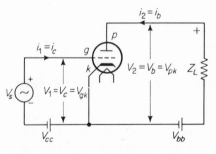

Figure 7-2 Common cathode configuration.

where i_1 and i_2 are the total input and output currents; v_1 and v_2 are the total input and output voltages, measured with respect to a common terminal; and F and G are functions determined by the tube characteristics.

Figure 7-2 shows a common-cathode configuration, and the designations on that figure illustrate the notation to be followed in this development, namely:

V_{bb} is the plate supply voltage

V_{cc} is the grid bias voltage

Z_L is the load impedance

$i_1 = i_c$, the total instantaneous grid current

$i_2 = i_b$, the total instantaneous plate current

$v_1 = v_c = v_{gk}$, the total instantaneous difference of potential between the grid and the cathode

$v_2 = v_b = v_{pk}$, the total instantaneous difference of potential between the plate and the cathode

When the excitation voltage v_s is applied, the output voltage can be expressed as

$$v_2 = V_{b0} + \Delta v_2 \qquad [7.1\text{-}3]$$

where V_{b0} is the static or quiescent value of v_2 when v_s is zero. The incremental output voltage, Δv_2 in Eq. 7.1-3, can be expressed as an infinite Taylor series provided that the partial derivatives with respect to the independent variables, v_1 and i_2, exist. When the changes in the independent variables are small, however, the first two terms of the Taylor series give a good approximation to Δv_2 which can be expressed as

$$\Delta v_2 \approx \left(\frac{\partial v_2}{\partial v_1}\right) \Delta v_1 + \left(\frac{\partial v_2}{\partial i_2}\right) \Delta i_2 \qquad [7.1\text{-}4]$$

where it is assumed that Δv_1 and Δi_2 are small enough so that all powers above the first may be neglected.

The partial derivatives in Eq. 7.1-4 are the small-signal triode parameters. These parameters are traditionally defined for the common-cathode configuration, and are given by

$$\frac{\partial v_2}{\partial v_1} = \frac{\partial v_b}{\partial v_c} = -\mu \qquad [7.1\text{-}5]$$

$$\frac{\partial v_2}{\partial i_2} = \frac{\partial v_b}{\partial i_b} = r_p \qquad [7.1\text{-}6]$$

where μ is numerical, and is the amplification factor, and r_p is the plate resistance, measured in ohms.

The negative sign in Eq. 7.1-5 results from the physical condition that, when the grid voltage has a positive increment, the plate voltage must have a negative increment if the plate current is to remain constant. The fact that the plate current remains constant is inherent in the definition of the partial derivative of v_2 as defined in Eq. 7.1-5. Since the effect of the grid upon the plate current is greater than that of the plate, the numerical value of μ is greater than unity.

The amplification factor and the plate resistance are readily determined from the static characteristics of the tube. The term "static" refers to the fact that the changes in electrode voltages are made so slowly that effects such as those of interelectrode capacitance are negligible. Thus,

$$\mu = -\frac{\Delta v_b}{\Delta v_c}\bigg|_{i_b \text{ const}} = -\frac{\Delta v_2}{\Delta v_1}\bigg|_{i_2 \text{ const}} \qquad [7.1\text{-}7]$$

$$r_p = \frac{\Delta v_b}{\Delta i_b}\bigg|_{v_c \text{ const}} = \frac{\Delta v_2}{\Delta i_2}\bigg|_{v_1 \text{ const}} \qquad [7.1\text{-}8]$$

The ratio of the amplification factor to the plate resistance is given by

$$\frac{\mu}{r_p} = g_m \qquad [7.1\text{-}9]$$

where g_m is termed the grid-plate transconductance.

When Eqs. 7.1-7 and 7.1-8 are substituted into Eq. 7.1-4, the following result is obtained:

$$\Delta v_2 = -\mu \Delta v_1 + r_p \Delta i_2 \qquad [7.1\text{-}10]$$

Equation 7.1-10 can also be written as

$$\Delta v_2 = g_{fk} \Delta v_1 + g_{ok} \Delta i_2 \qquad [7.1\text{-}11]$$

where g_{fk} is numerical, and represents a forward transfer coefficient, and g_{ok} is a short-circuit output impedance. The subscript k, attached to the coefficients in Eq. 7.1-11, signifies that the coefficients are defined for the common-cathode configuration. Similar coefficients will be derived later for other configurations. Equation 7.1-11 has the form of the hybrid g parameter equations of Sec. 1.3. *These parameters must not be confused with the symbol for conductance.*

It follows from Eqs. 7.1-10 and 7.1-11 that:

$$g_{fk} = -\mu \qquad [7.1\text{-}12]$$

$$g_{ok} = r_p \qquad [7.1\text{-}13]$$

The application of Eq. 7.1-10 to electron-tube circuits is based upon the following two assumptions:

(1) The increments, Δv_1 and Δi_2, are so small that the first two terms of the Taylor series in Eq. 7.1-4 are adequate to determine Δv_2. Hence, Eq. 7.1-10 is essentially a small-signal equality, and analysis based upon it is termed small-signal analysis.

(2) The partial derivatives, $\partial v_2/\partial v_1$ and $\partial v_2/\partial i_2$, remain substantially

constant for the range of Δv_1 and Δi_2 resulting from small-signal excitation, and may be placed respectively equal to the constants $-\mu$ and r_p.

These may seem as stringent restrictions, but practice has shown that Eq. 7.1-10 has wide application. The usefulness of Eq. 7.1-10 stems from the fact that since the coefficients are constant, linear circuit analysis may be applied to electron tubes. This will be brought out in the following section, where the analysis will be confined to sinusoidal excitation.

7.2 SINUSOIDAL EXCITATION

Assume that the variables in Eq. 7.1-4 are sinusoidal in time, and that they are given by

$$\Delta v_1 = \Delta v_{1,m} \epsilon^{j\omega t} \qquad [7.2\text{-}1]$$

$$\Delta v_2 = \Delta v_{2,m} \epsilon^{j\omega t} \qquad [7.2\text{-}2]$$

$$\Delta i_2 = \Delta i_{2,m} \epsilon^{j\omega t} \qquad [7.2\text{-}3]$$

where $\Delta v_{1,m}$, $\Delta v_{2,m}$, and $\Delta i_{2,m}$ respectively denote the maximum values of Δv_1, Δv_2, and Δi_2. For sinusoidal excitation, Eq. 7.1-4 becomes

$$\Delta v_{2,m}\epsilon^{j\omega t} = \left(\frac{\partial v_2}{\partial v_1}\right) \Delta v_{1,m}\epsilon^{j\omega t} + \left(\frac{\partial v_2}{\partial i_2}\right) \Delta i_{2,m}\epsilon^{j\omega t} \qquad [7.2\text{-}4]$$

where it is assumed that $\partial v_2/\partial v_1$ and $\partial v_2/\partial i_2$ are constant for the small variations under consideration. It follows from Eq. 7.1-11 that Eq. 7.2-4 can be written as

$$\Delta v_{2,m}\epsilon^{j\omega t} = g_{fk}\Delta v_{1,m}\epsilon^{j\omega t} + g_{ok}\Delta i_{2,m}\epsilon^{j\omega t} \qquad [7.2\text{-}5]$$

Dividing both sides of Eq. 7.2-5 by $\sqrt{2}\epsilon^{j\omega t}$ yields

$$V_2 = g_{fk}V_1 + g_{ok}I_2 \qquad [7.2\text{-}6]$$

where V_1, V_2, and I_2 are respectively the phasors corresponding to the input voltage, output voltage, and output current. These values must be small if the approximation implicit in Eq. 7.1-4 is to hold. It is also assumed that g_{fk} and g_{ok} remain substantially constant for the small variations about the static operating point. This makes possible the application of linear circuit theory to the analysis of electron-tube equivalent circuits.

Equation 7.2-6 is the equation for the common-cathode configuration, and is a special case of the following general relation:

$$V_2 = g_f V_1 + g_o I_2 \qquad [7.2\text{-}7]$$

where g_f is a general forward transfer coefficient, and g_o is a short-circuit output impedance. In Eq. 7.2-7, g_f may have three possible values: g_{fk}, g_{fp}, or g_{fg}, depending upon whether the cathode, plate, or grid is the common terminal.

The companion relation to Eq. 7.2-7, corresponding to Eq. 7.1-1, is

$$I_1 = g_i V_1 + g_r I_2 \qquad [7.2\text{-}8]$$

where g_i is an open-circuit input admittance and g_r is a reverse transfer coefficient. When there is no input admittance caused by conductance or capacitance, and when there is no feedback caused by interelectrode capacitance or external circuits, then

$$g_i = g_r = 0 \qquad [7.2\text{-}9]$$

When Eq. 7.2-9 is valid, the input admittance is zero, and Eq. 7.2-7 is sufficient to specify the operation of the tube.* Equations 7.2-7 and 7.2-8 are the hybrid or mixed set of equations developed in Sec. 1.3. The g parameters are defined in terms of the input and output voltages and currents as follows:

$$g_f = \left. \frac{V_2}{V_1} \right|_{I_2 = 0} \qquad [7.2\text{-}10]$$

$$g_o = \left. \frac{V_2}{I_2} \right|_{V_1 = 0} \qquad [7.2\text{-}11]$$

$$g_i = \left. \frac{I_1}{V_1} \right|_{I_2 = 0} \qquad [7.2\text{-}12]$$

$$g_r = \left. \frac{I_1}{I_2} \right|_{V_1 = 0} \qquad [7.2\text{-}13]$$

The parameters g_{fk} and g_{ok} may theoretically be determined from a-c measurements and Eqs. 7.2-10 and 7.2-11. Realization of the conditions imposed in Eq. 7.2-10, namely that the plate circuit be essentially open, requires that the quiescent plate voltage be fed through an impedance that is large compared to the output impedance of the tube. It is difficult to realize this condition in the case of a pentode having a very high plate resistance. However, the amplification factor and plate resistance can readily be determined from the static characteristics, and the above-

---

* Equation 7.2-9 is usually assumed to hold in the analysis of common-cathode and common-plate configurations.

mentioned difficulty is not encountered. The amplification factor is determined from the slope of a curve showing the variation of the plate voltage with the grid voltage for a constant plate current. Physical conditions require that this slope be always negative. The plate resistance is determined from the slope of a curve showing the variation of the plate current with the plate voltage for a constant grid voltage.

7.3 GENERALIZED GAIN AND EQUIVALENT
CIRCUITS FOR TRIODES

When the input admittance is zero, the input current is zero, and the current and power gains (the ratio of output to input) are infinite. Under these conditions, only the voltage gain is significant. In Fig. 7-3, a triode is shown as a "black box" with a load impedance, Z_L, connected between the output terminal, 2, and the common terminal, 3. The voltage gain is defined as

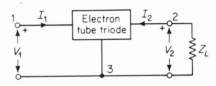

Figure 7-3 Electron tube triode with load.

$$A_V = \frac{V_2}{V_1} \qquad [7.3\text{-}1]$$

where both V_1 and V_2 are measured with respect to the common terminal, 3. Inspection of Fig. 7-3 shows that

$$I_2 = -\frac{V_2}{Z_L} \qquad [7.3\text{-}2]$$

The minus sign in Eq. 7.3-2 results from the reference current and the assumed polarity of the voltage at the output terminals. Substitution of Eq. 7.3-2 into Eq. 7.2-7 yields

$$V_2 = g_f V_1 - \left(\frac{g_o}{Z_L}\right) V_2 \qquad [7.3\text{-}3]$$

It follows from Eq. 7.3-3 that

$$V_2 \left(1 + \frac{g_o}{Z_L}\right) = g_f V_1 \qquad [7.3\text{-}4]$$

$$A_V = \frac{V_2}{V_1} = \frac{g_f}{1 + g_o/Z_L} \qquad [7.3\text{-}5]$$

Equation 7.3-5 is the general expression for the voltage gain of a triode for any of the three possible configurations and is independent of the values of g_i and g_r.

The equations

$$I_1 = g_i V_1 + g_r I_2 \qquad\qquad [7.3\text{-}6]$$

$$V_2 = g_f V_1 + g_o I_2 \qquad\qquad [7.3\text{-}7]$$

can be used directly to construct the general equivalent circuit shown in Fig. 7-4. Note that g_i is an admittance, $g_r I_2$ represents a current generator, g_o is a resistance, and $g_f V_1$ is a voltage generator with the indicated polarity. When it is assumed that the effects of interelectrode capacitance, grid circuit conductance, and current feedback are negligible, $g_i = g_r = 0$.

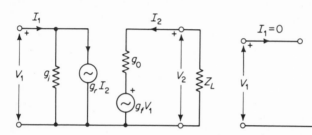
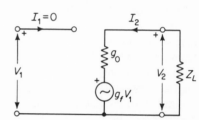

Figure 7-4   Equivalent circuit of triode using g parameters.

Figure 7-5   Low-frequency equivalent circuit for common-cathode and common-plate configurations.

Since $V_2 = -Z_L I_2$, Eq. 7.3-7 can be written as

$$-Z_L I_2 = g_f V_1 + g_o I_2 \qquad\qquad [7.3\text{-}8]$$

Hence,

$$I_2 = -\frac{g_f V_1}{g_o + Z_L} \qquad\qquad [7.3\text{-}9]$$

Substitution of Eq. 7.3-9 into Eq. 7.3-6 yields

$$I_1 = g_i V_1 - \left(\frac{g_f g_r}{g_o + Z_L}\right) V_1 = V_1 \left(g_i - \frac{g_f g_r}{g_o + Z_L}\right) \qquad [7.3\text{-}10]$$

It follows from Eq. 7.3-10 that the input admittance is given by

$$Y_{\text{in}} = \frac{I_1}{V_1} = g_i - \frac{g_f g_r}{g_o + Z_L} \qquad\qquad [7.3\text{-}11]$$

and that the input impedance is given by

$$Z_{\text{in}} = \frac{1}{Y_{\text{in}}} = \frac{1}{g_i - g_f g_r/(g_o + Z_L)} \qquad\qquad [7.3\text{-}12]$$

It can be seen from Eqs. 7.3-11 and 7.3-12 that, when $g_i = g_r = 0$, $Y_{in} = 0$ and Z_{in} is infinite.

When $g_i = g_r = 0$, Fig. 7-4 is reduced to Fig. 7-5, which is the conventional low-frequency equivalent circuit for the common-cathode and common-plate configurations when the input impedance is assumed to be infinite. Figure 7-5 is the equivalent circuit when interelectrode capacitance, grid circuit conductance, and current feedback are neglected.

The parameters in Eqs. 7.3-6 and 7.3-7 and Figs. 7-4 and 7-5 may have three possible values, depending upon the circuit configuration. These configurations are considered in the following section.

7.4 GAIN AND EQUIVALENT CIRCUITS FOR SPECIAL CONFIGURATIONS

The common-cathode configuration is shown in Fig. 7-6. The output voltage, measured between the plate and the cathode, is given by

$$V_2 = g_{fk}V_1 + g_{ok}I_2 \qquad [7.4-1]$$

where, as shown in Eqs. 7.1-12 and 7.1-13,

$$g_{fk} = -\mu \qquad [7.4-2]$$

$$g_{ok} = r_p \qquad [7.4-3]$$

If it is assumed that the effects of interelectrode capacitance and grid conductance are negligible, then $g_i = g_r = 0$, and the input admittance

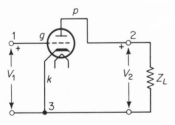

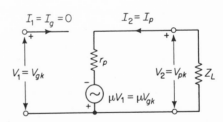

Figure 7-6 Common-cathode configuration.

Figure 7-7 Equivalent circuit of common-cathode configuration.

is zero. Under these conditions, the simplified equivalent circuit of Fig. 7.5 may be used. This circuit is shown in Fig. 7-7 with the appropriate values of g_f and g_o. It is to be noted that in the common cathode configuration, $V_1 = V_{gk}$, $V_2 = V_{pk}$, $I_1 = I_g$, and $I_2 = I_p$.

It follows from Fig. 7-7 that

$$V_{pk} = -\mu\, V_{gk} + r_p I_p \qquad\qquad [7.4\text{-}4]$$

Equation 7.4-4 is the fundamental equation for the plate circuit of a triode. This equation will be used in the analysis of all triode configurations.

The voltage gain of the common-cathode amplifier is found by substituting Eqs. 7.4-2 and 7.4-3 into Eq. 7.3-5 that holds for the general case. The result is the following:

$$A_V = -\frac{\mu}{1 + r_p/Z_L} = -\frac{\mu Z_L}{r_p + Z_L} \qquad [\text{common cathode}] \qquad [7.4\text{-}5]$$

The negative sign in Eq. 7.4-5 is consistent with the voltage phase reversal shown in Fig. 7-7. Note again that both the input and the output voltages are measured with respect to the common terminal, which in this case is the cathode. It can be seen from Eq. 7.4-5 that the maximum value of A_V is μ.

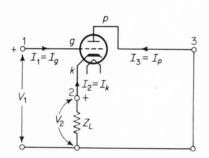

Figure 7-8 Common-plate configuration.

Consider now the common-plate configuration, which is shown in Fig. 7-8. Using the adopted notation for the currents and voltages, in Fig. 7-8, $I_1 = I_g$; $I_2 = I_k$; $V_1 = V_{gp}$; and $V_2 = V_{kp}$. The input and output voltages and currents are related by the equation

$$V_2 = g_{fp}V_1 + g_{op}I_2 \qquad\qquad [7.4\text{-}6]$$

where the second subscript, p, denotes that a common-plate configuration is under consideration. The analysis of this circuit requires the evaluation of g_{fp} and g_{op} in terms of μ and r_p, the conventional tube parameters.

It follows from Kirchhoff's voltage equation that:

$$V_{gp} + V_{pk} + V_{kg} = 0 \qquad\qquad [7.4\text{-}7]$$

Hence,

$$V_{kg} = -(V_{pk} + V_{gp}) \qquad\qquad [7.4\text{-}8]$$

and

$$V_{gk} = -V_{kg} = V_{pk} + V_{gp} \qquad\qquad [7.4\text{-}9]$$

The substitution of Eq. 7.4-9 into Eq. 7.4-4 yields

$$V_{pk} = -\mu(V_{pk} + V_{gp}) + r_p I_p \qquad [7.4\text{-}10]$$

$$(1 + \mu)V_{pk} = -\mu V_{gp} + r_p I_p \qquad [7.4\text{-}11]$$

It follows from Kirchhoff's current equation that:

$$I_g + I_p + I_k = 0 \qquad [7.4\text{-}12]$$

Inasmuch as it is assumed that $I_g = 0$,

$$I_p = -I_k \qquad [7.4\text{-}13]$$

The substitution of Eq. 7.4-13 into Eq. 7.4-11 gives the following results:

$$(1 + \mu)V_{pk} = -\mu V_{gp} - r_p I_k \qquad [7.4\text{-}14]$$

$$V_{pk} = \left(\frac{-\mu}{1 + \mu}\right) V_{gp} - \left(\frac{r_p}{1 + \mu}\right) I_k \qquad [7.4\text{-}15]$$

Since $V_{kp} = -V_{pk}$, Eq. 7.4-15 can be written as

$$V_{kp} = \left(\frac{\mu}{1 + \mu}\right) V_{gp} + \left(\frac{r_p}{1 + \mu}\right) I_k \qquad [7.4\text{-}16]$$

Using the adopted notation for currents and voltages, Eq. 7.4-16 becomes

$$V_2 = \left(\frac{\mu}{1 + \mu}\right) V_1 + \left(\frac{r_p}{1 + \mu}\right) I_2 = g_{fp} V_1 + g_{op} I_2 \qquad [7.4\text{-}17]$$

The equivalent circuit corresponding to Eq. 7.4-17, assuming that $I_1 = 0$, is shown in Fig. 7-9. It should be carefully noted that, unlike Fig. 7-7, there is no phase reversal of the output voltage with respect to the input voltage.*

The gain of the common-plate configuration is found by making the following substitutions in Eq. 7.3-5:

$$g_{fp} = \frac{\mu}{1 + \mu} \qquad [7.4\text{-}18]$$

$$g_{op} = \frac{r_p}{1 + \mu} \qquad [7.4\text{-}19]$$

* This can be seen by referring to the polarities of the equivalent voltage generators.

Equations 7.4-18 and 7.4-19 follow directly from Eq. 7.4-17. It follows from Eq. 7.3-5 that

$$A_V = \frac{\mu/(1+\mu)}{1 + \dfrac{r_p}{(1+\mu)Z_L}} = \frac{\mu Z_L}{r_p + (1+\mu)Z_L} \qquad \text{[common plate]} \quad \text{[7.4-20]}$$

Equation 7.4-20 shows that the voltage gain of the common-plate configuration is always less than unity. For values of r_p and Z_L used in practice, the voltage gain is of the order of 0.9. In other words, the common-plate configuration is essentially a unity gain device. It follows that the cathode and grid potentials are essentially equal both in magnitude and phase. Because the cathode and grid potentials rise and fall together, the common-plate configuration is known as a *cathode follower*. Inspection of Fig. 7-9 shows that the effective internal impedance of the cathode follower is $r_p/(1+\mu)$. Since μ is usually much greater than unity, the

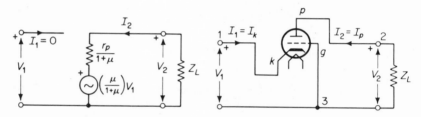

Figure 7-9 Equivalent circuit of common-plate configuration.

Figure 7-10 Common-grid configuration.

effective internal impedance is essentially $r_p/\mu = g_m$. The grid-plate transconductance, g_m, of most tubes varies from 1,000 to 10,000 micro-ohms. Hence, the range of the effective internal impedance of the cathode follower is between 100 and 1,000 ohms. When interelectrode capacitance and grid conductance are neglected, the input impedance is infinite. In any case, the input impedance to a cathode follower has a high value. Because of its high input impedance and low internal or output impedance, the cathode follower finds extensive application as a matching device between sources of high impedance and loads of low impedance.

The common-grid configuration is shown in Fig. 7-10. This is essentially a cathode input circuit. It is seen that $I_1 = I_k$; $I_2 = I_p$; $V_1 = V_{kg}$; and $V_2 = V_{pg}$. The currents and voltages are related by the following equations:

$$I_1 = g_{ig}V_1 + g_{rg}I_2 \qquad \text{[7.4-21]}$$

$$V_2 = g_{fg}V_1 + g_{og}I_2 \qquad \text{[7.4-22]}$$

where the second subscript, g, denotes the common-grid configuration. It follows from Eq. 7.4-7 that:

$$V_{pk} = -(V_{kg} + V_{gp}) \qquad [7.4\text{-}23]$$

Substituting Eq. 7.4-23 into Eq. 7.4-4, and multiplying through by -1, gives the following results:

$$V_{kg} + V_{gp} = \mu V_{gk} - r_p I_p \qquad [7.4\text{-}24]$$

$$(1 + \mu)V_{kg} = V_{pg} - r_p I_p \qquad [7.4\text{-}25]$$

The solution of Eq. 7.4-25 for V_{pg}, the output voltage, yields

$$V_{pg} = (1 + \mu)V_{kg} + r_p I_p \qquad [7.4\text{-}26]$$

In the adopted notation, Eq. 7.4-26 becomes

$$V_2 = (1 + \mu)V_1 + r_p I_2 = g_{fg}V_1 + g_{og}I_2 \qquad [7.4\text{-}27]$$

Equation 7.4-27 shows that

$$g_{fg} = 1 + \mu \qquad [7.4\text{-}28]$$

$$g_{og} = r_p \qquad [7.4\text{-}29]$$

The solution of Eq. 7.4-26 for I_p yields

$$I_p = \frac{V_{pg}}{r_p} - \left(\frac{1 + \mu}{r_p}\right) V_{kg} \qquad [7.4\text{-}30]$$

As shown in Eq. 7.4-13, $I_p = -I_k$. Hence, Eq. 7.4-30 can be written as

$$I_k = -\frac{V_{pg}}{r_p} + \left(\frac{1 + \mu}{r_p}\right) V_{kg} \qquad [7.4\text{-}31]$$

For the common-grid configuration, Eq. 7.4-31 can also be written as

$$I_1 = -\left(\frac{1}{r_p}\right) V_2 + \left(\frac{1 + \mu}{r_p}\right) V_1 \qquad [7.4\text{-}32]$$

The substitution of V_2, as given by Eq. 7.4-27, into Eq. 7.4-32 yields

$$I_1 = -\left(\frac{1 + \mu}{r_p}\right) V_1 - I_2 + \left(\frac{1 + \mu}{r_p}\right) V_1 \qquad [7.4\text{-}33]$$

$$I_1 = (0)V_1 - (1)I_2 = g_{ig}V_1 + g_{rg}I_2 \qquad [7.4\text{-}34]$$

It follows from Eq. 7.4-34 that, in the common-grid configuration,

$$g_{ig} = 0 \qquad \text{[7.4-35]}$$

$$g_{rg} = -1 \qquad \text{[7.4-36]}$$

The voltage gain of the common-grid configuration is found by substituting Eqs. 7.4-28 and 7.4-29 into the general expression given by 7.3-5. The result is

$$A_V = \frac{1 + \mu}{1 + r_p/Z_L} = \frac{(1 + \mu)Z_L}{r_p + Z_L} \quad \text{(common grid)} \quad \text{[7.4-37]}$$

The input admittance is found by substituting Eqs. 7.4-28, 7.4-29, 7.4-35, and 7.4-36 into the general expression given by Eq. 7.3-11. The result is

$$Y_{in} = -\frac{(-1)(1 + \mu)}{r_p + Z_L} = \frac{1 + \mu}{r_p + Z_L} \qquad \text{[7.4-38]}$$

The input impedance is given by Eq. 7.3-12 as

$$Z_{in} = \frac{r_p + Z_L}{1 + \mu} \qquad \text{[7.4-39]}$$

Equations 7.4-38 and 7.4-39 show that when Z_L is finite an input current exists in the common-grid configuration even when the interelectrode capacitance and the grid circuit conductance are neglected. The common-grid configuration always has a finite input impedance. This results from the fact that the common-grid configuration is essentially a cathode-input circuit. The complete equivalent circuit for the common-grid configuration is shown in (a) and (b) of Fig. 7-11. It should be noted that, in addition

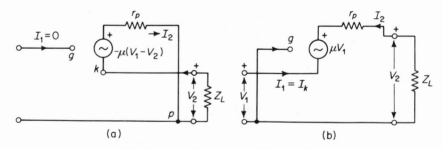

(a)   (b)

Figure 7-11   Equivalent circuits of common-grid configuration.

to the facts that I_1 exists and that the input impedance is finite, there is no phase reversal of the output voltage with respect to the input voltage in the common-grid configuration.

It follows from Eq. 7.4-39 and Fig. 7-11 that, under certain conditions, the input impedance of a common-grid amplifier is very low. Inspection of Fig. 7-11 shows that the internal or output impedance of the common-grid configuration is the same as for the common-cathode configuration.

Because of its low input impedance and high output impedance, the common-grid circuit may be used to connect a low-impedance source such as a transmission line to a high-impedance load.

The method for obtaining the gain and equivalent plate circuits for the various configurations from the generalized equations will now be summarized. The basic relation is Eq. 7.4-4, which is expressed in terms of the conventional tube parameters. These parameters are assumed to remain constant for small variations about the operating or quiescent point on the tube characteristic curve. Equation 7.4-4 is then modified by applying Eqs. 7.4-7 and 7.4-12 (Kirchhoff's voltage and current equations) until the variables represent the input and output voltages and currents for the particular configuration. The configuration depends upon the element that is selected as the common terminal. The resulting equations are then compared with Eqs. 7.2-7 and 7.2-8 to determine the appropriate g parameters. These parameters are then substituted into Eq. 7.3-5 to find the voltage gain, and into Eq. 7.3-12 to determine the input impedance. It is again stressed that $g_f = -\mu$ and $g_o = r_p$ only for the common-cathode configuration. For all other configurations, the g parameters must be calculated in terms of the conventional parameters, μ and r_p.

The g parameters can also be found by applying Eqs. 7.2-10, 7.2-11, 7.2-12, and 7.2-13 directly to the equivalent plate circuit that is determined by Eq. 7.4-4 and illustrated in Fig. 7-7. The equivalent plate circuit for the common-plate configuration is shown in (a) of Fig. 7.12; (b) of Fig.

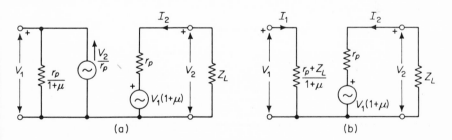

Figure 7-12 Equivalent plate circuits. (a) common-plate configuration. (b) common-grid configuration.

7.12 illustrates the common-grid configuration. Interelectrode capacitance and grid conductance are neglected in both cases. Note that the direction of I_2 is so chosen that $I_2 = -V_2/Z_L$, as required by Eq. 7.3-2.

Also, the generator voltage in Fig. 7.12(b) is μV_1, rather than $-\mu V_1$, because the cathode is at a positive a-c potential with respect to the grid.

Referring to Fig. 7.12(a), it is seen that

$$g_{ip} = \frac{I_1}{V_1}\bigg|_{I_2=0} = 0 \qquad\qquad [7.4\text{-}40]$$

$$g_{rp} = \frac{I_1}{I_2}\bigg|_{V_1=0} = 0 \qquad\qquad [7.4\text{-}41]$$

$$g_{fp} = \frac{V_2}{V_1}\bigg|_{I_2=0} = \frac{\mu(V_1 - V_2)}{V_1}$$

$$= \frac{\mu(V_1 - g_{fp}V_1)}{V_1} = \mu(1 - g_{fp}) \qquad [7.4\text{-}42]$$

Equation 7.4-42 follows from the fact that

$$V_2 = g_{fp}V_1 \qquad\qquad [7.4\text{-}43]$$

when $I_2 = 0$.

The solution of Eq. 7.4-42 for g_{fp} yields

$$g_{fp} = \frac{\mu}{1 + \mu} \qquad\qquad [7.4\text{-}44]$$

It follows from Eq. 7.2-11 and Fig. 7-12(a) that

$$g_{op} = \frac{V_2}{I_2}\bigg|_{V_1=0} = \frac{V_2}{(V_2 + \mu V_2)/r_p} = \frac{r_p}{1 + \mu} \qquad [7.4\text{-}45]$$

Equations 7.4-44 and 7.4-45 agree with Eqs. 7.4-18 and 7.4-19.

Referring now to Fig. 7-12(b), it is seen that, since $V_1 + \mu V_1 = V_2$ when $I_2 = 0$,

$$g_{fo} = \frac{V_2}{V_1}\bigg|_{I_2=0} = \frac{V_1 + \mu V_1}{V_1} = 1 + \mu \qquad [7.4\text{-}46]$$

Also,

$$g_{og} = \frac{V_2}{I_2}\bigg|_{V_1=0} = r_p \qquad\qquad [7.4\text{-}47]$$

Since $I_1 = -I_2$

$$g_{ig} = \frac{I_1}{V_1}\bigg|_{I_2=0} = 0 \qquad\qquad [7.4\text{-}48]$$

and

$$g_{r\theta} = \left.\frac{I_1}{I_2}\right|_{V_1=0} = -1 \qquad [7.4\text{-}49]$$

Equations 7.4-46, 7.4-47, 7.4-48, and 7.4-49 agree with Eqs. 7.4-28, 7.4-29, 7.4-35, and 7.4-36.

7.5 EFFECTS OF INTERELECTRODE CAPACITANCE AND FEEDBACK IN TRIODES

As previously noted, physical capacitance exists between the elements of an electron tube. In a triode, these capacitances are the following:

(a) C_{gp}, the capacitance between the grid and the plate

(b) C_{gk}, the capacitance between the grid and the cathode

(c) C_{kp}, the capacitance between the cathode and the plate

These capacitances are illustrated in Fig. 7-13, which represents the common-cathode configuration. In addition to these capacitances, a certain amount of wiring capacitance is always present.

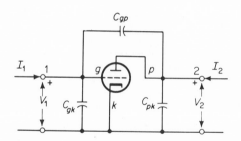

Figure 7-13 Interelectrode capacitances in a triode.

The susceptance of a capacitor increases directly with frequency. Hence, the effects of interelectrode capacitance become important at high frequencies, and must be taken into account in the analysis of the operation of electron tubes at high frequencies. One of the effects of interelectrode capacitance is to cause current I_1 to be different from zero. Hence the tube has a finite input impedance. Another effect is to produce feedback between the plate and the grid circuits. Mathematically, this means that g_i and g_r are different from zero in all three basic configurations.

In certain applications, external circuit elements are connected to produce feedback between the plate circuit and the grid circuit. Nodal analysis provides an efficient method for considering tube circuits when interelectrode capacitance and feedback are taken into account. The equivalent plate circuit of Fig. 7-7 can be transformed into one with a current source by the application of Norton's theorem. The result is shown in Fig. 7-14(a), where $g_p = 1/r_p$, and $g_m = \mu/r_p$, and the reference node is

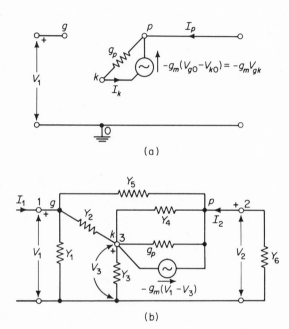

(a)

(b)

Figure 7-14   (a) Equivalent plate circuit with current source.
(b) Equivalent plate circuit with feedback.

considered to be an arbitrary point, O, at ground potential. The interelectrode capacitances are not shown. The current flowing out of the cathode and into the plate is given by the product of the negative of the grid-plate transconductance and the difference of potential between the grid and the plate. Thus

$$I_p = -I_k = -g_m(V_{go} - V_{ko}) = -g_m V_{gk} \qquad [7.5\text{-}1]$$

where point O is at ground or reference potential.

A generalized nodal circuit is shown in Fig. 7-14(b), where complex admittances offer feedback paths between the three elements of the tube and also between each element and ground. The grid is designated as node 1, the plate as node 2, and the cathode as node 3. The grid voltage is V_1, the plate voltage is V_2, and the cathode voltage is V_3, all taken with respect to the ground or reference potential of point O.

The node voltage equations for the network in Fig. 7-14(b) are the following:

$$I_1 = (Y_1+Y_2+Y_5)V_1-Y_5V_2-Y_2V_3$$
$$0 = (g_m-Y_5)V_1+(g_p + Y_4+Y_5+Y_6)V_2 - (g_p+g_m+Y_4)V_3 \qquad [7.5\text{-}2]$$
$$0 = -(g_m+Y_2)V_1 + (g_p+Y_4)V_2 + (g_m+g_p+Y_2+Y_3+Y_4)V_3$$

In Eqs. 7.5-2, the current sources, $-g_m(V_1-V_2)$ and $g_m(V_1-V_2)$, at nodes 2 and 3, have been transposed to the right sides of the equations. The matrix form of Eqs. 7.5-2 is

$$\begin{bmatrix} I_1 \\ 0 \\ 0 \end{bmatrix} = \begin{bmatrix} (Y_1+Y_2+Y_5) & -Y_5 & -Y_2 \\ (g_m-Y_5) & -(g_p+Y_4+Y_5+Y_6) & -(g_p+g_m+Y_4) \\ -(g_m+Y_2) & -(g_p+Y_4) & (g_m+g_p+Y_2+Y_3+Y_4) \end{bmatrix}$$
$$\times \begin{bmatrix} V_1 \\ V_2 \\ V_3 \end{bmatrix} \qquad [7.5\text{-}3]$$

The voltage gain is given by

$$A_V = \frac{V_2}{V_1} = \frac{\Delta_{12}}{\Delta_{11}}$$

$$= \frac{-[(g_m-Y_5)(g_m+g_p+Y_2+Y_3+Y_4) - (g_p+g_m+Y_4)(g_m+Y_2)]}{(g_p+Y_4+Y_5+Y_6)(g_m+g_p+Y_2+Y_3+Y_4) - (g_p+g_m+Y_4)(g_p+Y_4)}$$
$$[7.5\text{-}4]$$

The input admittance is given by

$$Y_{\text{in}} = \frac{I_1}{V_1} = \frac{\Delta_y}{\Delta_{11}} \qquad [7.5\text{-}5]$$

Under certain conditions, the real part of the input admittance or impedance becomes negative. This is caused by feedback between the output and input circuits. Interelectrode capacitance is an intrinsic cause of feedback in amplifiers. A negative resistance is associated with the conversion of d-c power into a-c power without the control of external excitation. This type of conversion also occurs in amplifiers, but is under the control of an external excitation, namely the input signal. The conversion of d-c power into a-c power without an externally applied signal is termed *oscillation*. Oscillations cannot be tolerated if the amplifier is to operate in a satisfactory manner with the frequencies of the input and output signals being the same. Therefore, the input admittance or impedance of an amplifier must be examined to determine whether its real part may become negative for certain types of loading.

In the case of a grounded-cathode amplifier, the real part of the input admittance may be negative when the load, represented by Y_6 in Fig. 7-14(b), is inductive. Assuming that interelectrode capacitance does not substantially alter the gain, it follows from Eq. 7.4-5 that, for inductive loading, the gain of a grounded-cathode amplifier is

$$A_V = -(a_1 + ja_2) \qquad [7.5\text{-}6]$$

where a_1 and a_2 are real and positive quantities. The input current is different from zero when interelectrode capacitance is taken into consideration, and it is seen from Fig. 7-13 that the input current is

$$I_1 = j\omega C_{gk} V_1 + j\omega C_{gp}(V_1 - V_2) \qquad [7.5\text{-}7]$$

Since $V_2 = A_V V_1$, where A_V is given by Eq. 7.5-6, Eq. 7.5-7 can be written as

$$I_1 = j\omega C_{gk} V_1 + j\omega C_{gp}(1 + a_1 + ja_2) V_1 \qquad [7.5\text{-}8]$$

It follows from Eq. 7.5-8 that

$$Y_{\text{in}} = \frac{I_1}{V_1} = -\omega a_2 C_{gp} + j\omega[C_{gk} + (1 + a_1)]C_{gp} \qquad [7.5\text{-}9]$$

Equation 7.5-9 illustrates two important points. The real part of Y_{in} is negative and may cause oscillations, and the grid-plate capacitance is multiplied by the factor $(1 + a_1)$. The latter result is referred to as the Miller effect. Reference to Eqs. 7.5-6 and 7.5-8 shows that the 180-degree phase shift associated with the voltage gain of the grounded-cathode amplifier is responsible for the negative component of the input admittance. Because of this negative component, the network determinant has poles in the right-hand half of the complex plane. When such poles are present, the steady-state response does not approach a finite limit unless non-linear network elements limit the response. Negative resistance or conductance, poles in the right-hand half of the complex plane, and oscillations of increasing amplitude are interrelated phenomena. A better insight to this subject will be obtained from a study of Chap. 11, where the time-domain response is associated with s-plane characteristics by Laplace transforms.

Reference to Eq. 7.4-37 shows that there is no 180-degree phase shift associated with the voltage gain of the grounded-grid amplifier. Because of this, feedback in the grounded-grid amplifier does not tend to produce oscillations. It is for this reason that the grounded-grid amplifier is used in high-frequency applications where the effect of feedback is an important consideration.

In the case of the grounded-cathode amplifer, $V_3 = 0$. The third column of the matrix in Eq. 7.5-3 disappears because $V_3 = 0$, and the third row disappears because node 3 is connected to the reference node. The node voltage equations for the grounded-cathode amplifier then have the following matrix form:

$$\begin{bmatrix} I_1 \\ 0 \end{bmatrix} = \begin{bmatrix} (Y_1 + Y_2 + Y_5) & -Y_5 \\ (g_m - Y_5) & (g_p + Y_4 + Y_5 + Y_6) \end{bmatrix} \times \begin{bmatrix} V_1 \\ V_2 \end{bmatrix} \qquad [7.5\text{-}10]$$

For the grounded-plate amplifier or cathode follower, $V_2 = 0$, and the second row and the second column of the matrix in Eq. 7.5-3 disappear. The resulting equations have the following form:

$$\begin{bmatrix} I_1 \\ 0 \end{bmatrix} = \begin{bmatrix} (Y_1 + Y_2 + Y_5) & -Y_2 \\ -(g_m + Y_2) & (g_m + g_p + Y_2 + Y_3 + Y_4) \end{bmatrix} \times \begin{bmatrix} V_1 \\ V_3 \end{bmatrix}$$

$$[7.5\text{-}11]$$

A part of the admittance Y_3 in Eq. 7.5-11 may be considered as the load on the cathode follower.

In the case of the grounded-grid amplifier, $V_1 = 0$, and the first row and the first column of the matrix in Eq. 7.5-3 disappear. The equations for this amplifier have the following form:

$$\begin{bmatrix} 0 \\ I_3 \end{bmatrix} = \begin{bmatrix} (g_p + Y_4 + Y_5 + Y_6) & -(g_p + g_m + Y_4) \\ -(g_p + Y_4) & (g_m + g_p + Y_2 + Y_3 + Y_4) \end{bmatrix} \times \begin{bmatrix} V_2 \\ V_3 \end{bmatrix}$$

$$[7.5\text{-}12]$$

where I_3 is the current applied to the cathode at node 3. The trivial case for $I_3 = 0$ corresponds to no a-c excitation.

The matrix equations for an electron tube at low frequencies for small signals, with the common-cathode connection, are as follows:

$$\begin{bmatrix} I_1 \\ I_2 \end{bmatrix} = \begin{bmatrix} 0 & 0 \\ g_m & g_p \end{bmatrix} \times \begin{bmatrix} V_1 \\ V_2 \end{bmatrix} \qquad [7.5\text{-}13]$$

Where $I_2 = -Y_6 V_2$. It is to be noted that, unlike the condition existing in reciprocal networks, y_{12} does not equal y_{21} in the admittance matrix. The zeros in the first row result from the fact that the effects of interelectrode capacitance are neglected, and it is assumed that the grid bias is of such magnitude as to cause the grid current to be zero.

In operation at higher frequencies, the interelectrode capacitances become of importance, and the admittance matrix may be written for the interelectrode capacitance shown in (a) of Fig. 7-15 and connected in parallel with the tube in (b) of Fig. 7-15.

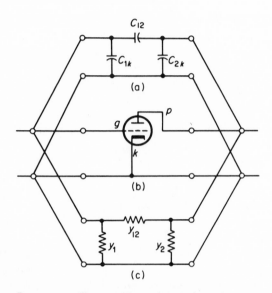

Figure 7-15 Electron tube with interelectrode capacitances connected in parallel with general network.

The y matrix for the interelectrode capacitances in Fig. 7-15(a) is

$$[y]_c = \begin{bmatrix} j\omega(C_{1k} + C_{12}) & -j\omega C_{12} \\ -j\omega C_{12} & j\omega(C_{2k} + C_{12}) \end{bmatrix} \qquad [7.5\text{-}14]$$

The y matrix for the tube in Fig. 7-15(b) is given in Eq. 7.5-13. The complete y matrix for networks (a) and (b) in Fig. 7-15 is formed by adding the matrices in Eqs. 7.5-13 and 7.5-14, and is given by

$$[y]_{ab} = \begin{bmatrix} j\omega(C_{1k} + C_{12}) & -j\omega C_{12} \\ (g_m - j\omega C_{12}) & g_p + j\omega(C_{2k} + C_{12}) \end{bmatrix} \qquad [7.5\text{-}15]$$

To carry this process one step further, a general y-system network shown in Fig. 7-15(c) may be added in parallel with the electron tube. The matrix of such a network is given by

$$[y] = \begin{bmatrix} y_1 + y_{12} & -y_{12} \\ -y_{21} & y_2 + y_{12} \end{bmatrix} \qquad [7.5\text{-}16]$$

In Eq. 7.5-16, y_1 may represent the grid conductance or admittance, y_2 represents the admittance of the plate load on the tube, and y_{12} may be zero or may exist as an additional circuit element. Adding all three networks in Fig. 7-15, we have the following complete matrix equation:

$$\begin{bmatrix} I_1 \\ 0 \end{bmatrix} = \begin{bmatrix} y_1 + y_{12} + j\omega(C_{1k} + C_{12}) & -(y_{12} + j\omega C_{12}) \\ g_m - y_{12} - j\omega C_{12} & g_p + y_2 + y_{12} + j\omega(C_{2k} + C_{12}) \end{bmatrix}$$
$$\times \begin{bmatrix} V_1 \\ V_2 \end{bmatrix} \qquad [7.5\text{-}17]$$

Equation 7.5-17 serves to illustrate the matrix method of obtaining the resultant matrix of an electron-tube circuit network by adding the admittance matrices of simpler networks.

The voltage gain for the complete network can always be written as

$$A_V = \frac{V_2}{V_1} = \frac{\Delta_{12}}{\Delta_{11}} \qquad [7.5\text{-}18]$$

where the determinant and its cofactor refer to the admittance matrix in Eq. 7.5-17.

The input admittance can be determined from the relation

$$Y_{in} = \frac{I_1}{V_1} = \frac{\Delta_y}{\Delta_{11}} \qquad [7.5\text{-}19]$$

Referring to Eq. 7.5-13, it can be seen that the admittance matrix of a triode amplifier at low frequencies can be written as

$$\begin{bmatrix} 0 & 0 \\ g_m & g_p \end{bmatrix} = \begin{bmatrix} 0 & \tfrac{1}{2}g_m \\ \tfrac{1}{2}g_m & g_p \end{bmatrix} + \begin{bmatrix} 0 & -\tfrac{1}{2}g_m \\ \tfrac{1}{2}g_m & 0 \end{bmatrix} \qquad [7.5\text{-}20]$$

Inspection of Eq. 7.5-20 shows that the original admittance matrix which is not reciprocal can be expressed as the sum of a matrix corresponding to a reciprocal network and another matrix having the characteristic that

$$y_{12} = -y_{21} \qquad [7.5\text{-}21]$$

A network characterized by Eq. 7.5-21 is termed a *gyrator*.* It follows from

---

* The student is referred to the following analyses of gyrators: J. Shekel, "The Gyrator as a 3-Terminal Element," *Proceeding of the I.R.E.*, vol. 41 (August 1953), pp. 1014–1016; also, L. de Pian, *Linear Active Network Theory* (Prentice-Hall, Inc., Englewood Cliffs, N.J.; 1962), pp. 236–241.

Eq. 7.5-20 that the triode amplifier at low frequencies can be represented by a reciprocal network followed by a gyrator.

The admittance matrix of a general nonreciprocal network can be expressed, as follows:

$$\begin{bmatrix} y_{11} & y_{12} \\ y_{21} & y_{22} \end{bmatrix} = \begin{bmatrix} y_{11} & \frac{1}{2}(y_{12} + y_{21}) \\ \frac{1}{2}(y_{12} + y_{21}) & y_{22} \end{bmatrix} + \begin{bmatrix} 0 & \frac{1}{2}(y_{12} - y_{21}) \\ \frac{1}{2}(y_{12} - y_{21}) & 0 \end{bmatrix}$$

$$[7.5\text{-}22]$$

where the first matrix on the right-hand side of Eq. 7.5-22 corresponds to a reciprocal network and the second matrix represents a gyrator. Equation 7.5-20 is a special case of Eq. 7.5-22 when $y_{11} = y_{12} = 0$.

7.6 TRANSISTOR CIRCUIT CONFIGURATIONS

Transistors, like electron-tube triodes, are three-terminal devices that become two-terminal pair networks when one terminal is common to both the input and output circuits. The elements of transistors are the emitter,

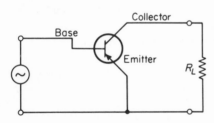

Figure 7-16   Elements of a transistor (common-emitter configuration).

circuit configurations are shown in Fig. 7-16, which is a common-emitter configuration. The common-base and the common-collector circuit configurations are shown in Fig. 7-17.

Figure 7-16 is analogous to the common-cathode electron-tube triode. Positive voltage is applied to the collector, which corresponds to the plate of the electron tube, and collects the electrons emitted by the emitter. The control signal is applied to the base, which corresponds to the grid of the triode. Figures 7-17(a) and

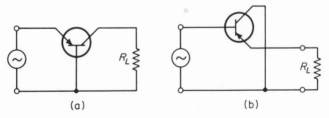

(a)   (b)

Figure 7-17   Transistor configurations: (a) common-base, (b) common-collector.

(b) are respectively analogous to the common- or grounded-grid and grounded-plate triodes.

7.7 TRANSISTOR PARAMETERS

In describing the operation of transistors, it is convenient to consider the input current and output voltage as the independent variables, and the output current and input voltage as the dependent variables. This leads to the following mixed or hybrid equations:

$$v_1 = H(i_1, v_2) \qquad\qquad [7.7\text{-}1]$$

$$i_2 = J(i_1, v_2) \qquad\qquad [7.7\text{-}2]$$

It will be shown that the selection of these variables facilitates the determination of the transistor parameters from a-c measurements.

For small variations about the quiescent operating point, the increments in voltage and current are given by

$$\Delta v_1 = \left(\frac{\partial v_1}{\partial i_1}\right)\Delta i_1 + \left(\frac{\partial v_1}{\partial v_2}\right)\Delta v_2 \qquad\qquad [7.7\text{-}3]$$

$$\Delta i_1 = \left(\frac{\partial v_2}{\partial i_1}\right)\Delta i_1 + \left(\frac{\partial i_2}{\partial v_2}\right)\Delta v_2 \qquad\qquad [7.7\text{-}4]$$

Equations 7.7-3 and 7.7-4 are approximations and can be applied only for small signals, in which case the first two terms of the Taylor series yield results that are valid.

For sinusoidal excitation, Eqs. 7.7-3 and 7.7-4 can be written as follows:

$$\Delta v_1(t) = \Delta v_{1,m}\epsilon^{j\omega t} = \left(\frac{\partial v_1}{\partial i_1}\right)\Delta i_{1,m}\epsilon^{j\omega t} + \left(\frac{\partial v_1}{\partial v_2}\right)\Delta v_{2,m}\epsilon^{j\omega t} \qquad [7.7\text{-}5]$$

$$\Delta i_2(t) = \Delta i_{2,m}\epsilon^{j\omega t} = \left(\frac{\partial i_2}{\partial i_1}\right)\Delta i_{1,m}\epsilon^{j\omega t} + \left(\frac{\partial i_2}{\partial v_2}\right)\Delta v_{2,m}\epsilon^{j\omega t} \qquad [7.7\text{-}6]$$

where it is assumed that all the coefficients are real numbers, and where the second subscript, m, denotes the maximum value of the sinusoid. Dividing both sides of Eqs. 7.7-5 and 7.7-6 by $\sqrt{2}\epsilon^{j\omega t}$, and assuming that the values of the partial derivatives remain constant for small variations about the quiescent operating point, gives the following results:

$$V_1 = h_{11}I_1 + h_{12}V_2 \qquad\qquad [7.7\text{-}7]$$

$$I_2 = h_{21}I_1 + h_{22}V_2 \qquad\qquad [7.7\text{-}8]$$

where V_1, V_2, I_1, and I_2 are the phasors corresponding to the input and output voltages and the input and output currents.

Equations 7.7-7 and 7.7-8 are a set of the hybrid or mixed equations developed in Sec. 1.3. The h parameters in Eqs. 7.7-7 and 7.7-8 are defined as follows:

$$h_{11} = \left.\frac{\partial v_1}{\partial i_1}\right|_{\Delta v_2 = 0} = \left.\frac{V_1}{I_1}\right|_{V_2 = 0} \tag{7.7-9}$$

$$h_{12} = \left.\frac{\partial v_1}{\partial v_2}\right|_{\Delta i_1 = 0} = \left.\frac{V_1}{V_2}\right|_{I_1 = 0} \tag{7.7-10}$$

$$h_{21} = \left.\frac{\partial i_2}{\partial i_1}\right|_{\Delta v_2 = 0} = \left.\frac{I_2}{I_1}\right|_{V_2 = 0} \tag{7.7-11}$$

$$h_{22} = \left.\frac{\partial i_2}{\partial v_2}\right|_{\Delta i_1 = 0} = \left.\frac{I_2}{V_2}\right|_{I_1 = 0} \tag{7.7-12}$$

The h parameters are determined from a-c measurements and Eqs. 7.7-9, 7.7-10, 7.7-11, and 7.7-12. The condition for the determination of h_{11} and h_{21} is that $V_2 = 0$. It should be noted that V_2 is an a-c voltage, and that a d-c voltage always exists. The required condition, $V_2 = 0$, is realized by connecting a capacitor across the output supply voltage. The impedance of the capacitor must be negligible compared to the output impedance of the transistor at the signal frequency. The quiescent input current is supplied through a resistor having a magnitude that is large compared to the input impedance of the transistor. This condition is realizable because, as will be shown in Sec. 7.8, the input impedance of a transistor in normal use is finite. The resistor through which the quiescent current is fed can be used to realize the condition imposed by Eqs. 7.7-10 and 7.7-12, namely that the a-c input current be negligible.

It is thus seen that the h parameters lend themselves to a-c measurement. On the other hand, a-c measurement of the z parameters requires a substantially open-circuited output ($I_2 = 0$) to determine z_{11} and z_{21}. To obtain this condition, the quiescent voltage must be fed through a very high resistance. The same condition exists in the determination of the g parameters. Measurement of the y parameters requires a short-circuited input ($V_1 = 0$) to determine y_{12} and y_{22}. To obtain this condition, a capacitance of very low impedance must be connected across the quiescent input source. Under certain conditions, an inordinately high capacitance is required. It is for these reasons that the h parameters are generally used to specify the operation of transistors.

Inspection of Eqs. 7.7-9, 7.7-10, 7.7-11, and 7.7-12 shows that h_{11} is a *short-circuit input impedance*, h_{12} is a *reverse-voltage transfer coefficient*, h_{21} is a *forward-current transfer coefficient*, and h_{22} is an *open-circuit output admit-*

tance. In view of these definitions, Eqs. 7.7-7 and 7.7-8 can be written as:

$$V_1 = h_i I_1 + h_r V_2 \qquad [7.7\text{-}13]$$

$$I_2 = h_f I_1 + h_o V_2 \qquad [7.7\text{-}14]$$

where the subscripts i, o, f, and r respectively denote input, output, forward, and reverse.

Equations 7.7-13 and 7.7-14 hold for all transistor configurations. For the common-emitter configuration in Fig. 7-16, Eqs. 7.7-13 and 7.7-14 have the following form:

$$V_1 = h_{ie} I_1 + h_{re} V_2 \qquad [7.7\text{-}15]$$

$$I_2 = h_{fe} I_1 + h_{oe} V_2 \qquad [7.7\text{-}16]$$

where the second subscript, e, denotes that the equations apply to the common-emitter configuration.

The form of the equations for the common-base configuration in Fig. 7-17(a) is

$$V_1 = h_{ib} I_1 + h_{rb} V_2 \qquad [7.7\text{-}17]$$

$$I_2 = h_{fb} I_1 + h_{ob} V_2 \qquad [7.7\text{-}18]$$

where the second subscript, b, denotes the common-base configuration.

Finally, the form of the hybrid equations for the common-collector configuration in Fig. 7-17(b) is

$$V_1 = h_{ic} I_1 + h_{rc} V_2 \qquad [7.7\text{-}19]$$

$$I_2 = h_{fc} I_1 + h_{oc} V_2 \qquad [7.7\text{-}20]$$

where the second subscript, c, denotes that the equations apply to the common-collector configuration.

It is seen from Eqs. 7.7-15 through 7.7-20 that there exist *twelve* h parameters (three sets of four each) to specify the small-signal operation of transistors.

7.8 GENERALIZED GAIN AND EQUIVALENT CIRCUITS FOR TRANSISTORS

As noted in Sec. 7.7, standard transistor terminology recognizes the existence of three sets of h parameters, depending upon whether the configuration represents a common base, a common emitter, or a common collector. This constitutes a fundamental difference between transistor and electron-tube terminology, where the tube parameters are traditionally defined for a single configuration, namely the one employing a common cathode. Using the broader transistor terminology, and considering the input as terminal 1 and the output as terminal 2, the input and output voltages and currents are related, as in Eqs. 7.7-13 and 7.7-14, by

$$V_1 = h_i I_1 + h_r V_2 \qquad\qquad [7.8\text{-}1]$$

$$I_2 = h_f I_1 + h_o V_2 \qquad\qquad [7.8\text{-}2]$$

where the subscripts denote only an input impedance, an output admittance, and the forward and reverse ratios, without regard to the circuit configuration. In applying Eqs. 7.8-1 and 7.8-2, it is to be understood that the values to be used for h_i, h_r, h_f, and h_o, must be appropriate to the given circuit configuration.* The equivalent circuit corresponding to Eqs. 7.8-1 and 7.8-2 is shown in Fig. 7-18.

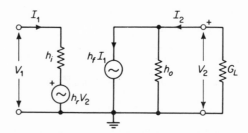

Figure 7-18   Equivalent circuit of a transistor.

Inspection of Fig. 7-18 shows that $I_2 = -V_2 G_L$. It follows from Eq. 7.8-2 that:

$$V_2 = -\frac{h_f I_1}{h_o + G_L} \qquad\qquad [7.8\text{-}3]$$

The substitution of V_2 from Eq. 7.8-3 into Eq. 7.8-2 gives the following result:

$$I_2 = h_f I_1 - \left(\frac{h_o h_f}{h_o + G_L}\right) I_1 = \left(h_f - \frac{h_o h_f}{h_o + G_L}\right) I_1 \qquad [7.8\text{-}4]$$

It follows from Eq. 7.8-4 that the current gain is given by

$$A_I = \frac{I_2}{I_1} = h_f - \frac{h_o h_f}{h_o + G_L} = \frac{h_f G_L}{h_o + G_L} = \frac{h_f}{1 + h_o Z_L} \qquad [7.8\text{-}5]$$

where A_I is the current gain and $Z_L = 1/G_L$.

* The parameters h_r and h_f are ratios that are expressed only in numbers; but h_i (the input impedance) and h_o (the output admittance) can be expressed in physical units, ohms and mhos, respectively.

The voltage gain is found by substituting I_1 from Eq. 7.8-1 into Eq. 7.8-3. The solution of Eq. 7.8-1 for I_1 yields

$$I_1 = \frac{V_1 - h_r V_2}{h_i} \qquad [7.8\text{-}6]$$

The substitution of I_1 from Eq. 7.8-6 into Eq. 7.8-3 gives the following result:

$$V_2 = \frac{h_r h_f V_2 - h_f V_1}{h_i(h_o + G_L)} \qquad [7.8\text{-}7]$$

The solution of Eq. 7.8-7 for V_2 yields

$$(h_r h_f - h_i h_o - h_i G_L)V_2 = h_f V_1 \qquad [7.8\text{-}8]$$

It follows from Eq. 7.8-8 that the voltage gain is

$$A_V = \frac{V_2}{V_1} = \frac{h_f}{h_r h_f - h_i h_o - h_i G_L} = -\frac{h_f}{|h| + h_i G_L} \qquad [7.8\text{-}9]$$

where $|h|$ is the determinant of the h parameters. Division of the numerator and denominator of the right-hand side of Eq. 7.8-9 by h_f gives the following result:

$$A_V = \frac{1}{h_r - h_i G_L \left(\dfrac{1 + h_o/G_L}{h_f} \right)}$$

$$= \frac{1}{h_r - \dfrac{h_i}{Z_L} \left(\dfrac{1 + h_o Z_L}{h_f} \right)} \qquad [7.8\text{-}10]$$

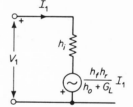

Figure 7-19 Equivalent input circuit of a transistor.

where $Z_L = 1/G_L$.

Using the expression for V_2 in Eq. 7.8-3, the input circuit in Fig. 7-18 can be represented as shown in Fig. 7-19. Note the change in polarity of the voltage generator caused by the minus sign in Eq. 7.8-3.

Inspection of Fig. 7.19 shows that the input impedance is

$$Z_{\text{in}} = h_i - \frac{h_f h_r}{h_o + G_L} = h_i - \frac{h_f h_r Z_L}{1 + h_o Z_L} \qquad [7.8\text{-}11]$$

Equation 7.8-11 shows that the input impedance of a transistor is always finite, and may have a real component that is negative. This constitutes a fundamental difference between transistors and electron tubes, where the input impedance at low frequencies may be considered infinite for certain configurations. In applying Eqs. 7.8-5, 7.8-10, and 7.8-11, it should always be borne in mind that these equations are general. Three equations can be formed by adding the suitable second subscript (b, c, or e) to the h parameter, depending upon the circuit configuration. The relations between the h parameters for the various circuit configurations are developed in Sec. 7.9.

The impedance and gain characteristics of the three transistor configurations are summarized in Table 7-1. The similarities between the transis-

TABLE 7-1

COMPARISON OF TRANSISTOR AND ELECTRON TUBE CONFIGURATIONS

Transistor configuration	Characteristics	Electron tube analogues
1. Common (Grounded) Emitter	Moderate input and output impedance; high current and voltage gain	Common (Grounded) Cathode
2. Common (Grounded) Base	Lowest input impedance, highest output impedance; nearly unity current gain and high voltage gain.	Common (Grounded) Grid
3. Common (Grounded) Collector (Emitter Follower)	Highest input impedance, lowest output impedance; high current gain and nearly unity voltage gain	Common (Grounded) Plate (Cathode Follower)

tor configurations and the analogous electron tube configurations are noted. Their applications are similar. Actual numerical values can be determined from solution of the problems at the end of this chapter.

7.9 RELATIONS AMONG TRANSISTOR PARAMETERS

Consider the common-emitter configuration (base input) shown in Fig. 7-16. The hybrid equations for this configuration are the following:

$$V_{be} = h_{ie}I_b + h_{re}V_{ce} \qquad [7.9\text{-}1]$$

$$I_c = h_{fe}I_b + h_{oe}V_{ce} \qquad [7.9\text{-}2]$$

where V_{be} and V_{ce} are the base (input) and collector (output) voltages measured with respect to the emitter, and I_b and I_c are the base (input) and collector (output) currents. The second subscript, e, of the h parameters denotes the common-emitter configuration.

The corresponding equations for the common-base configuration shown in (a) of Fig. 7-17 are

$$V_{eb} = h_{ib}I_e + h_{rb}V_{cb} \qquad [7.9\text{-}3]$$

$$I_c = h_{fb}I_e + h_{ob}V_{cb} \qquad [7.9\text{-}4]$$

where V_{eb} and V_{cb} are the emitter (input) and collector (output) voltages measured with respect to the base, and I_e and I_c are the emitter (input) and collector (output) currents. The second subscript, b, of the h parameters denotes the common-base configuration.

Assume that h_{ie}, h_{re}, h_{fe}, and h_{oe} in Eqs. 7.9-1 and 7.9-2 have been experimentally determined and are known. It is desired to find h_{ib}, h_{rb}, h_{fb}, and h_{ob} in Eqs. 7.9-3 and 7.9-4 in terms of the common-emitter parameters in Eqs. 7.9-1 and 7.9-2. This can be accomplished by applying Kirchhoff's voltage and current equations to express Eqs. 7.9-1 and 7.9-2 in terms of V_{eb}, V_{cb}, I_e, and I_c. This procedure is essentially the same as that used to determine the equivalent g parameters of the electron-tube triode in Sec. 7.4.

Kirchhoff's voltage and current equations for the transistor configurations in Figs. 7-16 and 7-17 are the following:

$$V_{ce} + V_{eb} + V_{bc} = 0 \qquad [7.9\text{-}5]$$

$$I_b + I_c + I_e = 0 \qquad [7.9\text{-}6]$$

It follows from Eqs. 7.9-5 and 7.9-6 that:

$$V_{ce} = V_{cb} + V_{be} \qquad [7.9\text{-}7]$$

$$I_b = -(I_c + I_e) \qquad [7.9\text{-}8]$$

Substituting Eqs. 7.9-7 and 7.9-8 into Eqs. 7.9-1 yields

$$V_{be} = -h_{ie}(I_c + I_e) + h_{re}(V_{cb} + V_{be}) \qquad [7.9\text{-}9]$$

$$(1 - h_{re})V_{be} = -h_{ie}I_e + h_{re}V_{cb} - h_{ie}I_c \qquad [7.9\text{-}10]$$

If Eq. 7.9-10 is to have the same form as Eq. 7.9-3 for the common-base configuration, I_c must be eliminated and expressed in terms of V_{cb}, V_{eb}, and I_e. Again, use the relations

$$V_{ce} = V_{cb} + V_{be} \qquad [7.9\text{-}11]$$

$$I_b = -(I_c + I_e) \qquad [7.9\text{-}12]$$

The substitution of Eqs. 7.9-11 and 7.9-12 into Eq. 7.9-2 gives the following expressions for I_c:

$$I_c = -h_{fe}(I_c + I_e) + h_{oe}(V_{cb} + V_{be}) \qquad [7.9\text{-}13]$$

$$I_c = -\left(\frac{h_{fe}}{1+h_{fe}}\right)I_e + \left(\frac{h_{oe}}{1+h_{fe}}\right)V_{cb} + \left(\frac{h_{oe}}{1+h_{fe}}\right)V_{be} \quad [7.9\text{-}14]$$

The substitution of Eq. 7.9-14 into Eq. 7.9-10 yields

$$(1-h_{re})V_{be} = -\left(h_{ie} - \frac{h_{ie}h_{fe}}{1+h_{fe}}\right)I_e + \left(h_{re} - \frac{h_{ie}h_{oe}}{1+h_{fe}}\right)V_{cb} - \left(\frac{h_{ie}h_{oe}}{1+h_{fe}}\right)V_{be}$$

$$[7.9\text{-}15]$$

Since $V_{be} = -V_{eb}$, Eq. 7.9-15 can be written as

$$(1-h_{re})V_{eb} = \left(\frac{h_{ie}(1+h_{fe}) - h_{ie}h_{fe}}{1+h_{fe}}\right)I_e$$

$$+ \left(\frac{h_{ie}h_{oe}}{1+h_{fe}} - h_{re}\right)V_{cb} - \left(\frac{h_{ie}h_{oe}}{1+h_{fe}}\right)V_{eb} \quad [7.9\text{-}16]$$

Note that the sign of the last term on the right-hand side of Eq. 7.9-16 has been changed twice, and is therefore unaltered. It follows from Eq. 7.9-16 that:

$$\left[\frac{(1-h_{re})(1+h_{fe}) + h_{ie}h_{oe}}{1+h_{fe}}\right]V_{eb} = \left[\frac{h_{ie}}{1+h_{fe}}\right]I_e + \left[\frac{h_{ie}h_{oe}}{1+h_{fe}} - h_{re}\right]V_{cb}$$

$$[7.9\text{-}17]$$

Equation 7.9-17 can be rewritten as

$$\left[\frac{1+h_{fe} - h_{re} + |h_e|}{1+h_{fe}}\right]V_{eb} = \left[\frac{h_{ie}}{1+h_{fe}}\right]I_e + \left[\frac{h_{ie}h_{oe}}{1+h_{fe}} - h_{re}\right]V_{cb}$$

$$[7.9\text{-}18]$$

where

$$|h_e| = \begin{vmatrix} h_{ie} & h_{re} \\ h_{fe} & h_{oe} \end{vmatrix} \quad [7.9\text{-}19]$$

and $|h_e|$ is the determinant of the h parameters for the grounded-emitter configuration. Typical numerical values of the h parameters for the three configurations shown in Figs. 7.16 and 7.17 are given in Table 7-2. It follows from Table 7-2 that:

$$|h_e| = \begin{vmatrix} 1400 & 3.37 \times 10^{-4} \\ 44 & 27 \times 10^{-6} \end{vmatrix} = 0.023 \quad [7.9\text{-}20]$$

It can be seen from Table 7-2 and Eq. 7.9-20 that $|h_e| \ll 1$, $h_{fe} \gg h_{re}$,

TABLE 7-2

Typical h Parameters of Transistor Configurations

Parameter	Common emitter	Common base	Common collector
h_i	1400 ohms	31 ohms	1400 ohms
h_r	3.37×10^{-4}	5×10^{-4}	1.00
h_f	44	-0.98	-45.0
h_o	27×10^{-6} mho	0.60×10^{-6} mho	27×10^{-6} mho

and $h_{fe} \gg 1$. Therefore, the coefficient of V_{eb} in Eq. 7.9-18 is approximately unity, and V_{eb} is approximately given by

$$V_{eb} \cong \left[\frac{h_{ie}}{1 + h_{fe}} \right] I_e + \left[\frac{h_{ie}h_{oc}}{1 + h_{fe}} - h_{re} \right] V_{cb} \qquad [7.9\text{-}21]$$

A comparison of Eqs. 7.9-3 and 7.9-21 shows that

$$h_{ib} \cong \frac{h_{ie}}{1 + h_{fe}} \qquad [7.9\text{-}22]$$

$$h_{rb} \cong \frac{h_{ie}h_{oe}}{1 + h_{fe}} - h_{re} \qquad [7.9\text{-}23]$$

The coefficients in Eq. 7.9-4 for the collector current when the base is common are determined from the coefficients in Eq. 7.9-2 for the common emitter in a similar manner. The derivation follows:

$$I_c = h_{fe}I_b + h_{oe}V_{ce} = -h_{fe}(I_c + I_e) - h_{oe}(V_{eb} + V_{bc}) \qquad [7.9\text{-}24]$$

$$(1 + h_{fe})I_c = -h_{fe}I_e - h_{oe}V_{bc} - h_{oe}V_{eb} \qquad [7.9\text{-}25]$$

It is possible to eliminate V_{eb} from Eq. 7.9-25 by the use of Eq. 7.9-1. Thus

$$V_{be} = h_{ie}I_b + h_{re}V_{ce} = -h_{ie}(I_c + I_e) - h_{re}(V_{eb} + V_{bc}) \qquad [7.9\text{-}26]$$

$$V_{eb} = \left[\frac{h_{ie}}{1 - h_{re}} \right] I_c + \left[\frac{h_{ie}}{1 - h_{re}} \right] I_e + \left[\frac{h_{re}}{1 + h_{re}} \right] V_{bc} \qquad [7.9\text{-}27]$$

The substitution of Eq. 7.9-27 into Eq. 7.9-25 yields

$$\left[1 + h_{fe} + \frac{h_{oe}h_{ie}}{1 - h_{re}} \right] I_c = - \left[h_{fe} + \frac{h_{oe}h_{ie}}{1 - h_{re}} \right] I_e + h_{oe} \left[1 + \frac{h_{re}}{1 - h_{re}} \right] V_{cb}$$

$$[7.9\text{-}28]$$

Inspection of Table 7-2 shows that

$$h_{fe} \gg \frac{h_{oe}h_{ie}}{1 - h_{re}} \qquad [7.9\text{-}29]$$

$$1 \gg \frac{h_{re}}{1 - h_{re}} \qquad [7.9\text{-}30]$$

Therefore a good approximation to Eq. 7.9-28 is the following:

$$(1 + h_{fe})I_c \cong -h_{fe}I_e + h_{oe}V_{cb} \qquad [7.9\text{-}31]$$

It follows from Eq. 7.9-31 that:

$$I_c \cong -\left[\frac{h_{fe}}{1 + h_{fe}}\right]I_e + \left[\frac{h_{oe}}{1 + h_{fe}}\right]V_{cb} \qquad [7.9\text{-}32]$$

A comparison of Eqs. 7.9-2 and 7.9-32 shows that

$$h_{fb} \cong -\frac{h_{fe}}{1 + h_{fe}} \qquad [7.9\text{-}33]$$

$$h_{ob} \cong \frac{h_{oe}}{1 + h_{fe}} \qquad [7.9\text{-}34]$$

The relations between the other h parameters are derived in a similar manner; those derivations are left as exercises for the student. These and other relations among the parameters of transistor circuits have been tabulated and published.*

7.10 EQUIVALENT T NETWORKS OF TRANSISTORS

The equivalent T network of a transistor is useful because it approximates the actual structure of the transistor. This network is derived from the z parameters. The relations between the h parameters and the z parameters are found from Table 1-2 to be the following:

$$z_{11} = \frac{|h|}{h_{22}} = \frac{|h|}{h_o} \qquad [7.10\text{-}1]$$

$$z_{12} = \frac{h_{12}}{h_{22}} = \frac{h_r}{h_o} \qquad [7.10\text{-}2]$$

$$z_{21} = -\frac{h_{21}}{h_{22}} = -\frac{h_f}{h_o} \qquad [7.10\text{-}3]$$

---

* Several manufacturers of transistors include such information in their handbooks or catalogues. For example, a convenient table appears in the *Transistor Handbook* of the General Electric Company, Syracuse, New York (Sixth Edition, 1962; page 55).

$$z_{22} = \frac{1}{h_{22}} = \frac{1}{h_o} \qquad [7.10\text{-}4]$$

Since $h_r \neq -h_f$, it follows that

$$z_{12} \neq z_{21} \qquad [7.10\text{-}5]$$

In other words, the network is nonreciprocal.

If the frequency is low enough so that the h parameters may be considered to be real, the equivalent T network is purely resistive. A resistive T network where $r_{12} \neq r_{21}$ is shown in Fig. 7-20. The difference between

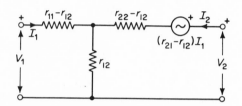

Figure 7-20 Representation of a transistor by a resistive T network.

r_{21} and r_{12} is taken into account by a voltage generator having a voltage of $(r_{21} - r_{12})I_1$ with the indicated polarity.

As a consequence of Eq. 7.10-2,

$$r_{12} = \frac{h_r}{h_o} \qquad [7.10\text{-}6]$$

It follows from Eqs. 7.10-1 and 7.10-6 that:

$$r_{11} - r_{12} = \frac{|h| - h_r}{h_o} = \frac{h_i h_o - h_r h_f - h_r}{h_o} \qquad [7.10\text{-}7]$$

$$r_{11} - r_{12} = h_i - \frac{h_r}{h_o}(1 + h_f) \qquad [7.10\text{-}8]$$

Also, it follows from Eqs. 7.10-4 and 7.10-6 that:

$$r_{22} - r_{12} = \frac{1 - h_r}{h_o} \qquad [7.10\text{-}9]$$

Further, it follows from Eqs. 7.10-3 and 7.10-6 that:

$$r_{21} - r_{12} = -\left(\frac{h_f + h_r}{h_o}\right) = r_m \qquad [7.10\text{-}10]$$

A modified equivalent circuit is shown in Fig. 7-21, where the difference between r_{21} and r_{12} is taken into account by a current generator. Approximations may be made in the components shown in Fig. 7-21. For example,

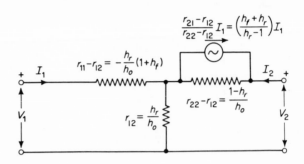

Figure 7-21 Modified equivalent circuit for transistor.

in a typical common-base configuration, $h_{fb} = -0.98$ and $h_{rb} = 5 \times 10^{-4}$. Hence, for a common-base configuration,

$$\frac{r_{21} - r_{12}}{r_{22} - r_{12}} = \frac{h_{fb} + h_{rb}}{h_{rb} - 1} \cong -h_{fb} \qquad [7.10\text{-}11]$$

The approximate equivalent circuit is shown in Fig. 7-22.

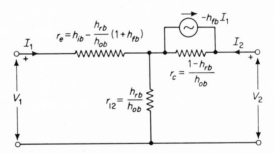

Figure 7-22 Approximate equivalent circuit for transistor.

A T section model that is somewhat analogous in structure to the actual transistor is shown in Fig. 7-23, where each branch of the network is associated with one of the physical terminals of the transistor. Figure 7-23(a) is obtained directly from Fig. 7-20 when the resistors leading respectively to the emitter, base, and collector have the following values:

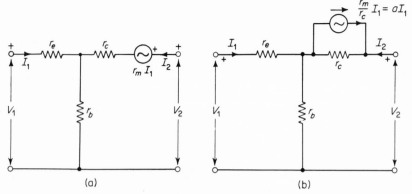

Figure 7-23   T section model of transistor (a) with voltage source (b) with current source.

$$r_l = r_{11} - r_{12}$$

$$r_b = r_{12} \qquad\qquad [7.10\text{-}12]$$

$$r_c = r_{22} - r_{12}$$

The voltage to account for the nonreciprocity of the network is $r_m I_1$, where r_m is given by Eq. 7.10-10. Nonreciprocity is taken into account in Fig. 7-23(b) by means of a current source of magnitude, $a\, I_1$, where

$$a = \frac{r_m}{r_c} \qquad\qquad [7.10\text{-}13]$$

is the *current amplification factor*. The *short-circuit current amplification factor*, α, is given by

$$\alpha = \frac{I_2}{I_1}\bigg|_{V_2=0} = h_f \qquad\qquad [7.10\text{-}14]$$

Equation 7.10-14 follows directly from Eq. 7.7-14.

The mesh-current equation for the mesh connected to the output terminals in Fig. 7-23(a) is

$$(r_b + r_m)I_1 + (r_b + r_c)I_2 = V_2 \qquad\qquad [7.10\text{-}15]$$

It follows from Eq. 7.10-15 that, when $V_2 = 0$,

$$\frac{I_2}{I_1} = -\left(\frac{r_b + r_m}{r_b + r_c}\right) = \alpha \qquad\qquad [7.10\text{-}16]$$

If $r_m \gg r_b$, and also if $r_c \gg r_b$, then

$$\alpha \cong - \frac{r_m}{r_c} \qquad [7.10\text{-}17]$$

Under these conditions, it follows from Eqs. 7.10-12 and 7.10-17 that

$$\alpha \cong -a \qquad [r_m \gg r_b, \quad r_c \gg r_b] \qquad [7.10\text{-}18]$$

PROBLEMS

7-1 A certain triode, connected as a common-cathode amplifier, has a plate resistance of 10,000 ohms and an amplification factor of 20. Assume that all interelectrode capacitances are equal to 5 $\mu\mu$f. The grid resistor, from grid to cathode, has a value of 10,000 ohms, and the load is a resistor having a conductance of 20×10^{-6} mho. Calculate the voltage gain at an angular frequency of 2×10^6 radians per second.

7-2 Find the input admittance in Prob. 7-1.

7-3 Solve Prob. 7-1 if the load admittance is a pure susceptance of $-j30 \times 10^{-6}$ mho.

7-4 Solve Prob. 7-2 if the load admittance is a pure susceptance of $j30 \times 10^{-6}$ mho.

7-5 Neglect the grid resistor in Prob. 7-1. Calculate the gain for a common-plate configuration.

7-6 Find the input admittance in Prob. 7-5.

7-7 Solve Prob. 7-5 for a common-grid configuration.

7-8 Find the input admittance in Prob. 7-7.

7-9 Given the following parameters for a common-base transistor circuit: $h_{ib} = $ 31 ohms, $h_{rb} = 5 \times 10^{-4}$, $h_{fb} = -0.98$ and $h_{ob} = 0.60 \times 10^{-6}$ mho. Calculate the h parameters of the common-emitter circuit.

7-10 Use the values given in prob. 7-9 to calculate the h parameters of the common-collector circuit.

7-11 Given the following parameters of a common-collector circuit: $h_{ic} = 1400$ ohms, $h_{rc} = 1.00$, $h_{fc} = -45$, $h_{oc} = 27 \times 10^{-6}$ mho. Calculate the h parameters of the common-emitter circuit.

7-12 Use the values given in Prob. 7-11 to calculate the h parameters of the common-base circuit.

7-13 Find the equivalent T network for the circuit in Prob. 7-9.

7-14 Find the equivalent T network for the circuit in Prob. 7-11.

7-15 In a common-emitter transistor circuit, $h_{ie} = 1400$ ohms, $h_{re} = 3.37 \times 10^{-4}$, $h_{fe} = 44$, $h_{oe} = 27 \times 10^{-6}$ mho. The load resistance is 5000 ohms. Calculate the following:

(a) the input impedance

(b) the current gain

(c) the voltage gain

(d) the power gain

7-16 Solve Prob. 7-15 using the equivalent T network.

7-17 Solve Prob. 7-15 if the load resistance is 1000 ohms.

7-18 Solve Prob. 7-15 if the load impedance is 10,000 + j10,000 ohms.

7-19 Solve Prob. 7-15 if the load resistance is 10,000 ohms.

7-20 Solve Prob. 7-1 if the signal (input) generator has an internal resistance of 1,000 ohms.

7-21 Derive an expression for the voltage gain of a common-grid triode amplifier if the signal (input) generator has a resistance of R_g.

7-22 Derive an expression for the power gain of the common-grid triode amplifier: (a), neglecting the resistance of the signal generator; and (b), assuming that the signal generator has a resistance of R_g.

7-23 The currents (in amperes) and the voltages (in volts) of a three-terminal device, A, in the accompanying sketch, are related as follows:

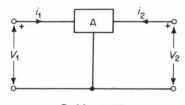

Problem 7-23

$$i_1 = 10^{-6}v_1$$

$$i_2 = 10^{-4}(v_2 + 20v_1) + 10^{-6}(v_2 + 20v_1)^2$$

Find a low-frequency, small-signal equivalent circuit that is valid at the operating point described by $V_1 = -5.0$ volts and $V_2 = 200$ volts.

7-24 Find the small-signal voltage and current gains, and the input impedance when the device of Prob. 7-23 is used in the circuit sketched below.

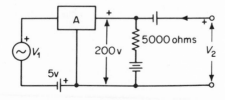

Problem 7-24

circuit theory of lossless

transmission lines

8.0 INTRODUCTION

In all of the preceding analyses, it has been assumed that the circuit configurations consisted of *lumped* circuit elements. In other words, it was assumed that at a given instant the current at every point of a series circuit had the same value, and that the voltages between all pairs of opposite points on the connecting leads were identical at a given instant. These assumptions are valid and exceedingly useful at low frequencies and in other special cases. For the more general analyses that are to be valid for higher frequencies and for conductors of appreciable lengths, however, the essentially *distributed* character of the circuit elements must be considered.

In order to transmit energy from a source to a load, a feeding line and its return must be used. This simple geometric configuration is shown in (a) Fig. 8-1. Lossless transmission lines are ideal lines without resistance or losses of any kind. In such lines, the power is transmitted without loss along the line by the magnetic and electric fields that link the conductors. These fields exist at all points of the circuit, and (neglecting losses), their effects can be represented by series inductance and shunt capacitance that are uniformly distributed throughout the length of a uniform line.

The electrical equivalent of the geometric configuration of Fig. 8-1(a) is shown approximately in Fig. 8-1(b). Because of the uniform distribution of the circuit parameters, it is possible to construct an equivalent circuit only in the limiting case when $\Delta x \rightarrow 0$ in Fig. 8-1(b). When the distributed nature of the circuit parameters is taken into consideration, the feed and return wires in Fig. 8-1 are termed a *transmission line*. In this text, such lines are analyzed by applying lumped circuit theory to the equivalent circuit shown in Fig. 8-1(b).

Inspection of Fig. 8-1(b) shows that a transmission line consists of series impedances and shunt admittances. Hence at any instant, the current and voltage vary at different points along the line, and the fundamental assumption upon which lumped circuit theory is based is no longer valid. In the study of transmission lines, the student must at once realize that a

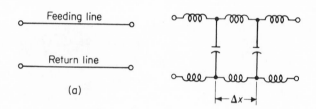

Feeding line

Return line

(a)

Figure 8-1   Lossless line and electrical equivalent.

series geometrical configuration is not necessarily a simple series electrical configuration when the distributed nature of the circuit parameters is taken into account. The distributed line constants introduce mathematical complications because the voltage and current are functions of distance as well as of time, and are therefore related by partial differential equations. These equations describe the propagation of the wave consisting of mutually sustaining electric and magnetic fields. Before a solution of these equations is attempted, an introduction to wave propagation will be given in order to show how the frequency of the wave and the length of the line determine the need for applying distributed parameter circuit analysis.

8.1 ELEMENTS OF WAVE PROPAGATION

A *wave* is defined, for the purposes of this text, as a group of disturbances that occur at one place at a given time and are reproduced at other places at later times, with the time delay proportional to the space separation from the first location. The disturbances need not be recurrent, although they may be recurrent as for example in a sinusoid (also termed a sine wave), which is a recurrent function of time at a given point. The definition given above for the term "wave" applies in the present discussion.

The motion of the disturbance is termed *propagation*. The propagation of a rectangular pulse is illustrated in Fig. 8-2, in which the space origin is assumed to be fixed and where

$$\frac{\Delta x}{\Delta t} = \frac{x_2 - x_1}{t_2 - t_1} = \frac{x_3 - x_2}{t_3 - t_2} = u \qquad [8.1\text{-}1]$$

where u is the *velocity of propagation*.

The velocity of propagation of electrical energy is finite. This can be seen from an inspection of Fig. 8-1(b), which implies that a finite amount of time, Δt, is required to charge the capacitor and to overcome the counter-emf of self-inductance present in an elementary length, Δx. Hence $\Delta x / \Delta t$

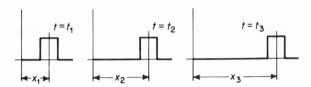

Figure 8-2 Propagation of a rectangular pulse.

is finite. Electromagnetic theory shows that the velocity of propagation of a uniform plane wave, where both the electric and magnetic fields exist entirely in planes that are perpendicular to the direction of propagation, is given by

$$u = \frac{1}{\sqrt{\mu_r \mu_\nu \epsilon_r \epsilon_\nu}}$$ [8.1-2]

where u is the velocity of propagation, μ_ν and ϵ_ν are the permeability and dielectric constants of free space, and μ_r and ϵ_r are the *relative* values of the permeability and dielectric constant of the medium in which propagation takes place. The waves on coaxial cables and parallel-wire transmission lines, to be studied in this chapter, are uniform plane waves to which Eq. 8.1-2 applies. Such waves are known as transverse electromagnetic (TEM) waves to denote that both the electric (E) and magnetic (M) fields are transverse (T) to the direction of propagation. The velocity of propagation of a TEM wave in free space where, $\mu_r = \epsilon_r = 1$, is given by

$$c = \frac{1}{\sqrt{\mu_\nu \epsilon_\nu}}$$ [8.1-3]

Since $\mu_\nu = 4\pi \times 10^{-7}$ henry per meter, and since $\epsilon_\nu = 1/36\pi \times 10^{-9}$ farad per meter in the rationalized MKS system,

$$c = \frac{1}{\sqrt{4\pi/36\pi \times 10^{-16}}} = \frac{1}{1/3 \times 10^{-8}} = 3 \times 10^8 \text{ meters per second}$$

[8.1-4]

Experiment has shown that c is numerically equal to the velocity of propagation of light waves in free space or air. This experiment is one of the links that establish the connection between electromagnetic waves and light waves. The velocity of propagation of light is also about 3×10^8 meters or 186,000 miles per second in free space.

Consider now the propagation of a repetitive TEM sine function along a transmission line. Assume that a sinusoidal generator of frequency f is connected to the input terminals of a transmission line. These cycles are repeated along the line with a time delay caused by the finite velocity of propagation. At the end of one second in the steady state, the first impulse has traveled u meters and the distribution of the disturbance (current or voltage) along the line appears as shown in Fig. 8-3, where the wavelength

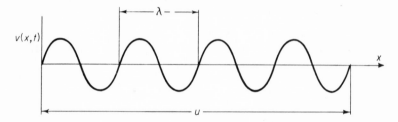

Figure 8-3 Propagation of a sine wave along a transmission line.

along the line is denoted by λ. Since f complete cycles, each occupying a distance of λ along the line, are transmitted per second, the velocity of propagation is given by

$$u = f\lambda \qquad [8.1\text{-}5]$$

where u and λ have the same units of distance.

The instantaneous voltage at any point along the line can be denoted by $v(x,t)$, showing that the voltage is a function of both time and distance. Assume that, at $x = 0$, the input voltage is given by

$$v(0,t) = v(t) = |V_m| \sin \omega t \qquad [8.1\text{-}6]$$

The voltage at a distance x is delayed by the factor x/u, corresponding to the time required by the finite velocity of propagation; this voltage is given by

$$v(x,t) = |V_m| \sin \omega \left(t - \frac{x}{u} \right) = |V_m| \sin (\omega t - \beta x) = |V_m| \sin (\omega t - \theta)$$

$$[8.1\text{-}7]$$

where
$$\beta = \frac{\omega}{u} = \frac{2\pi f}{u} \qquad [8.1\text{-}8]$$

and
$$\theta = \beta x = 2\pi \left(\frac{x}{\lambda} \right) \qquad [8.1\text{-}9]$$

In Eq. 8.1-7, $\theta = \beta x$ represents the phase angle of lag or delay caused by the retardation resulting from the finite velocity of propagation.

The magnitude of the maximum value of the phase angle of delay is critical in determining the effect of the distributed parameters on the behavior of the transmission line. It follows from Eqs. 8.1-8 and 8.1-9 that this phase angle depends upon both the frequency and the ratio of the length of the line to the wavelength. For example, at a frequency of 60 cycles in air, the wavelength in miles is given by

$$\lambda_1 = \frac{186,000}{60} = 3,100 \text{ miles} \qquad [8.1\text{-}10]$$

It follows that a power line 50 miles long, operating at 60 cycles per second, corresponds to only 1/62 wavelength, and has a maximum phase delay of

$$\theta_1 = 2\pi \left(\frac{1}{62}\right) = 5.8° \qquad [8.1\text{-}11]$$

Power lines that are less than 50 miles in length can usually be analyzed on a lumped parameter basis with the distributed inductance and capacitance represented by single lumped circuit elements as shown in Fig. 8-4, where $\bar{L}$ is the inductance per unit length, $\bar{L}\ell$ is the lumped inductance of a line of length ℓ, $\bar{C}$ is the capacitance per unit length, and $\bar{C}\ell$ is the total lumped capacitance. The validity of this representation is based upon the assumptions that the phase delay is negligible and that all currents and voltages along the line are identical at any instant of time.

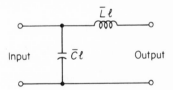

Figure 8-4 Electrical equivalent of a power line.

Consider now a different line, only 1 meter in length and operating at a frequency of 10^8 cycles per second. The wavelength in this case is

$$\lambda_2 = \frac{3 \times 10^8}{10^8} = 3 \text{ meters} \qquad [8.1\text{-}12]$$

It follows that a line, 1 meter in length and operating at 10^8 cycles per second, corresponds to 1/3 wavelength, and has a maximum phase delay of

$$\theta_2 = 2\pi \left(\frac{1}{3}\right) = 120° \qquad [8.1\text{-}13]$$

Such a line cannot be represented by lumped parameters because the phase difference of the voltages and currents along the line is not negligible.

The two examples given above show that, when the length of the line is comparable to the wavelength, lumped circuit analysis is not applicable. The ratio of line length to wavelength depends upon the frequency and the physical length of the line. It follows that at high frequencies and for long lines (in terms of wavelength), a circuit theory that takes into account both time and distance variations of the current and voltage must be developed. This requires a solution of the wave equation based upon distributed parameters. Before this is undertaken, formulas for the distributed inductance and capacitance will be derived.

8.2 DISTRIBUTED INDUCTANCE AND CAPACITANCE

Formulas for the distributed inductance and capacitance of coaxial cables and parallel-wire transmission lines can be derived by applying the following two basic relations of field theory that hold in the rationalized system of units:

(1) The total electric flux through a closed surface equals the total charge enclosed by the surface.

(2) The line integral of the magnetic field intensity around a closed path equals the current enclosed by the path.

Consider the coaxial cable shown sectioned in Fig. 8-5. The inner radius is r_1, the outer radius is r_2, and the length is ℓ. Assume that the charge per unit length on the conductors is $\bar{q}$. It follows from symmetry that the electric flux extends radially from the central conductor. The total flux, ϕ, passing through a cylinder of radius r, and concentric with the inner cylinder of length ℓ, is given by basic relation (1) of the field theory as

$$\phi = \bar{q}\ell = 2\pi r\ell D_r \qquad [8.2\text{-}1]$$

where D_r is the radial electric flux density measured in charge per unit area. Since

$$D_r = \epsilon_r\epsilon_\nu E_r \qquad [8.2\text{-}2]$$

where E_r is the radial electric field intensity shown in Fig. 8-5, it follows from Eqs. 8.2-1 and 8.2-2 that

$$E_r = \frac{\bar{q}}{2\pi\epsilon_r\epsilon_\nu r} \qquad [8.2\text{-}3]$$

The difference of potential between the inner and outer conductors is given by

$$V_0 = -\int_{r_2}^{r_1} E_r\,dr = \int_{r_1}^{r_2} \frac{\bar{q}\,dr}{2\pi\epsilon_r\epsilon_\nu r} = \left(\frac{\bar{q}}{2\pi\epsilon_r\epsilon_\nu}\right)\ln\left(r_2/r_1\right) \qquad [8.2\text{-}4]$$

Hence, the capacitance per unit length is

$$\frac{\bar{q}}{V} = \overline{C} = \frac{2\pi\epsilon_r\epsilon_\nu}{\ln (r_2/r_1)} \qquad [8.2\text{-}5]$$

Since $\epsilon_\nu = 1/36\pi \times 10^{-9}$ in the rationalized MKS system,

$$\overline{C} = \frac{\epsilon_r \times 10^{-9}}{18 \ln (r_2/r_1)} \text{ farads per meter} \qquad [8.2\text{-}6]$$

where ϵ_r is the relative dielectric constant of the medium between the conductors, and where the bar denotes that the parameter is per unit length.

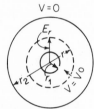

Figure 8-5 Section of a coaxial cable showing electric field intensity.

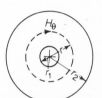

Figure 8-6 Section of a coaxial cable showing magnetic field intensity.

Assume now that a current, i, exists in the conductors, and that this current is completely confined to the outer surface of the conductors. The validity of this approximation increases with the frequency.* The lines of magnetic force are circular, as shown in Fig. 8-6 where H_θ represents the magnetic field strength. It follows from basic relation (2) that:

$$2\pi r H_\theta = i \qquad [8.2\text{-}7]$$

$$H_\theta = \frac{i}{2\pi r}$$

The flux density is given by

$$B_\theta = \mu_r\mu_\nu H_\theta = \frac{\mu_r\mu_\nu i}{2\pi r} \qquad [8.2\text{-}8]$$

and the total flux between conductors is

* This phenomenon is termed "the skin effect."

$$\phi = \int_{r_1}^{r_2} \left(\frac{\mu_r \mu_\nu i}{2\pi r} \right) (\ell \, dr) = \left(\frac{\mu_r \mu_\nu \ell i}{2\pi} \right) \ln (r_2/r_1) \qquad [8.2\text{-}9]$$

The inductance is

$$L = \frac{\phi}{i} = \left(\frac{\mu_r \mu_\nu \ell}{2\pi} \right) \ln (r_2/r_1) \qquad [8.2\text{-}10]$$

and the inductance per unit length is

$$\overline{L} = \frac{L}{\ell} = \left(\frac{\mu_r \mu_\nu}{2\pi} \right) \ln (r_2/r_1) \qquad [8.2\text{-}11]$$

In Eqs. 8.2-10 and 8.2-11 the internal flux linkages are neglected, and only the flux between the conductors is considered. Since $\mu_\nu = 4\pi \times 10^{-7}$ in the rationalized MKS system,

$$\overline{L} = 2\mu_r \times 10^{-7} \ln (r_2/r_1) \text{ henrys per meter} \qquad [8.2\text{-}12]$$

where μ_r is the relative permeability of the medium between the conductors.

It can be shown, in a manner similar to that used to derive Eqs. 8.2-6 and 8.2-12, that the inductance and capacitance of a parallel-wire line per unit length are given by

$$\overline{L} = \left(\frac{\mu_r \mu_\nu}{\pi} \right) \ln (D/r) = 4\mu_r \times 10^{-7} \ln (D/r) \text{ henrys per meter} \qquad [8.2\text{-}13]$$

and

$$\overline{C} = \frac{\pi \epsilon_r \epsilon_\nu}{\ln (D/r)} = \frac{10^{-9} \times \epsilon_r}{36 \ln (D/r)} \text{ farads per meter} \qquad [8.2\text{-}14]$$

where D is the distance between the centers of the wires, r is the radius of each wire, and μ_r and ϵ_r are the relative permeability and dielectric constant of the medium between the wires.* The internal flux linkages are neglected in Eq. 8.2-13. The derivation of Eqs. 8.2-13 and 8.2-14 is left as an exercise for the student.

---

* Equations 8.2-13 and 8.2-14 are based on the assumption that $D/2r \gg 1$. When this assumption is not valid, the formulas for $\overline{L}$ and $\overline{C}$ are

$$\overline{L} = \frac{\mu_r \mu_\nu}{\pi} \ln \left[\frac{D}{2r} + \sqrt{\left(\frac{D}{2r} \right)^2 - 1} \right] = \left(\frac{\mu_r \mu_\nu}{\pi} \right) \cosh^{-1} \frac{D}{2r}$$

$$\overline{C} = \frac{\pi \epsilon_r \epsilon_\nu}{\ln \left[\dfrac{D}{2r} + \sqrt{\left(\dfrac{D}{2r} \right)^2 - 1} \right]} = \frac{\pi \epsilon_r \epsilon_\nu}{\cosh^{-1} \dfrac{D}{2r}}$$

8.3 DERIVATION OF THE WAVE EQUATION

The wave equation is the partial differential equation that gives the variation of the voltage and current (or the electric and magnetic field strengths) with both time and distance measured with respect to a specified origin. An incremental length, Δx, of a two-wire transmission line is shown in Fig. 8-7. For future calculations, it will be found convenient to select the origin at the receiving end of the line, and to assume that distances measured to the left, from the receiver to the transmitter, are positive.* The reference instantaneous voltage polarities and current directions are as shown in Fig. 8-7. Other combinations of voltage polarity and current

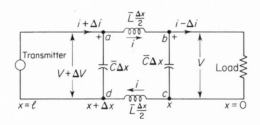

Figure 8-7 Two-wire transmission line with illustration of an incremental length.

direction may be assumed. Since the instantaneous voltage and current are functions of both distance and time, v and i in Fig. 8-7 represent $v(x,t)$ and $i(x,t)$ respectively.

The basic concept involved is that as $\Delta x \rightarrow 0$ in Fig. 8-7, lumped circuit theory may be applied to the incremental section. Since the algebraic sum of the voltage drops around a closed circuit equals zero, the algebraic sum of the voltage drops taken around $abcd$ in Fig. 8-7 equals zero. Therefore,

$$\left(\frac{\overline{L}\,\Delta x}{2}\right)\frac{\partial i}{\partial t} + v + \left(\frac{\overline{L}\,\Delta x}{2}\right)\frac{\partial i}{\partial t} - (v + \Delta v) = 0 \qquad [8.3\text{-}1]$$

where the partial derivative, $\partial i/\partial t$, is used because the current, i, is a function of distance as well as of time. It follows from Eq. 8.3-1 that

$$\overline{L}\,\Delta x\,\frac{\partial i}{\partial t} = \Delta v \qquad [8.3\text{-}2]$$

In the limit, as $\Delta x \rightarrow 0$, Eq. 8.3-2 becomes

$$\overline{L}\,\frac{\partial i}{\partial t} = \frac{\partial v}{\partial x} \qquad [8.3\text{-}3]$$

* The receiver is the load.

Inasmuch as the current flowing *into* node a equals the current flowing *out of* node a, the following relation holds:

$$i + \Delta i = i + \frac{\partial}{\partial t} \Delta q \qquad [8.3\text{-}4]$$

where Δq is the charge on the capacitor representing the distributed capacitance between points a and d. Therefore,

$$\Delta q = v\overline{C}\, \Delta x \qquad [8.3\text{-}5]$$

The substitution of Eq. 8.3-5 into Eq. 8.3-4 yields

$$i + \Delta i = i + \overline{C}\, \Delta x\, \frac{\partial v}{\partial t} \qquad [8.3\text{-}6]$$

where the partial derivative, $\partial v/\partial t$, is used because the voltage is a function of the distance as well as of time. In the limit, as $\Delta x \to 0$, Eq. 8.3-6 becomes

$$\overline{C}\, \frac{\partial v}{\partial t} = \frac{\partial i}{\partial x} \qquad [8.3\text{-}7]$$

When Eq. 8.3-3 is differentiated with respect to x, the following result is obtained:

$$\frac{\partial^2 v}{\partial x^2} = \overline{L}\, \frac{\partial}{\partial x}\, \frac{\partial i}{\partial t} \qquad [8.3\text{-}8]$$

Assuming that the order of differentiation on the right-hand side of Eq. 8.3-8 may be reversed, Eq. 8.3-8 may be written as

$$\frac{\partial^2 v}{\partial x^2} = \overline{L}\, \frac{\partial}{\partial t}\, \frac{\partial i}{\partial x} \qquad [8.3\text{-}9]$$

The substitution of $\partial i/\partial x$ from Eq. 8.3-7 into Eq. 8.3-9 yields

$$\frac{\partial^2 v}{\partial x^2} = \overline{L}\, \overline{C}\, \frac{\partial^2 v}{\partial t^2} \qquad [8.3\text{-}10]$$

Equation 8.3-10 is the *wave equation for the voltage* and gives the variation of the voltage with respect to both distance and time.

Differentiation of Eq. 8.3-7 with respect to x yields

$$\frac{\partial^2 i}{\partial x^2} = \overline{C}\, \frac{\partial}{\partial x}\, \frac{\partial v}{\partial t} \qquad [8.3\text{-}11]$$

Equation 8.3-11 may also be written as

$$\frac{\partial^2 i}{\partial x^2} = \overline{C} \frac{\partial}{\partial t} \frac{\partial v}{\partial x} \qquad [8.3\text{-}12]$$

The substitution of $\partial v/\partial x$ from Eq. 8.3-3 into Eq. 8.3-12 yields

$$\frac{\partial^2 i}{\partial x^2} = \overline{L}\,\overline{C} \frac{\partial^2 i}{\partial t^2} \qquad [8.3\text{-}13]$$

Equation 8.3-13 is the *wave equation for the current*, and has exactly the same form as Eq. 8.3-10.

8.4 SOLUTION OF THE WAVE EQUATION

Equation 8.3-10 can be written as

$$\frac{\partial^2 v}{\partial x^2} - \overline{L}\,\overline{C} \frac{\partial^2 v}{\partial t^2} = 0 \qquad [8.4\text{-}1]$$

The classical operational equivalent* of Eq. 8.4-1 is the following:

$$(D_x - \sqrt{\overline{L}\,\overline{C}}\, D_t)(D_x + \sqrt{\overline{L}\,\overline{C}}\, D_t)v = 0 \qquad [8.4\text{-}2]$$

where D_x and D_t respectively denote the partial derivatives with respect to x and t. The following relations are derived directly from Eq. 8.4-2:

$$(D_x - \sqrt{\overline{L}\,\overline{C}}\, D_t)v = 0 \qquad [8.4\text{-}3]$$

$$\frac{\partial v}{\partial x} = \sqrt{\overline{L}\,\overline{C}} \frac{\partial v}{\partial t} \qquad [8.4\text{-}4]$$

$$(D_x + \sqrt{\overline{L}\,\overline{C}}\, D_t)v = 0 \qquad [8.4\text{-}5]$$

$$\frac{\partial v}{\partial x} = -\sqrt{\overline{L}\,\overline{C}} \frac{\partial v}{\partial t} \qquad [8.4\text{-}6]$$

It is seen from Eqs. 8.4-3 and 8.4-6 that, in order to satisfy the wave equation, the voltage must be such a function of time and distance that its derivative with respect to distance equals its derivative with respect to time multiplied by $\pm\sqrt{\overline{L}\,\overline{C}}$. Such a function is

* The classical operator is discussed in *Transient Analysis in Electrical Engineering* by Sylvan Fich (Prentice-Hall, Inc., Englewood Cliffs, New Jersey, 1951), pages 14–18.

$$v(x,t) = f(t + t_1 + \sqrt{L\,C}\, x) \qquad [8.4\text{-}7]$$

where f denotes any function, and t_1 is an arbitrary constant. Partial differentiation of Eq. 8.4-7 with respect to t yields

$$\frac{\partial v}{\partial t} = f'(t + t_1 + \sqrt{L\,C}\, x) \qquad [8.4\text{-}8]$$

where f' denotes $\partial f/\partial y$, and $y = (t + t_1 + \sqrt{L\,C}\, x)$.* Partial differentiation of Eq. 8.4-7 with respect to x yields

$$\frac{\partial v}{\partial x} = \frac{\partial v}{\partial y}\frac{\partial y}{\partial x} = \sqrt{LC}\, f'(t + t_1 + \sqrt{L\,C}\, x) \qquad [8.4\text{-}9]$$

where $\partial y/\partial x = \sqrt{L\,C}$.

Equations 8.4-8 and 8.4-9 show that $v(x,t)$ in Eq. 8.4-7 satisfies the wave equation. Assume now that

$$v(x,t) = f(t + t_2 - \sqrt{L\,C}\, x) \qquad [8.4\text{-}10]$$

where t_2 is an arbitrary constant. Partial differentiation of Eq. 8.4-10 with respect to t and to x yields

$$\frac{\partial v}{\partial t} = f'(t + t_2 - \sqrt{L\,C}\, x) \qquad [8.4\text{-}11]$$

$$\frac{\partial v}{\partial x} = -\sqrt{L\,C}\, f'(t + t_2 - \sqrt{L\,C}\, x) \qquad [8.4\text{-}12]$$

Equations 8.4-11 and 8.4-12 show that $v(x,t)$ in Eq. 8.4-10 satisfies the wave equation. It follows that the instantaneous voltage along a lossless transmission line is given by

$$v(x,t) = f_1(t + t_1 + \sqrt{L\,C}\, x) + f_2(t + t_2 - \sqrt{L\,C}\, x) \qquad [8.4\text{-}13]$$

where f_1 and f_2 are arbitrary functions depending upon the type of excitation. Inspection of Eq. 8.4-13 shows that $\sqrt{L\,C}\, x$ has the dimension of

---

* Note that $\dfrac{\partial y}{\partial t} = 1$ in Eq. 8.4-8. If $v(x,t) = \sin \omega(t + t_1 + \sqrt{L\,C}\, x) = \sin y$, then

$\dfrac{\partial}{\partial t}\, v(x,t) = \dfrac{\partial v}{\partial y}\dfrac{\partial y}{\partial t} = \omega \cos \omega(t + t_1 + \sqrt{L\,C}\, x)$. In this case, $\dfrac{\partial y}{\partial t} = \omega$. In general,

$\dfrac{\partial v}{\partial t} = \dfrac{\partial v}{\partial y}\dfrac{\partial y}{\partial t}$.

time. Hence, $1/\sqrt{\overline{L}\,\overline{C}}$ has the dimension of a velocity, and is the actual velocity of propagation of the wave. A discussion of phase velocities is reserved for Sec. 8.6.

8.5 VOLTAGE AND CURRENT DISTRIBUTIONS

For arbitrary excitation, the instantaneous voltage is given by

$$v(x,t) = f_1(t + t_1 + \sqrt{\overline{L}\,\overline{C}}\,x) + f_2(t + t_2 - \sqrt{\overline{L}\,\overline{C}}\,x) \qquad [8.5\text{-}1]$$

As shown by Eq. 8.3-3,

$$\frac{\partial i}{\partial t} = \frac{1}{\overline{L}}\frac{\partial v}{\partial x} \qquad [8.5\text{-}2]$$

It follows that the current can be determined by differentiating the voltage with respect to x, dividing by $\overline{L}$, and integrating with respect to t. Thus,

$$\frac{\partial v}{\partial x} = \sqrt{\overline{L}\,\overline{C}}\,f_1'(t + t_1 + \sqrt{\overline{L}\,\overline{C}}\,x) - \sqrt{\overline{L}\,\overline{C}}\,f_2'(t + t_2 - \sqrt{\overline{L}\,\overline{C}}\,x) \quad [8.5\text{-}3]$$

$$\frac{\partial i}{\partial t} = \frac{1}{\overline{L}}\frac{\partial v}{\partial x} = \sqrt{\frac{\overline{C}}{\overline{L}}}\,f_1'(t + t_1 + \sqrt{\overline{L}\,\overline{C}}\,x) - \sqrt{\frac{\overline{C}}{\overline{L}}}\,f_2'(t + t_2 - \sqrt{\overline{L}\,\overline{C}}\,x) \quad [8.5\text{-}4]$$

The integration of Eq. 8.5-4 with respect to t yields

$$i(x,t) = \sqrt{\frac{\overline{C}}{\overline{L}}}\,f_1(t + t_1 + \sqrt{\overline{L}\,\overline{C}}\,x)$$

$$- \sqrt{\frac{\overline{C}}{\overline{L}}}\,f_2(t + t_2 - \sqrt{\overline{L}\,\overline{C}}\,x) + F(x) \qquad [8.5\text{-}5]$$

where $F(x)$ is independent of t, and is an arbitrary constant in integrating with respect to t.

The value of $F(x)$ can be determined by applying Eq. 8.3-7 to Eq. 8.5-5 to find $\partial v/\partial t$, then integrating with respect to t, and finally comparing the resulting expression for $v(x,t)$ with Eq. 8.5-1. It follows from Eq. 8.3-7 that

$$\frac{\partial v}{\partial t} = \frac{1}{\overline{C}}\frac{\partial i}{\partial x} \qquad [8.5\text{-}6]$$

The differentiation of Eq. 8.5-5 with respect to x yields

$$\frac{\partial i}{\partial x} = \overline{C} f_1'(t + t_1 + \sqrt{L\,\overline{C}}\ x) + \overline{C} f_2'(t + t_2 - \sqrt{L\,\overline{C}}\ x) + F'(x) \qquad [8.5\text{-}7]$$

where $F'(x) = dF/dx$. It follows from Eqs. 8.5-6 and 8.5-7 that

$$\frac{\partial v}{\partial t} = f_1'(t + t_1 + \sqrt{L\,\overline{C}}\ x) + f_2'(t + t_2 - \sqrt{L\,\overline{C}}\ x) + \left(\frac{1}{C}\right) F'(x) \qquad [8.5\text{-}8]$$

The integration of Eq. 8.5-8 with respect to t yields

$$\begin{aligned} v(x,t) &= f_1(t + t_1 + \sqrt{L\,\overline{C}}\ x) \\ &\quad + f_2(t + t_2 - \sqrt{L\,\overline{C}}\ x) + \left(\frac{t}{C}\right) F'(x) + F_1(x) \end{aligned} \qquad [8.5\text{-}9]$$

where $F_1(x)$ is an arbitrary function of x.

A comparison of Eqs. 8.5-1 and 8.5-9 shows that

$$\left(\frac{t}{C}\right) F'(x) + F_1(x) = 0 \qquad [8.5\text{-}10]$$

If Eq. 8.5-10 is to be valid for all values of x and t, both $F'(x)$ and $F_1(x)$ must vanish. In other words $F_1(x)$ must be equal to zero, and $F(x)$ can at most be a constant. Since a constant added to the expression for $v(x,t)$ simply determines the level about which the voltage varies, it contributes no information concerning wave propagation, and may therefore be disregarded or considered equal to zero.

When $F(x) = 0$, Eq. 8.5-5 becomes

$$i(x,t) = \sqrt{\frac{\overline{C}}{L}} f_1(t + t_1 + \sqrt{L\,\overline{C}}\ x) - \sqrt{\frac{\overline{C}}{L}} f_2(t + t_2 - \sqrt{L\,\overline{C}}\ x) \qquad [8.5\text{-}11]$$

A comparison of Eqs. 8.5-1 and 8.5-11 shows that both the voltage wave and the current wave consist of two components, and that the current component is derived from the voltage component by multiplying the first voltage component by $\sqrt{C/L}$, and the second by $-\sqrt{C/L}$. It will be shown later that the two components correspond to the direct and reflected waves. The ratio

$$Y_0 = G_0 = \sqrt{\frac{\overline{C}}{L}} \qquad [8.5\text{-}12]$$

is termed the *characteristic admittance* of the line, and the ratio

$$Z_0 = R_0 = \sqrt{\frac{\overline{L}}{C}} \qquad [8.5\text{-}13]$$

is termed the *characteristic impedance* of the line. In lossless lines, both Y_0 and Z_0 are real numbers.

It follows from Eqs. 8.2-6 and 8.2-12 that the characteristic impedance of coaxial cables is given by

$$Z_0 = 60 \sqrt{\frac{\mu_r}{\epsilon_r}} \ln (r_2/r_1) \text{ ohms} \qquad [8.5\text{-}14]$$

It follows from Eqs. 8.2-13 and 8.2-14 that the characteristic impedance of parallel-wire lines is given by

$$Z_0 = 120 \sqrt{\frac{\mu_r}{\epsilon_r}} \ln (D/r) \text{ ohms} \qquad [8.5\text{-}15]$$

It is important to note that the characteristic impedance is the absolute value of the ratio of the voltage to the current in each of the two components of the total wave.

In the case of steady-state sinusoidal excitation (sine or cosine), $f_1(t)$ and $f_2(t)$ in Eqs. 8.5-1 and 8.5-11 may be replaced by exponentials* of the form $|V_{m1}|\epsilon^{j\omega t}$ and $|V_{m2}|\epsilon^{j\omega t}$, and the instantaneous voltage and current are given by

$$v(x,t) = V_{m1}\epsilon^{j\omega(t+t_1+\sqrt{LC}\,x)} + V_{m2}\epsilon^{j\omega(t+t_2-\sqrt{LC}\,x)} \qquad [8.5\text{-}16]$$

$$i(x,t) = \frac{|V_{m1}|}{Z_0} e^{j\omega(t+t_1+\sqrt{LC}\,x)} - \frac{|V_{m2}|}{Z_0} e^{j\omega(t+t_2-\sqrt{LC}\,x)} \qquad [8.5\text{-}17]$$

where $|V_{m1}|$ and $|V_{m2}|$ are respectively the maximum values of the two components of the voltage wave. The real part of the expression is used for cosine excitation, and the imaginary part is used for sine excitation. Thus, when a cosine voltage is impressed,

$$v(x,t) = |V_{m1}| \cos \omega(t + t_1 + \sqrt{L\,C}\,x)$$
$$+ |V_{m2}| \cos \omega(t + t_2 - \sqrt{L\,C}\,x) \qquad [8.5\text{-}18]$$

and when a sine voltage is impressed,

$$v(x,t) = |V_{m1}| \sin \omega(t + t_1 + \sqrt{L\,C}\,x)$$
$$+ |V_{m2}| \sin \omega(t + t_2 - \sqrt{L\,C}\,x) \qquad [8.5\text{-}19]$$

* The exponential replacement of sine and cosine functions is presented in *Theory of A-C Circuits*, by S. Fich and J. L. Potter (Prentice-Hall, Inc., Englewood Cliffs, New Jersey, 1958), pages 45–49.

Equations 8.5-18 and 8.5-19 can also be written as follows:

$$v(x,t) = |V_{m1}| \cos [\omega(t + t_1) + \beta x] + |V_{m2}| \cos [\omega(t + t_2) - \beta x] \quad [8.5\text{-}20]$$
$$v(x,t) = |V_{m1}| \sin [\omega(t + t_1) + \beta x] + |V_{m2}| \sin [\omega(t + t_2) - \beta x] \quad [8.5\text{-}21]$$

where $\beta = \omega\sqrt{L\,C}$.

8.6 PHASE VELOCITIES OF PROPAGATION

Considering only the second terms in Eqs. 8.5-18 and 8.5-19, it is seen that the voltage remains constant if x and t change at such a rate that the angle $\omega(t + t_2 - \sqrt{L\,C}\,x)$ remains constant. The rate of change of x with respect to t required to maintain the angle constant when both x and t are varied is the *phase velocity*. This term is derived from the fact that motion along the line with such a velocity is required to maintain the instantaneous phase of the disturbance constant. Assume that x is changed by motion along the line to $(x + dx)$, and that this change in position requires a time interval, dt. In other words, when x becomes $(x + dx)$, t becomes $(t + dt)$. The condition for constant phase is

$$t + t_1 - \sqrt{L\,C}\,x = (t + dt) + t_1 - \sqrt{L\,C}\,(x + dx) \quad [8.6\text{-}1]$$

The solution of Eq. 8.6-1 yields

$$u_p = \frac{dx}{dt} = \frac{1}{\sqrt{L\,C}} \quad [8.6\text{-}2]$$

where u_p is the phase velocity. It should be noted that, in lossless lines, the phase velocity is independent of the frequency if L and C are assumed constant. It will be shown later that, when losses occur, the phase velocity generally depends upon the frequency.

Considering only the first terms in Eqs. 8.5-18 and 8.5-19, the condition for constant phase is

$$t + t_1 + \sqrt{L\,C}\,x = (t + dt) + t_1 + \sqrt{L\,C}\,(x + dx) \quad [8.6\text{-}3]$$

The solution of Eq. 8.6-3 yields

$$u_p = \frac{dx}{dt} = -\frac{1}{\sqrt{L\,C}} \quad [8.6\text{-}4]$$

A comparison of Eqs. 8.6-2 and 8.6-4 with Eqs. 8.5-18 and 8.5-19 shows that the second terms in Eqs. 8.5-18 and 8.5-19 denote a wave travelling in the positive direction with a phase velocity of $1/\sqrt{L\,C}$, whereas the first terms represent a wave travelling in the negative direction with the same velocity. The same result is obtained from Eq. 8.5-1, which holds for arbitrary excitation.* It follows that the solution of the wave equation indicates the possibility of the simultaneous existence along a transmission line of two waves travelling with equal and opposite velocity along the line. One of these waves is termed the *direct wave*, and the other is termed the *reflected wave*. The direct wave travels from the source or transmitter to the load or receiver; the reflected wave travels from the receiver to the transmitter. At this point it should be carefully noted that either the direct or the reflected wave may have a positive or a negative phase velocity. This depends solely upon the choice of the origin. Referring to Fig. 8-7, it is seen that when the origin is selected as in that figure, the reflected wave has a positive phase velocity and the direct wave has a negative phase velocity. If the origin were chosen at the transmitter, with distances measured to the right as positive, the direct wave would have a positive velocity, and the velocity of the reflected wave would be negative. Derivations in this chapter will conform to the coordinate system shown in Fig. 8-7.

Inspection of Eqs. 8.5-16 and 8.5-17 shows that the ratio of voltage to current in the reflected wave is opposite to that in the direct wave, and has an absolute value of Z_0 for both waves. The physical reason for the change in sign is that the flow of power in the reflected wave is opposite to that in the direct wave. This condition requires a change of sign in either the voltage or current in the reflected wave with respect to the direct wave.

It follows from Eqs. 8.2-6 and 8.2-12 that the phase velocity in coaxial cables is given by

$$u_p = \frac{1}{\sqrt{L\,C}} = \left[\frac{18 \ln (r_2/r_1)}{2\mu_r\epsilon_r \times 10^{-16} \ln (r_2/r_1)} \right]^{1/2} = \frac{3 \times 10^8}{\sqrt{\mu_r\epsilon_r}} \qquad [8.6\text{-}5]$$

In free space, where $\mu_r = \epsilon_r = 1$,

$$u_p = c = 3 \times 10^8 \text{ meters per sec} \qquad [8.6\text{-}6]$$

Similarly, it follows from Eqs. 8.2-13 and 8.2-14 that, in parallel-wire lines,

$$u_p = \frac{1}{\sqrt{L\,C}} = \left[\frac{36 \ln (D/r)}{4\mu_r\epsilon_r \times 10^{-16} \ln (D/r)} \right]^{1/2} = \frac{3 \times 10^8}{\sqrt{\mu_r\epsilon_r}} \qquad [8.6\text{-}7]$$

* It follows that the phase velocity on lossless lines is independent of the type of excitation.

In free space, where $\mu_r = \epsilon_r = 1$,

$$u_p = c = 3 \times 10^8 \text{ meters per sec} \qquad [8.6\text{-}8]$$

Reference to Eqs. 8.5-20 and 8.5-21 shows that the angular phase displacement caused by propagation over a distance x is given by

$$\theta = \omega \sqrt{L\,C}\, x = \beta x \qquad [8.6\text{-}9]$$

Hence,

$$\beta = \omega \sqrt{L\,C} = \frac{\omega}{u_p} = \frac{2\pi f}{f\lambda} = \frac{2\pi}{\lambda} \qquad [8.6\text{-}10]$$

where λ is the wavelength corresponding to the phase velocity u_p at the given frequency. Inasmuch as u_p is a constant in lossless lines, β is always a constant multiple of the frequency in lossless lines. When losses exist, both β and u_p are functions of the frequency, and the components of different frequency in a signal have different velocities of propagation.

8.7 REFLECTION AND STANDING WAVES

In the general case, when reflection exists, the electromagnetic propagation may be represented by two waves travelling with equal and opposite velocities on the line. These waves are termed the *direct wave* and the *reflected wave*. At some points along the line, the direct and reflected waves reinforce each other, and the resultant effect is greater than that of the direct wave alone; at other points, the resultant effect is less than that of the direct wave. This phenomenon is known as interference. In the case of sinusoidal excitation, the voltage and the current at every point on the line vary sinusoidally with time, but the maximum value of the voltage and of the current varies with the distance. The variation of the maximum or effective voltage and current with distance produces a *standing wave pattern*. A standing wave pattern of voltage is shown in Fig. 8-8, where it is assumed that the amplitude of the reflected wave equals that of the direct wave. In such a case, the voltage along the line varies from twice the voltage of the direct wave to zero, resulting from complete reinforcement or constructive interference at some points, and from complete destructive interference at other points.

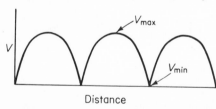

Figure 8-8 Voltage standing wave pattern.

In order to study the effects of reflection on standing wave patterns, the equations for the voltage and current distributions are written in the following form:

$$v(x,t) = |V_m(x)| \epsilon^{j(\omega t + \theta_1)}$$

$$= |V_{m1}| \epsilon^{j\omega(t+t_1)} \epsilon^{j\beta x} + |V_{m2}| \epsilon^{j\omega(t+t_2)} \epsilon^{-j\beta x} \qquad [8.7\text{-}1]$$

$$i(x,t) = |I_m(x)| \epsilon^{j(\omega t + \theta_2)}$$

$$= \left(\frac{|V_{m1}|}{Z_0}\right) \epsilon^{j\omega(t+t_1)} \epsilon^{j\beta x} - \left(\frac{|V_{m2}|}{Z_0}\right) \epsilon^{j\omega(t+t_2)} \epsilon^{-j\beta x} \qquad [8.7\text{-}2]$$

where $|V_m(x)|$ and $|I_m(x)|$ respectively represent the maximum voltage and current at a point located a distance x from the receiver, and where $\beta = \omega \sqrt{L\,C}$. The equations are written so as to demonstrate that the maximum current and maximum voltage are functions of the distance in a standing wave pattern.

The time variables in Eqs. 8.7-1 and 8.7-2 are eliminated by dividing by $\epsilon^{j\omega t}$, and the maximum values are reduced to effective values by dividing by $\sqrt{2}$. Dividing both sides of Eqs. 8.7-1 and 8.7-2 by $\sqrt{2}\ \epsilon^{j\omega t}$ yields

$$V(x) \doteq |V_1| \epsilon^{j\omega t_1} \epsilon^{j\beta x} + |V_2| \epsilon^{j\omega t_2} \epsilon^{-j\beta x}$$

$$\qquad\qquad\qquad\qquad\qquad\qquad [8.7\text{-}3]$$

$$I(x) = \frac{|V_1|}{Z_0} \epsilon^{j\omega t_1} \epsilon^{j\beta x} - \frac{|V_2|}{Z_0} \epsilon^{j\omega t_2} \epsilon^{-j\beta x}$$

where $\quad V(x) = \dfrac{|V_m(x)| \epsilon^{j\theta_1}}{\sqrt{2}}$

$$I(x) = \dfrac{|I_m(x)| \epsilon^{j\theta_2}}{\sqrt{2}}$$

$$|V_1| = \dfrac{|V_{m1}|}{\sqrt{2}}$$

$$|V_2| = \dfrac{|V_{m2}|}{\sqrt{2}}$$

In Eqs. 8.7-3, $V(x)$ and $I(x)$ are the complex numbers, termed phasors or sinors, that generate the sinusoidal functions of time at the angular frequency, ω, at points along the line. Equations 8.7-3 can be written as follows:

$$V(x) = |V_1| \epsilon^{j\omega t_1} \epsilon^{j\beta x} \left[1 + \left(\frac{|V_2|}{|V_1|}\right) \epsilon^{j\omega(t_2-t_1)} \epsilon^{-2j\beta x} \right] \qquad [8.7\text{-}4]$$

$$I(x) = \frac{|V_1|}{Z_0} \epsilon^{j\omega t_1} \epsilon^{j\beta x} \left[1 - \left(\frac{|V_2|}{|V_1|}\right) \epsilon^{j\omega(t_2-t_1)} \epsilon^{-2j\beta x} \right] \qquad [8.7\text{-}5]$$

The ratio

$$\rho = |\rho|\epsilon^{j\phi} = \left(\frac{|V_2|}{|V_1|}\right)\epsilon^{j\omega(t_2 - t_1)} \qquad [8.7\text{-}6]$$

is the *complex voltage reflection coefficient* at the receiver; it is the ratio of the reflected voltage to the direct voltage measured at the receiver or origin where $x = 0$. In Eq. 8.7-6,

$$|\rho| = \frac{|V_2|}{|V_1|} \qquad [8.7\text{-}7]$$

and

$$\phi = \omega(t_2 - t_1) \qquad [8.7\text{-}8]$$

It may now be seen that the purpose of introducing the constants t_1 and t_2 into the solution of the wave equation in Eqs. 8.4-7 and 8.4-10 was to provide for a *phase shift* when reflection occurs at the load.

The standing wave pattern can now be described by the following equations:

$$V(x) = V_1\epsilon^{j\beta x}[1 + |\rho|\epsilon^{-j(2\beta x - \phi)}] \qquad [8.7\text{-}9]$$

$$I(x) = \left(\frac{V_1}{Z_0}\right)\epsilon^{j\beta x}[1 - |\rho|\epsilon^{-j(2\beta x - \phi)}] \qquad [8.7\text{-}10]$$

where $V_1 = |V_1|\epsilon^{j\omega t_1}$, $\beta = \omega\sqrt{L\,C}$, and $|\rho|$ and ϕ are given by Eqs. 8.7-7 and 8.7-8.

An inspection of Eq. 8.7-9 shows that the voltage is a maximum when

$$2\beta x - \phi = 2n\pi \qquad [8.7\text{-}11]$$

when n equals zero or any integer.

The maximum absolute value of the voltage is

$$|V(x)|_{\max} = (1 + |\rho|)|V_1| \qquad [8.7\text{-}12]$$

The voltage is a minimum when

$$2\beta x - \phi = (2n + 1)\pi \qquad [8.7\text{-}13]$$

when n equals zero or any integer. The minimum absolute value of the voltage is

$$|V(x)|_{\min} = (1 - |\rho|)|V_1| \qquad [8.7\text{-}14]$$

An inspection of Eq. 8.7-10 shows that the current is a maximum when Eq. 8.7-13 is satisfied; the current has a maximum absolute value of

$$|I(x)|_{\mathrm{max}} = \frac{|V_1|}{Z_0}\,(1 + |\rho|) \qquad\qquad [8.7\text{-}15]$$

The minimum current occurs when Eq. 8.7-11 is satisfied. The minimum absolute value of the current is

$$|I(x)|_{\mathrm{min}} = \frac{|V_1|}{Z_0}\,(1 - |\rho|) \qquad\qquad [8.7\text{-}16]$$

The points of minima are termed *nodes;* the points of maxima are termed *anti-nodes.* The ratio of the amplitude of a standing wave at an anti-node to the amplitude at a node is defined as the *standing wave ratio,* and is denoted by the symbol S. It follows from Eqs. 8.7-12 and 8.7-14 and from Eqs. 8.7-15 and 8.7-16 that the standing wave ratio is

$$S = \frac{1 + |\rho|}{1 - |\rho|} \qquad\qquad [8.7\text{-}17]$$

It should be noted from Eqs. 8.7-9 and 8.7-10 that the standing wave pattern is a function of $2\beta x$. Hence, the pattern is repeated when the value of βx is changed by an integral multiple of π. Voltage and current standing wave patterns are shown in Fig. 8-9 for an assumed value of

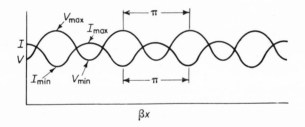

Figure 8-9 Voltage and current standing wave patterns ($S = 3$).

$S = 3$. Note that the voltage maxima coincide with the current minima, and the voltage minima coincide with the current maxima. It is also seen in Fig. 8-9 that the period, considered as a function of βx, is π.

The receiver impedance, Z_r, determines the ratio of voltage to current at the receiver where, $x = 0$. In fact, the reflected waves of voltage and current have the proper amplitude and phase so that, when combined with the direct waves, the following relation holds:

$$\frac{V_r}{I_r} = \frac{V(0)}{I(0)} = Z_r \qquad\qquad [8.7\text{-}18]$$

where the subscript, r, denotes the receiver. Setting x equal to zero in Eqs. 8.7-9 and 8.7-10, and substituting the resulting equations in Eq. 8.7-18, yields

$$Z_r = Z_0 \left(\frac{1 + \rho}{1 - \rho}\right) \qquad [8.7\text{-}19]$$

where ρ is the complex voltage reflection coefficient given by Eq. 8.7-6. The solution of Eq. 8.7-19 for ρ yields

$$\rho = \frac{Z_r - Z_0}{Z_r + Z_0} \qquad [8.7\text{-}20]$$

In a lossless line, ρ is a real number when Z_r is a pure resistance.*

It follows from Eq. 8.7-20 that when a line is terminated in its characteristic impedance $(Z_r = Z_0)$, there is no reflected wave. The reason for this is that the ratio of voltage to current in the direct wave is satisfied at the termination, and there is no need of a reflected wave to satisfy the terminal conditions. The reflected wave stems from a need to satisfy terminal conditions. The reflection coefficient for the current is

$$\rho' = \frac{Z_0 - Z_r}{Z_0 + Z_r} = -\rho \qquad [8.7\text{-}21]$$

The derivation of Eq. 8.7-21 is left as an exercise for the student.

A relative standing wave pattern can be constructed from a knowledge of the amplitude and phase of the reflection coefficient. Assume that

$$\rho = 0.5\epsilon^{-j\pi/6} \qquad [8.7\text{-}22]$$

In other words, the amplitude is 0.5 and the phase angle is 30°, lagging. The total relative voltage at the receiver, $V(0)$, is the resultant of a phasor of unit amplitude and another phasor of half that amplitude and lagging by 30°, as shown in (a) of Fig. 8-10. At 60°, or one-sixth wavelength from the receiver, the direct phasor is rotated 60° in a *positive* direction and the reflected phasor is rotated 60° in a *negative* direction, as shown in Fig. 8-10(b). The amplitudes of the phasors remain unchanged because it is assumed that the line is lossless. At a displacement of 90° from the receiver, the direct, reflected, and resultant phasors are as shown in Fig. 8-10(c). Fig. 8-10(d) gives the resultant voltage at a displacement of 180° or half a wavelength. The amplitude of the resultant in Fig. 8-10(d) is the same

---

* It follows from Eqs. 8.7-11 and 8.7-13 that either a voltage maximum or a voltage minimum exists at a resistive termination of a lossless line. In this case, the value of ϕ is either 0 or π, depending on whether $Z_r > Z_0$ or $Z_r < Z_0$.

as the amplitude in Fig. 8-10(a) because the standing wave pattern as a function of βx has a period of π. The standing wave pattern can be readily drawn with the aid of a series of phasor diagrams as shown in Fig. 8-10. In connection with Fig. 8-10, it should be noted that it follows directly

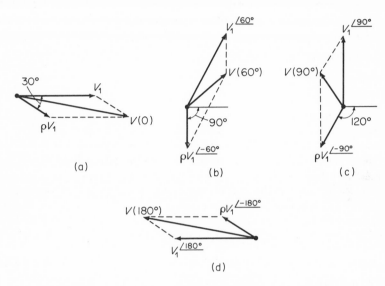

Figure 8-10   Phasor diagrams for constructing voltage standing wave pattern.

from Eq. 8.7-9 that the ratio of the reflected voltage component to the direct component at any point is given by

$$\rho(x) = \rho\epsilon^{-2j\beta x} \qquad [8.7\text{-}23]$$

where ρ is the reflection coefficient evaluated at the receiver and given by Eq. 8.7-20, and $\rho(x)$ is a complex number of constant amplitude $|\rho|$ and has a variable phase angle equal to $\phi - 2\beta x$.

The location of a voltage maximum or minimum, and the specification of the standing wave ratio, completely determine the reflection coefficient and the terminating impedance when the characteristic impedance of the line and the operating frequency are known. The voltage minimum is usually specified because it is more sharply defined than the voltage maximum. The voltage minimum nearest the load, corresponding to $n = 0$ in Eq. 8.7-13, is usually given.

Assume, for example, that a lossless line in air has a characteristic impedance of 300 ohms and is terminated by an unknown impedance. Assume further that when the frequency is 200 megacycles, the standing wave ratio is 4.48, and that the first voltage minimum is situated at 6 centimeters from the load. It is required to determine the complex reflection coefficient and the terminating impedance of the line. The wavelength at 200 megacycles and at an assumed velocity of propagation of 3×10^8 meters per second is 1.50 meters. Therefore,

$$\beta = \frac{2\pi}{\lambda} = \frac{2\pi}{1.5} = 4.18$$

It follows from Eq. 8.7-13 that:

$$2\beta x_{min} - \phi = \pi$$

where x_{min} denotes the distance of the first voltage minimum from the load. Hence,

$$\phi = 2\beta x_{min} - \pi = 0.50 - 3.14 = -2.64 \text{ radians}$$

The amplitude of the reflection coefficient is found by solving Eq. 8.7-17 for $|\rho|$ in terms of the known value of S. Thus

$$|\rho| = \frac{S-1}{S+1} = \frac{4.48-1}{4.48+1} = \frac{3.48}{5.48} = 0.635$$

Hence, $\rho = 0.635\epsilon^{-j2.64} = 0.635\underline{/-150°}$.

It follows from Eq. 8.7-19 that

$$\rho = \frac{Z_r - 300}{Z_r + 300} = 0.635\underline{/-150°} = -0.550 - j0.308$$

Hence,

$$Z_r - 300 = -0.550Z_r - j0.308Z_r - 165.0 - j92.4$$

$$(1.550 + j0.308)Z_r = 135.0 - j92.4$$

$$(1.57\underline{/11.3°})Z_r = 164.0\underline{/-34.4°}$$

$$Z_r = \frac{164.0\underline{/-34.4°}}{1.57\underline{/11.3°}} = 104.4\underline{/-45.7°} \text{ ohms}$$

This method is a standard technique of impedance measurement at frequencies that exceed the frequency ranges of ordinary bridges and the Q meter.

8.8 EQUATIONS FOR LOSSLESS LINES

Reference to Eqs. 8.7-9 and 8.7-10 shows that V_1 has not yet been evaluated. The reader is cautioned against the error of assuming that V_1 is either the input or the output voltage. For the evaluation of V_1 and the derivation of the transmission equations for lossless lines, Eqs. 8.7-9 and 8.7-10 will be written in the following form:

$$V(x) = V_1 \epsilon^{j\beta x}[1 + \rho \epsilon^{-2j\beta x}] \qquad [8.8\text{-}1]$$

$$I(x) = \left(\frac{V_1}{Z_0}\right) \epsilon^{j\beta x}[1 - \rho \epsilon^{-2j\beta x}] \qquad [8.8\text{-}2]$$

where

$$\rho = \frac{Z_r - Z_0}{Z_r + Z_0} \qquad [8.8\text{-}3]$$

and

$$V(0) = V_r \qquad [8.8\text{-}4]$$

where V_r is the receiver voltage.

It follows from Eqs. 8.8-1 and 8.8-4 that

$$V_r = (1 + \rho)V_1$$

$$V_1 = \frac{V_r}{1 + \rho} = \frac{V_r}{1 + (Z_r - Z_0)/(Z_r + Z_0)} = \frac{(Z_r + Z_0)V_r}{2Z_r} \qquad [8.8\text{-}5]$$

The substitution of Eq. 8.8-5 into Eqs. 8.8-1 and 8.8-2 yields

$$V(x) = \frac{V_r}{Z_r}\left[\left(\frac{Z_r + Z_0}{2}\right)\epsilon^{j\beta x} + \left(\frac{Z_r + Z_0}{2}\right)\left(\frac{Z_r - Z_0}{Z_r + Z_0}\right)\epsilon^{-j\beta x}\right] \qquad [8.8\text{-}6]$$

$$V(x) = \frac{V_r}{Z_r}\left[Z_r\left(\frac{\epsilon^{j\beta x} + \epsilon^{-j\beta x}}{2}\right) + Z_0\left(\frac{\epsilon^{j\beta x} - \epsilon^{-j\beta x}}{2}\right)\right] \qquad [8.8\text{-}7]$$

$$I(x) = \frac{V_r}{Z_0 Z_r}\left[\left(\frac{Z_r + Z_0}{2}\right)\epsilon^{j\beta x} - \left(\frac{Z_r + Z_0}{2}\right)\left(\frac{Z_r - Z_0}{Z_r + Z_0}\right)\epsilon^{-j\beta x}\right] \qquad [8.8\text{-}8]$$

$$I(x) = \frac{V_r}{Z_0 Z_r}\left[Z_0\left(\frac{\epsilon^{j\beta x} + \epsilon^{-j\beta x}}{2}\right) + Z_r\left(\frac{\epsilon^{j\beta x} - \epsilon^{-j\beta x}}{2}\right)\right] \qquad [8.8\text{-}9]$$

Substituting the relations

$$\cos \beta x = \frac{\epsilon^{j\beta x} + \epsilon^{-j\beta x}}{2}$$

$$j \sin \beta x = \frac{\epsilon^{j\beta x} - \epsilon^{-j\beta x}}{2}$$

into Eqs. 8.8-7 and 8.8-9, and simplifying, gives the following results:

$$V(x) = V_r \cos \beta x + jI_r Z_0 \sin \beta x \qquad [8.8\text{-}10]$$

$$I(x) = I_r \cos \beta x + j\left(\frac{V_r}{Z_0}\right) \sin \beta x \qquad [8.8\text{-}11]$$

where

$$I_r = \frac{V_r}{Z_r} \qquad [8.8\text{-}12]$$

Equations 8.8-10 and 8.8-11 give the voltage and current distributions in terms of the receiver quantities at $x = 0$. These equations can be modified to give the voltage and current along the line, in terms of the voltage and current at any point on the line taken as the origin, with distances measured to the left of the reference point taken as positive as in Fig. 8-7. Hence, when the transmitting or sending end is taken as the origin, and V_s and I_s are respectively the sending-end voltage and current, the voltage and current at any point at a distance z from the transmitter is given by

$$V(z) = V_s \cos(-\beta z) + jI_s Z_0 \sin(-\beta z) \qquad [8.8\text{-}13]$$

$$I(z) = I_s \cos(-\beta z) + j\left(\frac{V_s}{Z_0}\right) \sin(-\beta z) \qquad [8.8\text{-}14]$$

The minus signs are used in Eqs. 8.8-13 and 8.8-14 because the distance z is necessarily measured to the right of the transmitter in Fig. 8-7. Since $\cos(-\beta z) = \cos \beta z$, and since $\sin(-\beta z) = -\sin \beta z$, Eqs. 8.8-13 and 8.8-14 can be written as

$$V(z) = V_s \cos \beta z - jZ_0 I_s \sin \beta z \qquad [8.8\text{-}15]$$

$$I(z) = I_s \cos \beta z - j\left(\frac{V_s}{Z_0}\right) \sin \beta z \qquad [8.8\text{-}16]$$

where z is the distance from the transmitter at the sending end of the line.

8.9 VARIATION OF IMPEDANCE

The ratio of the voltage to the current at any point along a line is the impedance at that point. In general, the voltage and the current each consists of two components, the direct and the reflected. Although the absolute value of the ratio of voltage to current is Z_0 for both the direct and the reflected wave, the impedance at any point when reflection occurs is different from Z_0 and is also a function of x, the distance from the receiver. For this reason, the impedance is to be denoted by $Z(x)$. The reason why $Z(x)$ is different from Z_0 and varies with position when the reflection occurs, is that the direct and the reflected components are a function of position as shown in Fig. 8-10. Reference to Fig. 8-9 shows that the ratio of total voltage to total current (the sum of the direct and the reflected components) is a function of position when a standing wave pattern exists. It follows directly from Eqs. 8.7-9 and 8.7-10 that the impedance is

$$\frac{V(x)}{I(x)} = Z(x) = Z_0 \left[\frac{1 + |\rho| \epsilon^{-j(2\beta x - \phi)}}{1 - |\rho| \epsilon^{-j(2\beta x - \phi)}} \right] \qquad [8.9\text{-}1]$$

At a voltage maximum, $2\beta x - \phi = 2n\pi$, and

$$Z_{\max} = Z_0 \left[\frac{1 + |\rho|}{1 - |\rho|} \right] = S Z_0 \qquad [8.9\text{-}2]$$

where S is the standing wave ratio. At a voltage minimum, $2\beta x - \phi = (2n + 1)\pi$, and

$$Z_{\min} = Z_0 \left[\frac{1 - |\rho|}{1 + |\rho|} \right] = \frac{Z_0}{S_0} \qquad [8.9\text{-}3]$$

Since the line is assumed to be lossless, Z_0 is real in Eqs. 8.9-2 and 8.9-3.

It follows from Eqs. 8.9-2 and 8.9-3 that, regardless of the termination and regardless of the amplitude or phase of the reflection coefficient, the impedance is purely resistive and has its maximum value at a voltage maximum; and, at a voltage minimum, the impedance is also purely resistive and has its minimum value. It should again be noted that when Z_r is a pure resistance, either a voltage maximum or a voltage minimum exists at the termination. This follows directly from Eqs. 8.7-11 and 8.7-13.*

The trigonometric form of the impedance is found by taking the ratio of $V(x)$ and $I(x)$ in Eqs. 8.8-10 and 8.8-11. Thus,

$$Z(x) = Z_0 \left[\frac{V_r \cos \beta x + j I_r Z_0 \sin \beta x}{I_r Z_0 \cos \beta x + j V_r \sin \beta x} \right] \qquad [8.9\text{-}4]$$

Substituting $V_r = I_r Z_r$ into Eq. 8.9-4, and dividing the numerator and denominator by I_r, gives the following result:

$$Z(x) = Z_0 \left[\frac{Z_r \cos \beta x + j Z_0 \sin \beta x}{Z_0 \cos \beta x + j Z_r \sin \beta x} \right] \qquad [8.9\text{-}5]$$

Equations 8.9-3 and 8.9-5 can be used to find the terminating impedance when the standing wave ratio and the location of a voltage minimum are known, as illustrated in Fig. 8-11. If point a is a voltage minimum, the input impedance at terminals ab is given by

* When Z_r is real and greater than Z_0, $\phi = 0$; when Z_r is real and less than Z_0, $\phi = \pi$.

$$Z_{ab} = \frac{Z_0}{S} = Z_0 \left[\frac{Z_r \cos \beta x_{min} + jZ_0 \sin \beta x_{min}}{Z_0 \cos \beta x_{min} + jZ_r \sin \beta x_{min}} \right] \qquad [8.9\text{-}6]$$

The solution of Eq. 8.9-6 for Z_r yields

$$Z_r = Z_0 \left[\frac{\cos \beta x_{min} - jS \sin \beta x_{min}}{S \cos \beta x_{min} - j \sin \beta x_{min}} \right] \qquad [8.9\text{-}7]$$

The application of Eq. 8.9-7 to find the terminating impedance in the illustrative example of Sec. 8.7 is left as an exercise for the student.

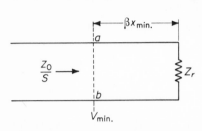

Figure 8-11 Input impedance at a voltage minimum.

Figure 8-12 shows the variation of $|Z(\beta x)|$ with the angle, βx, where $|Z(\beta x)|$ is the absolute value of the impedance at a distance, x, from the termination. This curve is formed by taking the ratio of the voltage to the current in the standing wave pattern as in the derivation of Eq. 8.9-5. The impedance is periodic, with recurrent values for a change of π in βx. The angle, βx, can be changed linearly by varying x or the frequency. This follows from the fact that $\beta = \omega/u_p$ where u_p is the phase velocity that is assumed constant in lossless lines. When the frequency is varied, the successive maxima and minima in practice will not generally have the same magnitudes as shown. This

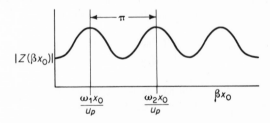

Figure 8-12 Input impedance of line with fault as a function of frequency.

results from the variation of the circuit parameters with frequency and from the effect of losses. The general effect is to raise the impedance levels at the higher frequencies. On lossless lines, the separation between adjacent maxima and minima is always $\beta x = \pi$. This relation can be applied in the location of faults on smooth lines.

A fault, or an abrupt change of impedance*, will cause reflection,

* Open or short circuits are extreme cases.

and an impedance variation is shown in Fig. 8-12. Assume that a fault exists at a distance x_0 from the transmitter. This can be considered to be the load, or termination, of the line between the transmitter and the fault. As the frequency is varied, the impedance $|Z(\beta x_0)|$, as measured at the transmitter, will follow a curve similar to the one shown in Fig. 8-12. The angular displacement of the fault from the transmitter will be equivalent to $\beta_1 x_0$ radians at a frequency f_1, and $\beta_2 x_0$ at a frequency f_2. Assume that the impedance is a maximum at f_1, and that f_2 is the frequency at an adjacent maximum. Then it follows from Fig. 8-12 that

$$\beta_2 x_0 - \beta_1 x_0 = x_0(\beta_2 - \beta_1) = \pi \qquad [8.9\text{-}8]$$

When β is expressed in terms of ω and the phase velocity, Eq. 8.9-8 becomes

$$\left(\frac{\omega_2 - \omega_1}{u_p}\right) x_0 = \pi \qquad [8.9\text{-}9]$$

where u_p is the velocity of propagation at frequencies f_1 and f_2. Solving Eq. 8.9-9 for x_0, the distance from the fault to the transmitter, gives the following result:

$$x_0 = \frac{\pi u_p}{\omega_2 - \omega_1} = \frac{u_p}{2(f_2 - f_1)} \qquad [8.9\text{-}10]$$

In the case of parallel-wire lines or coaxial cables in air, Eq. 8.9-10 can be written as

$$x_0 = \frac{c}{2\Delta f} \qquad [8.9\text{-}11]$$

where c is the velocity of propagation of light, and Δf is the frequency spread between two adjacent impedance maxima. Equation 8.9-11 is of considerable practical importance.

8.10 CALCULATIONS FOR LOSSLESS LINES

To illustrate the use of the lossless line relations, the received voltage and current will be calculated for a lossless line. Assume that the line is one kilometer long in air, has a characteristic impedance of 100 ohms, and is terminated by a 200-ohm resistor. Let the transmitter be an oscillator having a generated voltage of 10 volts and an internal resistance of 50 ohms at $\omega = 3 \times 10^5$ radians per second. Recalling that x in Eq. 8.8-9 is the distance from the receiver to the transmitter, it can be seen that the right-hand side of this equation gives the sending-end voltage, provided that $x = \ell$, where ℓ is the length of the line. Thus

$$V(\ell) = V_s = I_r(Z_r \cos \beta\ell + jZ_0 \sin \beta\ell) \qquad [8.10\text{-}1]$$

Inasmuch as the transmitter has a finite internal impedance and is delivering current, its output voltage is less than the generated voltage. In other words, V_s in Eq. 8.10-1 is not 10 volts, but is given by

$$V_s = \left(\frac{Z_{\text{in}}}{Z_{\text{in}} + 50}\right) 10 \qquad [8.10\text{-}2]$$

where $Z_{\text{in}} = Z(\ell)$ and is the input impedance of the line as measured at the transmitter, and is found from Eq. 8.9-5 to be

$$Z(\ell) = Z_{\text{in}} = Z_0 \left[\frac{Z_r \cos \beta\ell + jZ_0 \sin \beta\ell}{Z_0 \cos \beta\ell + jZ_r \sin \beta\ell}\right] \qquad [8.10\text{-}3]$$

When $\omega = 3 \times 10^5$ radians per second,

$$\beta = \frac{\omega}{c} = \frac{3 \times 10^5}{3 \times 10^8} = 10^{-3} \text{ radians per meter}$$

and $\beta\ell = 1000 \, (10^{-3}) = 1$ radian.
Hence,

$$Z_{\text{in}} = 100 \left[\frac{200 \cos 1 + j100 \sin 1}{100 \cos 1 + j200 \sin 1}\right] \qquad [8.10\text{-}4]$$

where $\cos 1$ radian $= 0.54$ and $\sin 1$ radian $= 0.84$.
The value of the input impedance is given by

$$Z_{\text{in}} = 100 \left[\frac{108 + j84}{54 + j168}\right] = \frac{13{,}700\underline{/37.8^\circ}}{177\underline{/72.2^\circ}}$$

$$= 77.4\underline{/-34.4^\circ} = 64.4 - j43.7 \text{ ohms} \qquad [8.10\text{-}5]$$

The substitution of Z_{in} from Eq. 8.10-5 into Eq. 8.10-2 yields

$$V_s = \frac{774.0\underline{/-34.4^\circ}}{114 - j43.7} = \frac{774\underline{/-34.4^\circ}}{122\underline{/-21^\circ}} = 6.34\underline{/-13.4^\circ} \text{ volts} \quad [8.10\text{-}6]$$

The receiver current for the case under consideration is found from Eq. 8.10-1 to be

$$I_r = \frac{V_s}{Z_r \cos \beta\ell + jZ_0 \sin \beta\ell} = \frac{6.34\underline{/-13.4^\circ}}{108 + j84} = \frac{6.34\underline{/-13.4^\circ}}{137\underline{/37.8^\circ}}$$

$$= 0.046\underline{/-51.2^\circ} \text{ ampere} \qquad [8.10\text{-}7]$$

The receiver voltage is

$$V_r = Z_r I_r = 200\underline{/0°} \times 0.046\underline{/-51.2°} = 9.2\underline{/-51.2°} \text{ volts} \quad [8.10\text{-}8]$$

The power delivered to the receiver is

$$P_r = |V_r|\,|I_r| = 9.2 \times 0.046 = 0.43 \text{ watt} \quad [8.10\text{-}9]$$

The power input at the sending end is

$$P_s = |V_s|\,|I_s|\cos\theta \quad [8.10\text{-}10]$$

where $|V_s|$ is the absolute value of the sending-end voltage in Eq. 8.10-6; $|I_s| = |V_s|/|Z_{in}|$, where Z_{in} is given by Eq. 8.10-5; and θ is the angle between V_s and I_s. It follows from Eqs. 8.10-5 and 8.10-6 that

$$I_s = \frac{V_s}{Z_{in}} = \frac{6.34\underline{/-13.4°}}{77.4\underline{/-34.4°}} = \frac{6.34}{77.4}\underline{/21°} \quad [8.10\text{-}11]$$

The substitution of I_s from Eq. 8.10-11 and V_s from Eq. 8.10-6 into Eq. 8.10-10 gives the following result:

$$P_s = \frac{6.34 \times 6.34}{77.4}\cos 34.4° = 0.43 \text{ watt} \quad [8.10\text{-}12]$$

The values of P_s in Eq. 8.10-12 and P_r in Eq. 8.10-9 are equal because the line was assumed to be lossless and all the power input is delivered to the receiver.

PROBLEMS

8-1 The outer diameter of the shield of a coaxial cable is 0.795 inch, and the outer radius of the inner conductor is 0.250 inch. The thickness of the shield is 0.065 inch. Assuming that the dielectric is polyethylene ($\epsilon_r = 2.25$), calculate: (a) the capacitance per mile of cable; and (b) the inductance per mile of cable.

8-2 The conductors of an open-wire transmission line in air have a diameter of 0.104 inch, and are 1 foot apart, center to center. Calculate: (a) the capacitance per mile of line; and (b) the inductance per mile of line.

8-3 Assuming that the voltage between the conductors of a coaxial cable is V and that the axial current is I, prove the following:
(a) The radial component of the electric field at a distance r from the center is given by $E_r = \dfrac{V}{r \ln{(r_2/r_1)}}.$

(b) The tangential component of the magnetic field is given by $H_\theta = I/2\pi r$.

(c) $\iint E_r H_\theta \, dA = VI$, where A is the cross-sectional area of the dielectric perpendicular to the direction of the current, and the integral in polar coordinates is taken over the cross-section. The vector product, $E_r \times H_\theta$, is the Poynting vector, and is measured in watts per unit area.

8-4 Calculate the reading of the voltmeter connected as shown in the accompanying sketch. Assume that Z, the impedance of the voltmeter, is infinite.

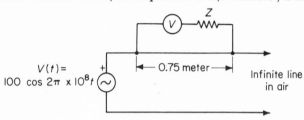

$$V(t) = 100 \cos 2\pi \times 10^8 t$$

Problem 8-4

8-5 Assuming that the dielectric strength of polyethylene is 4×10^7 volts per meter, find the maximum voltage that can be applied to the cable in Prob. 8-1 without exceeding the dielectric strength of the material.

8-6 Derive the partial differential equations for the voltage and current on the lossless line having the indicated origin, voltage polarities, and reference current shown in the diagram below. Derive the wave equations for the voltage and the current.

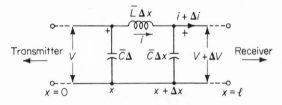

Problem 8-6

8-7 Prove that, when a transverse electromagnetic wave travels along a lossless line, the energy stored per unit length in the electric field of a single wave equals the energy stored per unit length in the magnetic field for all types of excitation.

8-8 (a) Find the outer radius of the inner conductor in Prob. 8-1 if the characteristic impedance of the cable is to be 50 ohms.

(b) Calculate the velocity of propagation along the cable.

8-9 (a) Find the required spacing of the conductors in Prob. 8-2 if the characteristic impedance of the line is to be 700 ohms.

(b) What is the velocity of propagation along the line?

8-10 A coaxial cable contains two dielectrics having relative dielectric constants of ϵ_{r1} when $r_1 < r < r_0$, and ϵ_{r2} when $r_0 < r < r_2$. Derive a formula for the characteristic impedance of the cable, assuming $\mu = \mu_r$ through both dielectrics.

8-11 A 100-volt sinusoidal source is connected to the input terminals of a 300-ohm lossless line, and a 100-ohm resistor is connected across the output terminals. The line is $\frac{1}{4}$ wavelength long.
(a) What is the standing wave ratio?
(b) Find the minimum effective voltage.
(c) Find the maximum effective current.

8-12 Prove that, when a line of characteristic impedance Z_0 is terminated by a load Z_r, the reflection coefficient of the current, defined as the ratio of the reflected to the direct current at the load, is $(Z_0 - Z_r)/(Z_0 + Z_r)$. Note that the current reflection coefficient is the negative of the voltage reflection coefficient.

8-13 The transmission coefficient is defined as the ratio of the total voltage or current transmitted to the load, to the direct or incident voltage or current.
(a) Prove that the voltage transmission coefficient is $2Z_r/(Z_r + Z_0)$.
(b) Prove that the current transmission coefficient is $2Z_0/(Z_r + Z_0)$.

8-14 A generator with an internal resistance of 100 ohms has a sinusoidal voltage of 10 volts at a frequency of 100 megacycles. This generator is connected to a lossless transmission line, 4.50 meters long in air, having a characteristic impedance of 300 ohms. Calculate the voltage and current at a distance of 1.0 meter from the generator when the line is terminated by a 300-ohm resistor. Find the power delivered by the generator.

8-15 Solve Prob. 8-14 when the line is terminated by a 500-ohm resistor.

8-16 Solve Prob. 8-14 when the line is terminated by a capacitor having a reactance of $-j500$ ohms.

8-17 Solve Prob. 8-14 when the line is terminated by an impedance of $300 + j100$ ohms.

8-18 Solve Prob. 8-14 when the output terminals are open.

8-19 Solve Prob. 8-14 when the output terminals are short-circuited.

8-20 Construct the standing wave patterns for the voltage and the current in Prob. 8-15.

8-21 Construct the standing wave patterns for the voltage and the current in Prob. 8-17.

8-22 Construct the standing wave patterns for the voltage and the current in Prob. 8-18.

8-23 Find the impedance at terminals ab of the lossless line in the following sketch. The characteristic impedance is Z_0.

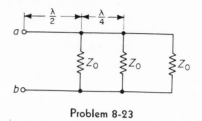

Problem 8-23

8-24 Calculate the voltage at the mid-point of the line in the diagram below.

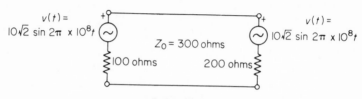

Problem 8-24

8-25 A lossless line has a characteristic impedance of 300 ohms, and is terminated by an impedance of $Z_r = 150\underline{/30°}$ ohms. The frequency of the source is 100 megacycles.

(a) Locate the current minimum nearest to the receiver.

(b) Locate the voltage minimum nearest to the receiver.

8-26 A lossless line in air having a characteristic impedance of 300 ohms is terminated by an unknown impedance. The first voltage minimum is located at 15 cm from the load, and the next voltage minimum is 30 cm from the load. The standing wave ratio is 3.3. Calculate the frequency and the terminating impedance.

8-27 Prove that the power transmitted along a lossless line, not terminated in its characteristic impedance, can be expressed as $P = \dfrac{S|V_{min}|^2}{Z_0}$, where S is the standing wave ratio and $|V_{min}|$ is the absolute value of the minimum effective voltage along the line.

8-28 Assuming the circuit shown below to be in the steady state, calculate the receiver voltage when $\omega t = 2n\pi$, where n is any integer.

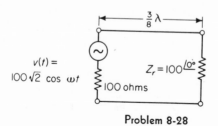

Problem 8-28

transmission lines

with losses

9.0 INTRODUCTION

Up to this point, only lossless or ideal lines have been considered. In an actual physical line, however, the wires have series resistance; in addition, the dielectric is not a perfect insulator, and it has an equivalent shunt conductance. Those conditions introduce losses.

One of the effects of losses is to reduce the amplitude of the voltage and current waves as they progress along the line from the transmitter to the receiver. This effect is termed *attenuation*. Another effect is to cause the phase velocity in most cases to be a function of the frequency. This effect is termed *dispersion*. The attenuation also is generally a function of the frequency.

In this chapter, the effects of losses will be analyzed, and some methods for improving transmission in practical lines will be studied.

9.1 CIRCUIT REPRESENTATION OF LINES WITH LOSSES

As already noted, the effect of losses is to introduce series resistance and shunt conductance. The equivalent circuit of an incremental length, Δx, of a line with losses is shown in Fig. 9-1, which is derived from Fig. 8-7 by the introduction of a series resistance $\bar{R}\Delta x$ and a shunt conductance $\bar{G}\Delta x$. The symbol $\bar{R}$ represents the resistance in ohms per unit length and $\bar{G}$ represents the shunt conductance in mhos per unit length.

In the frequency range where the skin effect is the predominant factor, $\bar{R}$ and $\bar{G}$ for copper parallel-wire lines of radius r and separation D, at a frequency f, are given by

$$\overline{R} = \frac{8.32\sqrt{f}}{r} \times 10^{-8} \text{ ohms per meter} \qquad [9.1\text{-}1]$$

$$\overline{G} = \frac{\pi\sigma}{\ln D/r} \text{ mhos per meter} \qquad [9.1\text{-}2]$$

where σ is the conductivity of the dielectric and is a function of the material, the moisture constant, and other factors.

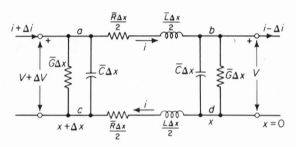

Figure 9-1 Incremental length of a transmission line with losses.

The corresponding formulas for copper coaxial cables of inner radius r_1 and outer radius r_2 are

$$\overline{R} = 4.2\sqrt{f}\left(\frac{1}{r_2} + \frac{1}{r_1}\right) \times 10^{-8} \text{ ohms per meter} \qquad [9.1\text{-}3]$$

$$\overline{G} = \frac{2\pi\sigma}{\ln (r_2/r_1)} \text{ mhos per meter} \qquad [9.1\text{-}4]$$

Three points should be noted concerning the equations above. First, Eqs. 9.1-1 and 9.1-3 are not valid for direct currents when $f = 0$. In that case the standard d-c formulas for the resistance of conductors are used. The d-c formulas can also be used to calculate the resistance at 60 cycles, where the skin effect is usually negligible. Second, it should also be noted that Eqs. 9.1-1 and 9.1-3 give the resistance of *both* conductors per unit length. Hence, the term "resistance per loop meter" is often used to describe $\overline{R}$. The third point to be noted is that Eqs. 9.1-2 and 9.1-4 can be obtained directly from Eqs. 8.2-5 and 8.2-14 by substituting σ for $\epsilon_r\epsilon_v$. The reason for this is that the electric field strength and the geometric configuration for both the charging current of $\overline{C}$ and the conduction current through $\overline{G}$ in Fig. 9-1 are identical. Since the charging current is directly proportional to the dielectric constant, and since the conduction current is directly proportional to the conductivity, the formulas for capacitance and shunt conductance are related by

$$\frac{\overline{G}}{\overline{C}} = \frac{\sigma}{\epsilon_r \epsilon_v} \qquad [9.1\text{-}5]$$

Equation 9.1-5 is general, and can be applied to other configurations.

9.2 DIFFERENTIAL EQUATIONS FOR VOLTAGE AND CURRENT

Equating to zero the voltage drops around the closed loop $abcd$, in Fig. 9-1, yields

$$\left(\frac{\overline{R}}{2}\right)\Delta x i + \left(\frac{\overline{L}}{2}\right)\Delta x \frac{\partial i}{\partial t} + v + \left(\frac{\overline{R}}{2}\right)\Delta x i + \left(\frac{\overline{L}}{2}\right)\Delta x \frac{\partial i}{\partial t} - (v + \Delta v) = 0$$

$$[9.2\text{-}1]$$

$$\overline{R}i + \overline{L}\frac{\partial i}{\partial t} = \frac{\Delta v}{\Delta x} \qquad [9.2\text{-}2]$$

In the limit, as $\Delta x \to 0$, Eq. 9.2-2 can be written as

$$\overline{R}i + \overline{L}\frac{\partial i}{\partial t} = \frac{\partial v}{\partial x} \qquad [9.2\text{-}3]$$

The equation for current continuity at node b yields

$$i = \overline{G}v\,\Delta x + \frac{\partial}{\partial t}(\Delta q) + (i - \Delta i) \qquad [9.2\text{-}4]$$

where

$$\frac{\partial}{\partial t}(\Delta q) = \overline{C}\,\Delta x\,\frac{\partial v}{\partial t} \qquad [9.2\text{-}5]$$

The substitution of Eq. 9.2-5 into Eq. 9.2-4 yields

$$\overline{G}v + \overline{C}\frac{\partial v}{\partial t} = \frac{\Delta i}{\Delta x} \qquad [9.2\text{-}6]$$

In the limit, as $\Delta x \to 0$, Eq. 9.2-6 can be written as

$$\overline{G}v + \overline{C}\frac{\partial v}{\partial t} = \frac{\partial i}{\partial x} \qquad [9.2\text{-}7]$$

A comparison of Eq. 8.3-3 with Eq. 9.2-3, and of Eq. 8.3-7 with Eq. 9.2-7, shows that the effect of losses is to introduce the term $\overline{R}i$ into Eq. 9.2-3 and the term $\overline{G}v$ into Eq. 9.2-7. In the case of sinusoidal excitation,

$$v(x,t) = |V_m(x)| \epsilon^{j(\omega t + \theta_1)} \qquad [9.2\text{-}8]$$

$$i(x,t) = |I_m(x)| \epsilon^{j(\omega t + \theta_2)} \qquad [9.2\text{-}9]$$

where $|V_m(x)|$ and $|I_m(x)|$ represent the maximum voltage and current at a distance x from the receiver. The substitution of Eqs. 9.2-8 and 9.2-9 into Eqs. 9.2-3 and 9.2-7 gives the following results:

$$(\overline{R} + j\omega\overline{L})|I_m(x)|\epsilon^{j(\omega t + \theta_2)} = \frac{\partial}{\partial x}|V_m(x)|\epsilon^{j(\omega t + \theta_1)} \qquad [9.2\text{-}10]$$

$$(\overline{G} + j\omega\overline{C})|V_m(x)|\epsilon^{j(\omega t + \theta_1)} = \frac{\partial}{\partial x}|I_m(x)|\epsilon^{j(\omega t + \theta_2)} \qquad [9.2\text{-}11]$$

Division of both sides of Eqs. 9.2-10 and 9.2-11 by $\sqrt{2}(\epsilon^{j\omega t})$ gives the following phasor or sinor equations for the voltage and current.

$$(\overline{R} + j\omega\overline{L})I = \frac{dV}{dx} \qquad [9.2\text{-}12]$$

$$(\overline{G} + j\omega\overline{C})V = \frac{dI}{dx} \qquad [9.2\text{-}13]$$

where total derivatives are shown because the time variable has been removed, and where V and I are voltage and current phasors that generate the instantaneous voltage and current at any point along the line.*

The phasor equations for lossless lines are formed by setting $\overline{R} = \overline{G} = 0$ in Eqs. 9.2-12 and 9.2-13, giving the following result:

$$(j\omega\overline{L})I = \frac{dV}{dx} \qquad [9.2\text{-}14]$$

$$(j\omega\overline{C})V = \frac{dI}{dx} \qquad [9.2\text{-}15]$$

Equations 9.2-12 and 9.2-13, which are for lines with losses and sinusoidal excitation, can be written in the same form as Eqs. 9.2-14 and 9.2-15 for lines without losses, by using the complex inductance and capacitance, $\overline{L}'$ and $\overline{C}'$, defined as follows:

$$\overline{L}' = \overline{L} + \frac{\overline{R}}{j\omega} = \overline{L} - j\left(\frac{\overline{R}}{\omega}\right) \qquad [9.2\text{-}16]$$

---

* Note that the phasors V and I are functions only of x:

$$V = V(x) = \left(\frac{|V_m(x)|}{\sqrt{2}}\right)\epsilon^{j\theta_1}; \quad \text{and} \quad I = I(x) = \left(\frac{|I_m(x)|}{\sqrt{2}}\right)\epsilon^{j\theta_2}$$

$$\overline{C}' = \overline{C} + \frac{\overline{G}}{j\omega} = \overline{C} - j\left(\frac{\overline{G}}{\omega}\right) \qquad [9.2\text{-}17]$$

Note particularly that Eqs. 9.2-16 and 9.2-17 define the complex inductance and capacitance at only a single frequency.

Substituting the complex inductance $\overline{L}'$ and capacitance $\overline{C}'$, from Eqs. 9.2-16 and 9.2-17, for $\overline{L}$ and $\overline{C}$ in Eqs. 9.2-14 and 9.2-15, yields

$$(j\omega\overline{L}')I = j\omega\left(\overline{L} + \frac{\overline{R}}{j\omega}\right)I = (\overline{R} + j\omega\overline{L})I = \frac{dV}{dx} \qquad [9.2\text{-}18]$$

$$(j\omega\overline{C}')V = j\omega\left(\overline{C} + \frac{\overline{G}}{j\omega}\right)V = (\overline{G} + j\omega\overline{C})V = \frac{dI}{dx} \qquad [9.2\text{-}19]$$

It is seen that Eqs. 9.2-18 and 9.2-19 are the same as Eqs. 9.2-12 and 9.2-13.

It follows that the voltage and current distributions for sinusoidal excitation on lines with losses can be found by substituting the complex inductance and the complex capacitance in the distributions previously calculated for lossless lines. It is to be emphasized that the complex parameters have no essential physical significance, but are simply a mathematical artifice. This artifice is to be employed in the following section.

9.3 APPLICATION OF COMPLEX PARAMETERS

Equations 8.8-1 and 8.8-2 for the phasor distributions on lossless lines can be written as follows:

$$V(x) = V_1[\epsilon^{\gamma x} + \rho\epsilon^{-\gamma x}] = \left(\frac{V_r}{1 + \rho}\right)[\epsilon^{\gamma x} + \rho\epsilon^{-\gamma x}] \qquad [9.3\text{-}1]$$

$$I(x) = \left(\frac{V_r}{(1 + \rho)Z_0}\right)[\epsilon^{\gamma x} - \rho\epsilon^{-\gamma x}] \qquad [9.3\text{-}2]$$

where V_1 is expressed in terms of V_r as in Eq. 8.8-5, and where

$$\gamma = j\omega\sqrt{\overline{L}\,\overline{C}} \qquad [9.3\text{-}3]$$

$$Z_0 = \sqrt{\frac{\overline{L}}{\overline{C}}} \qquad [9.3\text{-}4]$$

$$\rho = \frac{Z_r - Z_0}{Z_r + Z_0} \qquad [9.3\text{-}5]$$

It will be found convenient to consider the exponent γ, in Eqs. 9.3-1 and 9.3-2, as a propagation function that determines the amplitude and phase of the direct and reflected waves. In lossless lines, γ is purely imaginary and is directly proportional to the frequency. It will be found that, in lines with losses, γ is complex, and in general is a more complicated function of the frequency.

It follows from the analysis of the preceding section that the propagation function and the characteristic impedance of lines with losses can be found by substituting the complex parameters, $\overline{L}'$ and $\overline{C}'$, for $\overline{L}$ and $\overline{C}$ in Eqs. 9.3-3 and 9.3-4. This operation gives the following results for lines with losses:

$$\gamma = j\omega\sqrt{\overline{L}'\,\overline{C}'} = j\omega\sqrt{\left(\overline{L} + \frac{\overline{R}}{j\omega}\right)\left(\overline{C} + \frac{\overline{G}}{j\omega}\right)} \qquad [9.3\text{-}6]$$

$$\gamma = \sqrt{(\overline{R} + j\omega\overline{L})(\overline{G} + j\omega\overline{C})} = \alpha + j\beta \qquad [9.3\text{-}7]$$

where α and β are the real and imaginary components of γ.

For the characteristic impedance,

$$Z_0 = \sqrt{\frac{\overline{L}'}{\overline{C}'}} = \sqrt{\frac{\overline{L} + \overline{R}/j\omega}{\overline{C} + \overline{G}/j\omega}} = \sqrt{\frac{\overline{R} + j\omega\overline{L}}{\overline{G} + j\omega\overline{C}}} \qquad [9.3\text{-}8]$$

The complex reflection coefficient is found by substituting Z_0 from Eq. 9.3-8 into Eq. 9.3-5.

Consider now a single wave travelling in the positive direction and given by

$$V(x) = V\epsilon^{-\gamma x} \qquad [9.3\text{-}9]$$

where $V(0)$ is the voltage at $x = 0$, and it is to be understood that Eq. 9.3-9 is a phasor relation from which the time variable has been eliminated. The substitution of γ from Eq. 9.3-7 into Eq. 9.3-9 yields

$$V(x) = V(0)\epsilon^{-(\alpha+j\beta)x} = V(0)\epsilon^{-\alpha x}\epsilon^{-j\beta x} \qquad [9.3\text{-}10]$$

The component $\epsilon^{-\alpha x}$ shows that as x increases in the positive direction, the amplitude decreases and is said to be attenuated. The term $\epsilon^{-j\beta x}$ denotes a phase shift; and when x is changed from x_0 to $(x_0 + 2\pi/\beta)$, the phase shift is 360°, corresponding to one wavelength. Hence,

$$\lambda = \frac{2\pi}{\beta} \qquad [9.3\text{-}11]$$

where β is the wavelength function, and is in general not a linear function of the frequency, as is the case in lossless lines.

The instantaneous voltage corresponding to the phasor relations in Eqs. 9.3-9 and 9.3-10 is

$$v(x,t) = |V_\mathrm{m}|\epsilon^{-\alpha x}\epsilon^{j(\omega t - \beta x)} = |V_\mathrm{m}|\epsilon^{-\alpha t}\epsilon^{j\omega(t - \beta x/\omega)} \qquad [9.3\text{-}12]$$

where the real and imaginary parts correspond respectively to cosine and sine excitation. In Eq. 9.3-12, the exponent $-\beta x/\omega$ has the dimension of time. Hence, ω/β is a phase velocity and

$$\frac{x}{\omega/\beta} = \frac{x}{u_p} \qquad [9.3\text{-}13]$$

is the delay time, where u_p is the phase velocity.

It follows from Eqs. 9.3-11 and 9.3-13 that

$$\frac{\omega}{\beta} = \frac{2\pi f}{2\pi/\lambda} = f\lambda = u_p \qquad [9.3\text{-}14]$$

where λ is the wavelength on the line with losses. Here λ cannot be calculated by simply dividing the velocity of light by the frequency, but is determined from Eq. 9.3-11 where β is the imaginary part of the propagation function, γ, in Eq. 9.3-7. The real component, α, is the attenuation function, and is measured in nepers per unit length.

A real ratio, r, can be expressed in both nepers and decibels as follows:

$$r = \epsilon^N \qquad [9.3\text{-}15]$$

$$20 \log_{10} r = \mathrm{db} \qquad [9.3\text{-}16]$$

where the exponent denotes the number of nepers, and where db is the number of decibels required to measure the same ratio. The substitution of Eq. 9.3-15 in Eq. 9.3-16 yields

$$20 \log_{10} \epsilon^N = 20N \log_{10} \epsilon = 8.686N = \mathrm{db} \qquad [9.3\text{-}17]$$

It follows from Eq. 9.3-17 that the number of decibels required to represent a given ratio is 8.686 times the number of nepers. Hence, the neper is the larger unit, and equals 8.686 decibels.

9.4 ALTERNATE DERIVATION OF PHASOR EQUATIONS

The voltage and current, the propagation function, and the characteristic impedance of lines with losses were derived in Sec. 9.3 by the application of complex parameters. After the parameters were defined, the derivations were very simple. The same results can be derived by the classical method of solving the differential equations for the voltage and current. This procedure will now be followed.

Equations 9.2-12 and 9.2-13 can be written as

$$\frac{dV}{dx} = (\overline{R} + j\omega\overline{L})I = \overline{Z}\,I \qquad\qquad [9.4\text{-}1]$$

$$\frac{dI}{dx} = (\overline{G} + j\omega\overline{C})V = \overline{Y}\,V \qquad\qquad [9.4\text{-}2]$$

where $\overline{Z}$ is the series impedance per unit length, and $\overline{Y}$ is the shunt admittance per unit length. Differentiating Eq. 9.4-1 with respect to x yields

$$\frac{d^2V}{dx^2} = \overline{Z}\frac{dI}{dx} \qquad\qquad [9.4\text{-}3]$$

The substitution of dI/dx from Eq. 9.4-2 into 9.4-3 yields

$$\frac{d^2V}{dx^2} = \overline{Z}\,\overline{Y}\,V = \gamma^2 V \qquad\qquad [9.4\text{-}4]$$

where

$$\gamma = \sqrt{\overline{Z}\,\overline{Y}} = \sqrt{(\overline{R} + j\omega\overline{L})(\overline{G} + j\omega\overline{C})} \qquad\qquad [9.4\text{-}5]$$

Differentiation of Eq. 9.4-2 with respect to x, and the substitution of dV/dx from Eq. 9.4-1, give the following result:

$$\frac{d^2I}{dx^2} = \overline{Z}\,\overline{Y}\,I = \gamma^2 I \qquad\qquad [9.4\text{-}6]$$

Equations 9.4-4 and 9.4-6 are second-order differential equations having solutions of the following form:

$$V(x) = A_1\epsilon^{\gamma x} + A_2\epsilon^{-\gamma x} \qquad\qquad [9.4\text{-}7]$$
$$I(x) = B_1\epsilon^{\gamma x} + B_2\epsilon^{-\gamma x} \qquad\qquad [9.4\text{-}8]$$

The substitution of $V(x)$ and $I(x)$ from Eqs. 9.4-7 and 9.4-8 into Eq. 9.4-1 yields

$$\gamma A_1\epsilon^{\gamma x} - \gamma A_2\epsilon^{-\gamma x} = \overline{Z}\,B_1\epsilon^{\gamma x} + \overline{Z}\,B_2\epsilon^{-\gamma x} \qquad\qquad [9.4\text{-}9]$$

If Eq. 9.4-9 is to hold for all values of x, the coefficients must be related, as follows:

$$\overline{Z}\,B_1 = \gamma A_1 \qquad\qquad [9.4\text{-}10]$$
$$\overline{Z}\,B_2 = -\gamma A_2 \qquad\qquad [9.4\text{-}11]$$

$$B_1 = \left(\frac{1}{\overline{Z}}\right)\gamma A_1 = \frac{1}{\overline{Z}}\sqrt{\overline{Z}\,\overline{Y}}\,A_1 = \left(\sqrt{\frac{\overline{Y}}{\overline{Z}}}\right)A_1 = \left(\sqrt{\frac{\overline{G} + j\omega\overline{C}}{\overline{R} + j\omega\overline{L}}}\right)A_1 = \frac{A_1}{Z_0}$$

$$[9.4\text{-}12]$$

$$B_2 = -\left(\frac{1}{Z}\right)\gamma A_2 = -\frac{1}{Z}\sqrt{Z\,\overline{Y}}A_2 = -\left(\sqrt{\frac{\overline{Y}}{Z}}\right)A_2$$

$$= -\left(\sqrt{\frac{\overline{G} + j\omega\overline{C}}{\overline{R} + j\omega\overline{L}}}\right)A_2 = -\frac{A_2}{Z_0} \qquad [9.4\text{-}13]$$

where Z_0 is the characteristic impedance of the line.

The substitution of B_1 and B_2 from Eqs. 9.4-12 and 9.4-13 into Eq. 9.4-8 gives the following expression for the current:

$$I(x) = \frac{1}{Z_0}\left[A_1\epsilon^{\gamma x} - A_2\epsilon^{-\gamma x}\right] \qquad [9.4\text{-}14]$$

At the receiver, $x = 0$, $V(0) = V_r$, and $I(0) = I_r$. The substitution of these conditions into Eqs. 9.4-7 and 9.4-14 yields:

$$V(0) = V_r = A_1 + A_2 \qquad [9.4\text{-}15]$$

$$I(0) = I_r = \frac{1}{Z_0}(A_1 - A_2) \qquad [9.4\text{-}16]$$

since

$$\frac{V_r}{I_r} = Z_r$$

where Z_r is the receiver impedance, it follows from Eqs. 9.4-15 and 9.4-16 that:

$$Z_0\left(\frac{A_1 + A_2}{A_1 - A_2}\right) = Z_r \qquad [9.4\text{-}17]$$

It follows from Eq. 9.4-15 that

$$A_2 = V_r - A_1 \qquad [9.4\text{-}18]$$

The substitution of Eq. 9.4-18 into Eq. 9.4-17 yields the following relations:

$$\frac{Z_0 V_r}{2A_1 - V_r} = Z_r \qquad [9.4\text{-}19]$$

$$A_1 = \left(\frac{Z_0 + Z_r}{2Z_r}\right)V_r \qquad [9.4\text{-}20]$$

$$A_2 = V_r - A_1 = \frac{2Z_r V_r - (Z_0 + Z_r)V_r}{2Z_r} = \left(\frac{Z_r - Z_0}{2Z_r}\right)V_r \qquad [9.4\text{-}21]$$

When A_2 and A_1, as given by Eqs. 9.4-20 and 9.4-21, are substituted into

Eqs. 9.4-7 and 9.4-14, the following expressions for the voltage and current result:

$$V(x) = V_r \left[\left(\frac{Z_0 + Z_r}{2Z_r} \right) \epsilon^{\gamma x} + \left(\frac{Z_r - Z_0}{2Z_r} \right) \epsilon^{-\gamma x} \right] \qquad [9.4\text{-}22]$$

$$V(x) = \left(\frac{(Z_0 + Z_r)}{2Z_r} \right) V_r \left[\epsilon^{\gamma x} + \left(\frac{Z_r - Z_0}{Z_r + Z_0} \right) \epsilon^{-\gamma x} \right] = \left(\frac{V_r}{1 + \rho} \right) (\epsilon^{\gamma x} + \rho \epsilon^{-\gamma x})$$

$$[9.4\text{-}23]$$

$$I(x) = \left(\frac{(Z_0 + Z_r)}{2Z_r} \right) \left(\frac{V_r}{Z_0} \right) \left[\epsilon^{\gamma x} - \left(\frac{Z_r - Z_0}{Z_r + Z_0} \right) \epsilon^{-\gamma x} \right]$$

$$= \left(\frac{V_r}{(1 + \rho)Z_0} \right) (\epsilon^{\gamma x} - \rho \epsilon^{-\gamma x}) \qquad (9.4\text{-}24]$$

where ρ is the voltage reflection coefficient defined by Eq. 9.3-5.

Equations 9.4-23 and 9.4-24 agree with Eqs. 9.3-1 and 9.3-2, when γ is given by Eq. 9.3-7. The efficiency of deriving these equations by the concept of complex inductance and complex capacitance rather than by the classical solution of differential equations is apparent. The concept of a complex parameter has no intrinsic physical meaning, but is a very powerful tool in the solution of sinusoidal field problems involving dielectrics with losses. In that case, the complex dielectric constant finds extensive application. It must always be borne in mind that the use of a complex parameter is limited to applications where the forcing function is a pure sinusoid.

9.5 VOLTAGE, CURRENT, AND IMPEDANCE

The voltage, current, and impedance at points along a transmission line with losses can be conveniently expressed in terms of hyperbolic functions. Using the relation

$$\rho = \frac{Z_r - Z_0}{Z_r + Z_0} \qquad [9.5\text{-}1]$$

Eqs. 9.4-23 and 9.4-24 can be written in the following forms:

$$V(x) = \left(\frac{V_r}{1 + (Z_r - Z_0)/(Z_r + Z_0)} \right) \left[\epsilon^{\gamma x} + \left(\frac{Z_r - Z_0}{Z_r + Z_0} \right) \epsilon^{-\gamma x} \right] \qquad [9.5\text{-}2]$$

$$I(x) = \left(\frac{V_r/Z_0}{1 + (Z_r - Z_0)/(Z_r + Z_0)} \right) \left[\epsilon^{\gamma x} - \left(\frac{Z_r - Z_0}{Z_r + Z_0} \right) \epsilon^{-\gamma x} \right] \qquad [9.5\text{-}3]$$

Equation 9.5-2 can be simplified as follows:

$$V(x) = \left(\frac{V_r}{2Z_r}\right) [(Z_r + Z_0)\epsilon^{\gamma x} + (Z_r - Z_0)\epsilon^{-\gamma x}] \qquad [9.5\text{-}4]$$

$$V(x) = \left(\frac{V_r}{Z_r}\right) \left[Z_r \left(\frac{\epsilon^{\gamma x} + \epsilon^{-\gamma x}}{2}\right) + Z_0 \left(\frac{\epsilon^{\gamma x} - \epsilon^{-\gamma x}}{2}\right) \right] \qquad [9.5\text{-}5]$$

Hence

$$V(x) = V_r \cosh \gamma x + I_r Z_0 \sinh \gamma x \qquad [9.5\text{-}6]$$

where

$$I_r = \frac{V_r}{Z_r} \qquad [9.5\text{-}7]$$

Similarly, Eq. 9.5-3 can be simplified to yield

$$I(x) = \left(\frac{V_r}{2Z_r Z_0}\right) [(Z_r + Z_0)\epsilon^{\gamma x} - (Z_r - Z_0)\epsilon^{-\gamma x}] \qquad [9.5\text{-}8]$$

$$I(x) = \left(\frac{V_r}{Z_r Z_0}\right) \left[Z_0 \left(\frac{\epsilon^{\gamma x} + \epsilon^{-\gamma x}}{2}\right) + Z_r \left(\frac{\epsilon^{\gamma x} - \epsilon^{-\gamma x}}{2}\right) \right] \qquad [9.5\text{-}9]$$

Hence,

$$I(x) = I_r \cosh \gamma x + \left(\frac{V_r}{Z_0}\right) \sinh \gamma x \qquad [9.5\text{-}10]$$

In the lossless case, $\gamma = j\beta$; and, since

$$\cosh j\beta x = \cos \beta x \qquad [9.5\text{-}11]$$
$$\sinh j\beta x = j \sin \beta x \qquad [9.5\text{-}12]$$

Eqs. 9.5-6 and 9.5-10 for lossless lines become

$$V(x) = V_r \cos \beta x + j I_r Z_0 \sin \beta x \qquad [9.5\text{-}13]$$

$$I(x) = I_r \cos \beta x + j \left(\frac{V_r}{Z_0}\right) \sin \beta x \qquad [9.5\text{-}14]$$

Equations 9.5-13 and 9.5-14 agree with Eqs. 8.8-10 and 8.8-11, which were developed for lossless lines.

As in the case of voltage and current, the impedance at any point can be expressed in either the exponential or the hyperbolic form. The impedance in the exponential form is given by

$$Z(x) = \frac{V(x)}{I(x)} = \frac{V_1[\epsilon^{\gamma x} + \rho\epsilon^{-\gamma x}]}{(V_1/Z_0)[\epsilon^{\gamma x} - \rho\epsilon^{-\gamma x}]} = Z_0 \left[\frac{\epsilon^{\gamma x} + \rho\epsilon^{-\gamma x}}{\epsilon^{\gamma x} - \rho\epsilon^{-\gamma x}}\right] \qquad [9.5\text{-}15]$$

The impedance in the hyperbolic form is given by the ratio of Eq. 9.5-6 to Eq. 9.5-10 as follows:

$$Z(x) = \frac{V(x)}{I(x)} = \frac{I_r Z_r \cosh \gamma x + I_r Z_0 \sinh \gamma x}{(1/Z_0) [I_r Z_0 \cosh \gamma x + I_r Z_r \sinh \gamma x]} \qquad [9.5\text{-}16]$$

$$Z(x) = Z_0 \left[\frac{Z_r \cosh \gamma x + Z_0 \sinh \gamma x}{Z_0 \cosh \gamma x + Z_r \sinh \gamma x} \right] \qquad [9.5\text{-}17]$$

where x is the distance from the receiver.

Inspection of Eq. 9.5-15 shows that when $\rho = 0$ (which is the case when $Z_r = Z_0$), $Z(x) = Z_0$. Equation 9.5-15 can also be written as

$$Z(x) = Z_0 \left[\frac{\epsilon^{\gamma x} + |\rho| \epsilon^{j\varphi} \epsilon^{-\gamma x}}{\epsilon^{\gamma x} - |\rho| \epsilon^{j\varphi} \epsilon^{-\gamma x}} \right] = Z_0 \left[\frac{\epsilon^{2\gamma x} + |\rho| \epsilon^{j\varphi}}{\epsilon^{2\gamma x} - |\rho| \epsilon^{j\varphi}} \right] \qquad [9.5\text{-}18]$$

The input impedance of a line of length ℓ can be expressed as

$$Z_{\text{in}} = Z_0 \left[\frac{\epsilon^{2\alpha\ell} \epsilon^{j2\beta\ell} + |\rho| \epsilon^{j\varphi}}{\epsilon^{2\alpha\ell} \epsilon^{j2\beta\ell} - |\rho| \epsilon^{j\varphi}} \right] \qquad [9.5\text{-}19]$$

where α is the attenuation function, and β is the wavelength function. The maximum absolute value of $|\rho| \epsilon^{j\varphi}$ is unity. When $\alpha\ell = 3$, $\epsilon^{2\alpha\ell} = 403$, and the first term in both the numerator and denominator in Eq. 9.5-19 exceeds the second by over 400. Under such conditions the second terms are negligible, and

$$Z_{\text{in}} = Z_0 \qquad (\alpha\ell \geq 3) \qquad [9.5\text{-}20]$$

Equation 9.5-20 shows that when the attenuation $(\alpha\ell)$ equals or exceeds 3, the input impedance can safely be considered to be the characteristic impedance of the line. The reason for this is that when the attenuation is of such magnitude, the reflected wave becomes negligible compared to the direct wave, and the input impedance is simply the ratio of the voltage to the current in a single (direct) wave. When reflection exists, a wave of voltage travels from the transmitter to the receiver, where it is reflected back to the transmitter. The total distance traveled is twice the line length, ℓ. If $\alpha\ell = 3$, the ratio of the reflected to the direct voltage at the transmitter is ϵ^{-6}.* Since $\epsilon^{-6} = 0.00248$, it is evident that the effect of reflection is negligible under these conditions. Hence, in this case, the input impedance equals the characteristic impedance of the line. When $\alpha\ell = 2$, the reflected wave is less than 2 per cent of the direct wave, and for certain applications may be neglected, giving an input impedance substantially equal to the characteristic impedance. Thus, whenever the attenuation is of sufficient magnitude to cause the reflected wave to be negligible compared to the direct wave, the input impedance is the characteristic impedance of the line. This condition prevails whenever $\alpha\ell \geq 3$, and in some

*This is also the ratio of the reflected to the direct current.

cases when $\alpha\ell \geqq 2$. In certain applications, resistance attenuators are inserted in a line to cause the input impedance to be independent of the terminating impedance. This technique is of considerable practical value.

It follows from Eq. 9.4-7 that in lines where $\alpha\ell \geqq 3$, the term in $\epsilon^{-\gamma x}$ that represents the reflected wave can be neglected, and

$$V(x) = A_1\epsilon^{\gamma x} = V_r\epsilon^{\gamma x} \qquad [9.5\text{-}21]$$

since $V(x) = V_r$ when $x = 0$ at the receiver. The input voltage at $x = \ell$ is given by

$$V(\ell) = V_{\text{in}} = V_r\epsilon^{\gamma\ell} \qquad [9.5\text{-}22]$$

It follows from Eq. 9.5-22 that $V_r = V_{\text{in}}\epsilon^{-\gamma\ell}$ and substituting this expression for V_r into Eq. 9.5-21 gives the following expression for the voltage:

$$V(x) = V_{\text{in}}\epsilon^{\gamma(x-\ell)} = V_{\text{in}}\epsilon^{-\gamma z} \qquad [9.5\text{-}23]$$

where z is the distance from the transmitter.

Since only the direct wave exists, the expression for the current is

$$I(x) = \frac{V_{\text{in}}}{Z_0}\epsilon^{\gamma(x-\ell)} = \frac{V_{\text{in}}}{Z_0}\epsilon^{-\gamma z} \qquad [9.5\text{-}24]$$

The concept of an *infinite line* is also useful. In a line of infinite length with losses of a finite amount, no matter how small, the reflected wave vanishes because $\epsilon^{-\alpha\ell}$ approaches zero as ℓ becomes infinite, when α is any positive quantity. The infinite line is a convenient device to simulate conditions under which the reflected voltage and current waves can be neglected. Equations 9.5-23 and 9.5-24 give the voltage and current distributions on infinite lines in terms of the distance from the transmitter.

The input impedance to a line is Z_0 whenever there is no reflected wave. It follows from the analysis above that the input impedance can be made equal to Z_0 by the introduction of sufficient attenuation, regardless of the termination. A short length of line of high loss can be used to cause an unknown impedance to appear as Z_0 to the transmitter. It should be noted that for a line with losses, Z_0 is in general complex, as shown in Eq. 9.3-8. In practical communication lines of great length, the input impedance is almost independent of the termination and is approximately equal to Z_0.

For small values of $|\gamma x|$, sinh γx approaches zero and cosh γx approaches unity. It follows from Eq. 9.5-17 that when $|\gamma x| \ll 1$, $Z(x)$ approaches Z_r, the terminating impedance. In this case, the attenuation and phase shift between the transmitter and receiver are negligible, and the line approaches a series circuit in the lumped sense. In summary, it can be stated that the input impedance of long lines with losses is determined by the characteristic impedance of the line and is independent of the terminating impedance; the input impedance of short lines is determined by the terminating impedance and is independent of the characteristic impedance.

Equations 9.5-6 and 9.5-10 give the voltage and current at any point in terms of the voltage and current at the receiver. If the transmitter is taken as the origin, and if V_s and I_s are the transmitter voltage and current, the distributions are given by

$$V(z) = V_s \cosh(-\gamma z) + I_s Z_0 \sinh(-\gamma z) \qquad [9.5\text{-}25]$$

$$I(z) = I_s \cosh(-\gamma z) + \left(\frac{V_s}{Z_0}\right) \sinh(-\gamma z) \qquad [9.5\text{-}26]$$

where z is the distance measured from the transmitter and is in the negative direction. Since $\cosh(-\gamma z) = \cosh \gamma z$, and since $\sinh(-\gamma z) = -\sinh \gamma z$, Eqs. 9.5-25 and 9.5-26 can be written as

$$V(z) = V_s \cosh \gamma z - I_s Z_0 \sinh \gamma z \qquad [9.5\text{-}27]$$

$$I(z) = I_s \cosh \gamma z - \left(\frac{V_s}{Z_0}\right) \sinh \gamma z \qquad [9.5\text{-}28]$$

Since $I_s = V_s/Z_s$, where Z_s is the sending-end impedance, alternative forms of Eqs. 9.5-27 and 9.5-28 are the following:

$$V(z) = V_s \left(\cosh \gamma z - \frac{Z_0}{Z_s} \sinh \gamma z \right) \qquad [9.5\text{-}29]$$

$$I(z) = V_s \left(\frac{1}{Z_s} \cosh \gamma z - \frac{1}{Z_0} \sinh \gamma z \right) \qquad [9.5\text{-}30]$$

where Z_s is found by substituting $x = \ell$ in Eq. 9.5-17, where ℓ is the length of the line. Hence,

$$Z_s = Z_0 \left[\frac{Z_r \cosh \gamma \ell + Z_0 \sinh \gamma \ell}{Z_0 \cosh \gamma \ell + Z_r \sinh \gamma \ell} \right] \qquad [9.5\text{-}31]$$

9.6 CALCULATIONS FOR LINES WITH LOSSES

To illustrate the application of the equations developed in Sec. 9.5 for transmission lines with losses, the received voltage, current, and power will be calculated for a line fifty miles long, terminated by a 300-ohm resistor and having the following parameters per mile: $\overline{R} = 10.4$ ohms; $\overline{L} = 0.00367$ henry; $\overline{C} = 0.00835$ microfarad; and $\overline{G} = 0.8 \times 10^{-6}$ mho. The generator supplies 10 volts at 1000 cycles, and is assumed to have a negligible internal impedance.

The received voltage, V_r, can be calculated from Eq. 9.3-1 or Eq. 9.4-23 by letting $x = \ell$, the length of the line, and by placing $V(\ell)$ equal to the sending-end voltage. This requires the calculation of the values of Z_0, ρ, and γ. The characteristic impedance of the given line at a frequency of 1000 cyles is

$$Z_0 = \sqrt{\frac{10.4 + j23.0}{(0.8 + j52.6)10^{-6}}} = \sqrt{\frac{25.2\underline{/66°}}{52.6 \times 10^{-6}\underline{/90}}}$$

$$= 692\underline{/-12°} = 677 - j144 \text{ ohms} \qquad [9.6\text{-}1]$$

Use of the lossless line formula, $Z_0 = \sqrt{L/C}$, gives a value of $665\underline{/0°}$.

The value of ρ is found by substituting $Z_r = (300 + j0)$ and $Z_0 = (677 - j144)$ into Eq. 9.5-1, giving the following result:

$$\rho = \frac{300 - (677 - j144)}{300 + (677 - j144)} = \frac{-377 + j144}{977 - j144} = \frac{404\underline{/159.1°}}{985\underline{/-8.4°}}$$

$$= 0.41\underline{/167.5°} = -0.394 + j0.087 \qquad [9.6\text{-}2]$$

The propagation function is found from Eq. 9.3-7 to be

$$\gamma = \alpha + j\beta = \sqrt{25.2\underline{/66°} \times 52.6(10^{-6})\underline{/90°}}$$

$$= 0.036\underline{/78°} = 0.00755 + j0.0355 \qquad [9.6\text{-}3]$$

Hence, $\alpha\ell = 0.00755 \times 50 = 0.3775$ neper, and $\beta\ell = 0.0355 \times 50 = 1.775$ radians $= 101.8°$.

The substitution of the calculated values of Z_0, ρ, $\alpha\ell$, and $\beta\ell$ into Eq. 9.3-1 or Eq. 9.4-23, with $x = \ell = 50$, and with the left-hand side placed equal to $V_s = 10$ (since there is no internal impedance), yields the following expressions for V_r:

$$V_r = \frac{(1 + \rho)V_s}{\epsilon^{\gamma\ell} + \rho\epsilon^{-\gamma\ell}}$$

$$= \frac{(1 - 0.394 + j0.087)10}{\epsilon^{0.3775}\epsilon^{j1.775} + (0.41\underline{/167.5°} \times \epsilon^{-0.3775}\epsilon^{-j1.775})} \qquad [9.6\text{-}4]$$

$$V_r = \frac{6.1\underline{/8.2°}}{1.46\underline{/101.8°} + (0.41\underline{/167.5°} \times 0.685\underline{/-101.8°})}$$

$$= \frac{6.1\underline{/8.2°}}{-0.3 + j1.43 + 0.116 + j0.256} \qquad [9.6\text{-}5]$$

$$V_r = \frac{6.1\underline{/8.2^\circ}}{-0.184 + j1.686} = \frac{6.1\underline{/8.2^\circ}}{1.7\underline{/96.2^\circ}} = 3.60\underline{/-88^\circ}$$

$$= 0.14 - j3.58 \text{ volts} \qquad\qquad [9.6\text{-}6]$$

The output current, I_r, is given by

$$I_r = \frac{V_r}{Z_r} = \frac{3.60\underline{/-88^\circ}}{300} = 0.012\underline{/-88^\circ} \text{ ampere} \qquad [9.6\text{-}7]$$

The output power, P_r, is

$$P_r = 300\,|I_r|^2 = 300(0.012)^2 = 0.0432 \text{ watt} \qquad [9.6\text{-}8]$$

The input current, I_s, is V_s/Z_s, where Z_s is the sending-end impedance which can be found by setting $x = \ell = 50$ in Eq. 9.5-15. This gives the following result:

$$Z_s = Z_0\left[\frac{\epsilon^{\gamma\ell} + \rho\epsilon^{-\gamma\ell}}{\epsilon^{\gamma\ell} - \rho\epsilon^{-\gamma\ell}}\right] \qquad\qquad [9.6\text{-}9]$$

where the numerator in the expression for Z_s has already been found in Eq. 9.6-6 to be $1.7\underline{/96.2^\circ}$. The value for Z_s is thus given by

$$Z_s = 692\underline{/-12^\circ}\left[\frac{1.7\underline{/96.2^\circ}}{1.46\underline{/101.8^\circ} - (0.41\underline{/167.5^\circ} \times 0.685\underline{/-101.8^\circ})}\right]$$

$$= \frac{692\underline{/-12^\circ} \times 1.7\underline{/96.2^\circ}}{-0.3 + j1.43 - 0.116 - j0.256}$$

$$Z_s = \frac{692\underline{/-12^\circ} \times 1.7\underline{/96.2^\circ}}{-0.416 + j1.17} = \frac{1156\underline{/84.2^\circ}}{1.24\underline{/109.6}} = 934\underline{/-25.4^\circ} \text{ ohms} \qquad [9.6\text{-}10]$$

Note that reflection has caused Z_s to be considerably different from Z_0.

Inasmuch as the input or sending-end voltage has been taken as the reference, the sending-end power, P_s is given by

$$P_s = V_s I_s \cos\theta_s \qquad\qquad [9.6\text{-}11]$$

$$P_s = 10\left(\frac{10}{934}\right)\cos 25.4^\circ = 0.0960 \text{ watt} \qquad [9.6\text{-}12]$$

The efficiency of transmission is given by

$$\eta = \frac{P_r}{P_s} \times 100 = \frac{0.0430}{0.0960} \times 100 = 45.6 \text{ per cent} \qquad [9.6\text{-}13]$$

To illustrate the use of hyperbolic functions, Eq. 9.5-29 will now be applied to find the receiver voltage in the illustrative problem of this section. An expression for the receiver voltage is found by substituting $z = \ell$ in Eq. 9.5-29, yielding

$$V_r = V(\ell) = V_s\left(\cosh \gamma\ell - \frac{Z_0}{Z_s}\sinh \gamma\ell\right) \qquad [9.6\text{-}14]$$

The hyperbolic functions of the complex angle, $\gamma\ell$, are expanded as follows:

$$\cosh \gamma\ell = \cosh (\alpha + j\beta)\ell = \cosh \alpha\ell \cos \beta\ell + j \sinh \alpha\ell \sin \beta\ell \qquad [9.6\text{-}15]$$
$$\sinh \gamma\ell = \sinh (\alpha + j\beta)\ell = \sinh \alpha\ell \cos \beta\ell + j \cosh \alpha\ell \sin \beta\ell \qquad [9.6\text{-}16]$$

where $\alpha\ell = 0.3775$ and $\beta\ell = 1.775$. Standard tables give the following values for the hyperbolic and trigonometric functions:*

$$\begin{aligned}\cosh \alpha\ell &= \cosh 0.3775 = 1.072 \\ \sinh \alpha\ell &= \sinh 0.3775 = 0.387\end{aligned} \qquad [9.6\text{-}17]$$

$$\begin{aligned}\cos \beta\ell &= \cos 1.775 = \cos 101.8° = -0.204 \\ \sin \beta\ell &= \sin 1.775 = \sin 101.8° = 0.978\end{aligned} \qquad [9.6\text{-}18]$$

Hence,

$$\cosh \gamma\ell = 1.072(-0.204) + j0\,.387(0.978)$$
$$= -0.218 + j0.379 = 0.437\underline{/120.1°} \qquad [9.6\text{-}10]$$

$$\sinh \gamma\ell = 0.387(-0.204) + j1.072(0.978)$$
$$= -0.079 + j1.05 = 1.06\underline{/94.2°} \qquad [9.6\text{-}20]$$

Equations 9.6-19 and 9.6-20 can also be derived from Eqs. B-28 and B-29 of Appendix B.

Since Z_s was found to equal $934\underline{/-25.4°}$, Z_0/Z_s is given by

$$\frac{Z_0}{Z_s} = \frac{692\underline{/-12°}}{934\underline{/-25.4°}} = 0.730\underline{/13.4°} \qquad [9.6\text{-}21]$$

The substitution of this value into Eq. 9.6-14 gives the following value for V_r:

$$V_r = 10[-0.218 + j0.379 - (0.730\underline{/13.4°} \times 1.06\underline{/94.2°})] \qquad [9.6\text{-}22]$$

* Tables of the values of hyperbolic and exponential functions are given in Appendix C.

$$V_r = 10(-0.218 + j0.379 - 0.775\underline{/107.6°}) \qquad [9.6\text{-}23]$$

$$V_r = 10[-0.218 + j0.379 - (-0.232 + j0.737)]$$
$$= 0.14 - j3.58 \text{ volts} \qquad [9.6\text{-}24]$$

This is the same result as was obtained in Eq. 9.6-6.

9.7 EQUIVALENT LUMPED NETWORKS

A transmission line is a two-terminal pair network, consisting of two terminals at the input or sending end and two terminals at the receiving or output end. T and π networks are also two-terminal pairs. It will now be shown that these networks can be used to represent a general transmission line at a single frequency. In other words, for a given input voltage and current, the output voltage and current will be the same for the simulating network as for the transmission line at the given frequency.

The sending-end current on a transmission line of length ℓ can be expressed in terms of the receiving-end current and voltage by letting $x = \ell$ in Eq. 9.5-10. This gives the following expression:

$$I_s = I_r \cosh \gamma\ell + \frac{V_r}{Z_0} \sinh \gamma\ell \qquad [9.7\text{-}1]$$

The receiving-end current can be expressed in terms of the sending-end current and voltage by letting $z = \ell$ in Eq. 9.5-28. This gives the following result:

$$I_r = I_s \cosh \gamma\ell - \frac{V_s}{Z_0} \sinh \gamma\ell \qquad [9.7\text{-}2]$$

The solution of Eqs. 9.7-1 and 9.7-2 for V_s and V_r yields

$$V_s = I_s Z_0 \left(\frac{\cosh \gamma\ell}{\sinh \gamma\ell}\right) - \frac{I_r Z_0}{\sinh \gamma\ell} \qquad [9.7\text{-}3]$$

$$V_r = \frac{I_s Z_0}{\sinh \gamma\ell} - I_r Z_0 \left(\frac{\cosh \gamma\ell}{\sinh \gamma\ell}\right) \qquad [9.7\text{-}4]$$

Equations 9.7-3 and 9.7-4 can be written to conform to the mesh equations of a T network having the reference voltages and currents shown in Fig. 9-2 as follows:

$$I_s Z_0 \coth \gamma\ell - I_r Z_0 \operatorname{csch} \gamma\ell = V_s \qquad [9.7\text{-}5]$$

$$-I_s Z_0 \operatorname{csch} \gamma\ell + I_r Z_0 \coth \gamma\ell = -V_r \qquad [9.7\text{-}6]$$

The mesh-current equations of the symmetrical T network shown in Fig. 9-2 are:

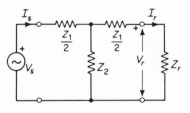

Figure 9-2 Symmetrical T network.

$$I_s\left(\frac{Z_1}{2} + Z_2\right) - I_r Z_2 = V_s \qquad [9.7\text{-}7]$$

$$-I_s Z_2 + I_r\left(\frac{Z_1}{2} + Z_2\right) = -V_r \qquad [9.7\text{-}8]$$

A comparison of Eqs. 9.7-5 and 9.7-6 with 9.7-7 and 9.7-8 shows that the T network is equivalent to the transmission line provided that

$$Z_2 = Z_0 \operatorname{csch} \gamma\ell \qquad [9.7\text{-}9]$$

$$\frac{Z_1}{2} + Z_2 = Z_0 \coth \gamma\ell \qquad [9.7\text{-}10]$$

The substitution of Z_2 from Eq. 9.7-9 into Eq. 9.7-10 gives the following expressions for Z_1:

$$\frac{Z_1}{2} = Z_0(\coth \gamma\ell - \operatorname{csch} \gamma\ell) = Z_0(\operatorname{csch} \gamma\ell)(\cosh \gamma\ell - 1) \qquad [9.7\text{-}11]$$

$$\frac{Z_1}{2} = \frac{Z_0}{\sinh \gamma\ell}\left(\frac{\epsilon^{\gamma\ell} + \epsilon^{-\gamma\ell}}{2} - 1\right) = \frac{Z_0}{\sinh \gamma\ell}\left(\frac{\epsilon^{\gamma\ell} - 2 + \epsilon^{-\gamma\ell}}{2}\right) \qquad [9.7\text{-}12]$$

$$\frac{Z_1}{2} = \frac{2Z_0}{\epsilon^{\gamma\ell} - \epsilon^{-\gamma\ell}}\left(\frac{\epsilon^{\gamma\ell/2} - \epsilon^{-\gamma\ell/2}}{2}\right)^2 = \frac{Z_0(\epsilon^{\gamma\ell/2} - \epsilon^{-\gamma\ell/2})^2}{(\epsilon^{\gamma\ell/2} + \epsilon^{-\gamma\ell/2})(\epsilon^{\gamma\ell/2} - \epsilon^{-\gamma\ell/2})} \qquad [9.7\text{-}13]$$

$$\frac{Z_1}{2} = \frac{Z_0 \sinh \gamma\ell/2}{\cosh \gamma\ell/2} = Z_0 \tanh \frac{\gamma\ell}{2} \qquad [9.7\text{-}14]$$

The equivalent T section can also be derived by applying the bisection principle. This is left as an exercise.

It follows from Eqs. 9.7-9 and 9.7-14 that the T network shown in Fig. 9-3 is the equivalent of the general transmission line of length ℓ, *at* and *only at the* frequency at which Z_0 and γ have been calculated. The corresponding π section is shown in Fig. 9-4. The equivalent π section can also be derived from the bisection principle.

For small values of $|\gamma\ell|$, the following approximations hold:

$$\left.\begin{aligned} \tanh \frac{\gamma\ell}{2} &\cong \frac{\gamma\ell}{2} \\[2mm] \operatorname{csch} \gamma\ell &\cong \frac{1}{\gamma\ell} \end{aligned}\right| \quad |\gamma\ell| \ll 1 \qquad [9.7\text{-}15]$$

The approximations given by Eq. 9.7-15 hold very well for $|\gamma\ell| \leqq 0.2$. Since the absolute value of γ is usually slightly greater than the wavelength function, β, it is safe to state that the relations given by Eq. 9.7-15 hold within engineering accuracy for lines in which $\beta\ell \leqq 10°$. This corre-

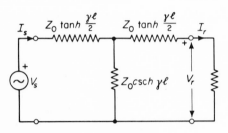

Figure 9-3 Representation of a transmission line by a symmetrical T network.

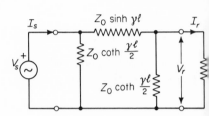

Figure 9-4 Representation of a transmission line by a symmetrical π network.

sponds to power lines having a length of less than 86 miles, and the range can probably be extended to 100 miles. When these approximations can be used, the elements of the equivalent T shown in Fig. 9-3 are:

$$Z_0 \tanh \frac{\gamma\ell}{2} \cong Z_0 \left(\frac{\gamma\ell}{2}\right) \cong \frac{\ell}{2} \sqrt{\frac{(\overline{R} + j\omega\overline{L})^2(\overline{G} + j\omega\overline{C})}{\overline{G} + j\omega\overline{C}}} \cong \frac{1}{2}(\overline{R} + j\omega\overline{L})\ell$$
[9.7-16]

$$Z_0 \operatorname{csch} \gamma\ell \cong \frac{Z_0}{\gamma\ell} \cong \frac{1}{\ell}\sqrt{\frac{(\overline{R} + j\omega\overline{L})}{(\overline{R} + j\omega\overline{L})(\overline{G} + j\omega\overline{C})^2}} \cong \frac{1}{(\overline{G} + j\omega\overline{C})\ell}$$
[9.7-17]

Equations 9.7-16 and 9.7-17 show that the series arm of the equivalent T section consists of a resistor, $\overline{R}\ell/2$, in series with an inductor, $\overline{L}\ell/2$; and that the shunt arm consists of a capacitor, $\overline{C}\ell$, in parallel with a conductance, $\overline{G}\ell$.

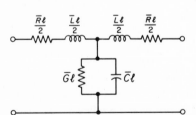

Figure 9-5 Equivalent T section of an electrically short transmission line.

The application of the approximations in Eqs. 9.7-16 and 9.7-17 to Fig. 9-3 results in Fig. 9-5, which is the equivalent T section for a line that has a length corresponding to 10° or less. The series arm corresponds to an impedance, and the shunt arm to an admittance.

The equivalent π section shown in Fig. 9-4 can be simplified in a similar manner when $|\gamma\ell| \ll 1$. The equivalent networks are useful in the design of *artificial lines* that consist of several

T or π sections, each section being the equivalent of a certain length of line. The length is chosen to satisfy the relation $|\gamma\ell| \ll 1$. Since the absolute value of γ is nearly equal to β in practice, the equivalent length per section is determined by the relation $\beta\ell \ll 1$. For example, if γ per mile for a certain line is given by

$$\gamma = 0.01 + j0.20 \qquad [9.7\text{-}18]$$

the relations in Eq. 9.7-15 are satisfied when

$$\gamma\ell = \beta\ell = 0.20\ell = 0.2 \qquad [9.7\text{-}19]$$

Hence,

$$\ell = \frac{0.2}{0.2} = 1.0 \text{ mile} \qquad [9.7\text{-}20]$$

Under these conditions, the section shown in Fig. 9-5 would be equivalent to 1.0 mile, and ten such sections would be equivalent to ten miles of line. It is assumed that the four line constants are known and that γ in Eq. 9.7-18 is given for the highest frequency of interest. Under these assumptions, the artificial line will be a satisfactory representation of the actual line for all frequencies up to and including the highest frequency for which γ is computed in Eq. 9.7-18. This follows from the fact that β increases with frequency. Hence, if $\beta\ell \ll 1$ at the highest frequency of interest, $\beta\ell \ll 1$ for all lower frequencies.

The division of Eq. 9.7-11 by Eq. 9.7-9 gives the following results:

$$\frac{Z_1}{2Z_2} = \frac{Z_0(\text{csch } \gamma\ell)(\cosh \gamma\ell - 1)}{Z_0 \text{ csch } \gamma\ell} = \cosh \gamma\ell - 1 \qquad [9.7\text{-}21]$$

$$\cosh \gamma\ell = 1 + \frac{Z_1}{2Z_2} = \cosh \gamma' \qquad [9.7\text{-}22]$$

where Z_1, Z_2, and γ' are, respectively, the equivalent T parameters and propagation function of a length, ℓ, of the transmission line.

9.8 DETERMINATION OF PARAMETERS FROM IMPEDANCE MEASUREMENTS

The characteristic impedance and the four parameters of a line can be determined from the input impedance of the line when its output terminals are open and when they are short-circuited. The input impedance of a line of length ℓ is given by Eq. 9.5-31 as

$$Z_{\text{in}} = Z_s = Z_0 \left[\frac{Z_r \cosh \gamma\ell + Z_0 \sinh \gamma\ell}{Z_0 \cosh \gamma\ell + Z_r \sinh \gamma\ell} \right] \qquad [9.8\text{-}1]$$

If $Z_r = 0$, Z_{in} represents the input impedance when the output terminals are short-circuited. This will be denoted by Z_{sc}, and has the following value:

$$Z_{sc} = Z_0 \tanh \gamma \ell \qquad [9.8\text{-}2]$$

When the output terminals are open, Z_{in} will be denoted by Z_{oc}, which is the limit of the right-hand side of Eq. 9.8-1 as $Z_r \to \infty$, and is given by

$$Z_{oc} = \operatorname*{Lim}_{Z_r \to \infty} Z_0 \left[\frac{\cosh \gamma \ell + (Z_0/Z_r) \sinh \gamma \ell}{(Z_0/Z_r) \cosh \gamma \ell + \sinh \gamma \ell} \right] = Z_0 \coth \gamma \ell \qquad [9.8\text{-}3]$$

It follows from Eqs. 9.8-2 and 9.8-3 that

$$Z_{sc} Z_{oc} = Z_0^2 \tanh \gamma \ell \coth \gamma \ell \qquad [9.8\text{-}4]$$

Hence,

$$Z_0 = \sqrt{Z_{sc} Z_{oc}} \qquad [9.8\text{-}5]$$

An expression for $\tanh \gamma \ell$ can be obtained by substituting Z_0 from Eq. 9.8-5 into Eq. 9.8-2, giving the following result:

$$Z_{sc} = \sqrt{Z_{sc} Z_{oc}} \tanh \gamma \ell \qquad [9.8\text{-}6]$$

$$\tanh \gamma \ell = \sqrt{\frac{Z_{sc}}{Z_{oc}}} \qquad [9.8\text{-}7]$$

It will now be shown that the solution of Eq. 9.8-7 for $\gamma \ell$, together with the determination of Z_0 from the open and short-circuited input impedance, makes possible the calculation of the transmission line parameters. Equation 9.8-7 can be written as

$$\frac{\epsilon^\gamma - \epsilon^{-\gamma \ell}}{\epsilon^{\gamma \ell} + \epsilon^{-\gamma \ell}} = \sqrt{\frac{Z_{sc}}{Z_{oc}}} \qquad [9.8\text{-}8]$$

Hence,

$$\epsilon^{\gamma \ell} - \epsilon^{-\gamma \ell} = (\epsilon^{\gamma \ell} + \epsilon^{-\gamma \ell}) \sqrt{\frac{Z_{sc}}{Z_{oc}}} \qquad [9.8\text{-}9]$$

$$\left(1 - \sqrt{\frac{Z_{sc}}{Z_{oc}}}\right) \epsilon^{\gamma \ell} = \left(1 + \sqrt{\frac{Z_{sc}}{Z_{oc}}}\right) \epsilon^{-\gamma \ell} \qquad [9.8\text{-}10]$$

Multiplying both sides of Eq. 9.8-10 by $\epsilon^{\gamma l}$ yields

$$\left(1 - \sqrt{\frac{Z_{sc}}{Z_{oc}}}\right) \epsilon^{2\gamma \ell} = 1 + \sqrt{\frac{Z_{sc}}{Z_{oc}}} \qquad [9.8\text{-}11]$$

$$\epsilon^{2\gamma \ell} = \frac{1 + \sqrt{Z_{sc}/Z_{oc}}}{1 - \sqrt{Z_{sc}/Z_{oc}}} \qquad [9.8\text{-}12]$$

It follows from Eq. 9.8-12 that:

$$2\gamma\ell = \ln\left(\frac{1 + \sqrt{Z_{sc}/Z_{oc}}}{1 + \sqrt{Z_{sc}/Z_{oc}}}\right) \qquad [9.8\text{-}13]$$

$$\gamma = \frac{1}{2\ell} \ln\left(\frac{1 + \sqrt{Z_{sc}/Z_{oc}}}{1 - \sqrt{Z_{sc}/Z_{oc}}}\right) \qquad [9.8\text{-}14]$$

It follows from Eqs. 9.3-7 and 9.3-8 that:

$$\gamma Z_0 = \sqrt{(\overline{R} + j\omega\overline{L})(\overline{G} + j\omega\overline{C})} \sqrt{\frac{\overline{R} + j\omega\overline{L}}{\overline{G} + j\omega\overline{C}}} = \overline{R} + j\omega\overline{L} \qquad [9.8\text{-}15]$$

and

$$\frac{\gamma}{Z_0} = \overline{G} + j\omega\overline{C} \qquad [9.8\text{-}16]$$

The derived equations will now be applied to calculate the characteristic impedance and parameters of a line 50 miles long, when Z_{oc} is measured by a bridge at 700 cycles to be $286\underline{/-40^\circ}$, and when Z_{sc} is $1520\underline{/16^\circ}$ ohms. It follows from Eq. 9.8-5 that:

$$Z_0 = \sqrt{286\underline{/-40} \times 1520\underline{/16}} = 660\underline{/-12^\circ} \text{ ohms} \qquad [9.8\text{-}17]$$

The impedance measurements yield the ratio

$$\sqrt{\frac{Z_{sc}}{Z_{oc}}} = \sqrt{\frac{1520\underline{/16^\circ}}{286\underline{/-40^\circ}}} = 2.31\underline{/28.0^\circ} = 2.04 + j1.08 \qquad [9.8\text{-}18]$$

It follows from Eq. 9.8-14 that:

$$\gamma = \frac{1}{100} \ln\left(\frac{3.04 + j1.08}{-1.04 - j1.08}\right)$$

$$= \frac{1}{100} \ln\left(\frac{3.23\underline{/21.1^\circ}}{1.54\underline{/-131.2^\circ}}\right) \qquad [9.8\text{-}19]$$

$$\gamma = \frac{1}{100} \ln\left(2.1\underline{/152.3^\circ}\right)$$

Hence,

$$\gamma = 0.00742 + j\left[\left(\frac{152.3}{100} \times \frac{\pi}{180}\right) + \frac{2\pi n}{100}\right] \qquad [9.8\text{-}20]$$

$$\gamma = 0.00742 + j\left[0.0266 + \frac{2\pi n}{100}\right] \qquad [9.8\text{-}21]$$

where n is an integer or zero.

312   transmission lines with losses

The addition of $2\pi n$ to the quadrature component of γ in Eq. 9.8-21 results from the fact that the logarithm of a complex number is not uniquely defined.* It follows from Eq. 9.8-21 that:

$$\gamma = \alpha + j\beta = 0.00742 + j(0.0266 + 0.0628n) \qquad [9.8\text{-}22]$$

where n is to be assigned a value to yield a reasonable velocity of phase propagation. If it is assumed that the measurements have been made on an open-wire line, the velocity of phase propagation is somewhat less than 186,000 miles per second, the value for a lossless line. If $n = 0$ in Eq. 9.8-22,

$$\lambda = \frac{2\pi}{\beta} = \frac{2\pi}{0.0266} = 235.5 \text{ miles}$$

$$u_p = 235.5 \times 700 = 164{,}850 \text{ miles per second}$$

Inasmuch as an increase of n to a value of unity would reduce the phase velocity by a factor of more than 3, values of n greater than zero are not permissible in Eq. 9.8-22. The value of n to be used in Eq. 9.8-22 can usually be determined from velocity considerations.

The complex propagation factor for this line is

$$\gamma = \alpha + j\beta = 0.00742 + j0.0266 = 0.0276\underline{/74.4°} \qquad [9.8\text{-}23]$$

It follows from Eq. 9.8-15 that:

$$\overline{R} + j\omega\overline{L} = \gamma Z_0 = 0.0276\underline{/74.4°} \times 660\underline{/-12°} = 18.2\underline{/62.4°} \qquad [9.8\text{-}24]$$

$$\overline{R} + j\omega\overline{L} = \overline{R} + j1400\pi(\overline{L}) = 8.35 + j16.1 \qquad [9.8\text{-}25]$$

Hence,

$$\overline{R} = 8.35 \text{ ohms per mile}$$

$$\overline{L} = \frac{16.1}{1400\pi} = 3.66 \text{ millihenrys per mile}$$

It follows from Eq. 9.8-16 that:

$$\overline{G} + j\omega\overline{C} = \frac{\gamma}{Z_0} = \frac{0.0276\underline{/74.4°}}{660\underline{/-12°}} = (41.8 \times 10^{-6})\underline{/86.4°} \qquad [9.8\text{-}26]$$

$$\overline{G} + j\omega\overline{C} = (2.18 \times 10^{-6}) + (j41.5 \times 10^{-6}) \qquad [9.8\text{-}27]$$

*A complex number can be expressed as $r = |r|\epsilon^{j(\theta+2n\pi)}$. Hence,

$$\ln r = \ln|r| + j(\theta + 2n\pi)$$

Hence,

$$\overline{G} = 2.18 \text{ micro-mho per mile}$$

$$\overline{C} = \frac{4.15}{1400\pi} = 0.00947 \text{ microfarad per mile}$$

9.9 DISTORTION

The signals usually transmitted over lines are complex and consist of many frequency components. Ideal transmission of such signals requires that all frequencies have the same attenuation and the same delay caused by a finite velocity of propagation. When these conditions are not satisfied, distortion is said to exist.

Distortion on transmission lines is usually of two forms. *Frequency distortion* is that form of distortion in which the various frequency components of the signal suffer different attenuations. In other words, when the attenuation function is a function of the frequency, frequency distortion exists. *Delay distortion* is that form of distortion in which the time required to transmit the various frequency components over the line and the consequent delay is not a constant. Since the phase velocity, u_p, is given by

$$u_p = \frac{\omega}{\beta} \qquad [9.9\text{-}1]$$

delay distortion exists whenever β, the phase function, is not equal to a constant multiplied by ω.

The general dependence of both the attenuation function, α, and the phase function, β, upon frequency can be seen from the equations for the real and imaginary components of the propagation function, γ. Recalling that

$$\gamma = \alpha + j\beta = \sqrt{(\overline{R} + j\omega\overline{L})(\overline{G} + j\omega\overline{C})} \qquad [9.9\text{-}2]$$

and squaring both sides of Eq. 9.9-2 to give

$$\alpha^2 - \beta^2 + 2j\alpha\beta = (\overline{R} + j\omega\overline{L})(\overline{G} + j\omega\overline{C}) = \overline{R}\,\overline{G} - \omega^2\overline{L}\,\overline{C}$$
$$+ j(\omega\overline{R}\,\overline{C} + \omega\overline{L}\,\overline{G}) \qquad [9.9\text{-}3]$$

yields the following two equations:

$$\alpha^2 - \beta^2 = \overline{R}\,\overline{G} - \omega^2\overline{L}\,\overline{C} \qquad [9.9\text{-}4]$$

$$2\alpha\beta = \omega(\overline{R}\,\overline{C} + \overline{L}\,\overline{G}) \qquad [9.9\text{-}5]$$

Squaring Eq. 9.9-5 and solving for β^2 yields

$$\beta^2 = \frac{\omega^2 (\overline{R}\,\overline{C} + \overline{L}\,\overline{G})^2}{4\alpha^2} \qquad [9.9\text{-}6]$$

The substitution of Eq. 9.9-6 into Eq. 9.9-4 gives the following expression:

$$\alpha^4 - \alpha^2(\overline{R}\,\overline{G} - \omega^2\overline{L}\,\overline{C}) - \frac{\omega^2}{4}(\overline{R}\,\overline{C} + \overline{L}\,\overline{G})^2 = 0 \qquad [9.9\text{-}7]$$

The solution of Eq. 9.9-7 yields the following expression for the attenuation function:

$$\alpha = \sqrt{\frac{(\overline{R}\,\overline{G} - \omega^2\overline{L}\,\overline{C}) + \sqrt{(\overline{R}\,\overline{G} - \omega^2\overline{L}\,\overline{C})^2 + \omega^2(\overline{R}\,\overline{C} + \overline{L}\,\overline{G})^2}}{2}} \qquad [9.9\text{-}8]$$

The substitution of Eq. 9.9-8 into Eq. 9.9-4 gives the following expression for the phase function:

$$\beta = \sqrt{\frac{(\omega^2\overline{L}\,\overline{C} - \overline{R}\,\overline{G}) + \sqrt{(\overline{R}\,\overline{G} - \omega^2\overline{L}\,\overline{C}) + \omega^2(\overline{R}\,\overline{C} + \overline{L}\,\overline{G})^2}}{2}} \qquad [9.9\text{-}9]$$

An inspection of Eqs. 9.9-8 and 9.9-9 shows that α and β are in general complicated functions of the frequency. However, under certain conditions, α is independent of frequency, and β is a constant multiplied by ω. In such cases, neither frequency nor phase distortion exists, and the line is said to be *distortionless*. The condition for distortionless transmission will be investigated by writing the expression for the propagation function as follows:

$$\gamma = \sqrt{(\overline{R} + j\omega\overline{L})(\overline{G} + j\omega\overline{C})} = \sqrt{\overline{L}\,\overline{C}}\sqrt{\left(\frac{\overline{R}}{\overline{L}} + j\omega\right)\left(\frac{\overline{G}}{\overline{C}} + j\omega\right)} \qquad [9.9\text{-}10]$$

Inspection of Eq. 9.9-10 shows that, when

$$\frac{\overline{R}}{\overline{L}} = \frac{\overline{G}}{\overline{C}} \qquad [9.9\text{-}11]$$

$$\gamma = \gamma_d = \left(\frac{\overline{R}}{\overline{L}} + j\omega\right)\sqrt{\overline{L}\,\overline{C}} = \left(\frac{\overline{G}}{\overline{C}} + j\omega\right)\sqrt{\overline{L}\,\overline{C}} \qquad [9.9\text{-}12]$$

Inspection of Eq. 9.9-12 shows that the real part of the propagation function is independent of the frequency and that the imaginary part is a constant multiplied by the frequency. This is the required condition for *distortionless transmission*, and the corresponding propagation function is denoted by γ_d in Eq. 9.9-12. Equation 9.9-11 gives the relation that the line parameters must satisfy for distortionless transmission. A line having parameters that satisfy Eq. 9.9-11 is termed a *distortionless line*. The condition for distortionless transmission was formulated by Oliver Heaviside.

The attenuation and wavelength functions of a distortionless line are found from Eq. 9.9-12 to be

$$\alpha_d = \overline{R}\sqrt{\frac{\overline{C}}{\overline{L}}} = \overline{G}\sqrt{\frac{\overline{L}}{\overline{C}}} \qquad [9.9\text{-}13]$$

$$\beta_d = \omega \sqrt{\overline{L}\,\overline{C}} \qquad [9.9\text{-}14]$$

where

$$\gamma_d = \alpha_d + j\beta_d \qquad [9.9\text{-}15]$$

In a distortionless line, all frequency components have the same attenuation and phase velocity. The received and transmitted wave forms have the same shape, but the received wave is reduced in amplitude because of attenuation. The above analysis assumes that the line parameters are independent of frequency. The characteristic impedance can be expressed as

$$Z_0 = \sqrt{\frac{\overline{R} + j\omega\overline{L}}{\overline{G} + j\omega\overline{C}}} = \sqrt{\frac{\overline{L}}{\overline{C}}}\sqrt{\frac{\overline{R}/\overline{L} + j\omega}{\overline{G}/\overline{C} + j\omega}} \qquad [9.9\text{-}16]$$

Since $\overline{R}/\overline{L} = \overline{G}/\overline{C}$ in a distortionless line, the characteristic impedance of a distortionless line is

$$Z_0 = \sqrt{\frac{\overline{L}}{\overline{C}}} \qquad [9.9\text{-}17]$$

Equation 9.9-17 shows that the characteristic impedance of a distortionless line is purely real, and is the same as for a lossless line.

It is seen from Eq. 9.9-12 that when $\overline{R} = \overline{G} = 0$, $\alpha = 0$ and $\beta = \beta_d$. Hence, a lossless line is distortionless. A line in which the parameters satisfy the relations

$$\frac{\overline{R}}{\omega\overline{L}} \ll 1 \qquad [9.9\text{-}18]$$

$$\frac{\overline{G}}{\omega\overline{C}} \ll 1 \qquad [9.9\text{-}19]$$

is a low-loss line and is almost distortionless. This can be seen by expressing the propagation function as

$$\gamma = \sqrt{(\overline{R} + j\omega\overline{L})(\overline{G} + j\omega\overline{C})}$$

$$= j\omega \sqrt{\overline{L}\,\overline{C}} \sqrt{\left(1 + \frac{\overline{R}}{j\omega\overline{L}}\right)\left(1 + \frac{\overline{G}}{j\omega\overline{C}}\right)} \qquad [9.9\text{-}20]$$

$$\gamma = j\omega \sqrt{\overline{L}\,\overline{C}} \left[1 + \frac{\overline{R}}{j\omega\overline{L}}\right]^{1/2} \left[1 + \frac{\overline{G}}{j\omega\overline{C}}\right]^{1/2} \qquad [9.9\text{-}21]$$

Expanding the square roots in Eq. 9.9-21 by the binomial theorem, and neglecting all powers greater than the first, gives the following expression:

$$\gamma = j\omega \sqrt{\overline{L}\,\overline{C}} \left[1 + \frac{1}{2}\left(\frac{\overline{R}}{j\omega\overline{L}}\right) + \frac{1}{2}\left(\frac{\overline{G}}{j\omega\overline{C}}\right)\right] = \alpha + j\beta \qquad [9.9\text{-}22]$$

Equating the real and the imaginary components in Eq. 9.9-22 yields

$$\alpha = \frac{1}{2}\left[\overline{R}\sqrt{\overline{C}/\overline{L}} + \overline{G}\sqrt{\overline{L}/\overline{C}}\right] \qquad [9.9\text{-}23]$$

$$\beta = \omega\sqrt{\overline{L}\,\overline{C}} \qquad [9.9\text{-}24]$$

Since α is independent of frequency, and since β is a multiple of the frequency, a line with parameters satisfying Eqs. 9.9-18 and 9.9-19 (which are actually inequalities) is distortionless within the approximations used in expanding Eq. 9.9-22. Also, under these conditions,

$$Z_0 = \sqrt{\frac{\overline{R} + j\omega\overline{L}}{\overline{G} + j\omega\overline{C}}} = \sqrt{\frac{\overline{L}}{\overline{C}}} \sqrt{\frac{1 + \overline{R}/j\omega\overline{L}}{1 + \overline{G}/j\omega\overline{C}}} = \sqrt{\frac{\overline{L}}{\overline{C}}} \qquad [9.9\text{-}25]$$

Hence, when Eqs. 9.9-18 and 9.9-19 are satisfied, the characteristic impedance is the same as for lossless or truly distortionless lines that satisfy Eq. 9.9-11. It should be noted that Eqs. 9.9-18 and 9.9-19 tend to be satisfied at the higher frequencies but cannot be satisfied for all frequencies, particularly those in the lower range. Hence, a non-sinusoidal or non-periodic wave form that includes all frequencies in its spectrum will be distorted in transmission unless the line is truly distortionless.

When a line is not distortionless, and its parameters do not satisfy Eq. 9.9-11 or Eqs. 9.9-18 and 9.9-19, the transmitted signal is distorted. Consider, for example, a telephone cable in which $\overline{R}$ and $\overline{C}$ are the predominant parameters, and $\omega\overline{L} \ll \overline{R}$ and $\omega\overline{C} \gg \overline{G}$. The propagation function is

$$\gamma \cong \sqrt{j\omega\overline{R}\,\overline{C}} = \sqrt{\omega\overline{R}\,\overline{C}} \left(\frac{1}{\sqrt{2}} + \frac{j}{\sqrt{2}}\right)$$

$$= (1 + j) \sqrt{\frac{\omega\overline{R}\,\overline{C}}{2}} \qquad [9.9\text{-}26]$$

where the effects of inductance and leakage have been neglected. It follows from Eq. 9.9-26 that in such a cable

$$\alpha = \beta = \sqrt{\frac{\omega \overline{R}\ \overline{C}}{2}}$$ [9.9-27]

The phase velocity is

$$u_p = \frac{\omega}{\beta} = \sqrt{\frac{2\omega}{\overline{R}\ \overline{C}}}$$ [9.9-28]

Equations 9.9-27 and 9.9-28 show that, in such a cable, the higher frequencies are attenuated more and travel faster than the lower frequencies. Hence, frequency and delay distortion result. Methods to reduce the distortion in cables and other lines are discussed in the following section.

9.10 LOADING

Efforts to decrease or eliminate distortion consist in modifying the line parameters to cause them to satisfy Eq. 9.9-11 or Eqs. 9.9-18 and 9.9-19. An example of such efforts is given in the following paragraphs.

The parameters of a 16-gauge paper-insulated cable pair are the following: $\overline{R} = 42.1$ ohms; $\overline{L} = 10^{-3}$ henry; $\overline{C} = 62 \times 10^{-9}$ farad; and $\overline{G} = 1.5 \times 10^{-6}$ mho. Hence,

$$\frac{\overline{R}}{\overline{L}} = \frac{42.1}{10^{-3}} = 42.1 \times 10^3$$ [9.10-1]

$$\frac{\overline{G}}{\overline{C}} = \frac{1.5 \times 10^{-6}}{62 \times 10^{-9}} = 0.0242 \times 10^3$$ [9.10-2]

It is seen that for the given cable

$$\frac{\overline{R}}{\overline{L}} \gg \frac{\overline{G}}{\overline{C}}$$ [9.10-3]

The distortionless condition can be approached in the following four ways:

(a) *The resistance can be decreased.* This method decreases the attenuation; but it requires larger conductors, and thus increases the cost.

(b) *The leakage can be increased.* This increase can be accomplished by lowering the quality of the insulation or by introducing shunt conductance along the line. This is a poor solution, however, because it increases the attenuation.

(c) *The capacitance can be decreased.* This approach involves increasing the spacing between the conductors, and cannot be accomplished in an air-insulated line of fixed dimensions.

(d) *The inductance can be increased.* An increase in inductance decreases the attenuation while reducing distortion. This can be accomplished in a line of fixed dimensions by inserting inductance in series with the line. Increasing the inductance is termed *loading.* The theory of loading was developed by Oliver Heaviside in connection with the derivation of Eq. 9.9-11. Professor M. I. Pupin developed the practical method of loading in which lumped inductors, known as *load coils,* are placed at suitable intervals along the line to increase the effective distributed inductance.

Returning to the 16-gauge cable, let us calculate the value of $\overline{L}$ required to satisfy Eq. 9.9-11 for distortionless transmission. This value of $\overline{L}$ is given by the relation

$$\frac{42.1}{\overline{L}} = \frac{\overline{G}}{\overline{C}} = 0.0242 \times 10^3 \qquad [9.10\text{-}4]$$

where $\overline{G}/\overline{C}$ is given in Eq. 9.10-2. Solution of Eq. 9.10-4 for the inductance yields

$$\overline{L} = \frac{42.1}{0.0242} \times 10^{-3} = 1740 \times 10^{-3} \text{ henrys per mile} \qquad [9.10\text{-}5]$$

Since the self-inductance of the cable is 10^{-3} henry, sufficient lumped inductance to obtain an equivalent distributed inductance of 1.739 henrys per mile must be added to satisfy Eq. 9.9-11. This is a very large inductance. In practice, smaller inductors are used to satisfy inequalities 9.9-18 and 9.9-19 to obtain a low-loss line.

It was shown that the distortion is low when $\overline{R}/\omega\overline{L} \ll 1$ and $\overline{G}/\omega\overline{C} \ll 1$. In applying these relations to telephone lines, it is assumed that $\omega = 5000$, corresponding to an *average* voice frequency of 796 cycles per second. For the cable under consideration,

$$\frac{\overline{G}}{\omega\overline{C}} = \frac{1.5 \times 10^{-6}}{5000 \times 62 \times 10^{-9}} = 0.0048 \qquad [9.10\text{-}6]$$

Hence, $\overline{G}/\omega\overline{C} \ll 1$. It is unnecessary for the ratio $\overline{R}/\omega\overline{L}$ to be as small as indicated in Eq. 9.10-6. Assume that

$$\frac{\overline{R}}{\omega\overline{L}} = \frac{42.1}{5000\,\overline{L}} = 0.3 \qquad [9.10\text{-}7]$$

Solution of Eq. 9.10-7 for $\overline{L}$ yields

$$\overline{L} = 28 \times 10^{-3} \text{ henrys per mile} \qquad [9.10\text{-}8]$$

Coils having inductance of 31 millihenrys and a resistance of 2.7 ohms, spaced 1.135 miles apart are used to load the cable under consideration. The equivalent distributed parameters of each coil are $\overline{L}_L = 31/1.135 = 27$ millihenrys per mile and $\overline{R}_L = 2.7/1.135 = 2.4$ ohms per mile.

The constants of the loaded cable are therefore the following: $\overline{R} = 44.5$; $\overline{L} = 28 \times 10^{-3}$; $\overline{C} = 62 \times 10^{-9}$; $\overline{G} = 1.5 \times 10^{-6}$. Note that $\overline{R}$ includes the resistance of the coils.

It follows from Eqs. 9.9-23 and 9.9-24 that the approximate attenuation and phase functions are

$$\alpha = \frac{1}{2}\left[44.5 \sqrt{\frac{62 \times 10^{-9}}{28 \times 10^{-3}}} + (1.5 \times 10^{-6}) \sqrt{\frac{28 \times 10^{-3}}{62 \times 10^{-9}}} \right]$$

$$= 33.9 \times 10^{-3} \text{ nepers per mile} \qquad [9.10\text{-}9]$$

$$\beta = 5000 \sqrt{(28 \times 10^{-3})(62 \times 10^{-9})}$$

$$= 5000 \times 42 \times 10^{-6} = 0.210 \text{ radians per mile} \qquad [9.10\text{-}10]$$

The phase velocity for *all* frequencies is substantially

$$u_p = \frac{\omega}{\beta} = \frac{5000}{5000 \times 42 \times 10^{-6}} = 23{,}800 \text{ miles per sec} \qquad [9.10\text{-}11]$$

Exact values of α and β can be obtained from the real and imaginary parts of

$$\gamma = \sqrt{\frac{[44.5 + (j5000 \times 28 \times 10^{-3})]}{[(1.5 \times 10^{-6}) + (j5000 \times 62 \times 10^{-9})]}}$$

$$= 0.214\underline{/81.2°} = 0.033 + j0.211 = \alpha + j\beta \qquad [9.10\text{-}12]$$

This calculation is left as an exercise. It should be carefully noted that although the phase velocity is substantially equal to $1/\sqrt{\overline{L}\,\overline{C}}$, it does not equal the velocity of light, because of the loading.

It is of interest to compare the attenuation and phase constants of the unloaded cable with those of the loaded cable. It follows from Eq. 9.9-27 that, when the effects of self-inductance and leakage are neglected, α and β at 796 cycles are given by

$$\alpha = \beta = \sqrt{\frac{\omega \overline{R}\,\overline{C}}{2}} = \sqrt{\frac{5000 \times 42.1 \times 62 \times 10^{-9}}{2}}$$

$$= 81 \times 10^{-3} \qquad [9.10\text{-}13]$$

Hence, the attenuation is 81×10^{-3} nepers per mile, and the phase velocity at 796 cycles is

$$u_p = \frac{\omega}{\beta} = \frac{5000}{81 \times 10^{-3}} = 61,700 \text{ miles per sec} \qquad [9.10\text{-}14]$$

As shown by Eqs. 9.10-9 and 9.10-10, the attenuation is reduced to less than one-half of its value for the unloaded cable, and the phase velocity is greatly reduced by loading. The characteristic impedance of the unloaded cable is found by substituting $\overline{L} = \overline{G} = 0$ in Eq. 9.9-16. This gives

$$Z_0 = \sqrt{\frac{\overline{R}}{j\omega\overline{C}}} = \sqrt{\frac{42.1}{j5000 \times 62 \times 10^{-9}}}$$

$$= 356\underline{/-45°} \text{ ohms} \qquad [9.10\text{-}15]$$

The characteristic impedance of the loaded cable is approximately

$$Z_0 = \sqrt{\frac{\overline{L}}{\overline{C}}} = \sqrt{\frac{28 \times 10^{-3}}{62 \times 10^{-9}}} = 670 \text{ ohms} \qquad [9.10\text{-}16]$$

The increase in the absolute value of the characteristic impedance caused by loading is evident. The exact characteristic impedance of the loaded cable can be found from Eq. 9.9-16. This is left as an exercise.

In the discussion of loading, it has been tacitly assumed that the equivalent inductance per unit length is found by dividing the lumped inductance of the loading coil by the separation between coils. The same procedure was used to find the contribution of the loading coils to the distributed resistance. This is an approximate solution. A more exact solution consists of representing the line between loading points by the equivalent T

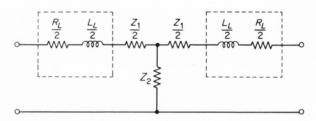

Figure 9-6   Representation of a section of a loaded transmission line by a T network.

network derived in Fig. 9-4. This representation is shown in Fig. 9-6, where the distributed and lumped parameters are combined into an equivalent T network and where the load coils are divided into two parts, each with resistance $R_L/2$ and inductance $L_L/2$. It follows from Fig. 9-6 that the equivalent T section between the centers of consecutive coils, a distance ℓ apart, is as shown in Fig. 9-7, where

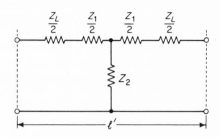

Figure 9-7 Equivalent T network of a transmission line and load coil.

$$Z_L/2 = R_L/2 + j\omega L_L/2 \quad [9.10\text{-}17]$$

It follows from Eq. 9.7-23 that the propagation function for the equivalent T section between loading points in Fig. 9-7 is given by

$$\cosh \gamma' = 1 + \frac{Z_1}{2Z_2} + \frac{Z_L}{2Z_2} \qquad [9.10\text{-}18]$$

where Z_L is the impedance of the load coil at the given frequency, and where $Z_1/2$ and Z_2 are given by Eqs. 9.7-9 and 9.7-11 as

$$Z_1/2 = Z_0 \, (\operatorname{csch} \gamma\ell)(\cosh \gamma\ell - 1) \qquad [9.10\text{-}19]$$

$$Z_2 = Z_0 \operatorname{csch} \gamma\ell \qquad [9.10\text{-}20]$$

where ℓ is the distance between the coils. The substitution of Eqs. 9.10-19 and 9.10-20 in Eq. 9.10-18 gives the following results:

$$\cosh \gamma' = 1 + \frac{Z_0 \, (\operatorname{csch} \gamma\ell)(\cosh \gamma\ell - 1)}{Z_0 \operatorname{csch} \gamma\ell} + \frac{Z_L}{2Z_0 \operatorname{csch} \gamma\ell} \qquad [9.10\text{-}21]$$

$$\cosh \gamma' = \cosh \gamma\ell + \frac{Z_L}{2Z_0} \sinh \gamma\ell \qquad [9.10\text{-}22]$$

Equation 9.10-22 was first derived by G. A. Campbell and is known as Campbell's formula.

Equation B-14 of Appendix B can be used to determine the exact propagation factor of a loaded line. For closely-spaced coils, the method used in Eq. 9.10-12 is much simpler, and gives a satisfactory result.

It can be shown from Eq. 9.10-22 that the inductively loaded line is a low-pass filter. The filter characteristic of the loaded line is readily seen if the losses in both the line and the loading coils are neglected in the application of Eq. 9.10-22. Under these assumptions, $\gamma' = j\beta'$, $\gamma = j\beta$, $Z_L = jX_L$, Z_0 is real, and Campbell's formula becomes

$$\cos \beta' = \cos \beta\ell - \frac{X_L}{2Z_0} \sin \beta\ell \qquad [9.10\text{-}23]$$

The pass range is defined by the relation

$$- 1 \leqq \cos \beta' \leqq 1 \qquad [9.10\text{-}24]$$

For frequencies at which Eq. 9.10-24 does not hold, β' is imaginary, and attenuation, *not caused by ohmic losses*, exists.* Inspection of Eq. 9.10-23 shows that since β and X_L are directly proportional to the frequency, and since $\cos \beta$ is negative and $\sin \beta$ is positive in the second quadrant, it is possible for the right-hand side of this equation to be less than -1. Under this condition, cutoff occurs. It is thus seen that the loaded line behaves as a low-pass filter.

Campbell's formula can also be derived by the use of transfer matrices. The general transmission line equations can be written in the following matrix form:

$$\begin{bmatrix} V_1 \\ I_1 \end{bmatrix} = \begin{bmatrix} \cosh \gamma x & Z_0 \sinh \gamma x \\ (\sinh \gamma x)/Z_0 & \cosh \gamma x \end{bmatrix} \times \begin{bmatrix} V_2 \\ -I_2 \end{bmatrix} \qquad [9.10\text{-}25]$$

where γ is the propagation function, where V_1 and I_1 are the sending-end voltage and current, and V_2 and $-I_2$ are the receiving-end voltage and current. Note that I_2 in Eq. 9.10-25 is the negative of I_r, the receiving-end current in Eq. 9.7-1.

The repetitive section, ab, of a loaded line consists of a length ℓ, of the unloaded line, connected in series with two lumped impedances of

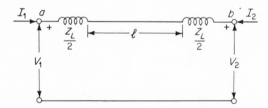

Figure 9-8 Repetitive section of a loaded line.

magnitude $Z_L/2$, as shown in Fig. 9-8. Let the input and output voltages and currents in Fig. 9-8 be related as in Eq. 9.10-25. Then

$$\begin{bmatrix} V_1 \\ I_1 \end{bmatrix} = \begin{bmatrix} \cosh \gamma_m \ell & Z_0 \sinh \gamma_m \ell \\ (\sinh \gamma_m \ell)/Z_0 & \cosh \gamma_m \ell \end{bmatrix} \times \begin{bmatrix} V_2 \\ -I_2 \end{bmatrix} \qquad [9.10\text{-}26]$$

where γ_m is the modified propagation factor per unit length of the loaded line, and the direction of I_2 is opposite to that of I_r.

* This follows from the fact that $\epsilon^{j(j\beta')} = \epsilon^{-\beta'}$, and denotes attenuation.

Figure 9-8 results from the cascading of the following three networks: a lumped impedance, $Z_L/2$, an unloaded transmission line of characteristic impedance Z_0 and length ℓ, and another lumped impedance, $Z_L/2$. The transfer matrix of $Z_L/2$ is given by Eq. 6.3-6 as

$$[T]_{Z_L/2} = \begin{bmatrix} 1 & Z_L/2 \\ 0 & 1 \end{bmatrix} \qquad [9.10\text{-}27]$$

and the transfer matrix of the transmission line is found from Eq. 9.10-25 to be:

$$[T]_\ell = \begin{bmatrix} \cosh \gamma\ell & Z_0 \sinh \gamma\ell \\ (\sinh \gamma\ell)/Z_0 & \cosh \gamma\ell \end{bmatrix} \qquad [9.10\text{-}28]$$

where γ is the propagation factor of the unloaded line of characteristic impedance Z_0.

Since the transfer matrix of a cascade equals the product of the transfer matrices of the component networks of the cascade, the input and output voltages and currents in Fig. 9-8 are related as follows:

$$\begin{bmatrix} V_1 \\ I_1 \end{bmatrix} = \begin{bmatrix} 1 & Z_L/2 \\ 0 & 1 \end{bmatrix} \times \begin{bmatrix} \cosh \gamma\ell & Z_0 \sinh \gamma\ell \\ (\sinh \gamma\ell)/Z_0 & \cosh \gamma\ell \end{bmatrix} \times \begin{bmatrix} 1 & Z_L/2 \\ 0 & 1 \end{bmatrix} \times \begin{bmatrix} V_2 \\ -I_2 \end{bmatrix}$$

$$[9.10\text{-}29]$$

The complete matrix multiplication indicated in Eq. 9.10-29 is complicated. However, only one term, namely the coefficient, A, of the resultant $ABCD$ matrix is required to determine the propagation function of the loaded line. This follows from the fact that:

$$\cosh \gamma = A \qquad [9.10\text{-}30]$$

Because the first column of the third matrix on the right-hand side of Eq. 9.10-29 consists of the terms, 1 and 0, it is only necessary to find the term, A', in the first row and first column of the product of the first two matrices, to determine the coefficient, A, of the resultant matrix. It is seen by inspection that

$$A' = \cosh \gamma\ell + \frac{Z_L}{2Z_0} \sinh \gamma\ell \qquad [9.10\text{-}31]$$

Since $A' = A$, it follows from Eqs. 9.10-26 and 9.10-31 that:

$$\cosh \gamma_m\ell = \cosh \gamma\ell + \frac{Z_L}{2Z_0} \sinh \gamma\ell \qquad [9.10\text{-}32]$$

Substituting $\gamma' = \gamma_m \ell$ in Eq. 9.10-32 gives

$$\cosh \gamma' = \cosh \gamma\ell + \frac{Z_L}{2Z_0} \sinh \gamma\ell \qquad [9.10\text{-}33]$$

Equation 9.10-33 is Campbell's formula, and agrees with Eq. 9.10-22.

9.11 DISPERSION AND GROUP VELOCITY

The phase velocity for sinusoidal excitation has been defined as ω/β. It has also been shown that, except in the case of a lossless or distortionless line, β is not a constant multiple of ω. Hence, the components of a complex wave form generally shift in relative phase during propagation along a line where β is not a constant multiple of ω. This phenomenon is known as *dispersion*. The result of dispersion is that the wave components at some point along the line may combine to yield a wave form that is quite different from the input wave form. This condition has been considered in the study of phase distortion. When dispersion exists, it is often difficult to define a significant velocity of propagation for a complex wave form.

In the case of small dispersion, a significant velocity of propagation is the *group velocity*. Small dispersion occurs when the maximum difference in frequency of the components of a given signal is small. An example of

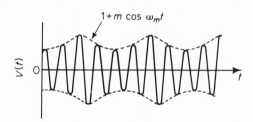

Figure 9-9   Amplitude modulated signal.

such a signal is the amplitude-modulated signal shown in Fig. 9-9, where the voltage is given by

$$v(t) = (1 + m \cos \omega_m t) \cos \omega_c t \qquad [9.11\text{-}1]$$

and where ω_c is the carrier (high) angular frequency, ω_m is the modulating (low) angular frequency, and m is the modulation factor. It will be assumed that $\omega_m \ll \omega_c$. Fig. 9-9 is essentially a high-frequency sinusoid with an amplitude that varies at a relatively low frequency. In other words, the *envelope* of the carrier varies slowly.

The presence of three closely-spaced frequency components in an amplitude-modulated signal is found by expressing Eq. 9.11-1 as

$$v(t) = \Re \epsilon^{j\omega_c t} \left[1 + \left(\frac{m}{2}\right) \epsilon^{j\omega_m t} + \left(\frac{m}{2}\right) \epsilon^{-j\omega_m t} \right] \qquad [9.11\text{-}2]$$

where the symbol $\Re$ denotes the real part corresponding to cosine excitation. It follows from Eq. 9.11-2 that

$$v(t) = \Re \left[\epsilon^{j\omega_c t} + \left(\frac{m}{2}\right) \epsilon^{j(\omega_c + \omega_m)t} + \left(\frac{m}{2}\right) \epsilon^{j(\omega_c - \omega_m)t} \right] \qquad [9.11\text{-}3]$$

It can be seen from Eq. 9.11-3 that the signal has three angular frequency components: the *carrier* frequency, ω_c; the *upper side frequency* $\omega_c + \omega_m$; and the *lower side frequency*, $\omega_c - \omega_m$. Under the assumption that $\omega_m \ll \omega_c$, these three components are closely spaced about the carrier frequency.

Consider the case where the phase function is not simply equal to a constant multiple of ω. Let the phase function for the carrier angular frequency be β_c. The phase functions for the side frequencies of angular frequencies $(\omega_c \pm \omega_m)$ are found by expanding β in a Taylor series about β_c. Thus, the phase function $\beta(\omega_c + \omega_m)$ for the upper side frequency is given by

$$\beta(\omega_c + \omega_m) = \beta_c + \omega_m \beta_c' + \frac{\omega_m^2}{2}\beta_c'' + \ldots \qquad [9.11\text{-}4]$$

and for the lower side frequency is

$$\beta(\omega_c - \omega_m) = \beta_c - \omega_m \beta_c' + \frac{\omega_m^2}{2}\beta_c'' + \ldots \qquad [9.11\text{-}5]$$

where β_c' and β_c'' are respectively the first and second derivatives of β with respect to ω evaluated at the carrier frequency, $\omega = \omega_c$. If only the first two terms of the Taylor series are used, it follows that:*

$$\beta(\omega_c + \omega_m) = \beta_c + \omega_m \beta_c' \qquad [9.11\text{-}6]$$

$$\beta(\omega_c - \omega_m) = \beta_c - \omega_m \beta_c' \qquad [9.11\text{-}7]$$

When an amplitude-modulated signal, as given by Eq. 9.11-3, is applied to a transmission line, the wave travelling in the positive direction is given by

*It is assumed that all other terms are negligible

$$v(x,t) = \Re \left[\epsilon^{j(\omega_c t - \beta_c x)} + \left(\frac{m}{2}\right) \epsilon^{j[(\omega_c + \omega_m)t - (\beta_c + \omega_m \beta_c')x]} \right.$$
$$\left. + \left(\frac{m}{2}\right) \epsilon^{j[(\omega_c - \omega_m)t - (\beta_c - \omega_m \beta_c')x]} \right] \qquad [9.11\text{-}8]$$

where the effect of attenuation has been neglected.

Equation 9.11-8 can be written as

$$v(x,t) = \Re \, \epsilon^{j(\omega_c t - \beta_c x)} \left[1 + \left(\frac{m}{2}\right) \epsilon^{j(\omega_m t - \omega_m \beta_c' x)} + \left(\frac{m}{2}\right) \epsilon^{-j(\omega_m t - \omega_m \beta_c' x)} \right] \qquad [9.11\text{-}9]$$

It follows from Eq. 9.11-9 that

$$v(x,t) = [1 + m \cos (\omega_m t - \omega_m \beta_c' x)] \cos (\omega_c t - \beta_c x) \qquad [9.11\text{-}10]$$

As in Eq. 9.11-1, the term involving m in Eq. 9.11-10 represents the effect of modulation. Inspection of Eq. 9.11-10 shows that this effect is propagated without distortion and with a time delay, τ, given by

$$\tau = \beta_c' x \qquad [9.11\text{-}11]$$

It follows that the group velocity, or the velocity of propagation of the frequency group, is

$$u_g = \frac{dx}{d\tau} = \frac{1}{\beta_c'} = \left[\frac{d\omega}{d\beta}\right]_{\omega - \omega_c} \qquad [9.11\text{-}12]$$

where $d\omega/d\beta$ is evaluated at the carrier or central frequency. The group velocity is the velocity at which the energy is propagated.

A relation between the group velocity and the phase velocity will now be developed. Since

$$u_p = \frac{\omega}{\beta} \qquad [9.11\text{-}13]$$

$$\frac{du_p}{d\omega} = \frac{\beta - \omega \, (d\beta/d\omega)}{\beta^2}$$

$$= \frac{1 - (\omega/\beta)(d\beta/d\omega)}{\beta} = \frac{1 - u_p/u_g}{\beta} \qquad [9.11\text{-}14]$$

It follows from Eq. 9.11-14 that

$$\beta \frac{du_p}{d\omega} = 1 - \frac{u_p}{u_g} \qquad [9.11\text{-}15]$$

$$\frac{u_p}{u_g} = 1 - \beta \frac{du_p}{d\omega} \qquad [9.11\text{-}16]$$

$$u_g = \frac{u_p}{1 - \beta(du_p/d\omega)} = \frac{u_p}{1 - (\omega/u_p)(du_p/d\omega)} \qquad [9.11\text{-}17]$$

It is seen from Eq. 9.11-17 that $u_g = u_p$ when $du_p/d\omega = 0$. This is consistent with the definition of group velocity.

PROBLEMS

9-1 The constants per mile of a certain cable are the following: $\overline{R} = 42.9$ ohms; $\overline{L} = 0.7$ mh; $\overline{C} = 0.1$ μf; and $\overline{G} = 2.4$ μmhos. Calculate the attenuation function, the characteristic impedance, and the phase velocity when $\omega = 5000$ radians per second.

9-2 The characteristic impedance of a certain line is $710\underline{/-16°}$ ohms when the frequency is 1000 cycles per second. At the given frequency, the attenuation function = 0.01 neper per mile, and the phase function is 0.035 radian per mile. Calculate the resistance, the leakage, the inductance, and the capacitance per mile. Find the velocity of propagation.

9-3 The propagation function at 1000 cycles for a certain line is $\gamma = 0.008 + j0.029$ radians per mile. The absolute value of the characteristic impedance is 700 ohms. Assuming that $\overline{G} = 0$, find $\overline{R}$, $\overline{L}$, and $\overline{C}$.

9-4 The line in Prob. 9-2 is 100 miles long, and is terminated by a 300-ohm resistor. Neglecting the internal impedance of the transmitter, calculate the ratio of the transmitter voltage to the receiver voltage in decibels and in nepers.

9-5 The characteristic impedance of a certain line is $710\underline{/14°}$ ohms, and $\gamma = 0.007 + j0.028$ radians per mile. The line is terminated in a 300-ohm resistor. Calculate the input impedance to the line if its length is 100 miles.

9-6 Repeat Prob. 9-5 if the length of the line is 500 miles.

9-7 Repeat Prob. 9-5 if the length of the line is 2 miles.

9-8 Assume that, in the line in Prob. 9-5, the transmitter has a generated voltage of 100 volts and an internal resistance of 300 ohms. Calculate the voltage at the receiving end.

9-9 A transmitter with a generated voltage of 100 volts and an internal resistance of 700 ohms is connected to the input terminals of the line in Prob. 9-5. Find the receiver voltage.

9-10 Calculate the efficiency of transmission in Prob. 9-9.

9-11 Derive the elements of the π network in Fig. 9-4. Derive the approximate network when $|\gamma\ell| \ll 1$.

9-12 Find the ratio of the internal generator (transmitter) voltage to the receiver voltage in Prob. 9-4 if the transmitter has an internal impedance of $100 + j50$.

9-13 The insertion loss is a measure of the voltage drop introduced by a transmission circuit and is defined as the ratio of the voltage across the load, when placed directly across the transmitter terminals, to the load voltage appearing at the output terminals of the transmission circuit. Calculate the decibel insertion loss of the transmission line in Prob. 9-12.

9-14 A 3-phase, 60-cycle transmission line is 80 miles long. The three conductors are soft-drawn stranded 300,000 circular-mil copper, equilaterally spaced 8 feet between centers. This construction results in the following values for the line parameters:

$\overline{R}$ = 0.1901 ohm per mile per conductor

$\overline{L}$ = 1.960 millihenrys per mile per conductor

$\overline{C}$ = 0.0156 microfarad per mile conductor to neutral

$\overline{G}$ = 0

The line delivers 24,000 kva at 0.8 power factor lagging, at 66,000 volts, to a balanced load. Determine the generator output in kva, the voltage regulation, and the transmission efficiency of the line, using transmission line equations.

9-15 Solve Prob. 9-14 using the equivalent π circuit for the line.

9-16 Solve Prob. 9-14 neglecting the distributed capacitance to neutral, and compare your result with that obtained in Prob. 9-15. What conclusion can be drawn from this comparison?

9-17 An open-wire unloaded line, 50 miles long, is operated at a frequency of 800 cycles. The open-circuit input impedance is found to be 330 $\underline{/-30°}$ ohms, and the short-circuit impedance is 1540 $\underline{/7°}$ ohms. Calculate the parameters of this line, assuming $u_p \cong$ 186,000 miles/sec.

9-18 Design a T section that is equivalent to 0.5 mile of the cable specified in Prob. 9-1.

9-19 A line with losses, and of length ℓ, is terminated in an open circuit. Show that the ratio of the output to the input voltage is a maximum when

$$\frac{\sinh 2\alpha l}{\sin 2\beta l} = \frac{\beta}{\alpha}$$

Neglect the internal impedance of the transmitter.

9-20 The cable in Prob. 9-1 is loaded with coils having an inductance of 18 millihenrys and a resistance of 1.4 ohms. The coils are spaced 1.135 miles apart. Assuming the inductance of the load coils to be uniformly distributed, calculate the attenuation function, the characteristic impedance, and the phase velocity of the loaded cable.

9-21 Solve Prob. 9-20 by applying Campbell's formula.

9-22 Prove that in a cable where $\overline{L} = \overline{G} = 0$, the product of the phase and group velocities is $4w/\overline{R}\,\overline{C}$.

9-23 Derive the equivalent T section of a transmission line (Fig. 9-3) by applying the bisection principle.

9-24 Derive the equivalent π section of a transmission line (Fig. 9-4) by applying the bisection principle.

9-25 Prove that the input resistance and the input reactance of an open-circuited line of length ℓ are given by

$$R_{in} = \frac{Z_0}{2} \left(\frac{\sinh 2\,\alpha\ell}{\cosh^2 \alpha\ell - \cos^2 \beta\ell} \right)$$

$$X_{in} = -\frac{Z_0}{2} \left(\frac{\sin 2\,\beta\ell}{\cosh^2 \alpha\ell - \cos^2 \beta\ell} \right)$$

9-26 Show that, if in Prob. 9-25 $\ell = \lambda/4$ and $\alpha\ell \ll 1$, then $R_{in} = \bar{R}\lambda/8$, assuming that $\bar{G} = 0$. What is the value of X_{in}?

9-27 A one-volt rectangular pulse, having a width of 10 microseconds, is applied to a distortionless line 2 miles long, for which $\bar{R} = 42.1$ ohms, $\bar{L} = 10^{-3}$ henry, and $\bar{C} = 62 \times 10^{-9}$ farad. Find the height and width of the output pulse if the line is terminated by its characteristic impedance.

high-frequency transmission

lines

10.0 INTRODUCTION

The circuit theory of high-frequency lines is essentially the same as that developed in the previous chapters. However, there is one important difference. Above frequencies of about 100 megacycles, the physical lengths of lines used in practical circuits are short. This follows from the fact that a single wavelength in air at a frequency of 100 megacycles is 3.0 meters, and a complete standing wave pattern occupies a length of 1.50 meters. Hence, at a frequency of 100 megacycles, an entire impedance variation, from the maximum to the minimum value, occurs in a distance of 1.50 meters in air. Therefore, when a high-frequency line is used as a circuit element of variable impedance, its physical length is usually short.

At high frequencies, ohmic and dielectric losses may be appreciable; but since the physical length of line is small, the effect of the losses is usually disregarded in specifying the voltage and current distributions. Distributions calculated on a lossless basis agree very well with those measured on high-frequency lines. It should be recognized that the basic reason for this agreement is not that losses are negligible at high frequencies, but that the physical lengths of practical lines are such that the total attenuation is small, and only the phase shift is of consequence in determining the voltage and current distributions. This condition would not be valid for physically long high-frequency lines that might conceivably be used for the transmission of high-frequency power. Only lines of short physical length are to be considered in this chapter, and the distributions for lossless lines will generally be used. When losses are taken into account, certain approximations that are valid at high frequencies will be made.

10.1 EQUATIONS FOR HIGH-FREQUENCY LINES

Assuming that the voltage and current distributions are unaffected by the attenuation in the relatively short physical lengths of the lines used in practice, these distributions are given by the equations derived for lossless lines in Chap. 8. Equations 8.8-10 and 8.8-11 give the voltage and current as

$$V(x) = V_r \cos \beta x + j I_r Z_0 \sin \beta x \qquad [10.1\text{-}1]$$

$$I(x) = I_r \cos \beta x + j \left(\frac{V_r}{Z_0} \right) \sin \beta x \qquad [10.1\text{-}2]$$

where

$$I_r = \frac{V_r}{Z_r} \qquad [10.1\text{-}3]$$

and

$$Z_0 = \sqrt{\frac{L}{C}} \qquad [10.1\text{-}4]$$

The impedance at any point is

$$Z(x) = \frac{V(x)}{I(x)} = Z_0 \left[\frac{Z_r \cos \beta x + j Z_0 \sin \beta x}{Z_0 \cos \beta x + j Z_r \sin \beta x} \right] \qquad [10.1\text{-}5]$$

If losses are taken into account, hyperbolic functions may be used to give the distributions as follows:

$$V(x) = V_r \cosh \gamma x + I_r Z_0 \sinh \gamma x \qquad [10.1\text{-}6]$$

$$I(x) = I_r \cosh \gamma x + \left(\frac{V_r}{Z_0} \right) \sinh \gamma x \qquad [10.1\text{-}7]$$

$$Z(x) = Z_0 \left[\frac{Z_r \cosh \gamma x + Z_0 \sinh \gamma x}{Z_0 \cosh \gamma x + Z_r \sinh \gamma x} \right] \qquad [10.1\text{-}8]$$

where the general expressions for γ and Z_0 are

$$\gamma = \sqrt{(R + j\omega L)(G + j\omega C)} \qquad [10.1\text{-}9]$$

$$Z_0 = \sqrt{\frac{R + j\omega L}{G + j\omega C}} \qquad [10.1\text{-}10]$$

Equation 10.1-9 can also be written as

$$\gamma = j\omega \sqrt{L C} \sqrt{\left(1 + \frac{R}{j\omega L} \right) \left(1 + \frac{G}{j\omega C} \right)}$$

$$= j\omega \sqrt{L C} \left[1 + \frac{R}{j\omega L} \right]^{1/2} \left[1 + \frac{G}{j\omega C} \right]^{1/2} \qquad [10.1\text{-}11]$$

Assuming that, at high frequencies, $\overline{R}/\omega\overline{L} \ll 1$ and $\overline{G}/\omega\overline{C} \ll 1$, expansion of the right-hand side of Eq. 10.1-11 by the binomial theorem (neglecting all powers above the first) gives the following result:

$$\gamma = j\omega\,\sqrt{\overline{L}\,\overline{C}}\left[1 + \frac{1}{2}\left(\frac{\overline{R}}{j\omega\overline{L}} + \frac{\overline{G}}{j\omega\overline{C}}\right)\right]$$

$$= \frac{1}{2}\left[\overline{R}\,\sqrt{\frac{\overline{C}}{\overline{L}}} + \overline{G}\,\sqrt{\frac{\overline{L}}{\overline{C}}}\right] + j\omega\,\sqrt{\overline{L}\,\overline{C}} = \alpha + j\beta \qquad [10.1\text{-}12]$$

Hence, at high frequencies,

$$\alpha = \frac{1}{2}\left[\overline{R}\,\sqrt{\frac{\overline{C}}{\overline{L}}} + \overline{G}\,\sqrt{\frac{\overline{L}}{\overline{C}}}\right] \qquad\qquad [10.1\text{-}13]$$

$$\beta = \omega\,\sqrt{\overline{L}\,\overline{C}} \qquad\qquad\qquad [10.1\text{-}14]$$

Equation 10.1-10 can also be written as

$$Z_0 = \sqrt{\frac{\overline{R} + j\omega\overline{L}}{\overline{G} + j\omega\overline{C}}} = \sqrt{\frac{\overline{L} + \overline{R}/j\omega}{\overline{C} + \overline{G}/j\omega}} \qquad [10.1\text{-}15]$$

Assuming that $|\overline{R}/j\omega| \ll \overline{L}$ and that $|\overline{G}/j\omega| \ll \overline{C}$ at high frequencies, Eq. 10.1-15 becomes

$$Z_0 = \sqrt{\frac{\overline{L}}{\overline{C}}} \qquad\qquad\qquad [10.1\text{-}16]$$

Substitution of Eq. 10.1-16 into Eq. 10.1-13 gives the following expression for the attenuation function:

$$\alpha = \frac{1}{2}\left[\frac{\overline{R}}{Z_0} + \overline{G}Z_0\right] \qquad\qquad [10.1\text{-}17]$$

Consider a single wave traveling on an infinite line or one that is terminated by its characteristic impedance. The absolute value of the voltage and current at a point a distance z from the transmitter is given by

$$|V(z)| = |V_{\text{in}}|\,\epsilon^{-\alpha z} \qquad\qquad [10.1\text{-}18]$$

$$|I(z)| = \frac{|V_{\text{in}}|}{Z_0}\,\epsilon^{-\alpha z} \qquad\qquad [10.1\text{-}19]$$

where $|V_{\text{in}}|$ is the absolute value of the input voltage. Assuming that Z_0

is a real number, as given by Eq. 10.1-16, the transmitted power at any point is

$$P(z) = |V(z)|\,|I(z)| = \frac{|V_{\text{in}}|^2}{Z_0}\,\epsilon^{-2\alpha z} = P_{\text{in}}\,\epsilon^{-2\alpha z} \qquad [10.1\text{-}20]$$

where P_{in} is the input power. Differentiation of Eq. 10.1-20 with respect to z gives the following results:

$$\frac{d}{dz}\,[P(z)] = -2\alpha P_{\text{in}}\,\epsilon^{-2\alpha z} = -2\alpha P(z) \qquad [10.1\text{-}21]$$

$$\alpha = \frac{-d/dz\,[P(z)]}{2P(z)} \qquad [10.1\text{-}22]$$

It follows from Eq. 10.1-22 that the attenuation function is equal to the power dissipated per unit length divided by twice the power transmitted.

Assume now that the attenuation is so small that the voltage and current distributions are essentially the same as on a lossless line. In that case

$$V(z) = |V_{\text{in}}|\,\epsilon^{-j\beta z} \qquad [10.1\text{-}23]$$

$$I(z) = \left|\frac{V_{\text{in}}}{Z_0}\right|\,\epsilon^{-j\beta z} \qquad [10.1\text{-}24]$$

where V_{in} is the absolute value of the input voltage. The transmitted power is

$$P(z) = V(z)\,I^*(z) = \frac{|V_{\text{in}}|^2}{Z_0} \qquad [10.1\text{-}25]$$

The power dissipated in series resistance per unit length is

$$P_R = |I_{\text{in}}|^2\overline{R} = \frac{|V_{\text{in}}|^2}{Z_0}\,\overline{R} \qquad [10.1\text{-}26]$$

where $|I_{\text{in}}|$ is the absolute value of the input current. No integration is necessary because under the assumed conditions the effective value of the voltage and current is constant at all points on the line, as shown by Eqs. 10.1-23 and 10.1-24.

The power dissipated per unit length in shunt conductance is

$$P_G = |V_{\text{in}}|^2\overline{G} \qquad [10.1\text{-}27]$$

Substitution of Eq. 10.1-25, 10.1-26, and 10.1-27 into Eq. 10.1-22 gives the following result:

$$\alpha = \frac{\overline{P}_R + \overline{P}_G}{2P(z)} = \frac{|V_{\text{in}}|^2\, \overline{R}/Z_0^2 + |V_{\text{in}}|^2\overline{G}}{2|V_{\text{in}}|^2/Z_0}$$

$$= \frac{1}{2}\left[\frac{\overline{R}}{Z_0} + \overline{G}Z_0\right] \qquad [10.1\text{-}28]$$

Equation 10.1-28 gives the same result as Eq. 10.1-17. This indicates that the approximation involved in neglecting the effect of attenuation upon the voltage and current distributions is of the same order as that made in the expansion of Eq. 10.1-11. The technique of neglecting losses in the distribution equation and applying Eq. 10.1-22 to such distributions to calculate attenuation finds considerable application in wave guides.

10.2 IMPEDANCE AND ADMITTANCE OF SHORT-CIRCUITED AND OPEN-CIRCUITED LINES

Short-circuited and open-circuited lines find considerable application as reactances at high frequencies. The input impedance of a lossless line of length ℓ is found by substituting $x = \ell$ in Eq. 10.1-5, giving the following result:

$$Z_{\text{in}} = Z_0\left[\frac{Z_r \cos \beta\ell + jZ_0 \sin \beta\ell}{Z_0 \cos \beta\ell + jZ_r \sin \beta\ell}\right] \qquad [10.2\text{-}1]$$

where Z_r is the terminating impedance.

The input impedance of a short-circuited line is found by setting

$$Z_r = 0 \qquad [10.2\text{-}2]$$

in Eq. 10.2-1. This gives the following expression for the input impedance, Z_{sc} to a short-circuited line:

$$Z_{\text{sc}} = jZ_0 \tan \beta\ell \qquad [Z_r = 0] \qquad [10.2\text{-}3]$$

A graph of the input impedance of a short-circuited line as a function of $\beta\ell$ is shown in Fig. 10-1, where it is seen that the input impedance assumes all possible reactive values ranging from positive infinity to negative infinity as $\beta\ell$ varies from 0 to π, or as the length of the line is varied from zero to one-half a wavelength at a given frequency. Anti-resonance with theoretically infinite impedance occurs when $\beta\ell$ is an odd multiple of $\pi/2$, and resonance with theoretically zero impedance occurs when $\beta\ell$ is an even multiple of $\pi/2$. The graph in Fig. 10-1 from $\beta\ell = 0$ to $\beta\ell = \pi$ has the same general form as the reactance curve of a parallel lumped L-C circuit when the frequency is varied. The poles and zeros in Fig. 10-1 alternate, and the slope of the reactance curve is always positive. Such a reactance function can be simulated by a cascade of parallel L-C circuits as in a Foster network.

It should be stressed that the results obtained in Fig. 10-1 hold for all frequencies. The theory is perfectly general; but, at low frequencies

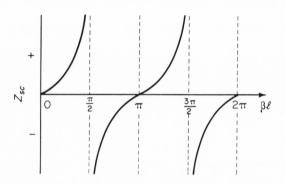

Figure 10-1   Input impedance of a short-circuited line.

and long wavelengths, it is impossible to obtain reasonable lengths to simulate a complete reactance variation. At high frequencies and short wavelengths, it is rather simple to obtain the complete reactance variation with manageable lengths of line. Such lines are frequently termed *stubs*. The use of short-circuited stubs as variable reactances is a common high-frequency technique. Open-circuited lines are rarely used because it is difficult to vary their lengths and because of radiation losses at the open ends.

When losses are taken into account, hyperbolic functions may be used in the expressions for the impedance. The input impedance of a short-circuited line with losses is found from Eq. 10.1-8 to be

$$Z_{sc} = Z_0 \tanh \gamma\ell = Z_0 \left(\frac{\sinh \gamma\ell}{\cosh \gamma\ell} \right) \qquad [10.2\text{-}4]$$

where Z_0 is given by Eq. 10.1-16 and where

$$\gamma = \alpha + j\beta \qquad [10.2\text{-}5]$$

and α and β are given by Eqs. 10.1-13 and 10.1-14.

Equation 10.2-4 can be expanded as follows:

$$Z_{sc} = Z_0 \left[\frac{\sinh \alpha\ell \cos \beta\ell + j \cosh \alpha\ell \sin \beta\ell}{\cosh \alpha\ell \cos \beta\ell + j \sinh \alpha\ell \sin \beta\ell} \right] \qquad [10.2\text{-}6]$$

For an antiresonant stub, $\beta\ell = \pi/2$; $\cos\beta\ell = 0$; and $\sin\beta\ell = 1$; with these values, Eq. 10.2-6 reduces to

$$Z_{sc} = Z_0 \left(\frac{\cosh\alpha\ell}{\sinh\alpha\ell} \right) \qquad [10.2\text{-}7]$$

Under the basic assumption that $\alpha\ell \ll 1$,

$$\cosh\alpha\ell = 1 \qquad [10.2\text{-}8]$$

$$\sinh\alpha\ell = \alpha\ell \qquad [10.2\text{-}9]$$

it follows that:

$$\dot{Z}_{sc} = \frac{Z_0}{\alpha\ell} \qquad [10.2\text{-}10]$$

If $\overline{G} = 0$, it follows from Eq. 10.1-13 that

$$\alpha = \frac{1}{2}\left(\overline{R} \sqrt{\frac{\overline{C}}{\overline{L}}} \right) = \frac{\overline{R}}{2Z_0} \qquad [\overline{G} = 0] \qquad [10.2\text{-}11]$$

The substitution of Eq. 10.2-11 into Eq. 10.2-10 gives the following expression for the input impedance of a resonant quarter-wavelength short-circuited stub with losses:

$$Z_{sc} = \frac{2Z_0^2}{R} \qquad [10.2\text{-}12]$$

where R is the total ohmic resistance of the stub and where radiation losses are neglected.

The input impedance to an open-circuited length ℓ is found by writing Eq. 10.1-5 in the following form:

$$Z_{in} = Z_0 \left[\frac{\cos\beta\ell + j(Z_0 \sin\beta\ell)/Z_r}{(Z_0 \cos\beta\ell)/Z_r + j\sin\beta\ell} \right] \qquad [10.2\text{-}13]$$

Taking the limit of the right-hand side of Eq. 10.2-13 as $Z_r \rightarrow \infty$ gives the following results:

$$Z_{oc} = \lim_{Z_r \to \infty} Z_0 \left[\frac{\cos\beta\ell + j(Z_0 \sin\beta\ell)/Z_r}{(Z_0 \cos\beta\ell)/Z_r + j\sin\beta\ell} \right] = \frac{Z_0 \cos\beta\ell}{j\sin\beta\ell} \qquad [10.2\text{-}14]$$

$$Z_{oc} = -jZ_0 \cot\beta\ell \qquad [Z_r \rightarrow \infty] \qquad [10.2\text{-}15]$$

The graph of Z_{oc} as a function of $\beta\ell$ is shown in Fig. 10-2.

It follows from Eqs. 10.2-3 and 10.2-15 that

$$Z_{sc}Z_{oc} = Z_0^2 \qquad [10.2\text{-}16]$$

The short-circuited and open-circuited lines are seen to have inverse input impedances with respect to Z_0.

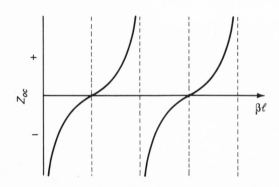

Figure 10-2 Input impedance of an open-circuited line.

The admittance of a short-circuited line is found from the reciprocal of Z_{sc} in Eq. 10.2-3 to be

$$Y_{sc} = \frac{1}{Z_{sc}} = \frac{1}{jZ_0 \tan \beta \ell} = -jY_0 \cot \beta \ell \qquad [10.2\text{-}17]$$

where Y_0 is the characteristic admittance of the line. The graph of Y_{sc} is similar to Fig. 10-2 for Z_{oc}.

The admittance of an open-circuited line is found from the reciprocal of Z_{oc} in Eq. 10.2-15 to be

$$Y_{oc} = \frac{1}{Z_{oc}} = \frac{1}{-jZ_0 \cot \beta \ell} = jY_0 \tan \beta \ell \qquad [10.2\text{-}18]$$

The graph of Y_{oc} is similar to Fig. 10-1 for Z_{sc}.

10.3 Q OF RESONANT LINES

The Q of a resonant line can be derived from either energy or bandwidth calculations. Q is defined in terms of energy as

$$Q = \omega \times \frac{\text{maximum energy stored}}{\text{energy dissipated per second}} = \frac{\omega W}{P} \qquad [10.3\text{-}1]$$

where W is the maximum stored energy and P is the average dissipated power.

The instantaneous voltage and current distributions along a line are

$$v(x,t) = \sqrt{2}|I_r| \, \epsilon^{j\omega t} (Z_r \cos \beta x + jZ_0 \sin \beta x) \qquad [10.3\text{-}2]$$

$$i(x,t) = \left[\frac{\sqrt{2}|I_r|}{Z_0} \right] \epsilon^{j\omega t} (Z_0 \cos \beta x + jZ_r \sin \beta x) \qquad [10.3\text{-}3]$$

where losses are at this point neglected and where the real part corresponds to cosine wave excitation, the imaginary part corresponds to sine wave excitation, and $|I_r|$ is the effective value of the receiver current.

The instantaneous voltage and current along a short-circuited line are found by letting $Z_r = 0$ in Eqs. 10.3-2 and 10.3-3. This gives the following expressions:

$$v(x,t) = j\sqrt{2}|I_r|Z_0\epsilon^{j\omega t} \sin \beta x = \sqrt{2}|I_r|Z_0\epsilon^{j(\omega t+\pi/2)} \sin \beta x$$

$$= \sqrt{2}|I_r|Z_0 \sin \beta x \left[\cos \left(\omega t + \frac{\pi}{2} \right) \right] + j \sin \left(\omega t + \frac{\pi}{2} \right) \right] \qquad [10.3\text{-}4]$$

$$i(x,t) = \sqrt{2}|I_r|\epsilon^{j\omega t} \cos \beta x = \sqrt{2}|I_r| \cos \beta x \, [\cos \omega t + j \sin \omega t] \qquad [10.3\text{-}5]$$

Equations 10.3-4 and 10.3-5 show that the voltage and current along a short-circuited line are 90° out of phase in time. Hence, when the current is a maximum, the voltage is zero; and when the voltage is a maximum, the current is zero at every point along the line. Also, the total energy stored in a resonant or anti-resonant line remains constant. It is therefore possible to calculate W in Eq. 10.3-1 from either the magnetic energy or the electric energy provided that the calculation is made at a time when either the voltage or current is zero at every point along the line. The calculation of W will be made at a time when the voltage, and hence the stored electrical energy, is everywhere zero. It will prove instructive for the student to perform the calculation at a time when the current is everywhere zero, and also at a time when neither the current nor the voltage is everywhere zero. The results should be the same.

Assuming cosine wave excitation, the current distribution along the line at a time when the voltage is everywhere zero is found by letting $\omega t = 2n\pi$ in the bracket in Eq. 10.3-5. The resulting current distribution is given by

$$i(x) = \sqrt{2}(I_r \cos \beta x) \qquad [10.3\text{-}6]$$

The stored magnetic energy for the entire line of length, ℓ, is

$$W = \frac{1}{2} \overline{L} \int_0^\ell [\sqrt{2}|I_r| \cos \beta x]^2 \, dx \qquad [10.3\text{-}7]$$

If the line is a quarter-wavelength long,

$$\ell = \frac{\lambda}{4} = \frac{2\pi/\beta}{4} = \frac{\pi}{2\beta} \qquad [10.3\text{-}8]$$

Hence,

$$W = \overline{L}|I_r|^2 \int_0^{\pi/2\beta} \cos^2 \beta x \, dx = \overline{L}|I_r|^2 \int_0^{\pi/2\beta} \left(\frac{1 + \cos 2\beta x}{2} \right) dx \qquad [10.3\text{-}9]$$

$$W = \overline{L}|I_r|^2 \left[\frac{x}{2} + \frac{1}{4} \sin 2\beta x \right]_0^{\pi/2\beta} = \frac{\pi \overline{L}|I_r|^2}{4\beta} \qquad [10.3\text{-}10]$$

since the second term in the bracket vanishes at both the upper and lower limits. If W had been calculated for the electric field at a time when the current was everywhere zero, the same result would have been obtained.

The denominator in Eq. 10.3-1 must include the average power dissipated in series resistance and shunt conductance. The average power, P_G, lost in shunt conductance is found from Eq. 10.3-4 for the voltage to be

$$P_G = \frac{\overline{G}}{2} \int_0^{\pi/2\beta} [\sqrt{2}|I_r|Z_0 \sin \beta x]^2 \, dx \qquad [10.3\text{-}11]$$

$$P_G = |I_r|^2 \overline{G} Z_0^2 \int_0^{\pi/2\beta} \left(\frac{1 - \cos 2\beta x}{2} \right) dx = \frac{|I_r|^2 \overline{G} Z_0^2 \pi}{4\beta} \qquad [10.3\text{-}12]$$

The average power lost in series resistance is found from Eq. 10.3-5 for the current to be

$$P_R = \frac{1}{2} \overline{R} \int_0^{\pi/2\beta} (\sqrt{2}|I_r| \cos \beta x)^2 \, dx \qquad [10.3\text{-}13]$$

$$P_R = |I_r|^2 \overline{R} \int_0^{\pi/2\beta} \left(\frac{1 + \cos 2\beta x}{2} \right) dx = \frac{\pi |I_r|^2 \overline{R}}{4\beta} \qquad [10.3\text{-}14]$$

It follows from Eqs. 10.3-1, 10.3-10, 10.3-12, and 10.3-14 that:

$$Q = \omega \left(\frac{W}{P_R + P_G} \right) = \frac{\overline{L}|I_r|^2 \omega}{|I_r|^2 (\overline{R} + Z_0^2 \overline{G})} = \frac{\omega \overline{L}\,\overline{C}}{\overline{R}\,\overline{C} + \overline{L}\,\overline{G}} \qquad [10.3\text{-}15]$$

It is interesting to note that if G is neglected in Eq. 10.3-15,

$$Q = \frac{\omega \overline{L}}{\overline{R}} \qquad [G = 0] \qquad [10.3\text{-}16]$$

This is analogous to the expression for lumped constants.

When the numerator and denominator of Eq. 10.3-15 are divided by $\sqrt{\overline{L}\,\overline{C}}$, the following result is obtained:

$$Q = \frac{\omega\sqrt{\overline{L}\,\overline{C}}}{\overline{R}/Z_0 + \overline{G}Z_0} = \frac{\beta_0}{2\alpha} \qquad [10.3\text{-}17]$$

where β_0 is the wavelength function of a resonant quarter-wave short-circuited line. The final transformation in Eq. 10.3-17 was made by referring to Eqs. 10.1-13 and 10.1-14.

The Q of a resonant line can also be calculated from the relation

$$Q = \frac{\omega_0}{2\Delta\omega} \qquad [10.3\text{-}18]$$

where $2\Delta\omega$ is the deviation in radians between the two half-power points, and where ω_0 is the resonant frequency.

Since losses are to be considered, Eq. 10.2-4 for the input impedance must be used. The input impedance when $Z_r = 0$ is given by

$$Z_{sc} = Z_0 \left[\frac{\sinh \gamma\ell}{\cosh \gamma\ell} \right]$$
$$= Z_0 \left[\frac{\sinh \alpha\ell \cos \beta\ell + j \cosh \alpha\ell \sin \beta\ell}{\cosh \alpha\ell \cos \beta\ell + j \sinh \alpha\ell \sin \beta\ell} \right] \qquad [10.3\text{-}19]$$

At the resonant frequency, $\beta\ell = \pi/2$, and

$$Z_{sc} = Z_0 \left[\frac{\cosh \alpha\ell}{\sinh \alpha\ell} \right] = Z_0 \coth \alpha\,\ell \qquad [10.3\text{-}20]$$

If the frequency is increased so that β changes from $\beta_0 = \omega_0/u_p$ to $\beta = (\omega_0 + \Delta\omega)/u_p$ where u_p is the phase velocity, the expression for the impedance of the short-circuited quarter-wave line becomes

$$Z_{sc} = Z_0 \left[\frac{\sinh \alpha\ell \cos[\pi/2 + (\Delta\omega/u_p)\ell] + j \cosh \alpha\ell \sin[\pi/2 + (\Delta\omega/u_p)\ell]}{\cosh \alpha\ell \cos[\pi/2 + (\Delta\omega/u_p)\ell] + j \sinh \alpha\ell \sin[\pi/2 + (\Delta\omega/u_p)\ell]} \right]$$

$$Z_{sc} = Z_0 \left[\frac{-\sinh \alpha\ell \sin(\Delta\omega/u_p)\ell + j \cosh \alpha\ell \cos(\Delta\omega/u_p)\ell}{-\cosh \alpha\ell \sin(\Delta\omega/u_p)\ell + j \sinh \alpha\ell \cos(\Delta\omega/u_p)\ell} \right] \qquad [10.3\text{-}21]$$

Since $\alpha\ell$ was assumed to be small, and since, for high-Q lines, $(\Delta\omega/u_p)\ell$ is also very small, the following approximations are permissible:

$$\left.\begin{aligned}
\sinh \alpha\ell &= \alpha\ell \\
\cosh \alpha\ell &= 1 \\
\sin (\Delta\omega/u_p)\ell &= (\Delta\omega/u_p)\ell \\
\cos (\Delta\omega/u_p)\ell &= 1
\end{aligned}\right\} \qquad [10.3\text{-}22]$$

With these approximations, Eq. 10.3-21 becomes

$$Z_{sc} = Z_0 \left[\frac{-\alpha\ell(\Delta\omega/u_p)\ell + j}{(-\Delta\omega/u_p)\ell + j\alpha\ell} \right] \qquad [10.3\text{-}23]$$

Since $\alpha\ell(\Delta\omega/u_p)\ell \ll 1$, the approximate expression for Z_{sc} becomes

$$Z_{sc} = \frac{jZ_0}{(-\Delta\omega/u_p)\ell + j\alpha\ell} = \frac{Z_0}{\alpha\ell + j(\Delta\omega/u_p)\ell} \qquad [10.3\text{-}24]$$

At a half-power point, the quadrature component in the denominator of Eq. 10.3-24 equals the real component. Hence, at a half-power point,

$$\alpha\ell = (\Delta\omega/u_p)\ell \qquad [10.3\text{-}25]$$

$$\Delta\omega = \alpha u_p \qquad [10.3\text{-}26]$$

Equation 10.3-26 gives the deviation in angular frequency of the half-power point. The substitution of Eq. 10.3-26 into Eq. 10.3-18 gives the following result:

$$Q = \frac{\omega_0}{2\alpha u_p} = \frac{\beta_0}{2\alpha} \qquad [10.3\text{-}27]$$

Equation 10.3-27 gives the same result as Eq. 10.3-17, which was derived from energy considerations. Note that Q is independent of the physical length of the line, provided that the line is equivalent to an odd number of quarter-wavelengths, and the total length is such that the approximations in Eq. 10.3-22 are valid.

10.4 EFFECTS OF MISMATCHED RECEIVER IMPEDANCE

When the receiver impedance, Z_r, is different from Z_0, the receiver impedance is said to be mismatched, and reflection occurs at the receiver. Under this condition, the input impedance at the source is given by

$$Z_{in} = Z_0 \left[\frac{Z_r \cos \beta\ell + jZ_0 \sin \beta\ell}{Z_0 \cos \beta\ell + jZ_r \sin \beta\ell} \right] \qquad [10.4\text{-}1]$$

where ℓ is the length of the line.

At high frequencies, a relatively short physical length may well include as many as 30 wavelengths.* Under this assumption,

$$\beta\ell = 60\pi = 10,800° \qquad\qquad [10.4\text{-}2]$$

It is impossible to obtain absolute stability in the frequency of the oscillator or signal generator at the input. Assuming a drift of one-half of one per cent in frequency, and recalling that at high frequencies β is directly proportional to the frequency, it follows from Eq. 10.4-2 that for such a change in frequency, the increment in $\beta\ell$ is

$$(\Delta\beta\ell) = 0.005 \times 10,800° = 54.0° \qquad\qquad [10.4\text{-}3]$$

Inspection of Eq. 10.4-1 shows that a change of 54° in $\beta\ell$ can cause a considerable variation in Z_{in}. It follows that when reflection exists simultaneously with a frequency drift, the input impedance does not remain constant. Under these conditions it is impossible to match the source to the line for maximum power input.

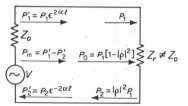

Another effect of a mismatched load is to reduce the efficiency of transmission in the presence of line losses. These effects occur at *all* frequencies. A line with a mismatched load is shown in Fig.

Figure 10-3 Power reflection caused by mismatched receiver impedance.

10-3. Assuming that the incident power at the load is P_1, the corresponding power input at the source is

$$P_1' = P_1\epsilon^{2\alpha\ell} \qquad\qquad [10.4\text{-}4]$$

where α is the attenuation function. The reflected power at the load is

$$P_2 = |\rho|^2 P_1 \qquad\qquad [10.4\text{-}5]$$

where $|\rho|$ is the absolute value of the reflection coefficient at the load. The reflected power arriving at the source is

$$P_2' = P_2\epsilon^{-2\alpha\ell} = |\rho|^2 P_1\epsilon^{-2\alpha\ell} \qquad\qquad [10.4\text{-}6]$$

Since only the effect of the mismatched load is under consideration, it may be assumed that all of P_2' is converted into input power without loss. Under this assumption, the net power input is

---

* A line 10 feet in length is approximately equivalent to 30 wavelengths at a frequency of 3000 megacycles when air is the dielectric.

$$P_{in} = P'_1 - P'_2 = P_1[\epsilon^{2\alpha\ell} - |\rho|^2 \epsilon^{-2\alpha\ell}] \qquad [10.4\text{-}7]$$

The power transmitted to the load is

$$P_0 = P_1[1 - |\rho|^2] \qquad [10.4\text{-}8]$$

The efficiency of transmission is

$$\eta = \frac{P_0}{P_{in}} = \frac{1 - |\rho|^2}{\epsilon^{2\alpha\ell} - |\rho|^2 \epsilon^{-2\alpha\ell}} \qquad [10.4\text{-}9]$$

Equation 10.4-9 can be written as follows:

$$\eta = \frac{1 - |\rho|^2}{\epsilon^{2\alpha\ell}[1 - |\rho|^2 \epsilon^{-4\alpha\ell}]} = \frac{\epsilon^{-2\alpha\ell}[1 - |\rho|^2]}{1 - (|\rho|\epsilon^{-2\alpha\ell})^2} \qquad [10.4\text{-}10]$$

In the case of a matched load, there is no reflection, and the power input and output are related by

$$P'_0 = P'_{in} \epsilon^{-2\alpha\ell} \qquad [10.4\text{-}11]$$

The corresponding efficiency of transmission is

$$\eta' = \frac{P'_0}{P'_{1n}} = \epsilon^{-2\alpha\ell} \qquad [10.4\text{-}12]$$

Substitution of Eq. 10.4-12 into Eq. 10.4-10 gives the following expression for the efficiency when the load is mismatched:

$$\eta = \frac{\eta'[1 - |\rho|^2]}{1 - (\eta'|\rho|)^2} \qquad [10.4\text{-}13]$$

Since η' and $|\rho|$ are always less than unity, it follows from Eq. 10.4-13 that $\eta < \eta'$.

Since $\eta < \eta'$, one effect of a mismatched load is to reduce the efficiency of transmission of a high-frequency line. In the case of power lines, a mismatch is deliberately created by the use of transformers in order to increase the efficiency of transmission. The reason for the difference in the effect of an impedance mismatch upon the transmission efficiency of high-frequency lines and power lines is that the length of a power line is usually a small fraction of a wavelength, and such a line may therefore be considered as essentially a lumped parameter network. Hence, there is a negligible phase shift in current and voltage along the line, and the magnitude of the input current determines the approximate magnitude of the current at every point along the line. It follows that a reduced input current serves to reduce the series resistance loss along the line. It is for this reason that transformers are used so that the power is transmitted along the line at a high voltage, low current, and high impedance level. The increase in voltage is limited by the dielectric strength of the medium and the power dissipated in the dielectric. It is thus seen that the efficiency of transmission of high-frequency and power lines is increased by different methods.

Even when dielectric loss is negligible, the dielectric strength of the medium limits the maximum voltage that may exist at any point along the line. When standing waves exist on a line, the voltage stress in the dielectric is not uniform, and the voltages existing at the anti-nodes are the limiting factors. When standing waves exist, the voltage at an anti-node may be greater than the input voltage, and the input voltage must be limited to such a value that the voltage at the anti-nodes is below the dielectric strength of the medium. Since the power input is proportional to the square of the input voltage, it follows that the effect of standing waves is to reduce the power capacity of the line. This effect may be significant in certain applications, and is another reason for eliminating standing waves by means of a matched load. Methods used for impedance transformation and matching are discussed in the following sections.

10.5 IMPEDANCE TRANSFORMATION BY QUARTER-WAVE LINES

A quarter-wavelength line can be used to transform a resistance of one magnitude into a resistance of another magnitude. If, in Eq. 10.4-1, $\beta \ell = \pi/2$, corresponding to a quarter-wavelength line,

$$Z_{in} = \frac{Z_0^2}{Z_r} \qquad [10.5\text{-}1]$$

The circuit is shown in (a) of Fig. 10-4. It is seen that a quarter-wavelength line transforms an impedance in a manner that is analogous to the way that a transformer with unity coupling in lumped circuits trans-

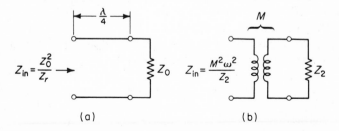

Figure 10-4   Quarter-wave line and analogous lumped circuit.

forms an impedance, Z_2, in the secondary to $M^2\omega^2/Z_2$ in the primary, where M is the mutual inductance [Fig. 10-4(b)]. The transformation property of a quarter-wavelength line is understandable when it is recalled that impedance (resistance) maxima and minima are a quarter-wavelength apart in the standing wave pattern. In that case, the quarter-wavelength line actually transforms the maximum impedance into the minimum impedance, and vice versa.

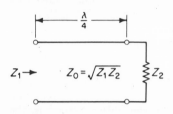

Figure 10-5 Quarter-wave line used for impedance transformation.

A quarter-wavelength line for transforming an impedance Z_2 into an impedance Z_1 is shown in Fig. 10-5. The characteristic impedance of the line is found from the following equations:

$$Z_1 = \frac{Z_0^2}{Z_2} \qquad [10.5\text{-}2]$$

$$Z_0 = \sqrt{Z_1 Z_2} \qquad [10.5\text{-}3]$$

Equation 10.5-3 shows that the characteristic impedance of the quarter-wavelength line must be chosen as the geometric mean of the two impedances that are to be matched. If Z_0 is a pure resistance, as is usually assumed for a high-frequency line, Z_1 and Z_2 must also be pure resistors. It will be shown that this statement does not limit the application of quarter-wavelength lines to matching resistive loads. Before considering this, it should be noted that the required characteristic impedance of the matching line can be realized by varying the dimensions of the line (r_2/r_1 for coaxial cables, D/r for open-wire lines) or by varying the dielectric, as for example by filling the air region in a coaxial cable with a quarter-wavelength dielectric slug having a relative dielectric constant greater than unity.* In the latter case, the phase velocity in the cable is reduced, and the wavelength must be computed on the basis of the reduced phase velocity and not on the basis of the free-space velocity. In other words, the physical length of the matching section must be less than a quarter-wavelength in free space.

As shown in Eqs. 8.7-9 and 8.7-10, the voltage and current standing wave patterns on lossless lines are given by

$$V(x) = V_1(\epsilon^{j\beta x} + \rho\epsilon^{-j\beta x}) = V_1\epsilon^{j\beta x}(1 + |\rho|\epsilon^{-j(2\beta x - \phi)}) \qquad [10.5\text{-}4]$$

* Practical considerations limit the range in Z_0 that can be attained, and limit the applicability of this method of impedance transformation.

$$I(x) = \frac{V_1}{Z_0}\left(\epsilon^{j\beta x} - \rho\epsilon^{-j\beta x}\right) = \left(\frac{V_1}{Z_0}\right)\epsilon^{j\beta x}\left(1 - |\rho|\epsilon^{-j(2\beta x - \phi)}\right) \quad [10.5\text{-}5]$$

where the complex reflection coefficient is

$$\rho = |\rho|\epsilon^{j\phi} \quad [10.5\text{-}6]$$

As given by Eq. 8.7-12, the magnitude of the maximum voltage is

$$|V_{\max}| = |V_1|(1 + |\rho|) \quad [10.5\text{-}7]$$

At the point of maximum voltage, the current has its minimum value given by

$$|I_{\min}| = \left(\frac{|V_1|}{Z_0}\right)(1 - |\rho|) \quad [10.5\text{-}8]$$

At a voltage maximum, the impedance has its maximum value given by

$$Z_{\max} = \left[\frac{1 + |\rho|}{1 - |\rho|}\right] Z_0 = SZ_0 \quad [10.5\text{-}9]$$

where S is the standing wave ratio.

Similarly, the minimum impedance is located at a voltage minimum and is

$$Z_{\min} = \left[\frac{1 - |\rho|}{1 + |\rho|}\right] Z_0 = \frac{Z_0}{S} \quad [10.5\text{-}10]$$

It is important to note that, since Z_0 is assumed to be purely real in high-frequency lines, both $Z_{\max}$ and $Z_{\min}$ are purely real. It follows that, regardless of the actual termination, there are always two points on a line, a quarter-wavelength apart, where the impedance is a pure resistance, equal to either SZ_0 or Z_0/S. Hence, a quarter-wavelength line can be used to match an impedance to a given line, provided that the matching line is connected at either a voltage maximum or a voltage minimum as shown in Figs. 10-6 and 10-7, and that the required characteristic impedance of the matching section is practically realizable.

In Fig. 10-6, the matching section is connected to a voltage maximum where the impedance is SZ_0. It follows from Eq. 10.5-3 that the characteristic impedance of the quarter-wavelength line is

$$Z_0' = \sqrt{S\, Z_0 Z_0} = Z_0\sqrt{S} \quad [10.5\text{-}11]$$

The length of the line is designated as $\lambda'/4$ to indicate the possible

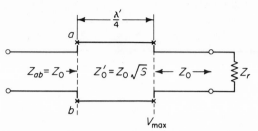

Figure 10-6 Quarter-wave line connected at voltage maximum to match load to line.

change in wavelength caused by a change in dielectric required to realize Eq. 10.5-11.

In Fig. 10-7, the matching section is connected to a voltage minimum where the impedance is Z_0/S. Hence, in Fig. 10-7, the impedance of the matching line is

$$Z_0' = \sqrt{Z_0 Z_0/S} = \frac{Z_0}{\sqrt{S}} \qquad [10.5\text{-}12]$$

One additional point should be noted. When Z_0 is the characteristic impedance of a line with air as the dielectric, and Z_0' for the matching

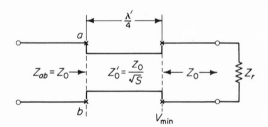

Figure 10-7 Quarter-wave line connected at voltage minimum to match load to line.

section is realized by varying the dielectric constant of the matching section, Z_0' of the matching section must be less than Z_0. This follows from the relations

$$Z_0 = \sqrt{\frac{L}{C}} \qquad [10.5\text{-}13]$$

$$Z_0' = \sqrt{\frac{L}{C'}} \qquad [10.5\text{-}14]$$

where $\overline{C}'$ is the capacitance per unit length resulting from increasing the dielectric constant. A decrease in the dielectric constant is impossible, because the dielectric constant of free space is a minimum. Since $\overline{L}$ is unaffected by a change in the dielectric constant, and since $C' > C$, $Z_0' < Z_0$. Under these conditions, the matching section must be connected at a voltage minimum, because only Eq. 10.5-12 can be satisfied since S is greater than unity.

10.6 IMPEDANCE TRANSFORMATION BY STUBBING

The impedance along a line with standing waves varies from its maximum value of a pure resistance of magnitude SZ_0, at a voltage maximum, to its minimum value of a pure resistance of magnitude Z_0/S, at a voltage minimum. It will be shown that at some intermediate point the real part of the impedance is Z_0. At this point, however, the impedance also has a reactive component.

It follows that at points situated between voltage maxima and minima the admittance can be represented by a conductance of $1/Z_0$ and an associated susceptance. Since an open or short-circuited line having a length of less than one-half a wavelength can be used to simulate any desired susceptance, the associated susceptance can be neutralized by connecting a section of suitable length across the line at the point where the conductance is $1/Z_0$. The section of open or short-circuited line that is connected across the given transmission line is termed a *stub*, and the process of matching impedances by this method is known as *stubbing*, as is shown in Fig. 10-8. At the stubbing point, the real component of the input admittance is $1/Z_0$, and the algebraic sum of the stub and line susceptance is zero. Hence, the input impedance at the stubbing position

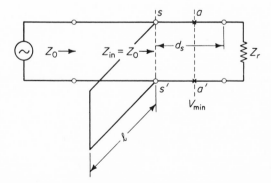

Figure 10-8   Use of short-circuited stub for impedance transformation.

is Z_0, and there are no standing waves to the left of the stubbing point, s, in Fig. 10-8. This method of impedance transformation is more flexible than the use of quarter-wave lines. It should be noted that standing waves do exist in the short portion of the transmission line to the right of point s.

In Fig. 10-8, d_s is the distance from the receiver to the first stubbing position, and ℓ represents the length of the short-circuited stub. An open-circuited stub may also be used, but the short-circuited stub is usually preferred. Inasmuch as the period of the standing wave pattern is π radians, possible stubbing positions occur along the line at intervals of π radians. For minimum line loss, the stub should be placed nearest the load. The point a in Fig. 10-8 denotes the voltage minimum nearest to the load.

The ratio of voltage to current, or impedance, at point a is a pure resistance of magnitude Z_0/S. Therefore, the effect of the line and load to the right of point a can be simulated by connecting a resistor of magnitude Z_0/S across aa'. This is shown in Fig. 10-9, where the distance from the voltage minimum, a, to the load is designated as x_m, and the distance from the stubbing point, s, to the voltage minimum is x_s. Note that the line to the right of aa' is disconnected after the insertion of the equivalent resistor, Z_0/S.

Since the process of stubbing consists in placing a section of short-circuited or open-circuited line across or in parallel with the given line, stubbing calculations must be based upon the expression for input admittance in order to determine the susceptance to be neutralized by the stub. It follows from Eq. 10.1-5 that the input admittance is given by

$$Y(x) = \frac{I(x)}{V(x)} = \frac{Z_0 \cos \beta x + jZ_r \sin \beta x}{Z_0(Z_r \cos \beta x + jZ_0 \sin \beta x)} \qquad [10.6\text{-}1]$$

where x is the distance measured to the left of the point at which the impedance is Z_r. When Z_0/S is substituted for Z_r in Eq. 10.6-1, $x = x_s$, the distance from point a, the voltage minimum, shown in Fig. 10-9.

From the preceding analysis in this section, it follows that the distance x_s of the stubbing point from the voltage minimum is defined by the following equation:

$$\frac{Z_0 \cos \beta x_s + j(Z_0/S) \sin \beta x_s}{Z_0(Z_0/S \cos \beta x_s + jZ_0 \sin \beta x_s)} = \frac{1}{Z_0} + jB_s \qquad [10.6\text{-}2]$$

Equation 10.6-2 assumes that the input conductance at the stubbing position is $1/Z_0$ and that the associated susceptance is B_s. When the numerator and denominator of the left-hand side of Eq. 10.6-2 are divided by $\cos \beta x_s$, the following result is obtained:

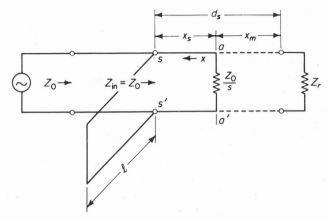

Figure 10-9 Further illustration of impedance transformation by stubbing.

$$\frac{1}{Z_0}\left[\frac{S + j \tan \beta x_s}{1 + jS \tan \beta x_s}\right] = \frac{1}{Z_0} + jB_s \qquad [10.6\text{-}3]$$

Rationalization of the left-hand side of Eq. 10.6-3 yields

$$\frac{S + S \tan^2 \beta x_s}{Z_0(1 + S^2 \tan^2 \beta x_s)} + j\left[\frac{\tan \beta x_s - S^2 \tan \beta x_s}{Z_0(1 + S^2 \tan^2 \beta x_s)}\right] = \frac{1}{Z_0} + jB_s \qquad [10.6\text{-}4]$$

It follows from Eq. 10.6-4 that:

$$\frac{S + S \tan^2 \beta x_s}{1 + S^2 \tan^2 \beta x_s} = 1 \qquad [10.6\text{-}5]$$

$$\frac{(1 - S^2) \tan \beta x_s}{Z_0(1 + S^2 \tan^2 \beta x_s)} = B_s \qquad [10.6\text{-}6]$$

where B_s is the reactive component of the admittance at the stubbing point. The solution of Eq. 10.6-5 yields:

$$S + S \tan^2 \beta x_s = 1 + S^2 \tan^2 \beta x_s \qquad [10.6\text{-}7]$$

$$S - 1 = S(S - 1) \tan^2 \beta x_s \qquad [10.6\text{-}8]$$

$$\tan \beta x_s = \pm \sqrt{\frac{1}{S}} \qquad [10.6\text{-}9]$$

Equation 10.6-9 gives the distance of the stubbing position from the voltage minimum in terms of the voltage standing wave ratio. The substitution of $\tan \beta x_s$ as given by Eq. 10.6-9 into Eq. 10.6-6 gives the following result:

$$\frac{(\pm 1/\sqrt{S})(1 - S^2)}{Z_0(1 + S)} = \frac{(\pm 1/\sqrt{S})(1 - S)}{Z_0} = B_s \qquad [10.6\text{-}10]$$

where B_s is the input susceptance at the stubbing point.

It follows directly from Eq. 10.2-17 that the admittance of a short-circuited section of length ℓ and characteristic impedance Z_0' is given by

$$jB' = \frac{1}{jZ_0' \tan \beta\ell} = \frac{-j \cot \beta\ell}{Z_0'} \qquad [10.6\text{-}11]$$

Since the purpose of stubbing is to neutralize the input susceptance at the stubbing position,

$$B' = - B_s \qquad [10.6\text{-}12]$$

It follows from Eqs. 10.6-10, 10.6-11, and 10.6-12 that:

$$\frac{(\pm 1/\sqrt{S})(1 - S)}{Z_0} = \frac{1}{Z_0'} \cot \beta\ell \qquad [10.6\text{-}13]$$

Hence,

$$\tan \beta\ell = \frac{\pm Z_0\sqrt{S}}{Z_0'(1 - S)} \qquad [10.6\text{-}14]$$

where ℓ is the length of the stub.

If the characteristic impedances of the stub and the line are equal, as is often the case, $Z_0 = Z_0'$ in Eq. 10.6-14, and the equation for the stub length then becomes:

$$\tan \beta\ell = \frac{\pm \sqrt{S}}{1 - S} \qquad [10.6\text{-}15]$$

Since the tangent is positive in the first quadrant and negative in the second, and $S > 1$, use of the negative sign in the numerator of Eq. 10.6-15 results in the stub of shorter length. Equation 10.6-15 defines the stub length in terms of the voltage standing wave ratio. Equations 10.6-9 and 10.6-15 can be written so as to give the stubbing position and length of a short-circuited stub as fractions of a wavelength. These relations are the following:

$$\frac{x_s}{\lambda} = \pm \frac{1}{2\pi} \tan^{-1}\left(\frac{1}{\sqrt{S}}\right) \qquad [10.6\text{-}16]$$

$$\frac{\ell}{\lambda} = \pm \frac{1}{2\pi} \tan^{-1}\left(\frac{\sqrt{S}}{1-S}\right) \qquad [10.6\text{-}17]$$

Equations 10.6-16 and 10.6-17 for the stubbing distances and lengths expressed as fractions of a wavelength are general relations, and are plotted as reference data.*

When a line is terminated by an impedance other than Z_0, the real part of the admittance along the line varies from Y_0/S at a voltage maximum to SY_0 at a voltage minimum. By placing a stub at some point between a voltage maximum and a voltage minimum, a terminal admittance $Y_r = G_r + jB_r$ can be transformed into an admittance,

$$Y = G + jB \quad [Y_0/S \leqq G \leqq SY_0] \qquad [10.6\text{-}18]$$

where Y_0 is the characteristic admittance of the line and B is the algebraic sum of the susceptance of the line at the stubbing position and the susceptance of the stub. Thus, stubbing can be used for impedance or admittance transformation within the limits prescribed for the real component of Y in Eq. 10.6-18. Note that B in Eq. 10.6-18 may have any value, depending upon the length of the stub.

Assume that at a distance, x_1, from a voltage minimum, the real part of the admittance is to be mY_0 where $1/S \leqq m \leqq S$. It follows directly from Eq. 10.6-4 that:

$$Y_0\left[\frac{S + S\tan^2 \beta x_1}{1 + S^2 \tan^2 \beta x_1} + j\left(\frac{\tan \beta x_1 - S^2 \tan \beta x_1}{1 + S^2 \tan^2 \beta x_1}\right)\right] = mY_0 + jB_1 \qquad [10.6\text{-}19]$$

Equating the real and imaginary components in both sides of Eq. 10.6-19 yields

$$\frac{S + S\tan^2 \beta x_1}{1 + S^2 \tan^2 \beta x_1} = m \qquad [10.6\text{-}20]$$

$$Y_0\left[\frac{\tan \beta x_1 - S^2 \tan \beta x_1}{1 + S^2 \tan \beta x_1}\right] = B_1 \qquad [10.6\text{-}21]$$

It follows from Eq. 10.6-20 that

$$\tan \beta x_1 = \pm \sqrt{\frac{S - m}{S(mS - 1)}} = \pm n \qquad [10.6\text{-}22]$$

* These curves are found in the following handbook: *Reference Data for Radio Engineers*, Federal Telephone and Radio Corp., New York, 4th Edition, 1957, page 584.

An inspection of Eq. 10.6-22 shows that if $\tan \beta x_1$ is to be real, then

$$\frac{1}{S} \leqq m \leqq S \qquad [10.6\text{-}23]$$

Equation 10.6-23 is consistent with Eq. 10.6-18.
It follows from Eqs. 10.6-21 and 10.6-22 that:

$$Y_0 \left[\frac{\pm n \mp nS^2}{1 \pm nS^2} \right] = B_1 \qquad [10.6\text{-}24]$$

If the required susceptance is B, the stub susceptance, B_s, is given by

$$B_s = B - B_1 \qquad [10.6\text{-}25]$$

where B_1 is given by Eq. 10.6-24. If a short-circuited stub of characteristic admittance Y_0' is used, the length of the stub must satisfy the following relation:

$$B_s = - \frac{1}{Z_0' \tan \beta \ell} = - Y_0' \cot \beta \ell \qquad [10.6\text{-}26]$$

It follows from Eqs. 10.6-24, 10.6-25, and 10.6-26 that:

$$\cot \beta \ell = - \frac{1}{Y_0'} \left[B - Y_0 \left(\frac{\pm n \mp nS^2}{1 + nS^2} \right) \right] \qquad [10.6\text{-}27]$$

Equations 10.6-22 and 10.6-27 determine the stub position and length required to transform an admittance Y_r to an admittance $G + jB$ where the limits of G are given in Eq. 10.6-18. The transformed impedance is given by

$$Z = \frac{1}{G + jB} = \frac{G}{G^2 + B^2} - \frac{jB}{G^2 + B^2} = R + jX \qquad [10.6\text{-}28]$$

10.7 APPLICATION OF STUBBING EQUATIONS

To illustrate the application of the stubbing equations, consider a lossless line in air, having a characteristic impedance of 300 ohms and operated at frequency of 200 megacycles. The voltage standing wave ratio is 4.48, and the first voltage minimum is located at 6 centimeters from the load. It is required to determine two stubbing positions nearest the load and the corresponding lengths of short-circuited stubs having a characteristic impedance of 300 ohms. No knowledge of the type or magnitude of the load is required.* The wavelength at a frequency of 200 megacycles and an assumed velocity of propagation of 3×10^8 meters per second is

$$\lambda = \frac{c}{f} = \frac{3 \times 10^8}{2 \times 10^8} = 1.50 \text{ meters} \qquad [10.7\text{-}1]$$

It follows from Eq. 10.6-16 that the two stubbing positions are given by:

$$\frac{x_s}{1.5} = \pm \left(\frac{1}{2\pi} \right) \tan^{-1} \left(\frac{1}{\sqrt{4.48}} \right) \qquad [10.7\text{-}2]$$

Since $\tan^{-1} (0.473) = 25.3°$, the value of x_s is given by

$$x_s = \pm \left(\frac{1.5}{2\pi} \right) \tan^{-1} (0.473) = \pm \left(\frac{1.5}{2\pi} \right) \left(25.3 \times \frac{\pi}{180} \right) = \pm 0.105 \text{ meter}$$

$$[10.7\text{-}3]$$

Hence, the two stubbing positions are

$$x_{s1} = 0.105 \text{ meter} \qquad [10.7\text{-}4]$$

$$x_{s2} = -0.105 \text{ meter} \qquad [10.7\text{-}5]$$

where x_{s1} is measured to the left of the voltage minimum, and x_{s2} is measured to the right. This follows from the assumed coordinate system. Since the voltage minimum is 0.06 meter from the load, x_{s2} falls off the line. Inasmuch as the standing wave pattern has a period equal to one-half wavelength, x_{s2} is also given by

$$x_{s2} = -0.105 + \frac{\lambda}{2} = -0.105 + 0.75 = 0.645 \text{ meter} \qquad [10.7\text{-}6]$$

The corresponding stub lengths are found from Eq. 10.6-17 to be

$$\frac{\ell}{1.5} = \pm \left(\frac{1}{2\pi} \right) \tan^{-1} \left[\frac{\sqrt{4.48}}{1 - 4.48} \right] = \pm \left(\frac{1}{2\pi} \right) \tan^{-1} \left(\frac{-2.12}{3.48} \right)$$

$$= \mp \left(\frac{1}{2\pi} \right) \tan^{-1} (0.610) \qquad [10.7\text{-}7]$$

Since $\tan^{-1} (0.610) = 31.4°$, the two stub lengths are

$$\ell = \mp \left(\frac{1.5}{2\pi} \right) (31.4) \times \frac{\pi}{180} = \mp 0.130 \text{ meter} \qquad [10.7\text{-}8]$$

* It will be recalled that the load is completely specified by the voltage standing wave ratio and the location of the voltage minimum.

A physically realizable stub corresponding to $\ell = -0.130$ meter has a length given by

$$\ell_1 = -0.130 + \frac{\lambda}{2} = -0.130 + 0.750 = 0.620 \text{ meter} \qquad [10.7\text{-}9]$$

where ℓ_1 is the length of the stub placed at a distance of 0.105 meter to the left of the voltage minimum. The stub placed at 0.645 meter to the left of the voltage minimum has a length of

$$\ell_2 = 0.130 \text{ meter} \qquad [10.7\text{-}10]$$

and is the shorter stub.

It should be carefully noted that, since the positive part of the $\pm$ sign is used to determine x_{s1} from Eq. 10.7-3, the positive part must also be used to determine the corresponding stub length, ℓ_1, in Eq. 10.7-7. The stubbing arrangements are shown in Fig. 10-10, where d_{s1} and d_{s2} denote the distances of the stubs from the load.

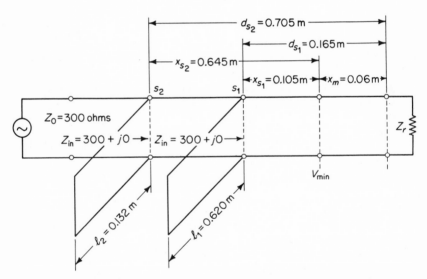

Figure 10-10   Two possible stub arrangements for matching a load to a line.

As already noted, when the positive part of the $\pm$ sign is used to determine the stubbing position, the positive part is also used to calculate the length of the stub. It follows from Eq. 10.6-17 that, since S is always greater than unity and since $(1 - S)$ is always negative, the use of the positive part of the $\pm$ sign results in a negative value of ℓ. To obtain a physically realizable stub, $\lambda/2$ must be added to the value of ℓ obtained from Eq. 10.6-17. This results in a stub having a length greater than $\lambda/4$. It follows that the use of the negative part of the $\pm$ sign in Eqs. 10.6-16 and 10.6-17 gives the shorter stub. The curves referred to in connection with Eqs. 10.6-16 and 10.6-17 give the length of the shorter stub.

10.8 THE SMITH TRANSMISSION LINE CHART

Transmission line calculations can be facilitated by use of the Smith Transmission Line Chart.* On this chart, the real and reactive components of input impedance lie along families of circles. The coordinates of these circles are the real and quadrature components of a general reflection coefficient, defined as the ratio of the reflected to the direct voltage at any point of the line. As often happens, the actual mathematical relations are much simpler than their description. The derivation of these equations follows.

The impedance at any point is given by

$$Z(x) = \frac{V(x)}{I(x)} = Z_0 \left[\frac{1 + |\rho| \epsilon^{j\theta}}{1 - |\rho| \epsilon^{j\theta}} \right] \qquad [10.8\text{-}1]$$

where

$$\theta = \phi - 2\beta x \qquad [10.8\text{-}2]$$

The ratio $Z(x)/Z_0$ is dimensionless, and is termed the per-unit or normalized impedance. It is designated by the symbol z, and is given by

$$z = \frac{Z(x)}{Z_0} = \frac{1 + |\rho| \epsilon^{j\theta}}{1 - |\rho| \epsilon^{j\theta}} \qquad [10.8\text{-}3]$$

Equation 10.8-3 can also be written as follows:

$$z = \frac{1 + w}{1 - w} \qquad [10.8\text{-}4]$$

where w is a complex number, given by

$$w = u + jv = |\rho| \epsilon^{j\phi} \epsilon^{-j2\beta x} \qquad [10.8\text{-}5]$$

It can be seen from Eq. 10.8-5 that u and v are the real and quadrature

* A description of this chart is given in "Transmission Line Calculator" by P. H. Smith, *Electronics*, vol. 12 (January 1939), pages 29–31; and in "An Improved Transmission Line Calculator" by P. H. Smith, *Electronics*, vol. 17 (January 1944), page 130.

components of the general reflection coefficient, defined as the ratio of the reflected voltage to the direct voltage at any point on the line.*

The per-unit impedance in Eq. 10.8-4 can now be expressed as follows:

$$z = r + jx = \frac{1 + u + jv}{1 - u - jv} \qquad [10.8-6]$$

where r and x are respectively the per-unit resistance and reactance. Rationalization of the right-hand side of Eq. 10.8-6 yields

$$r + jx = \frac{1 - u^2 - v^2}{(1 - u)^2 + v^2} + j\left[\frac{2v}{(1 - u)^2 + v^2}\right] \qquad [10.8-7]$$

It follows from Eq. 10.8-7 that:

$$r = \frac{1 - u^2 - v^2}{(1 - u)^2 + v^2} \qquad [10.8-8]$$

$$x = \frac{2v}{(1 - u)^2 + v^2} \qquad [10.8-9]$$

Equation 10.8-8 can be written in the following forms:

$$r(u^2 + v^2) - 2ru + r = 1 - u^2 - v^2 \qquad [10.8-10]$$

$$(1 + r)u^2 + (1 + r)v^2 - 2ru = 1 - r \qquad [10.8-11]$$

$$u^2 - \frac{2ru}{1 + r} + v^2 = \frac{1 - r}{1 + r} \qquad [10.8-12]$$

Since the coefficients of the squared terms are equal, Eq. 10.8-12 represents a circle in u-v coordinates. Completing the square of the terms in u yields

$$u^2 - \frac{2ru}{1 + r} + \frac{r^2}{(1 + r)^2} + v^2 = \frac{1 - r}{1 + r} + \frac{r^2}{(1 + r)^2} = \frac{1}{(1 + r)^2} \qquad [10.8-13]$$

$$\left(u - \frac{r}{1 + r}\right)^2 + v^2 = \left(\frac{1}{1 + r}\right)^2 \qquad [10.8-14]$$

Equation 10.8-14 represents a circle of radius $1/(1 + r)$, with its center at $u = r/(1 + r)$, $v = 0$.

In a similar manner, it follows from Eq. 10.8-9 that:

$$u^2 + v^2 - 2u - \frac{2v}{x} = -1 \qquad [10.8-15]$$

---

*This is not to be confused with the reflection coefficient at the receiver where $x = 0$.

$$u^2 - 2u + 1 + v^2 - \frac{2v}{x} + \frac{1}{x^2} = -1 + 1 + \frac{1}{x^2} = \frac{1}{x^2} \quad [10.8\text{-}16]$$

$$(u - 1)^2 + \left(v - \frac{1}{x}\right)^2 = \left(\frac{1}{x}\right)^2 \qquad [10.8\text{-}17]$$

Equation 10.8-17 thus represents a circle of radius $1/x$, with its center at $u = 1$, $v = 1/x$.

Equations 10.8-14 and 10.8-17 can also be derived from consideration of the inversion of straight lines not passing through the origin.

Equations 10.8-14 and 10.8-17 show that the loci of the per-unit or normalized input resistance and reactance are families of circles having centers and radii that are dependent upon the per-unit parameters. Since r and x are dimensionless, they can be assigned values such as $\frac{1}{4}$, $\frac{1}{2}$, 1, 2, 4, etc. It follows from Eq. 10.8-14 that when $r = 0$, corresponding to purely reactive input impedance, the circle is of unit radius, and has its center at the origin. This circle is known as the *unit circle*. Inspection of Eq. 10.8-14 shows that the circle for $r = 1$ passes through the origin. It follows from Eqs. 10.8-14 and 10.8-17 that all the circles pass through the point, $u = 1$, $v = 0$.

A Smith chart is shown in Fig. 10-11. The resistance circles intersect the axis of reals at right angles, and the reactance circles are tangent to the axis of reals at its right-hand extremity. The radius of the unit circle is arbitrary. All other circles fall within the unit circle and pass through the point 1, 0. The location of this point is determined by the scale chosen for the unit circle. The angular divisions above the unit circle are the intersections of radii emanating from the origin, which is the intersection of the $r = 1$ circle with the real axis. It follows from Eq. 10.8-5 that the angle associated with w is $\theta = \phi - 2\beta x$. Since $\phi - 2\beta x$ decreases as x increases for a given value of ϕ, distances measured toward the generator (positive x) are equivalent to decreasing θ. Therefore, distances measured toward the generator are measured in a clockwise direction on the Smith chart. These distances are given in terms of the wavelength and also in degrees in Fig. 10-11.

The Smith chart can be used for admittance calculations as well as for impedances. The input admittance is given by

$$Y(x) = \frac{I(x)}{V(x)} = \frac{1}{Z_0}\left[\frac{1 - |\rho|\epsilon^{j\theta}}{1 + |\rho|\epsilon^{j\theta}}\right] \qquad [10.8\text{-}18]$$

Equation 10.8-18 can also be written as

$$\frac{Y(x)}{Y_0} = \frac{1 - |\rho|\epsilon^{j\theta}}{1 + |\rho|\epsilon^{j\theta}} \qquad [10.8\text{-}19]$$

The left-hand side of Eq. 10.8-19 is the per-unit admittance, y. Hence,

$$y = \frac{1 - |\rho|\epsilon^{j\theta}}{1 + |\rho|\epsilon^{j\theta}} = g + jb \qquad [10.8\text{-}20]$$

where g and b are respectively the per-unit input conductance and susceptance.

A comparison of Eqs. 10.8-3 and 10.8-20 shows that the latter can be converted into the former by shifting the phase of the reflection coefficient by π. It will be recalled that the reflection coefficient of the current is equal in magnitude to the voltage reflection coefficient, but has a phase difference of π. If ρ' represents the current reflection coefficient, Eq. 10.8-20 can be written as

$$y = \frac{1 + |\rho'|\epsilon^{j\theta}}{1 - |\rho'|\epsilon^{j\theta}} \qquad [10.8\text{-}21]$$

Equation 10.8-21 has exactly the same form as Eq. 10.8-3. It follows that the circles in Fig. 10-11 are loci of constant conductance and susceptance as well as constant resistance and reactance.

The unit circle gives both the reactance and the susceptance of an open or short-circuited line. This is evident from the following equations:

$$\frac{Z_{oc}}{Z_0} = -j \cot \beta x = \frac{Y_{sc}}{Y_0} \qquad [10.8\text{-}22]$$

$$\frac{Z_{sc}}{Z_0} = j \tan \beta x = \frac{Y_{oc}}{Y_0} \qquad [10.8\text{-}23]$$

The impedances and admittances are given by Eqs. 10.2-3, 10.2-15, 10.2-17, and 10.2-18.

10.9 APPLICATION OF THE SMITH CHART

As the first example, let it be required to determine the length of a short-circuited stub having a characteristic impedance of 200 ohms and an input reactance of $-j100$ ohms. The per-unit or normalized reactance is $-j0.5$. The unit circle is the locus of pure reactance and pure susceptance. The origin for the reactance of a short-circuited stub and the susceptance of an open-circuited stub is the left-hand intersection of the axis of reals and the unit circle. The stub length is found by proceeding clockwise, corresponding to motion along the line from the short-circuited termination toward the input, through the entire upper half of the unit circle, where the reactance is positive, until the intersection of the lower 0.5 reactance circle with the unit circle is reached. This point is labelled A in Fig. 10-11. The displacement along the wavelength scale is from $\lambda = 0$ to $\lambda = 0.426$ wavelength, as shown by the intersection of OA′ with the outer wavelength scale. Hence, the required length is 0.426 wavelength or 153.4°. The right-hand intersection of the axis of reals and the unit circle is the origin for finding the reactance of an open-circuited stub or the susceptance of a short-circuited stub.

For the second example, let it be required to determine the input impedance of a 200-ohm line, three-eighths of a wavelength long, terminated by a 100-ohm resistor. The per-unit value of the termination is $0.5 + j0$, and is located at point B in Fig. 10-11. The length of OB is found to be one-third of the radius of the unit circle. Since the rectangular coordinates of a Smith chart are the real and quadrature components of the general reflection coefficient, the magnitude of the reflection coefficient for this termination is $\frac{1}{3}$. The angle is given by the intersection of OB (extended) with the Angle of Reflection Coefficient scale. The angle is found to be 180°. In motion along the line and the corresponding rotation on the Smith chart, the magnitude of the reflection coefficient and the standing wave ratio both remain constant. This follows from the fact that losses are neglected. Therefore, a displacement of $\frac{3}{8}$ wavelength along the line from the termination to the input corresponds to clockwise rotation along a circle of radius OB, as shown in Fig. 10-11. The intersection of this circle with the line OC, drawn to intersect the 0.375 coordinate on the wavelength scale, is point D, and gives the per-unit input impedance, which is found to be $0.8 - j0.6$. Hence, the actual input impedance is

$$Z_{in} = 200(0.8 - j0.6) = 160 - j120 \text{ ohms} \qquad [10.9\text{-}1]$$

Consider now a 300-ohm line terminated by an unknown impedance. The standing wave ratio is 4.48, and the first voltage minimum is situated at 6 cm from the termination when the frequency is 200 megacycles. It is required to find the terminating impedance, assuming that the line is in air and that the wavelength is 150 cm. Hence, the first voltage minimum is $6/150 = 0.04$ wavelength from the termination. The per-unit impedance at a voltage minimum is a pure resistance of magnitude $1/S$. In this case, the per-unit impedance is 0.22 ohm. The voltage minimum corresponds to point E in Fig. 10-11. The terminating impedance is found by rotating point E counterclockwise toward the load for a distance of 0.04 wavelength to point F. The coordinates of point F are $0.24 - j0.24$.

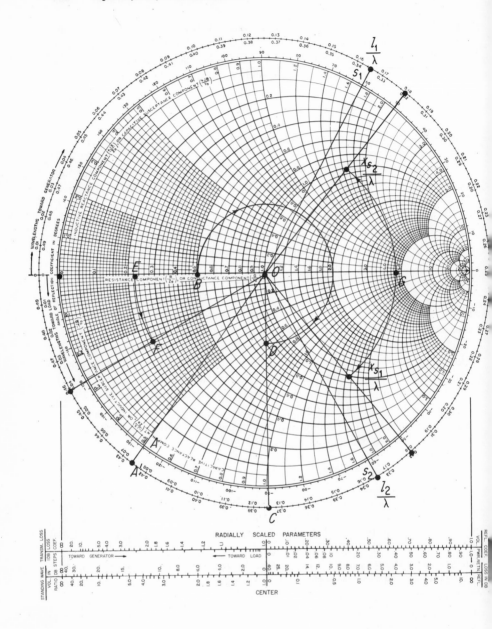

Figure 10-11 Smith chart showing impedance or admittance coordinates.

Therefore, the terminating impedance is

$$Z_r = 300(0.24 - j0.24) = 72 - j72 \text{ ohms} \qquad [10.9\text{-}2]$$

This agrees well with the analytical result obtained in Sec. 8.7.

The Smith chart is very useful for stubbing calculations. In this connection, several points must be noted. As in the algebraic calculations of Sec. 10.8, stubbing is based upon admittance values. Hence, in stubbing problems, the Smith chart must be used as an admittance diagram. A voltage minimum is an impedance minimum and an admittance maximum. At a voltage minimum, the per-unit admittance is S. The $r = 1$ circle is the locus of all possible stubbing positions because, at all points on this circle, the real part of the per-unit admittance is 1.0. The stubbing positions are found by rotation around a circle of radius S to intersect the $r = 1$ circle.

Consider now the problem of stubbing a lossless line having a standing wave ratio of 4.48, with the first voltage minimum at 6 cm from the load when the frequency is 200 megacycles. As previously noted, the voltage minimum is an admittance maximum, and in this case is located at point G on the 4.48 resistance circle in Fig. 10-11. The stubbing positions are found by rotating, with radius OG, to the intersection with the unit resistance circle, where the real part of the per unit admittance is 1.0. The stubbing points are labelled x_{s_1}/λ and x_{s_2}/λ in Fig. 10-11, and are situated at a distance of $\pm 0.07\lambda$ from the voltage minimum. This corresponds to

$$x_{s_1} = 0.07 \times 1.50 = 0.105 \text{ meter} \qquad [10.9\text{-}3]$$

Equation 10.9-3 gives the same result as Eq. 10.7-4.

The point x_{s_1}, found by clockwise rotation, represents a stubbing position measured toward the transmitter, and is positive; the point x_{s_2}, found by counterclockwise rotation, represents a stubbing position measured toward the receiver, and is negative. Since x_{s_2} falls off the line, the actual stubbing position is

$$x_{s_2} = -0.105 + \frac{\lambda}{2} = -0.105 + 0.750 = 0.645 \text{ meter} \qquad [10.9\text{-}4]$$

Equation 10.9-4 gives the same result as Eq. 10.7-6.

The per-unit or normalized susceptance existing at stubbing point x_{s_1} is $-j1.70$ mhos, and the per-unit susceptance at point x_{s_2} is $j1.70$ mhos. Since these susceptances are to be neutralized by short-circuited stubs having the same characteristic impedance as the line, the stub lengths are found by rotation in a clockwise direction around the unit circle, starting with the right-hand intersection of the unit circle and the axis of reals. This follows from the fact that the right-hand intersection is the origin for the susceptance of short-circuited stubs and the reactance of open-circuited stubs.

The stub lengths are given by

$$\frac{\ell_1}{\lambda} = 0.415 \qquad [10.9\text{-}5]$$

where ℓ_1 is the length of the stub when $x_{s_1} = 0.105$ meter. This position is indicated as point S_1 on the unit circle in Fig. 10-11. The actual stub length is

$$\ell_1 = 0.415\lambda = 0.415 \times 1.50 = 0.622 \text{ meter} \qquad [10.9\text{-}6]$$

Equation 10.9-6 agrees with Eq. 10.7-9.

The length of the stub when $x_{s_2} = 0.105$ meter is found at point S_2 in Fig. 10-11, and is given by

$$\frac{\ell_2}{\lambda} = 0.085 \qquad [10.9\text{-}7]$$

Note that the difference between the readings on the wavelength scale at points S_2 and S_0 gives the required ratio. The actual stub length is

$$\ell_2 = 0.085\lambda = 0.085 \times 1.50 = 0.128 \text{ meter} \qquad [10.9\text{-}8]$$

Equation 10.9-8 agrees closely with Eq. 10.7-10.

10.10 DOUBLE-STUB MATCHING

The use of a single stub of variable length and variable position is not practicable in coaxial cables. Matching in coaxial cables can, however, be accomplished by the use of two stubs of fixed position and variable length. This procedure is known as double-stub matching. A line with two stubs, spaced at a distance of $3\lambda/8$ apart, is shown in Fig. 10-12, where the first stub is placed at a distance of 0.1λ from the first voltage minimum.

Double-stub matching is most readily performed by use of the Smith chart. The construction for Fig. 10-12 with $S = 4.48$ is shown in Fig. 10-13. If the input admittance at c in Fig. 10-12 is to be Y_0, the point

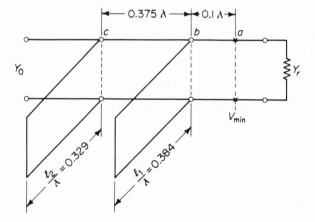

Figure 10-12 Illustration of double-stub matching.

corresponding to c on the Smith chart must be on the circle of unit conductance $(g = 1)$. The $g = 1$ circle, with its center at point o, is rotated counterclockwise by 0.375λ to coincide with point b, the first stubbing position in Fig. 10-12. The center of the rotated $g = 1$ circle is indicated as point o' in Fig. 10-13.

The per-unit admittance at point a, the voltage minimum, is

$$y = S = 4.48 + j0 \qquad [10.10\text{-}1]$$

The per-unit admittance at point b, resulting from a rotation of 0.1λ, is found from the Smith chart to be

$$y_1 = 0.6 - j1.20 \qquad [10.10\text{-}2]$$

Variation of the stub susceptance at point b corresponds to motion along a circle of constant conductance for which $g = 0.6$. The point of unit conductance is shown as b', where the per-unit admittance is found to be

$$y_1 + jb_{s1} = 0.60 - j0.08 \qquad [10.10\text{-}3]$$

where b_{s1} is the susceptance supplied by the first stub and is given by

$$b_{s1} = 1.2 - 0.08 = 1.12 \qquad [10.10\text{-}4]$$

The point b' is then rotated clockwise 0.375λ to point c on the $g = 1$ circle with its center at point o. The admittance at this point is found to be

$$y_2 = 1 - j0.54 \qquad [10.10\text{-}5]$$

In order for the input admittance at point c in Fig. 10-12 to be Y_0, the second stub must provide a susceptance of

$$b_{s2} = 0.54 \qquad [10.10\text{-}6]$$

The required lengths of the short-circuited stubs are found from the intersections with the unit circle to have the following values:

$$\frac{\ell_1}{\lambda} = 0.376 \qquad [10.10\text{-}7]$$

$$\frac{\ell_2}{\lambda} = 0.329 \qquad [10.10\text{-}8]$$

Two other stub lengths can be found by rotating counterclockwise from point b to the rotated $g = 1$ circle.

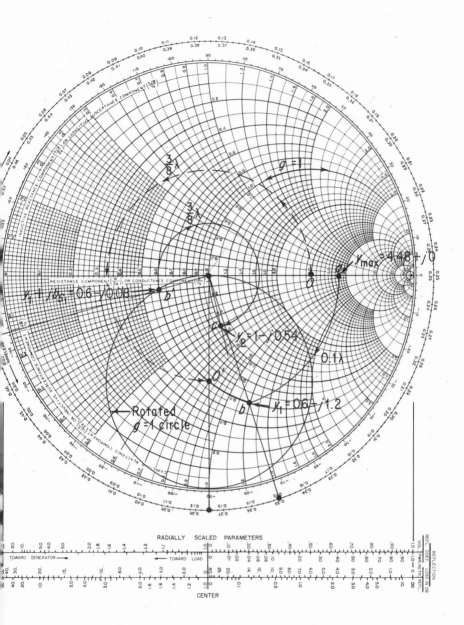

Figure 10-13   Use of Smith chart for double-stub matching.

10.11 THE EXPONENTIAL LINE

The exponential line is an impedance-matching device. It is essentially a non-uniform line where the inductance and capacitance per unit length are exponential functions of the distance along the line. The exponential variation is such that the $\bar{L}\,\bar{C}$ product remains constant while $\sqrt{\bar{L}/\bar{C}} = \epsilon^{kx}$, where k is a constant. Since the characteristic impedance of the exponential line is variable, it appears that it should be possible to obtain an impedance match between a load and the line.

Assume that the inductance and capacitance per unit length of an exponentially tapered line are given by

$$\bar{L} = (\bar{L}_0)\epsilon^{kx} \qquad [10.11\text{-}1]$$

$$\bar{C} = (\bar{C}_0)\epsilon^{-kx} \qquad [10.11\text{-}2]$$

where k is the taper coefficient, and where $\bar{L}_0$ and $\bar{C}_0$ are the inductance and capacitance per unit length when $x = 0$. It follows from Eqs. 10.11-1 and 10.11-2 that:

$$\bar{L}\,\bar{C} = \bar{L}_0\bar{C}_0 \qquad [10.11\text{-}3]$$

$$\sqrt{\frac{\bar{L}}{\bar{C}}} = \sqrt{\frac{\bar{L}_0}{\bar{C}_0}}\,(\epsilon^{kx}) \qquad [10.11\text{-}4]$$

Neglecting losses, the differential equations for the voltage and current phasors are:

$$\frac{dV}{dx} = (j\omega\bar{L})I \qquad [10.11\text{-}5]$$

$$\frac{dI}{dx} = (j\omega\bar{C})V \qquad [10.11\text{-}6]$$

where $\bar{L}$ and $\bar{C}$ are given by Eqs. 10.11-1 and 10.11-2.

Differentiation of Eq. 10.11-5 with respect to x yields

$$\frac{d^2V}{dx^2} = j\omega\bar{L}\frac{dI}{dx} + j\omega I\frac{d\bar{L}}{dx} \qquad [10.11\text{-}7]$$

The second term on the right-hand side of Eq. 10.11-7 vanishes for a uniform line.

It follows from Eq. 10.11-1 that:

$$\frac{d\bar{L}}{dx} = (k\bar{L}_0)\epsilon^{kx} = k\bar{L} \qquad [10.11\text{-}8]$$

The substitution of Eqs. 10.11-6 and 10.11-8 into Eq. 10.11-7 gives the following differential equation for the voltage phasor:

$$\frac{d^2V}{dx^2} = -\omega^2(\overline{L}\,\overline{C})V + jk\omega(\overline{L})I \qquad [10.11\text{-}9]$$

The solution of Eq. 10.11-5 for I yields

$$I = \left(\frac{1}{j\omega\overline{L}}\right)\frac{dV}{dx} \qquad [10.11\text{-}10]$$

When Eq. 10.11-10 is substituted into Eq. 10.11-9, the following result is obtained:

$$\frac{d^2V}{dx^2} - k\frac{dV}{dx} + \omega^2(\overline{L}\,\overline{C})V = 0 \qquad [10.11\text{-}11]$$

Equation 10.11-11 is a second-order differential equation with constant coefficients, and has the following solution:

$$V = A_1\epsilon^{r_1x} + A_2\epsilon^{r_2x} \qquad [10.11\text{-}12]$$

where r_1 and r_2 are roots of

$$y^2 - ky + \omega^2(\overline{L}\,\overline{C}) = 0 \qquad [10.11\text{-}13]$$

These roots are

$$r_1 = \frac{k}{2} + \sqrt{(k/2)^2 - \omega^2(\overline{L}\,\overline{C})} = \frac{k}{2} + \sqrt{(k/2)^2 - \omega^2(\overline{L}_0\,\overline{C}_0)} \qquad [10.11\text{-}14]$$

$$r_2 = \frac{k}{2} - \sqrt{(k/2)^2 - \omega^2(\overline{L}\,\overline{C})} = \frac{k}{2} - \sqrt{(k/2)^2 - \omega^2(\overline{L}_0\,\overline{C}_0)} \qquad [10.11\text{-}15]$$

Equation 10.11-3 was used in obtaining the final expressions for r_1 and r_2.

Inspection of Eqs. 10.11-14 and 10.11-15 shows that wave propagation with its associated phase shift occurs only when $\omega^2(\overline{L}_0\,\overline{C}_0) > (k/2)^2$, and r_1 and r_2 are complex. The condition for wave propagation is

$$\omega > \frac{k}{2\sqrt{\overline{L}_0\,\overline{C}_0}} \qquad [10.11\text{-}16]$$

Hence, the exponential line manifests its properties when the frequency exceeds

$$f_c = \frac{k}{4\pi\sqrt{\overline{L}_0\,\overline{C}_0}} \qquad [10.11\text{-}17]$$

where f_c is the cut-off frequency. When $f < f_c$, attenuation without phase shift occurs.

Assuming that Eq. 10.11-16 (which is actually an inequality) is satisfied, and using Eqs. 10.11-14 and 10.11-15, Eq. 10.11-12 can be written as

$$V = \epsilon^{(k/2)x}[A_1\epsilon^{j\beta x} + A_2\epsilon^{-j\beta x}]$$ [10.11-18]

where β in the exponent is given by

$$\beta = \sqrt{\omega^2(\overline{L}_0\,\overline{C}_0) - (k/2)^2}$$ [10.11-19]

An expression for the current is found by applying Eq. 10.11-10 to Eq. 10.11-18. The result is

$$I = \epsilon^{(k/2)x}\left[\left(\frac{j\beta + k/2}{j\omega\overline{L}}\right) A_1\epsilon^{j\beta x} - \left(\frac{j\beta - k/2}{j\omega\overline{L}}\right) A_2\epsilon^{-j\beta x}\right]$$ [10.11-20]

The division of Eq. 10.11-18 by Eq. 10.11-20 yields the following two characteristic impedances:

$$Z_{01} = \frac{j\omega\overline{L}}{j\beta + k/2}$$ [10.11-21]

$$Z_{02} = \frac{j\omega\overline{L}}{j\beta - k/2}$$ [10.11-22]

When the frequency and the taper coefficient have such values that $\beta \gg k/2$, it follows from Eqs. 10.11-21 and 10.11-22 that $Z_{01} = Z_{02} = Z_0$, and the characteristic impedance is approximately given by

$$Z_0 \approx \frac{\omega\overline{L}}{\beta} \approx \frac{\omega\overline{L}}{\omega\sqrt{\overline{L}\,\overline{C}}} \approx \sqrt{\frac{\overline{L}}{\overline{C}}} \approx \sqrt{\frac{\overline{L}_0}{\overline{C}_0}}\,(\epsilon^{kx})$$ [10.11-23]

Equation 10.11-23 shows that the expression given in Eq. 10.11-4 is approximately the characteristic impedance of the line.

It follows from Eq. 10.11-23 that a resistive load R_L, given by

$$R_L = \sqrt{\frac{\overline{L}_0}{\overline{C}_0}}\,(\epsilon^{k\ell})$$ [10.11-24]

connected at the terminals of a lossless line of length, ℓ, will appear approximately as $\sqrt{\overline{L}_0/\overline{C}_0}$ ohms at the input terminals, provided that the frequency exceeds the cut-off frequency given by Eq. 10.11-17. Reference to Eqs. 10.11-21 and 10.11-22 shows that a true impedance match cannot be obtained for a resistive load. For a true match, the load must have some reactance.

PROBLEMS

10-1 The outer diameter of the inner conductor of a coaxial line is 0.5 cm, and the inner diameter of the outer conductor is 2 cm. If the line is to be used at 60 megacycles, find the following:

(a) The minimum length of short-circuited line that can be used to simulate an inductive reactance of 200 ohms.

(b) The minimum length of short-circuited line to simulate a capacitive reactance of 200 ohms.

(c) The minimum length of open-circuited line to simulate an almost infinite input impedance.

10-2 Solve Prob. 10-1 for a two-wire parallel line in air composed of No. 10 B&S gauge copper wires placed 1 inch from center to center.

10-3 A two-wire line has a characteristic impedance of 300 ohms and is to feed a 90-ohm resistor at 100 megacycles. A quarter-wavelength line is to be used as a transformer to match the load to the line. This line is to be constructed of tube, 0.250 inch in diameter. Find the center-to-center spacing in air.

10-4 A lossless line has a characteristic impedance of 70 ohms and is operated at 200 megacycles. When this line is terminated by an unknown impedance, Z_r, the voltage standing wave ratio is 3.2 and the first voltage minimum is 15 cm from the receiving end. Calculate Z_r.

10-5 A high-frequency voltmeter consists of a quarter-wavelength lossless line with 300 ohms characteristic impedance, terminated by a radio-frequency ammeter of 2 ohms resistance. If the reading of the meter is 0.2 ampere, find the input voltage and the power taken by the meter from the line.

10-6 (a) A 100-ohm line operated at $\omega = 10^{10}$ radians per second is terminated by an unknown impedance. The standing wave ratio is infinite, and the first voltage minimum is situated at 180° from the load. Find the termination.

(b) Solve (a) if the first voltage maximum is located at 30° from the load.

10-7 A 100-ohm line is terminated by an unknown impedance, and has a standing wave ratio of 3.8. When the output terminals are short-circuited, the first voltage minimum is shifted toward the receiving end by 30°. Find the terminating impedance.

10-8 A 100-ohm lossless line operated at $\omega = 10^{10}$ radians per second is terminated by an unknown impedance. A short-circuited tuning stub ($Z_0 = 100$ ohms) is placed in parallel with the unknown impedance. When the length of this stub is equal to one-eighth of a wavelength, the standing wave ratio is 5.2 and a voltage minimum occurs at 180° from the termination. Find the unknown impedance.

10-9 In the illustrative problem of Sec. 10.7, find the required lengths of open-circuited stubs to eliminate reflections beyond the calculated stubbing positions, assuming that the characteristic impedance of the stub lines is 200 ohms.

10-10 A 300-ohm line feeding an antenna has a standing wave ratio of 4.0, and the distance from the load to the first voltage maximum is 28 cm. If the frequency is 150 megacycles, determine analytically the location and length of a short-circuited stub to eliminate standing waves from the maximum possible length of the line.

10-11 Show that the power, P, transmitted by a line in which reflections occur, is given by the following expression:

$$P = \frac{|V_{max}|^2}{SZ_0} = \frac{S|V_{min}|^2}{Z_0} = \frac{|V_{max}| \times |V_{min}|}{Z_0} = \frac{|V^+|^2 - |V^-|^2}{Z_0}$$

where S is the standing wave ratio, and V^+ and V^- are the direct and reflected voltages.

10-12 Solve Prob. 10-4 by use of the Smith transmission line chart.

10-13 Solve Prob. 10-7 by use of the Smith chart.

10-14 Solve Prob. 10-10 by use of the Smith chart.

10-15 The line shown in the diagram below is assumed to have uniformly distributed shunt inductive loading. Prove that wave propagation without attenuation occurs when $\omega > 1/\sqrt{L_2 C}$. (Examine the propagation function, and determine when it becomes imaginary.)

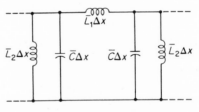

Problem 10-15

10-16 Prove that the product of the phase velocity and the group velocity in Prob. 10-15 is $1/\sqrt{L_1 C}$.

10-17 The line shown is assumed to have uniformly distributed series capacitive loading. Derive an expression for the propagation factor, and determine the frequency range for propagation without attenuation.

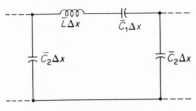

Problem 10-17

10-18 (a) Derive an expression for the phase velocity in Prob. 10-17.

(b) Derive an expression for the group velocity in Prob. 10-17.

10-19 The air dielectric lossless transmission lines shown in the sketch are to be cascaded to form a low-pass filter. The characteristic impedance of the first and third sections is equal to Z_0, and the characteristic impedance of the second section is equal to Z_0'.

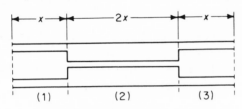

Problem 10-19

(a) Find the $ABCD$ coefficients for the three cascaded lines.

(b) Determine the propagation function of the cascaded lines in terms of the line parameters.

(c) If $x = 10$ cm, the velocity of propagation $c = 3 \times 10^{10}$ cm per sec, $Z_0 = 20$ ohms, and $Z_0' = 100$ ohms, find the cut-off frequency.

10-20 Find suitable values of the length and taper coefficient of an exponential line used to match approximately a 100-ohm load to a 400-ohm generator at a frequency of 10^9 cycles per second. Assume that air is the dielectric. Calculate the cut-off frequency.

10-21 The reflection coefficient of a non-uniform line may be defined as

$$\rho = \frac{[V(x)/I(x)] - Z_0(x)}{[V(x)/I(x)] + Z_0(x)}$$

where $V(x)$ and $I(x)$ are the voltage and current phasors at the point, and $Z_0(x)$ is the variable characteristic impedance. Prove that the differential equation for the reflection coefficient is

$$\frac{d\rho}{dx} + 2\rho\,\gamma(x) + \left(\frac{1 - \rho^2}{2}\right)\frac{d}{dx}\log Z_0(x) = 0$$

where $\gamma(x)$ is the propagation function.

Note: $Z_0(x) = \sqrt{\bar{Z}(x)/\bar{Y}(x)}$, and $\gamma(x) = \sqrt{\bar{Z}(x)[\bar{Y}(x)]}$, where $\bar{Z}(x)$ and $\bar{Y}(x)$ are the variable series impedance and shunt admittance per unit length.

10-22 Find two other lengths for the short-circuited stubs to provide double-stub impedance matching in the illustrative problem of Section 10-10.

10-23 A resistor is situated so near to a ground plane that at high frequencies it must be considered as a distributed RC circuit. Assuming $\bar{L} = \bar{G} = 0$, and a tapered construction such that $\bar{R} = \bar{R}_0\,\epsilon^{kx}$ and $\bar{C} = \bar{C}_0\,\epsilon^{-kx}$, prove that the voltage and current at points along the resistor are given by

(a) $V(x) = \epsilon^{kx/2}\,[A \sinh \gamma x + B \cosh \gamma x]$

(b) $I(x) = -\dfrac{\epsilon^{-kx/2}}{\bar{R}_0}\left[\left(\dfrac{Ak}{2} + B\gamma\right) \sinh \gamma x + \left(A\gamma + \dfrac{Bk}{2}\right) \cosh \gamma x\right]$

where x is measured to the right from one end of the resistor.

$$\gamma = \sqrt{\frac{k^2}{4} + j\omega\,\bar{R}_0\bar{C}_0}$$

and A and B are constants.

10-24 Find the equivalent T network of the resistor and ground plane in Prob. 10-23 considered as a two-terminal pair network. Assume that the length of the resistor is ℓ.

eleven

transients in networks

and lines

11.0 INTRODUCTION

Only the steady-state sinusoidal response of networks and lines has been studied in the previous chapters. The transient response, consisting of the response of networks and lines during the time when the steady-state response is being established and also the response to non-periodic forcing functions, is to be considered briefly in this chapter. The purpose is to present basic methods of analysis rather than to attempt the detailed solutions of particular problems. Transform analysis is to be used. This consists of first determining the frequency-domain response, and then transforming it into the time-domain response. Both the Fourier and Laplace transforms will be used.*

11.1 FOURIER AND LAPLACE TRANSFORMS

The Fourier transforms are the following:

$$F(\omega) = \int_{-\infty}^{\infty} f(t)\epsilon^{-j\omega t}\,dt \qquad [11.1\text{-}1]$$

$$f(t) = \frac{1}{2\pi}\int_{-\infty}^{\infty} F(\omega)\epsilon^{j\omega t}\,d\omega \qquad [11.1\text{-}2]$$

where $F(\omega)$ is the frequency spectrum and $f(t)$ is its transform in the time

---

* A detailed analysis of Fourier and Laplace transforms is given in *Transform Calculus for Electrical Engineers*, by R. Legros and A. V. J. Martin; Prentice-Hall, Inc., Englewood Cliffs, New Jersey, 1961, and *The Fourier Integral and Its Applications* by A. Papoulis; McGraw-Hill Book Company, Inc., New York, 1962.

domain. Whereas the Fourier transforms are stated with respect to the real frequency, the Laplace transforms are calculated with respect to the complex frequency, s.

The Laplace transforms are the following:

$$F(s) = \int_0^\infty f(t)\epsilon^{-st}\, dt = \mathcal{L}[f(t)] \qquad [11.1\text{-}3]$$

$$f(t) = \frac{1}{2\pi j} \int_{\sigma_0-j\infty}^{\sigma_0+j\infty} F(s)\epsilon^{st}\, ds = \mathcal{L}^{-1}[F(s)] \qquad [11.1\text{-}4]$$

where $F(s)$ is the Laplace transform of $f(t)$ and is denoted by $\mathcal{L}[f(t)]$; where $\mathcal{L}^{-1}[F(s)]$ denotes the inverse transform of $F(s)$; and where σ_0 is defined as the abscissa of absolute convergence.

The Laplace transform of the unit step function defined as

$$U(t) = 0 \qquad [-\infty < t < 0]$$
$$U(t) = 1 \qquad [0 < t < \infty]$$

is given by

$$\mathcal{L}[U(t)] = \frac{1}{s} \qquad [11.1\text{-}5]$$

Unless otherwise specified, it will be understood that $U(t)$ is a multiplier of all time functions for which the Laplace transform is given.

The transform of a constant, K, is

$$\mathcal{L}[K] = \frac{K}{s} \qquad [11.1\text{-}6]$$

An important transform is the following:

$$\mathcal{L}[\epsilon^{s_1 t}] = \frac{1}{s - s_1} \qquad [11.1\text{-}7]$$

where s_1 may be real, imaginary, or complex.

The Laplace transforms of sine and cosine functions are

$$\mathcal{L}[\sin \omega t] = \frac{\omega}{s^2 + \omega^2} \qquad [11.1\text{-}8]$$

$$\mathcal{L}[\cos \omega t] = \frac{s}{s^2 + \omega^2} \qquad [11.1\text{-}9]$$

Equations 11.1-8 and 11.1-9 can be derived by letting $s_1 = j\omega$ in Eq. 11.1-7, rationalizing, and equating the real and imaginary components.

The Laplace transforms of damped sine and cosine functions are given by

$$\mathcal{L}[\epsilon^{-at} \sin \omega t] = \frac{\omega}{(s + a)^2 + \omega^2} \qquad [11.1\text{-}10]$$

$$\mathcal{L}[\epsilon^{-at} \cos \omega t] = \frac{s + a}{(s + a)^2 + \omega^2} \qquad [11.1\text{-}11]$$

Equations 11.1-10 and 11.1-11 conform to the general rule that if $F(s) = \mathcal{L}[f(t)]$, then

$$\mathcal{L}[\epsilon^{-at} f(t)] = F(s + a) \qquad [11.1\text{-}12]$$

Another useful relation is

$$\mathcal{L}^{-1}[\epsilon^{-st_0} F(s)] = f(t - t_0)[U(t - t_0)] \qquad [11.1\text{-}13]$$

where $f(t) = \mathcal{L}^{-1}F(s)$, and $U(t - t_0)$ denotes the fact that $f(t - t_0)$ is zero until $t = t_0$.

The transform of a derivative is given by

$$\mathcal{L}\left[\frac{dy}{dt}\right] = sY(s) - y(0) \qquad [11.1\text{-}14]$$

where $Y(s)$ is the transform of $y(t)$, and $y(0)$ is the initial value of $y(t)$. The transform of a definite integral having zero as its lower limit is

$$\mathcal{L}\left[\int_0^t y\, dt\right] = \frac{1}{s}[Y(s)] \qquad [11.1\text{-}15]$$

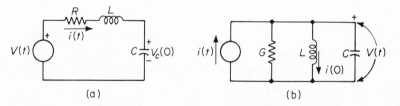

(a)   (b)

Figure 11-1 Series and parallel circuits.

Consider now the series R-L-C circuit shown in (a) of Fig. 11-1. The differential equation for the current in the time domain is

$$L\frac{di}{dt} + Ri + v_c(0) + \frac{1}{C}\int_0^t i\, dt = v(t) \qquad [11.1\text{-}16]$$

where $v_c(0)$ is the initial capacitor voltage having the indicated polarity.

It follows from Eqs. 11.1-6, 11.1-14, and 11.1-15 that transformation of Eq. 11.1-16 into the complex frequency domain yields

$$\left(R + Ls + \frac{1}{Cs}\right) I(s) + \frac{v_c(0)}{s} - Li(0) = V(s) \qquad [11.1\text{-}17]$$

where $V(s)$ is the transform of the arbitrary applied voltage $v(t)$; $I(s)$ is the transform of the current $i(t)$; and $i(0)$ is the initial current.

Equation 11.1-17 can also be written as

$$Z(s) I(s) = V(s) - \frac{v_c(0)}{s} + Li(0) \qquad [11.1\text{-}18]$$

where $Z(s) = R + Ls + 1/Cs$ and is the generalized impedance at the complex frequency.

The differential equation for the voltage in Fig. 11-1(b) is

$$Gv + C\frac{dv}{dt} + i(0) + \frac{1}{L}\int_0 v\, dt = i(t) \qquad [11.1\text{-}19]$$

The transformation of Eq. 11.1-19 yields

$$\left(G + Cs + \frac{1}{Ls}\right) V(s) + \frac{i(0)}{s} - Cv_c(0) = I(s) \qquad [11.1\text{-}20]$$

Equation 11.1-20 can also be written as

$$Y(s)V(s) = I(s) - \frac{i(0)}{s} + Cv_c(0) \qquad [11.1\text{-}21]$$

where $Y(s) = G + Cs + 1/Ls$ and is the generalized admittance. The dual relationship between Eqs. 11.1-18 and 11.1-21 is evident.

The transient solution of lumped parameter networks often leads to transforms of the following form:

$$F(s) = \frac{P(s)}{Q(s)} = \frac{P(s)}{(s - s_1) \ldots (s - s_{k-1})(s - s_k)(s - s_{k+1}) \ldots (s - s_n)}$$

$$[11.1\text{-}22]$$

where $Q(s)$ consists of n non-repeated linear factors.

In such cases the inverse transform is given by

$$f(t) = \mathcal{L}^{-1}[F(s)] = \sum_{k=1}^{k=n} \left[\frac{(s - s_k)P(s)\epsilon^{st}}{Q(s)}\right]_{s=s_k} \qquad [11.1\text{-}23]$$

Inspection of Eq. 11.1-23 shows that, if s_k is in the right-hand half of the complex plane, then $f(t)$ increases without limit. Hence, the transforms of the response of networks containing only passive elements have no poles in the right-hand half of the complex plane.

Another useful form of $f(t)$ is

$$f(t) = \sum_{k=1}^{k=n} \left[\frac{P(s)\epsilon^{st}}{(s-s_1)\dots(s-s_{k-1})(s-s_{k+1})\dots(s-s_n)} \right]_{s=s_k} \qquad [11.1\text{-}24]$$

Another form is the following:

$$f(t) = \sum_{k=1}^{k=n} \left[\frac{P(s)\epsilon^{st}}{Q'(s)} \right]_{s=s_k} \qquad [11.1\text{-}25]$$

where $Q'(s) = \dfrac{d}{ds} Q(s)$. Equations 11.1-23, 11.1-24, and 11.1-25 are forms of Heaviside's expansion theorem.

The inverse transform $i(t)$ of $I(s)$ in Eq. 11.1-17 can be found by applying Eq. 11.1-24. When $v(t)$ is a constant, V_0, the solution of Eq. 11.1-17 for $I(s)$ yields

$$I(s) = \frac{V_0/s + Li(0) - v_C(0)/s}{R + Ls + \dfrac{1}{sC}} = \frac{V_0 - v_C(0) + Li(0)s}{L\left(s^2 + \dfrac{R}{L}s + \dfrac{1}{LC}\right)} \qquad [11.1\text{-}26]$$

Equation 11.1-26 can be written as

$$I(s) = \frac{V_0 - v_C(0) + Li(0)s}{L(s-s_1)(s-s_2)} = \frac{P(s)}{Q(s)} \qquad [11.1\text{-}27]$$

where $s_1 = -\dfrac{R}{2L} + \sqrt{\dfrac{R^2}{4L^2} - \dfrac{1}{LC}} = -m + n$

$s_2 = -\dfrac{R}{2L} - \sqrt{\dfrac{R^2}{4L^2} - \dfrac{1}{LC}} = -m - n$

It follows from Eqs. 11.1-24 and 11.1-27 that:

$$i(t) = \frac{V_0 - v_C(0) + Li(0)s_1}{L(s_1 - s_2)}\epsilon^{s_1 t} - \frac{V_0 - v_C(0) + Li(0)s_2}{L(s_1 - s_2)}\epsilon^{s_2 t} \qquad [11.1\text{-}28]$$

Equation 11.1-28 reduces to

$$i(t) = \frac{1}{L(s_1 - s_2)} \epsilon^{-mt}\{[V_0 - v_C(0)](\epsilon^{nt} - \epsilon^{-nt})$$

$$+ Li(0)s_1\epsilon^{nt} - Li(0)s_2\epsilon^{-nt}\} \qquad [11.1\text{-}29]$$

Substituting $\epsilon^{nt} - \epsilon^{-nt} = 2 \sinh nt$ and $\epsilon^{\pm nt} = \cosh nt \pm \sinh nt$, Eq. 11.1-29 becomes

$$i(t) = \frac{1}{L(s_1 - s_2)} \epsilon^{-mt}\{2[V_0 - v_C(0)] \sinh nt + Li(0)(s_1 - s_2) \cosh nt$$

$$+ Li(0)(s_1 + s_2) \sinh nt\} \qquad [11.1\text{-}30]$$

Substituting $s_1 - s_2 = 2n$, $s_1 + s_2 = -2m$, and combining terms in Eq. 11.1-30 gives the following result:

$$i(t) = \epsilon^{-mt}\left\{i(0) \cosh nt + \frac{1}{n}\left[\frac{V_0 - v_C(0)}{L} - mi(0)\right] \sinh nt\right\} \qquad [11.1\text{-}31]$$

Other applications of Eqs. 11.1-24 and 11.1-25 will be given in the following sections.

11.2 TRANSIENT RESPONSE OF IDEAL FILTER TO PULSE INPUT

An ideal filter is one that has zero attenuation and a phase shift directly proportional to the frequency within the passband, with infinite attenuation outside the passband. It follows that the ratio of output to input of an ideal low-pass filter is given by

$$G(\omega) = \epsilon^{-j\omega t_1} \qquad [0 < \omega_c < \omega] \qquad [11.2\text{-}1]$$

$$G(\omega) = 0 \qquad [\omega_c < \omega < \infty] \qquad [11.2\text{-}2]$$

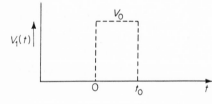

Figure 11-2 Rectangular pulse.

where ω_c is the cut-off frequency, and t_1 is the time delay. *A filter with the above characteristics is not realizable.*

Assume that the voltage pulse shown in Fig. 11-2 is applied to the input terminals of an ideal low-pass filter. The equation of this pulse is

$$v_1(t) = V_0 \qquad [0 < t < t_0] \qquad [11.2\text{-}3]$$

$$v_1(t) = 0 \qquad [\text{all other values of } t] \qquad [11.2\text{-}4]$$

It follows from Eq. 11.1-1 that the Fourier transform of the input to the filter is

$$V_1(\omega) = \int_0^{t_0} V_0 \epsilon^{-j\omega t} \, dt = -\frac{V_0}{j\omega} \left[\epsilon^{-j\omega t}\right]_0^{t_0}$$

$$V_1(\omega) = \frac{V_0}{j\omega} \left(1 - \epsilon^{-j\omega t_0}\right) \qquad [11.2\text{-}5]$$

It follows from Eqs. 11.2-1, 11.2-2, and 11.2-5 that the Fourier transform of the output is

$$V_2(\omega) = G(\omega)V_1(\omega) = \frac{V_0 \epsilon^{-j\omega t_1}}{j\omega} \left[1 - \epsilon^{-j\omega t_0}\right] \qquad [|\omega| < |\omega_c|] \qquad [11.2\text{-}6]$$

$$V_2(\omega) = 0 \qquad \text{[all other values of } \omega\text{]} \qquad [11.2\text{-}7]$$

The inverse transform of the output voltage in the time domain, $v_2(t)$, is found by applying Eq. 11.1-2 to Eqs. 11.2-6 and 11.2-7. The result is as follows:

$$v_2(t) = \frac{V_0}{2\pi} \int_{-\omega_c}^{\omega_c} \frac{\epsilon^{j\omega(t-t_1)}}{j\omega} \, d\omega - \frac{V_0}{2\pi} \int_{-\omega_c}^{\omega_c} \frac{\epsilon^{j\omega(t-t_1-t_0)}}{j\omega} \, d\omega \qquad [11.2\text{-}8]$$

The first integral in Eq. 11.2-8 can be written as

$$\frac{V_0}{2\pi} \int_{-\omega_c}^{\omega_c} \frac{\epsilon^{j\omega(t-t_1)}}{j\omega} \, d\omega = \frac{V_0}{2\pi} \int_{-\omega_c}^{\omega_c} \frac{\sin \omega(t - t_1)}{\omega} \, d\omega$$

$$- \frac{jV_0}{2\pi} \int_{-\omega_c}^{\omega_c} \frac{\cos \omega(t - t_1)}{\omega} \, d\omega \qquad [11.2\text{-}9]$$

Since $\sin x$ is an odd function of x, $\dfrac{\sin x}{x}$ is an even function of x; similarly, since $\cos x$ is an even function of x, $\dfrac{\cos x}{x}$ is an odd function of x. It follows that the first integrand on the right-hand side of Eq. 11.2-9 is an even function of ω; and, since the second integrand is an odd function of ω, the integral, taken over equal positive and negative limits, vanishes. Hence,

$$\frac{V_0}{2\pi} \int_{-\omega_c}^{\omega_c} \frac{\epsilon^{j\omega(t-t_1)}}{j\omega} \, d\omega = \frac{V_0}{2\pi} \int_{-\omega_c}^{\omega_c} \frac{\sin \omega(t - t_1)}{\omega} \, d\omega$$

$$= \frac{V_0}{\pi} \int_0^{\omega_c} \frac{\sin \omega(t - t_1)}{\omega} \, d\omega \qquad [11.2\text{-}10]$$

The last integral on the right-hand side of Eq. 11.2-10 results from the fact that the integrand is an even function of ω.

It can be shown in a similar manner that the second integral in Eq. 11.2-8 has the following form:

$$\frac{V_0}{2\pi} \int_{-\omega_c}^{\omega_c} \frac{\epsilon^{j\omega(t - t_1 - t_0)}}{j\omega}\, d\omega = \frac{V_0}{\pi} \int_0^{\omega_c} \frac{\sin \omega(t - t_1 - t_0)}{\omega}\, d\omega \qquad [11.2\text{-}11]$$

It follows from Eqs. 11.2-8, 11.2-10, and 11.2-11 that:

$$v_2(t) = \frac{V_0}{\pi} \int_0^{\omega_c} \frac{\sin \omega(t - t_1)}{\omega}\, d\omega - \frac{V_0}{\pi} \int_0^{\omega_c} \frac{\sin \omega(t - t_1 - t_0)}{\omega}\, d\omega \qquad [11.2\text{-}12]$$

In Eq. 11.2-12, let

$$\omega(t - t_1) = u \qquad [11.2\text{-}13]$$

Then

$$d\omega = \frac{du}{t - t_1} \qquad [11.2\text{-}14]$$

Also in Eq. 11.2-12, let

$$\omega(t_1 + t_0 - t) = v \qquad [11.2\text{-}15]$$

Then

$$d\omega = \frac{dv}{t_1 + t_0 - t} \qquad [11.2\text{-}16]$$

The substitution of Eqs. 11.2-13 through 11.2-16 into Eq. 11.2-12 gives the following result:

$$v_2(t) = \frac{V_0}{\pi} \int_0^{x_1} \frac{\sin u}{u}\, du + \frac{V_0}{\pi} \int_0^{x_2} \frac{\sin v}{v}\, dv \qquad [11.2\text{-}17]$$

where

$$x_1 = \omega_c(t - t_1) \qquad [11.2\text{-}18]$$

$$x_2 = \omega_c(t_1 + t_0 - t) \qquad [11.2\text{-}19]$$

The integrals in Eq. 11.2-17 are known as the Sine Integrals and are denoted by $Si(x_1)$ and $Si(x_2)$; they have been tabulated.* Equation 11.2-19 can be written as

---

* Tables of Sine Integrals are given in *Tables of Sine, Cosine, and Exponential Integrals* (National Bureau of Standards, Washington, D. C., 1940) and also in *Antennas*, by J. D. Kraus (McGraw-Hill Book Company, Inc., New York, 1956), pp. 537 ff.

$$v_2(t) = \frac{V_0}{\pi} [Si(x_1) + Si(x_2)] \qquad\qquad [11.2\text{-}20]$$

Figure 11-3 shows the output voltage, $v_2(t)$. The indicated response when $t < 0$ is attributable to the fact that the filter is not physically realizable.

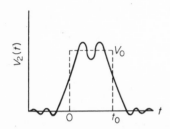

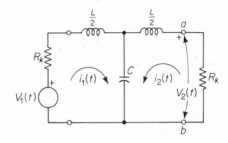

Figure 11-3 Response of ideal filter to pulse input.

Figure 11-4 T section of low-pass filter.

11.3 TRANSIENT RESPONSE OF T SECTION TO STEP INPUT

A single T section is shown in Fig. 11-4. This is also one section of the simplest type of low-pass filter, namely the constant-k prototype. It is assumed that the filter is terminated in its nominal characteristic impedance, $R_k = \sqrt{L/C}$, and also that the internal impedance of the generator at the input terminals is R_k. The output voltage is $v_2(t)$, appearing across the terminals ab.

Assuming that no initial currents or voltages exist in the network in Fig. 11-4, it follows directly from Eq. 11.1-17 that the transformed equations for the network are

$$\left(R_k + \frac{Ls}{2} + \frac{1}{Cs}\right) I_1(s) + \left(\frac{1}{Cs}\right) I_2(s) = V_1(s) \qquad [11.3\text{-}1]$$

$$\left(\frac{1}{Cs}\right) I_1(s) + \left(R_k + \frac{Ls}{2} + \frac{1}{Cs}\right) I_2(s) = 0 \qquad [11.3\text{-}2]$$

where $I_1(s)$ and $I_2(s)$ are respectively the Laplace transforms of $i_1(t)$ and $i_2(t)$; and where $V_1(s)$ is the Laplace transform of the input voltage, $v_1(t)$, which may have an arbitrary waveform.

Solving Eqs. 11.3-1 and 11.3-2 for $I_2(s)$ yields

$$I_2(s) = \cfrac{\begin{vmatrix} R_k + \dfrac{Ls}{2} + \dfrac{1}{Cs} & V_1(s) \\[2mm] \dfrac{1}{Cs} & 0 \end{vmatrix}}{\begin{vmatrix} R_k + \dfrac{Ls}{2} + \dfrac{1}{Cs} & \dfrac{1}{Cs} \\[2mm] \dfrac{1}{Cs} & R_k + \dfrac{Ls}{2} + \dfrac{1}{Cs} \end{vmatrix}} \qquad [11.3\text{-}3]$$

where $R_k = \sqrt{L/C}$.

The transform of the output voltage is given by

$$V_2(s) = -R_k I_2(s) \qquad [11.3\text{-}4]$$

where $V_2(s)$ is the transform of $v_2(t)$.

It follows from Eqs. 11.3-3 and 11.3-4 that:

$$V_2(s) = \frac{R_k V_1(s)}{Cs(L^2 s^2/4 + R_k Ls + L/C + R_k^2 + 2R_k/Cs)} \qquad [11.3\text{-}5]$$

Substituting $R_k = \sqrt{L/C}$ in Eq. 11.3-5, and converting the coefficient of the leading term in the denominator to unity yields

$$V_2(s) = \frac{4\sqrt{L/C}\ V_1(s)}{L^2 C \left(s^3 + \dfrac{4s^2}{\sqrt{LC}} + \dfrac{8s}{LC} + \dfrac{8}{LC\sqrt{LC}} \right)} \qquad [11.3\text{-}6]$$

Equation 11.3-6 can also be written as

$$V_2(s) = \frac{4u^3 V_1(s)}{s^3 + 4us^2 + 8u^2 s + 8u^3} \qquad [11.3\text{-}7]$$

where $u = 1/\sqrt{LC}$.

It is seen by inspection that $s = -2u$ is a zero of the denominator.* Hence $s + 2u$ is a factor, and the denominator can be expressed in factored form as follows:

$$s^3 + 4us^2 + 8u^2 s + 8u^3 = (s + 2u)(s^2 + 2us + 4u^2)$$

$$= (s + 2u)(s + u + j\sqrt{3}u)(s + u - j\sqrt{3}u)$$

$$[11.3\text{-}8]$$

*Rational zeroes must be factors of $8u^3$.

Substituting Eq. 11.3-8 into Eq. 11.3-7 yields

$$V_2(s) = \frac{4u^3 V_1(s)}{(s + 2u)(s + u + j\sqrt{3}u)(s + u - j\sqrt{3}u)} \qquad [11.3\text{-}9]$$

Equation 11.3-9 is a general expression for the transform of the output of the voltage in Fig. 11-4. When a unit step function is applied to the input, $V_1(s) = 1/s$, and it follows from Eqs. 11.3-8 and 11.3-9 that the transform of the output is given by

$$V_2(s) = \frac{4u^3}{s(s + 2u)(s^2 + 2us + 4u^2)}$$

$$= \frac{4u^3}{s(s + 2u)(s + u + j\sqrt{3}u)(s + u - j\sqrt{3}u)} \qquad [11.3\text{-}10]$$

The inverse transform, $v_2(t)$, is found by applying Eq. 11.1-24 to Eq. 11.3-10, giving the following results:

$$v_2(t) = \left[\frac{4u^3}{(s + 2u)(s^2 + 2us + 4u^2)}\right]_{s=0} + \left[\frac{4u^3 \epsilon^{st}}{s(s^2 + 2us + 4u^2)}\right]_{s=-2u}$$

$$+ \ldots + \left[\frac{4u^3 \epsilon^{st}}{s(s + 2u)(s + u + j\sqrt{3}u)}\right]_{s=-u+j\sqrt{3}u}$$

$$+ \left[\frac{4u^3 \epsilon^{st}}{s(s + 2u)(s + u - j\sqrt{3}u)}\right]_{s=-u-j\sqrt{3}u}$$

$$[11.3\text{-}11]$$

Performing the operations indicated in Eq. 11.3-11 yields

$$v_2(t) = 0.50 - 0.50\epsilon^{-2ut} - \frac{\epsilon^{(-u+j\sqrt{3}u)t}}{j2\sqrt{3}} + \frac{\epsilon^{(-u-j\sqrt{3}u)t}}{j2\sqrt{3}} \qquad [11.3\text{-}12]$$

$$v_2(t) = 0.50 - 0.50\epsilon^{-2ut} - 0.58\epsilon^{-t} \sin \sqrt{3}ut \qquad [11.3\text{-}13]$$

Equation 11.3-13 shows that when a unit step voltage is applied to the lumped-parameter T section in Fig. 11-4, the output voltage is a function of ut where $u = 1/\sqrt{LC}$. The output voltage for a unit step input voltage is plotted in Fig. 11-5 as a function of ut.

As the impedance of the generator is reduced, the output voltage not only exhibits an overshoot as shown in Fig. 11-5, but also shows oscillations about its steady-state value of 0.5 volt. The difference between the time required for the output voltage to attain nine-tenths of its steady-

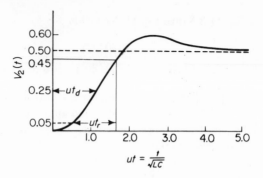

Figure 11-5   Response of low-pass filter to unit step input.

state value and the time required to attain one-tenth of its steady-state value is termed the *rise time*, and is denoted by the symbol, t_r. Figure 11-5 shows that the rise time for a single T section is given by

$$ut_r = 1.13 \qquad [11.3\text{-}14]$$

Since $u = 1/\sqrt{LC}$, it follows that

$$t_r = 1.13 \sqrt{LC} \qquad [11.3\text{-}15]$$

The time required for the output to attain one-half of its final value is termed the *delay time*, and is denoted by the symbol, t_d. Figure 11-5 shows that the delay time for a single T section is given by

$$ut_d = 1.07 \qquad [11.3\text{-}16]$$

Hence,

$$t_d = 1.07 \sqrt{LC} \qquad [11.3\text{-}17]$$

The rise and delay times are important parameters in the design of delay lines. An introduction to delay lines is given in Sec. 11.9.

11.4 TRANSFORMATION OF TRANSMISSION LINE EQUATIONS

An incremental length of parallel-wire transmission line is shown in Fig. 11-6. The mesh-current equation for mesh *abcd* is

$$\overline{R} \,\Delta x\, i + \overline{L}\, \Delta x\, \frac{\partial i}{\partial t} + v + \Delta v - v = 0 \qquad [11.4\text{-}1]$$

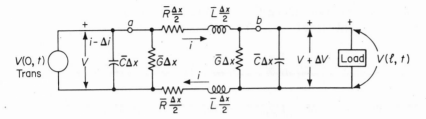

Figure 11-6   Incremental length of transmission line.

As Δx approaches zero, Eq. 11.4-1 becomes

$$\bar{R}i + \bar{L}\frac{\partial i}{\partial t} = -\frac{\partial v}{\partial x} \qquad [11.4\text{-}2]$$

The node voltage equation at node a is

$$\bar{G}\,\Delta x\, v + \bar{C}\,\Delta x\,\frac{\partial v}{\partial t} + i = i - \Delta i \qquad [11.4\text{-}3]$$

As Δx approaches zero, Eq. 11.4-3 becomes

$$\bar{G}v + \bar{C}\frac{\partial v}{\partial t} = -\frac{\partial i}{\partial x} \qquad [11.4\text{-}4]$$

Equations 11.4-2 and 11.4-4 are the partial differential equations for the voltage and the current. The difference in signs between the right-hand sides of Eqs. 11.4-2 and 11.4-4 and Eqs. 9.2-3 and 9.2-7 results from the change in origin from the receiving to the transmitting end of the line. The purpose of this change is to focus attention upon the nature of the transmitter voltage.

The transformation of Eqs. 11.4-2 and 11.4-4 is accomplished by multiplying both sides by ϵ^{-st}, and integrating from zero to infinity. This gives the following results:

$$(\bar{R} + \bar{L}s)I(x,s) - \bar{L}i(x,0) = -\frac{\partial}{\partial x}V(x,s) \qquad [11.4\text{-}5]$$

$$(\bar{G} + \bar{C}s)V(x,s) - \bar{C}v(x,0) = -\frac{\partial}{\partial x}I(x,s) \qquad [11.4\text{-}6]$$

Note that the transforms of the voltage and the current are functions of the distance, x, as well as of the complex frequency, s. It should also be noted that $i(x,0)$ and $v(x,0)$ respectively represent the initial current and voltage distributions along the line, and are functions of x, but not of t. Differentiation of Eq. 11.4-5 with respect to x yields

$$(\overline{R} + \overline{L}s) \frac{\partial}{\partial x} I(x,s) - \frac{\partial}{\partial x} \overline{L}i(x,0) = - \frac{\partial^2}{\partial x^2} V(x,s) \qquad [11.4\text{-}7]$$

The substitution of $\dfrac{\partial}{\partial x} I(x,s)$ from Eq. 11.4-6 into Eq. 11.4-7 gives the following result:

$$(\overline{R} + \overline{L}s)(\overline{G} + \overline{C}s)V(x,s) - (\overline{R} + \overline{L}s)\overline{C}v(x,0) + \frac{\partial}{\partial x} \overline{L}i(x,0) = \frac{\partial^2}{\partial x^2} V(x,s)$$

$$[11.4\text{-}8]$$

The differentiation of Eq. 11.4-6 with respect to x yields

$$(\overline{G} + \overline{C}s) \frac{\partial}{\partial x} V(x,s) - \frac{\partial}{\partial x} \overline{C}v(x,0) = - \frac{\partial^2}{\partial x^2} I(x,s) \qquad [11.4\text{-}9]$$

The substitution of $\dfrac{\partial}{\partial x} V(x,s)$ from Eq. 11.4-5 into Eq. 11.4-9 gives the following result:

$$(\overline{R} + \overline{L}s)(\overline{G} + \overline{C}s)I(x,s) - (\overline{G} + \overline{C}s)\overline{L}i(x,0) + \frac{\partial}{\partial x} \overline{C}v(x,0) = \frac{\partial^2}{\partial x^2} I(x,s)$$

$$[11.4\text{-}10]$$

Equation 11.4-8 can also be written as

$$(D^2 - \gamma^2)V(x_1s) = \frac{\partial}{\partial x} \overline{L}i(x,0) - (\overline{R} + \overline{L}s)\overline{C}v(x,0) \qquad [11.4\text{-}11]$$

where D^2 represents $\dfrac{\partial^2}{\partial x^2}$ and $\gamma = \sqrt{(\overline{R} + \overline{L}s)(\overline{G} + \overline{C}s)}$. Note that γ is a generalized propagation function for complex frequencies, and is reduced to the steady-state propagation function when $s = j\omega$.

Equation 11.4-10 can also be written as

$$(D^2 - \gamma^2)I(x,s) = \frac{\partial}{\partial x} \overline{C}v(x,0) - (\overline{G} + \overline{C}s)\overline{L}i(x,0) \qquad [11.4\text{-}12]$$

The solution of a particular problem involves solving Eqs. 11.4-11 and 11.4-12 for $V(x,s)$ and $I(x,s)$ subject to the terminal conditions, and then finding their inverse transforms, $v(x,t)$ and $i(x,t)$. The impedance of the transmitter at $x = 0$ must be known, as well as the nature of the load at

$x = \ell$. The form of the input voltage, $v(0,t)$, and its transform, $V(0,s)$, must also be known. As in the case of all linear differential equations, the solution consists of a *complementary function* and a *particular integral*.

The complementary function for the voltage transform is a solution of the differential equation

$$(D^2 - \gamma^2)V(x_1s) = 0 \qquad [11.4\text{-}13]$$

The solution of Eq. 11.4-13 is

$$V_1(x,s) = K_1\epsilon^{\gamma x} + K_2\epsilon^{-\gamma x} \qquad [11.4\text{-}14]$$

where $V_1(x,s)$ denotes the complementary function, and where K_1 and K_2 are independent of x, but may be functions of s.

The complementary function for the current transform is

$$I_1(x,s) = K_3\epsilon^{\gamma x} + K_4\epsilon^{-\gamma x} \qquad [11.4\text{-}15]$$

where $I_1(x,s)$ denotes the complementary function, and where K_3 and K_4 are independent of x, but may be functions of s.

The particular integral for the voltage transform is a solution of the differential equation

$$(D^2 - \gamma^2)V(x,s) = \frac{\partial}{\partial x}\overline{L}i(x,0) - (\overline{R} + \overline{L}s)\overline{C}v(x,0) \qquad [11.4\text{-}16]$$

The particular integral depends upon the initial voltage and current distributions, and will be denoted by $V_2(x,s)$.* The complete solution for the voltage transform is

$$V(x,s) = V_1(x,s) + V_2(x,s) \qquad [11.4\text{-}17]$$

where $V_1(x,s)$ is given by Eqs. 11.4-14 and $V_2(x,s)$ is the particular integral.

Similarly, the complete solution for the current transform is

$$I(x,s) = I_1(x,s) + I_2(x,s) \qquad [11.4\text{-}18]$$

where $I_2(x,s)$ is the particular integral that depends upon the initial voltage and current distributions, and $I_1(x,s)$ is given by Eq. 11.4-15.

The instantaneous voltage and current at any point along the line are the inverse transforms, and are given by

---

* Useful rules for determining both the particular integral and the complementary function are given in *Transient Analysis in Electrical Engineering*, by S. Fich (Prentice-Hall, Inc., Englewood Cliffs, N.J., 1951), Chap. 2.

$$v(x,t) = \mathcal{L}^{-1}[V(x,s)] \qquad [11.4\text{-}19]$$

$$i(x,t) = \mathcal{L}^{-1}[I(x,s)] \qquad [11.4\text{-}20]$$

11.5 THE INITIALLY QUIESCENT LINE

In an initially quiescent line there are no initial voltage or current distributions. Hence,

$$v(x,0) = i(x,0) = 0 \qquad [11.5\text{-}1]$$

in an initially quiescent line. Since the particular integral in the expression for $V(x,s)$ exists only when there are initial distributions, the complete solution for the quiescent line consists only of the complementary function, and is given by

$$V(x,s) = K_1 \epsilon^{-\gamma x} + K_2 \epsilon^{\gamma x} \qquad [11.5\text{-}2]$$

where

$$\gamma = \sqrt{(\overline{R} + \overline{L}s)(\overline{G} + \overline{C}s)} \qquad [11.5\text{-}3]$$

The first term in the right-hand side of Eq. 11.5-2 represents the direct wave, and the second term is the reflected wave. A comparison of Eqs. 9.3-1 and 11.5-2 shows that the signs of the exponents in the direct and reflected waves are interchanged. This is caused by shifting the origin from the receiving to the transmitting end.

It follows from Eq. 11.4-5 that, in an initially quiescent line,

$$(\overline{R} + \overline{L}s)I(x,s) = -\frac{\partial}{\partial x}V(x,s) \qquad [11.5\text{-}4]$$

The substitution of Eq. 11.5-2 into Eq. 11.5-4 yields the following expressions:

$$I(x,s) = \frac{\gamma}{\overline{R} + \overline{L}s}\left[K_1\epsilon^{-\gamma x} - K_2\epsilon^{\gamma x}\right] \qquad [11.5\text{-}5]$$

$$I(x,s) = \sqrt{\frac{\overline{G} + \overline{C}s}{\overline{R} + \overline{L}s}}\left[K_1\epsilon^{-\gamma x} - K_2\epsilon^{\gamma x}\right] \qquad [11.5\text{-}6]$$

$$I(x,s) = \frac{1}{Z_0(s)}\left[K_1\epsilon^{-\gamma x} - K_2\epsilon^{\gamma x}\right] \qquad [11.5\text{-}7]$$

where

$$Z_0(s) = \sqrt{\frac{\overline{R} + \overline{L}s}{\overline{G} + \overline{C}s}} \qquad [11.5\text{-}8]$$

denotes the characteristic impedance, and is the ratio of the voltage transform to the current transform in each wave. The steady-state equations for the voltage and current distributions are obtained by substituting $s = j\omega$, and replacing the current and voltage transforms by their respective phasors.

The solution of an initially quiescent line requires the evaluation of the constants K_1 and K_2. Assume that the line has a finite length, ℓ; that it is terminated in an impedance, $Z_r(s)$; that the transform of the generator voltage is $V_g(s)$; and that the generator has an impedance, $Z_g(s)$. It follows from Eq. 11.5-2 that:

$$V(0,s) = K_1 + K_2 \qquad [11.5\text{-}9]$$

where $V(0,s)$ is the transform of the input voltage at $x = 0$.

Since the transform of the input voltage to the line equals the transform of the generator voltage minus the internal voltage drop,

$$V(0,s) = V_g(s) - Z_g(s)I(0,s) \qquad [11.5\text{-}10]$$

where $I(0,s)$ is the transform of the input current at $x = 0$.

It follows from Eq. 11.5-7 that:

$$I(0,s) = \frac{1}{Z_0(s)}[K_1 - K_2] \qquad [11.5\text{-}11]$$

The relation between Eqs. 11.5-10 and 11.5-11 and the corresponding steady-state equations when s is replaced by $j\omega$ is again stressed.

It follows from Eqs. 11.5-9, 11.5-10, and 11.5-11 that:

$$K_1 + K_2 = V_g(s) - \left[\frac{Z_g(s)}{Z_0(s)}\right][K_1 - K_2] \qquad [11.5\text{-}12]$$

At the receiver, where $x = \ell$, the following relations hold:

$$\frac{V(\ell,s)}{I(\ell,s)} = Z_r(s) \qquad [11.5\text{-}13]$$

$$\frac{Z_0[K_1\epsilon^{-\gamma\ell} + K_2\epsilon^{\gamma\ell}]}{K_1\epsilon^{-\gamma\ell} - K_2\epsilon^{\gamma\ell}} = Z_r(s) \qquad [11.5\text{-}14]$$

The constants K_1 and K_2 can be found by solving Eqs. 11.5-12 and 11.5-14. When K_1 and K_2 have been found, $V(x,s)$ and $I(x,s)$ are determined. The calculation of the inverse transforms, $v(x,t)$ and $i(x,t)$, is in general not a simple matter. These transforms will be evaluated for some special cases in the following section.

11.6 EXAMPLES

The propagation characteristics of a transmission line are clearly brought out by a study of the initially quiescent line having a length that approaches infinity.

The general expression for the transform of the voltage is

$$V(x,s) = K_1 \epsilon^{-\gamma x} + K_2 \epsilon^{\gamma x} \qquad [11.6\text{-}1]$$

If x is allowed to approach infinity, K_2 must be zero if the voltage is to remain finite. Therefore, in the case of an infinite line, the transform of the voltage is given by

$$V(x,s) = K_1 \epsilon^{-\gamma x} \qquad [11.6\text{-}2]$$

where

$$K_1 = V(0,s) \qquad [11.6\text{-}3]$$

The current and voltage distributions are given by

$$V(x,s) = V(0,s)\epsilon^{-\gamma x} \qquad [11.6\text{-}4]$$

$$I(x,s) = \left(\frac{V(0,s)}{Z_0(s)}\right) \epsilon^{-\gamma x} \qquad [11.6\text{-}5]$$

Equations 11.6-4 and 11.6-5 hold for lines where the reflected wave does not exist or where it is negligible, as in the case of lines with high loss.

In Eqs. 11.6-4 and 11.6-5

$$\gamma = \sqrt{(\overline{R} + \overline{L}s)(\overline{G} + \overline{C}s)} \qquad [11.6\text{-}6]$$

$$Z_0(s) = \sqrt{\frac{\overline{R} + \overline{L}s}{\overline{G} + \overline{C}s}} \qquad [11.6\text{-}7]$$

Assume now that, in addition to being of infinite length, the line is also lossless. In other words $\overline{R} = \overline{G} = 0$. Under these conditions,

$$\gamma = s\sqrt{\overline{L}\,\overline{C}} \qquad [\overline{R} = \overline{G} = 0] \qquad [11.6\text{-}8]$$

$$Z_0 = \sqrt{\frac{\overline{L}}{\overline{C}}} \qquad [\overline{R} = \overline{G} = 0] \qquad [11.6\text{-}9]$$

It follows from Eqs. 11.6-4 and 11.6-5 that the transforms of the voltage and current along an infinite lossless line are given by

$$V(x,s) = V(0,s)\epsilon^{-s\sqrt{LC}\,x} \qquad [11.6\text{-}10]$$

$$I(x,s) = \left[\frac{V(0,s)}{Z_0}\right]\epsilon^{-s\sqrt{LC}\,x} \qquad [11.6\text{-}11]$$

$$I(x,s) = I(0,s)\epsilon^{-s\sqrt{LC}\,x} \qquad [11.6\text{-}12]$$

where $V(0,s)$ is the transform of the input voltage, and where $I(0,s)$ is the transform of the input current.

It is seen from Eqs. 11.6-10 and 11.6-12 that the transforms of the voltage and current at any point are equal to the corresponding input transforms multiplied by $\epsilon^{-s\sqrt{LC}\,x}$. Reference to Eq. 11.1-13 shows that the inverse transforms are

$$v(x,t) = v(0,t - x/u)\, U(t - x/u) \qquad [11.6\text{-}13]$$

$$i(x,t) = i(0,t - x/u)\, U(t - x/u) \qquad [11.6\text{-}14]$$

where $u = 1/\sqrt{L\,C}$

Equations 11.6-13 and 11.6-14 show that the waveforms of the voltage and current at any point are exactly the same as their input waveforms, but are delayed by x/u, which corresponds to the time required for propagation over a distance x at a velocity u. This is entirely consistent with the theory developed in Sec. 8.6.

Assume now that losses exist, but that the line parameters are related as follows:

$$\frac{R}{L} = \frac{G}{C} \qquad [11.6\text{-}15]$$

This is the condition given in Eq. 9.9-11 for a distortionless line.

When Eq. 11.6-15 holds,

$$\gamma = \gamma_d = \left(1 + \frac{R}{Ls}\right)s\sqrt{L\,C} = \left(s + \frac{R}{L}\right)\sqrt{L\,C} \qquad [11.6\text{-}16]$$

where γ_d denotes the propagation function of the distortionless line.

The substitution of Eq. 11.6-16 into Eq. 11.6-4 gives the following expression for the voltage transform at any point on an infinite distortionless line:

$$V(x,s) = V(0,s)\epsilon^{-s\sqrt{LC}\,x}\,\epsilon^{-R\sqrt{C/L}\,x} \qquad [11.6\text{-}17]$$

The inverse transform of Eq. 11.6-17 is

$$v(x,t) = \epsilon^{-R\sqrt{C/L}\,x}\,[v(0,t - x/u)\,U(t - x/u)] \qquad [11.6\text{-}18]$$

Equation 11.6-18 shows that the voltage at any point, x, is both retarded and attenuated, but that the wave form suffers no distortion. This holds for any type of excitation.

It follows from Eq. 11.6-7 that in a distortionless line

$$Z_0 = \sqrt{\frac{L}{C}} \qquad [11.6\text{-}19]$$

This result also is independent of the excitation.

It follows from Eq. 11.6-5 and 11.6-19 that the current along a distortionless line is given by

$$i(x,t) = \sqrt{\frac{C}{L}}\, \epsilon^{-R\sqrt{C/L}x} \left[v(0,t - x/u)\, U(t - x/u) \right] \qquad [11.6\text{-}20]$$

$$i(x,t) = \epsilon^{-R\sqrt{C/L}x} \left[i(0,t - x/u)\, U(t - x/u) \right] \qquad [11.6\text{-}21]$$

where $i(0,t)$ is the input current.

The results obtained in the previous two examples could have readily been found from steady-state analysis. Inasmuch as there is no attenuation on a lossless line, and all frequency components have the same phase velocity, the applied waveform, regardless of its shape, is transmitted without loss or distortion, and has a time delay directly proportional to the distance from the transmitter. The phase velocity and attenuation are also independent of frequency on distortionless lines. Hence, the waveform, regardless of its shape, is transmitted without distortion, but with attenuation and a time delay that is directly proportional to the distance from the transmitter.

As already noted, the previous examples serve only to illustrate transform methods, but these methods are not required to determine the solution. When the line is neither lossless nor distortionless, transform methods are essential for determining the response.

Consider, for example, an unloaded cable of finite length ℓ, short-circuited at its receiving end, and having a unit step voltage applied at the transmitting end, as shown in Fig. 11-7. It is assumed that there are

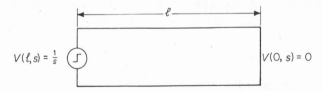

Figure 11-7 Short-circuited cable with unit step voltage applied.

no initial currents or voltages, and it is also assumed that $\overline{L} = \overline{G} = 0$. It is required to find an expression for the instantaneous voltage and current at any point along the cable.

In the work on this problem, it will be found convenient to express Eq. 11.6-1 in terms of hyperbolic functions as follows:

$$V(x,s) = K_3 \cosh \gamma x + K_4 \sinh \gamma x \qquad [11.6\text{-}22]$$

Equation 11.6-22 is also valid when the origin is at the receiver. Since $\overline{L} = \overline{G} = 0$,

$$\gamma = \sqrt{\overline{R}\,\overline{C}s} \qquad [11.6\text{-}23]$$

Inasmuch as the receiver terminals at $x = 0$ are short-circuited, $V(0,s) = 0$, and it follows from Eq. 11.6-22 that $K_3 = 0$. Hence,

$$V(x,s) = K_4 \sinh \gamma x \qquad [11.6\text{-}24]$$

Since the input is a unit step voltage, $V(\ell,s) = 1/s$, and substitution in Eq. 11.6-24 yields

$$\frac{1}{s} = K_4 \sinh \gamma\ell \qquad [11.6\text{-}25]$$

$$K_4 = \frac{1}{s \sinh \gamma\ell} \qquad [11.6\text{-}26]$$

It follows from Eqs. 11.6-24 and 11.6-26 that:

$$V(x,s) = \frac{\sinh \gamma x}{s \sinh \gamma\ell} = \frac{\sinh x\sqrt{\overline{R}\,\overline{C}s}}{s \sinh \ell\sqrt{\overline{R}\,\overline{C}s}} \qquad [11.6\text{-}27]$$

Expansion of the hyperbolic functions in Eq. 11.6-27 according to Eq. B-17 of Appendix B yields

$$V(x,s) = \frac{x[\overline{R}\,\overline{C}s]^{1/2} + \dfrac{x^3}{3!}[\overline{R}\,\overline{C}s]^{3/2} + \dfrac{x^5}{5!}[\overline{R}\,\overline{C}s]^{5/2} + \cdots}{s[\ell[\overline{R}\,\overline{C}s]^{1/2} + \dfrac{\ell^3}{3!}[\overline{R}\,\overline{C}s]^{3/2} + \dfrac{\ell^5}{5!}[\overline{R}\,\overline{C}s]^{5/2} + \cdots]} \qquad [11.6\text{-}28]$$

Division of the numerator and denominator of Eq. 11.6-28 by $[\overline{R}\,\overline{C}s]^{1/2}$ gives the following result:

$$V(x,s) = \frac{x + \dfrac{x^3}{3!}[\overline{R}\,\overline{C}s] + \dfrac{x^5}{5!}[\overline{R}\,\overline{C}s]^2 + \cdots}{s[\ell + \dfrac{\ell^3}{3!}[\overline{R}\,\overline{C}s] + \dfrac{\ell^5}{5!}[\overline{R}\,\overline{C}s]^2 + \cdots]} \qquad [11.6\text{-}29]$$

It follows directly from Eq. 11.6-29 that:

$$\underset{s \to 0}{\text{Lim}} \left[\frac{\sinh x \sqrt{\overline{R}\,\overline{C}s}}{s \sinh \ell\sqrt{\overline{R}\,\overline{C}s}} \right] = \underset{s \to 0}{\text{Lim}} \left[\frac{1}{s} \left(\frac{x}{\ell} \right) \right] \qquad [11.6\text{-}30]$$

Equation 11.6-30 shows that $V(x,s)$ has a pole at $s = 0$, and also that $\sinh \ell\sqrt{\overline{R}\,\overline{C}s}$ in the denominator does not contribute a pole at $s = 0$. The reason for this is that the numerator of $V(x,s)$ contains the factor $\sqrt{\overline{R}\,\overline{C}s}$.

The component of the inverse transform $v_1(x,t)$, resulting from the pole at $s = 0$, is found by applying Eq. 11.1-23 to Eq. 11.6-27, and is given by

$$v_1(x,t) = \left[\frac{\sinh x\sqrt{\overline{R}\,\overline{C}s}}{\sinh \ell\sqrt{\overline{R}\,\overline{C}s}} \right]_{s=0} \qquad [11.6\text{-}31]$$

It follows from Eqs. 11.6-28 and 11.6-31 that:

$$v_1(x,t) = \left[\frac{\sinh x\sqrt{\overline{R}\,\overline{C}s}}{\sinh \ell\sqrt{\overline{R}\,\overline{C}s}} \right]_{s=0} = \frac{x}{\ell} \qquad [11.6\text{-}32]$$

The second component, $v_2(x,t)$, of the inverse transform results from the infinite number of poles occurring when

$$\ell\sqrt{\overline{R}\,\overline{C}s_k} = jk\pi \qquad [11.6\text{-}33]$$

where k is any integer other than zero. This follows from the fact that $\sinh j\theta = j \sin \theta$, and $\sin k\pi$ vanishes for all integral values of k. The value of $k = 0$ is excluded because of the relation developed in Eq. 11.6-30, as previously noted.

The solution of Eq. 11.6-33 for s_k yields

$$s_k = - \frac{k^2\pi^2}{\overline{R}\,\overline{C}\ell^2} \qquad [11.6\text{-}34]$$

The application of Eq. 11.1-25 to Eq. 11.6-27, for the values of s_k given by Eq. 11.6-34, gives the following result:

$$v_2(x,t) = \sum_{k=1}^{k=\infty} \left[\frac{\sinh x(\sqrt{\overline{R}\,\overline{C}s_k})\epsilon^{s_k t}}{\frac{1}{2}s_k^{1/2} \ell\sqrt{\overline{R}\,\overline{C}} \cosh \ell\sqrt{\overline{R}\,\overline{C}s_k}} \right]_{s_k = -k^2\pi^2/R\overline{C}\ell^2} \qquad [11.6\text{-}35]$$

The summation in Eq. 11.6-35 includes only positive values of k, because s_k is independent of the sign of k, as shown by Eq. 11.6-34. It follows from Eq. 11.6-33 that:

$$\sqrt{R\,C}s_k = \frac{jk\pi}{\ell} \qquad [11.6\text{-}36]$$

The substitution of Eq. 11.6-36 into Eq. 11.6-35 yields

$$v_2(x,t) = 2\sum_{k=1}^{k=\infty} \left[\frac{\sinh j(k\pi x/\ell)\epsilon^{s_k t}}{s_k^{1/2}\,\ell\sqrt{R\,C}\,\cosh jk\pi}\right]_{s_k=-k^2\pi^2/R\bar{C}\ell^2} \qquad [11.6\text{-}37]$$

where

$$s_k^{1/2} = \frac{jk\pi}{\ell\sqrt{R\,C}} \qquad [11.6\text{-}38]$$

Since $\cosh jk\pi = \cos k\pi = (-1)^k$; and since $\sinh j(k\pi x/\ell) = j\sin k\pi x/\ell$, Eq. 11.6-37 can be written as

$$v_2(x,t) = 2\sum_{k=1}^{k=\infty} (-1)^k \left[\frac{\sin k\pi x/\ell}{k\pi}\right]\epsilon^{(-k^2\pi^2/R\bar{C}\ell^2)t} \qquad [11.6\text{-}39]$$

It follows from Eqs. 11.6-32 and 11.6-39 that the voltage distribution along the cable is given by

$$v(x,t) = v_1(x,t) + v_2(x,t) = \frac{x}{\ell} + 2\sum_{k=1}^{k=\infty} (-1)^k \left[\frac{\sin k\pi x/\ell}{k\pi}\right]\epsilon^{(-k^2\pi^2/R\bar{C}\ell^2)t}$$
$$[11.6\text{-}40]$$

Equation 11.6-40 shows that $v(0,t) = 0$, and $v(\ell,t) = 1$. Hence the terminal conditions are satisfied.

When $L = 0$, and the origin is at the receiver, the relation between the voltage and current for the reference voltages and currents in Fig. 11-6 is

$$i = \left(\frac{1}{R}\right)\frac{\partial v}{\partial x} \qquad [11.6\text{-}41]$$

The current distribution along the cable is found by applying Eq. 11.6-41 to Eq. 11.6-40. The result is

$$i(x,t) = \frac{1}{R}\left[\frac{1}{\ell}\left\{1 + 2\sum_{k=1}^{k=\infty} (-1)^k \cos\left(\frac{k\pi x}{\ell}\right)\epsilon^{(-k^2\pi^2/R\bar{C}\ell^2)t}\right\}\right] \qquad [11.6\text{-}42]$$

It follows from Eq. 11.6-42 that:

$$\operatorname*{Lim}_{t\to\infty} i(x,t) = \frac{1}{R\ell} = \frac{1}{R} \qquad [11.6\text{-}43]$$

where R is the total resistance of the line. Equation 11.6-43 shows that the steady-state current satisfies Ohm's law.

11.7 THE PULSE-FORMING LINE

The effect of initial conditions is brought out in the analysis of the pulse-forming line shown in Fig. 11-8. It is assumed that the line is of length ℓ and is lossless. Switch S_2 is initially open, and switch S_1 remains closed until the entire line is charged to the voltage V_0. When $t = 0$, switch S_1 is opened and switch S_2 is simultaneously closed. It will be shown that the resulting voltage across the terminating impedance, Z_0, is a rectangular pulse. The line derives its name from this phenomenon.

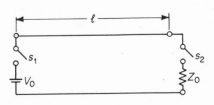

Figure 11-8 Pulse-forming line.

Since $\bar{R} = \bar{G} = 0$, and inasmuch as the initial current is zero and the initial voltage distribution is a constant V_0, it follows from Eq. 11.4-11 that

$$(D^2 - \gamma^2)\, V(x,s) = -(\bar{L}\,\bar{C}s)V_0 \qquad [11.7\text{-}1]$$

where

$$\gamma = s\sqrt{\bar{L}\,\bar{C}} \qquad [11.7\text{-}2]$$

The solution of Eq. 11.7-1 is

$$V(x,s) = K_1\epsilon^{-\gamma x} + K_2\epsilon^{\gamma x} + V_2(x,s) \qquad [11.7\text{-}3]$$

where $V_2(x,s)$ is the particular integral.

Since the right-hand side of Eq. 11.7-1 is independent of x, $V_2(x,s)$ is independent of x. Now assume that

$$V_2(x,s) = A(s) \qquad [11.7\text{-}4]$$

where A is independent of x, but may be a function of s.

The substitution of Eq. 11.7-4 into Eq. 11.7-1 yields

$$-s^2(\bar{L}\,\bar{C})A(s) = -(\bar{L}\,\bar{C}s)V_0 \qquad [11.7\text{-}5]$$

Hence,

$$A(s) = \frac{V_0}{s} = V_2(x,s) \qquad [11.7\text{-}6]$$

The substitution of Eq. 11.7-6 into Eq. 11.7-3 gives the following expression for the voltage transform:

$$V(x,s) = K_1 \epsilon^{-\gamma x} + K_2 \epsilon^{\gamma x} + \frac{V_0}{s} \qquad [11.7\text{-}7]$$

When $\overline{R} = i(x,0) = 0$, the transform of the current is found from Eq. 11.4-5 to be

$$I(x,s) = -\left(\frac{1}{Ls}\right)\frac{\partial}{\partial x} V(x,s) \qquad [11.7\text{-}8]$$

It follows from Eqs. 11.7-7 and 11.7-8 that:

$$I(x,s) = \left(\sqrt{\frac{\overline{C}}{L}}\right)[K_1 \epsilon^{-\gamma x} - K_2 \epsilon^{\gamma x}] \qquad [11.7\text{-}9]$$

Since switch S_1 is opened at $t = 0$, $I(0,s) = 0$ when $t > 0$. The substitution of $x = 0$ and $I(0,s) = 0$ in Eq. 11.7-9 yields

$$0 = K_1 - K_2 \qquad [11.7\text{-}10]$$
$$K_1 = K_2 = K \qquad [11.7\text{-}11]$$

Substituting Eq. 11.7-11 into Eqs. 11.7-7 and 11.7-9 gives the following expressions for the voltage and current transforms:

$$V(x,s) = \frac{V_0}{s} + K(\epsilon^{-\gamma x} + \epsilon^{\gamma x}) \qquad [11.7\text{-}12]$$

$$I(x,s) = K\left(\sqrt{\frac{\overline{C}}{L}}\right)(\epsilon^{-\gamma x} - \epsilon^{\gamma x}) \qquad [11.7\text{-}13]$$

When $x = \ell$,

$$V(\ell,s) = Z_0 \, I(\ell,s) = \sqrt{\frac{L}{C}} \, I(\ell,s) \qquad [11.7\text{-}14]$$

It follows from Eqs. 11.7-12, 11.7-13, and 11.7-14 that:

$$\frac{V_0}{s} + K(\epsilon^{-\gamma \ell} + \epsilon^{\gamma \ell}) = K(\epsilon^{-\gamma \ell} - \epsilon^{\gamma \ell}) \qquad [11.7\text{-}15]$$

The solution of Eq. 11.7-15 for K yields

$$K = -\left(\frac{V_0}{2s}\right)\epsilon^{-\gamma \ell} \qquad [11.7\text{-}16]$$

When Eq. 11.7-16 is substituted into Eq. 11.7-13, the following expression is obtained for the transform of the current:

$$I(x,s) = -\frac{V_0}{2s}\left(\sqrt{\frac{C}{L}}\right)\epsilon^{-\gamma\ell}[\epsilon^{-\gamma x} - \epsilon^{\gamma x}] \qquad [11.7\text{-}17]$$

Since, for a lossless line, $\gamma = s\sqrt{L\,C}$, Eq. 11.7-17 can be written as

$$I(x,s) = \frac{1}{2}\left(\sqrt{\frac{C}{L}}\right)V_0\left[\frac{\epsilon^{-s\sqrt{LC}(\ell-x)}}{s} - \frac{\epsilon^{-s\sqrt{LC}(\ell+x)}}{s}\right] \qquad [11.7\text{-}18]$$

The transform of the load current is found by substituting $x = \ell$ in Eq. 11.7-18, giving the following results:

$$I(\ell,s) = \frac{1}{2}\left(\sqrt{\frac{C}{L}}\right)V_0\left[\frac{1}{s} - \frac{\epsilon^{-2s\ell\sqrt{LC}}}{s}\right] \qquad [11.7\text{-}19]$$

$$I(\ell,s) = \frac{V_0}{2Z_0 s}[1 - \epsilon^{-2s\ell\sqrt{LC}}] \qquad [11.7\text{-}20]$$

The inverse transform of Eq. 11.7-20 is found from Eqs. 11.1-5 and 11.1-13 to be

$$i(\ell,t) = \frac{V_0}{2Z_0}[U(t) - U(t - 2\ell\sqrt{L\,C}] \qquad [11.7\text{-}21]$$

Inasmuch as the line is terminated in a pure resistance, Z_0, the instantaneous output voltage is

$$v(\ell,t) = Z_0 i(\ell,t) = \frac{V_0}{2}[U(t) - U(t - 2\ell\sqrt{L\,C}] \qquad [11.7\text{-}22]$$

Equation 11.7-22 represents a rectangular pulse of magnitude $V_0/2$, and width $2\ell\sqrt{L\,C}$. The pulse is shown in Fig. 11-9. It is seen that the pulse width depends upon the length of the line.

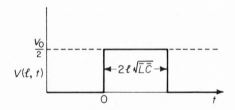

Figure 11-9 Voltage output of pulse forming line.

11.8 GENERAL THEORY OF FINITE LINES

Consider a line of finite length terminated by an arbitrary impedance, Z_r, and excited by a generator having an internal impedance, Z_g, as shown in Fig. 11-10. Assume that the line is initially quiescent. The voltage

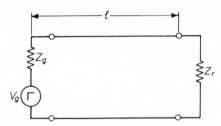

Figure 11-10 Line terminated by arbitrary impedance.

and current transforms at any point a distance x from the transmitter are given by

$$V(x,s) = K_1 \epsilon^{-\gamma x} + K_2 \epsilon^{\gamma x} \qquad [11.8\text{-}1]$$

$$I(x,s) = \frac{1}{Z_0} [K_1 \epsilon^{-\gamma x} - K_2 \epsilon^{\gamma x}] \qquad [11.8\text{-}2]$$

where $Z_0 = \sqrt{L/C}$. The constants K_1 and K_2 are determined by the general method outlined in Sec. 11.5. Thus,

$$V(0,s) = V_g(s) - Z_g I(0,s) \qquad [11.8\text{-}3]$$

where $V_g(s)$ is the transform of the generator voltage, and $V(0,s)$ and $I(0,s)$ are the transforms of the voltage and current at the input terminals of the line.

Also, when $x = \ell$,

$$\frac{V(\ell,s)}{I(\ell,s)} = Z_r \qquad [11.8\text{-}4]$$

The substitution of Eqs. 11.8-1 and 11.8-2 into Eqs. 11.8-3 and 11.8-4 gives the following results:

$$K_1 + K_2 = V_g(s) - \left[\frac{Z_g}{Z_0}\right][K_1 - K_2] \qquad [11.8\text{-}5]$$

$$\frac{Z_0[K_1 \epsilon^{-\gamma \ell} + K_2 \epsilon^{\gamma \ell}]}{[K_1 \epsilon^{-\gamma \ell} - K_2 \epsilon^{\gamma \ell}]} = Z_r \qquad [11.8\text{-}6]$$

The solution of Eq. 11.8-5 for K_2 yields

$$K_2 = \frac{V_g(s) - [1 + (Z_g/Z_0]K_1}{1 - Z_g/Z_0} \qquad [11.8\text{-}7]$$

It follows from Eq. 11.8-6 that:

$$K_1\epsilon^{-\gamma l} + K_2\epsilon^{\gamma l} = \frac{Z_r}{Z_0}[K_1\epsilon^{-\gamma l} - K_2\epsilon^{\gamma l}] \qquad [11.8\text{-}8]$$

$$K_1(Z_r/Z_0 - 1) = K_2(Z_r/Z_0 + 1)\epsilon^{2\gamma l} \qquad [11.8\text{-}9]$$

$$K_2 = K_1\left(\frac{(Z_r/Z_0 - 1)}{Z_r/Z_0 + 1}\right)\epsilon^{-2\gamma l} \qquad [11.8\text{-}10]$$

The substitution of Eq. 11.8-10 into Eq. 11.8-7 yields

$$\left[\frac{1 + Z_g/Z_0}{1 - Z_g/Z_0} + \left(\frac{Z_r/Z_0 - 1}{Z_r/Z_0 + 1}\right)\epsilon^{-2\gamma l}\right]K_1 = \frac{V_g(s)}{1 - Z_g/Z_0} \qquad [11.8\text{-}11]$$

Multiplying both sides of Eq. 11.8-11 by $\dfrac{1 - Z_g/Z_0}{1 + Z_g/Z_0}$ gives the following expression for K_1:

$$K_1 = \frac{\left(\dfrac{Z_0}{Z_0 + Z_g}\right)V_g(s)}{1 - \left(\dfrac{Z_g - Z_0}{Z_g + Z_0}\right)\left(\dfrac{Z_r - Z_0}{Z_r + Z_0}\right)\epsilon^{-2\gamma l}} \qquad [11.8\text{-}12]$$

It follows from Eqs. 11.8-10 and 11.8-12 that:

$$K_2 = \frac{\left(\dfrac{Z_r - Z_0}{Z_r + Z_0}\right)\left(\dfrac{Z_0}{Z_0 + Z_g}\right)\epsilon^{-2\gamma l}\,V_g(s)}{1 - \left(\dfrac{Z_g - Z_0}{Z_g + Z_0}\right)\left(\dfrac{Z_r - Z_0}{Z_r + Z_0}\right)\epsilon^{-2\gamma l}} \qquad [11.8\text{-}13]$$

Equations 11.8-12 and 11.8-13 can also be written as

$$K_1 = \frac{V'(s)}{1 - \rho_1\rho_2\epsilon^{-2\gamma l}} \qquad [11.8\text{-}14]$$

$$K_2 = \frac{\rho_1 V'(s)\epsilon^{-2\gamma l}}{1 - \rho_1\rho_2\epsilon^{-2\gamma l}} \qquad [11.8\text{-}15]$$

where ρ_1 and ρ_2 are respectively the voltage reflection coefficients at the receiver and generator, and where $V'(s) = [Z_0/(Z_0 + Z_g)]\,V_g(s)$.

The substitution of Eqs. 11.8-14 and 11.8-15 into Eq. 11.8-1 gives the following expression for the voltage transform:

$$V(x,s) = \left(\frac{V'(s)}{1-w}\right) \left[\epsilon^{-\gamma x} + \rho_1 \epsilon^{\gamma(x-2\ell)}\right] \qquad [11.8\text{-}16]$$

where

$$w = \rho_1 \rho_2 \epsilon^{-2\gamma\ell} \qquad [11.8\text{-}17]$$

An inspection of Eq. 11.8-17 shows that $|w| < 1$. The following expression will be utilized to illustrate the physical significance of Eq. 11.8-16:

$$\frac{1}{1-w} = 1 + w + w^2 + \ldots + w^{k-1} + \ldots \qquad [11.8\text{-}18]$$

The substitution of Eq. 11.8-18 into Eq. 11.8-16 gives the following result:

$$V(x,s) = V'(s)[(1 + \rho_1\rho_2\epsilon^{-2\gamma\ell} + \rho_1^2\rho_2^2\epsilon^{-4\gamma\ell} + \ldots)\epsilon^{-\gamma x}$$
$$+ (\rho_1\epsilon^{-2\gamma\ell} + \rho_1^2\rho_2^2\epsilon^{-4\gamma\ell} + \ldots)\epsilon^{\gamma x}] \qquad [11.8\text{-}19]$$

Equation 11.8-19 can be written as

$$V(x,s) = V'(s)[\epsilon^{-\gamma x} + \rho_1\epsilon^{-\gamma(2\ell-x)} + \rho_1\rho_2\epsilon^{-\gamma(2\ell+x)}$$
$$+ \rho_1^2\rho_2\epsilon^{-\gamma(4\ell-x)} + \rho_1^2\rho_2^2\epsilon^{-(\gamma 4\ell+x)} + \ldots] \qquad [11.8\text{-}20]$$

Fixing our attention at a point, x, on the line, it is seen that the first term in the bracket in Eq. 11.8-20 represents the transform of the direct wave; the second term represents the wave reflected from the load; the third term represents the wave reflected first from the load, and then from the generator; the fourth term represents the wave reflected first from the load, then from the generator, and then again at the load; etc.

It is seen that the voltage at any point is produced by an infinite number of components resulting from *multiple reflections* from the load and from the generator. An expression similar to Eq. 11.8-20 can be derived for the current. It may therefore be concluded that the voltage and current distributions are formed by multiple reflections from the load and generator terminals, and given by the terms in $\epsilon^{\gamma x}$ and $\epsilon^{-\gamma x}$.

11.9 INTRODUCTION TO DELAY LINES

A delay line or network is a device having the property that the output signal lags the input by a finite delay time. Delay lines find extensive application in coding and decoding devices, correlators, computers, etc. Delay lines may be of either the distributed-parameter or the lumped-parameter type. Problems involved in the design of delay lines are those concerned with obtaining the necessary delay with minimum distortion. Stability, volume, and cost are also important factors.

The velocity of propagation of electromagnetic waves along lossless lines is

$$u = \frac{3 \times 10^8}{\sqrt{\mu_r \epsilon_r}} \text{ meters per sec} \qquad [11.9\text{-}1]$$

where μ_r and ϵ_r are the relative permeability and dielectric constant. It follows that when air is the dielectric, the delay per meter is given by

$$t_d = \frac{1}{3 \times 10^8} = 0.0033 \times 10^{-6} \text{ sec} \qquad [11.9\text{-}2]$$

Thus a length of 300 meters is required for a 1-microsecond delay in air. It is possible to obtain delays of up to about 3 microseconds per meter by employing dielectrics other than air and by using helical constructions. If the loss is low, there is negligible distortion of the waveform.

Another method of obtaining a delay is by the use of a lumped-parameter network consisting of several sections, each similar to the T section shown in Fig. 11-4.* The output of this network is shown in Fig. 11-5, where both the rise time and the delay time are given.

The design parameters of a delay line are the nominal characteristic impedance, R_k, the total delay, T_d, and the effective rise time, T_r. When n similar lumped-parameter sections are connected in cascade, the total delay time is given by

$$T_d = nt_d \qquad [11.9\text{-}3]$$

where t_d is the delay per section.

It is customary to assume that the rise time varies approximately as the cube root of the number of sections.† Then,

$$T_r = t_r n^{1/3} \qquad [11.9\text{-}4]$$

where t_r is the rise time per section.

The division of Eq. 11.9-3 by Eq. 11.9-4 yields

$$\frac{T_d}{T_r} = n^{2/3} \left(\frac{t_d}{t_r} \right) \qquad [11.9\text{-}5]$$

It follows from Eq. 11.9-5 that the number of sections is given by

---

* These are similar to the artificial lines discussed in Sec. 9.7.

† This relation is given in *Pulse and Digital Circuits*, by J. Millman and H. Taub (McGraw-Hill Book Co., New York, 1956), pages 293–294; Chap. 10 of that text is devoted to delay lines.

$$n = \left(\frac{T_d}{T_r}\right)^{1.5}\left(\frac{t_r}{t_d}\right)^{1.5} \qquad\qquad [11.9\text{-}6]$$

It follows from Eqs. 11.3-15 and 11.3-17 that

$$\frac{t_r}{t_d} = \frac{1.13}{1.07} = 1.06 \qquad\qquad [11.9\text{-}7]$$

The substitution of Eq. 11.9-7 into Eq. 11.9-6 yields

$$n = 1.1\left[\frac{T_d}{T_r}\right]^{1.5} \qquad\qquad [11.9\text{-}8]$$

Equation 11.9-8 determines the required number of sections for specified delay and rise times.

Since $R_k = \sqrt{L/C}$,

$$L = CR_k^2 \qquad\qquad [11.9\text{-}9]$$

The substitution of L from Eq. 11.9-9 into Eq. 11.3-17 for the delay time per section gives the following result:

$$t_d = 1.07CR_k = \frac{T_d}{n} \qquad\qquad [11.9\text{-}10]$$

The solution of Eq. 11.9-10 for C yields

$$C = \frac{T_d}{1.07nR_k} \qquad\qquad [11.9\text{-}11]$$

The substitution of $C = L/R_k^2$ (from Eq. 11.9-9) in Eq. 11.9-11 yields

$$L = \frac{R_kT_d}{1.07n} \qquad\qquad [11.9\text{-}12]$$

Equations 11.9-8, 11.9-11, and 11.9-12 are the design equations of the lumped-parameter delay line.

A reduction in distortion, and a resulting improvement in the waveform, can be obtained by the use of an m-derived section with $m = 1.27$. The reader is referred to the previously cited work of Millman and Taub for the details of this design.

PROBLEMS

11-1 Plot the response of an ideal filter to a rectangular pulse input under these conditions: (a), when $\omega_c t_1 = 2\pi$; and (b), when $\omega_c t_1 = 12\pi$.

11-2 Derive an expression for $v_2(t)$ in Fig. 11-4, assuming that the internal impedance of the generator is zero.

11-3 Plot the result obtained for Prob. 11-2 for the coordinates used in Fig. 11-5. Compare your result with the curve shown in Fig. 11-5.

11-4 A lossless transmission line having a characteristic impedance of Z_0 is terminated by a resistance of $Z_0/2$. A 10-volt battery in series with a resistance of $Z_0/4$ is connected at the sending end. Derive an expression for the voltage across the termination.

11-5 Derive an expression for the input current to the line of Prob. 11-4.

11-6 The parameters of a line that is 100 meters in length are: $\overline{L} = 10^{-6}$ henry per meter; $\overline{C} = 6 \times 10^{-11}$ farad per meter; $\overline{R} = 0.4$ ohm per meter; and $\overline{G} = 0$. The line is terminated by its characteristic impedance. An ideal voltage source having $v(t) = 10 \cos 6\pi \times 10^6 t$ is applied at the input terminals. After the steady state is attained, the source is short-circuited. Derive an expression for the transform of the line voltage after the short-circuit.

11-7 Solve Prob. 11-6 if the source has an internal impedance of 100 ohms.

11-8 Solve Prob. 11-6 if the line is terminated by a 50-ohm resistor.

11-9 Refer to Fig. 11-8 (Sec. 11.7) and prove that the energy initially stored in the pulse-forming line is entirely dissipated in Z_0 after switch S_2 is closed.

11-10 Design a delay line using the T section of the form shown in Fig. 11.4. The impedance is to be 500 ohms. The total delay is to be 1.0 microsecond, and the rise time is to be 0.3 microsecond.

derivation of equation 1.1-11

A general proof of Eq. 1.1-11 will now be given. Consider the determinant given by

$$\Delta = \begin{vmatrix} a_{11} & a_{12} & a_{13} & a_{14} & \ldots & a_{1n} \\ a_{21} & a_{22} & a_{23} & a_{24} & \ldots & a_{2n} \\ a_{31} & a_{32} & a_{33} & a_{34} & \ldots & a_{3n} \\ a_{41} & a_{42} & a_{43} & a_{44} & \ldots & a_{4n} \\ \ldots & \ldots & \ldots & \ldots & \ldots & \ldots \\ \ldots & \ldots & \ldots & \ldots & \ldots & \ldots \\ a_{n1} & a_{n2} & a_{n3} & a_{n4} & \ldots & a_{nn} \end{vmatrix} \qquad [\text{A-1}]$$

Let another determinant Δ' be formed from the cofactors of Δ such that

$$\Delta' = \Delta_{11}\Delta_{22} - \Delta_{21}\Delta_{12} \qquad [\text{A-2}]$$

The determinant Δ' can be written as

$$\Delta' = \begin{vmatrix} \Delta_{11} & \Delta_{21} & 0 & 0 & \ldots & 0 \\ \Delta_{12} & \Delta_{22} & 0 & 0 & \ldots & 0 \\ \Delta_{13} & \Delta_{23} & 1 & 0 & \ldots & 0 \\ \Delta_{14} & \Delta_{24} & 0 & 1 & \ldots & 0 \\ \ldots & \ldots & \ldots & \ldots & \ldots & \ldots \\ \ldots & \ldots & \ldots & \ldots & \ldots & \ldots \\ \Delta_{1n} & \Delta_{2n} & 0 & 0 & \ldots & 1 \end{vmatrix} = \Delta_{11}\Delta_{22} - \Delta_{21}\Delta_{12} \qquad [\text{A-3}]$$

Equation A-3 is derived by expanding Δ' in terms of the cofactors of its first row. The product $\Delta\Delta'$ is given by

$$\Delta\Delta' = \begin{vmatrix} (a_{11}\Delta_{11} + a_{12}\Delta_{12} + \ldots + a_{1n}\Delta_{1n}) & (a_{11}\Delta_{21} + a_{12}\Delta_{22} + \ldots + a_{1n}\Delta_{2n}) & a_{13} & a_{14} & \ldots & a_{1n} \\ (a_{21}\Delta_{11} + a_{22}\Delta_{12} + \ldots + a_{2n}\Delta_{1n}) & (a_{21}\Delta_{21} + a_{22}\Delta_{22} + \ldots + a_{2n}\Delta_{2n}) & a_{23} & a_{24} & \ldots & a_{2n} \\ (a_{31}\Delta_{11} + a_{32}\Delta_{12} + \ldots + a_{3n}\Delta_{1n}) & (a_{31}\Delta_{21} + a_{32}\Delta_{22} + \ldots + a_{3n}\Delta_{2n}) & a_{33} & a_{34} & \ldots & a_{3n} \\ \ldots & \ldots & & & & \\ \ldots & \ldots & & & & \\ \ldots & \ldots & & & & \\ (a_{n1}\Delta_{11} + a_{n2}\Delta_{12} + \ldots + a_{nn}\Delta_{1n}) & (a_{n1}\Delta_{21} + a_{n2}\Delta_{22} + \ldots + a_{nn}\Delta_{2n}) & a_{n3} & a_{n4} & \ldots & a_{nn} \end{vmatrix}$$

$$[\text{A-4}]$$

It follows directly from the definition of a cofactor that

$$a_{11}\Delta_{11} + a_{12}\Delta_{12} + \ldots + a_{1n}\Delta_{1n} = \Delta$$

$$a_{21}\Delta_{21} + a_{22}\Delta_{22} + \ldots + a_{2n}\Delta_{2n} = \Delta$$

$$[\text{A-5}]$$

It also follows from the theory for the expansion of a determinant in terms of the elements of any row or column and the cofactors of *any other* row or column that:

$$a_{21}\Delta_{11} + a_{22}\Delta_{12} + \ldots + a_{2n}\Delta_{1n} = a_{31}\Delta_{21} + a_{32}\Delta_{22} + \ldots + a_{3n}\Delta_{2n}$$

$$= a_{n1}\Delta_{k1} + a_{n2}\Delta_{k2} + \ldots + a_{nn}\Delta_{kn} = 0 \quad [\text{A-6}]$$

Hence Eq. A-4 can be written as

$$\Delta\Delta' = \begin{vmatrix} \Delta & 0 & a_{13} & a_{14} & \ldots & a_{1n} \\ 0 & \Delta & a_{33} & a_{24} & \ldots & a_{2n} \\ 0 & 0 & a_{33} & a_{34} & \ldots & a_{3n} \\ \ldots & & & & & \\ \ldots & & & & & \\ 0 & 0 & a_{n3} & a_{n4} & \ldots & a_{nn} \end{vmatrix} \quad [\text{A-7}]$$

Expansion of the determinant on the right-hand side of Eq. A-7 yields

$$\Delta\Delta' = \Delta^2\Delta_{1122} \quad [\text{A-8}]$$

where Δ_{1122} is the determinant that remains after both the first row and the first column and the second row and the second column are eliminated from the original determinant Δ in Eq. A-1. Substitution of Δ' from Eq. A-2 into Eq. A-8 gives the following relation:

$$\Delta_{11}\Delta_{22} - \Delta_{21}\Delta_{12} = \Delta\Delta_{1122} \quad [\text{A-9}]$$

It follows from Eq. A-9 that:

$$\frac{\Delta_{11}\Delta_{22} - \Delta_{21}\Delta_{12}}{\Delta} = \Delta_{1122} \quad [\text{A-10}]$$

where the cofactors are those of Δ. Equation 1.1-11 is Eq. A-10.
To illustrate the application of Eq. A-10, consider the determinant

$$\Delta = \begin{vmatrix} 1 & -2 & 2 \\ -2 & 4 & 3 \\ 3 & 1 & -2 \end{vmatrix} \qquad \text{[A-11]}$$

for which

$$\Delta_{11} = -8-3 = -11 \qquad \Delta_{12} = -(4-9) = 5$$

$$\Delta_{13} = -2-12 = -14 \qquad \Delta_{21} = -(4-2) = -2$$

$$\Delta_{22} = -2-6 = -8 \qquad \Delta = \Delta_{11} - 2\Delta_{12} + 2\Delta_{13} = -49$$

Hence

$$\frac{\Delta_{11}\Delta_{22} - \Delta_{21}\Delta_{12}}{\Delta} = \frac{88 + 10}{-49} = -2 = \Delta_{1122} \qquad \text{[A-12]}$$

Inspection of Eq. A-11 shows that when the first row and the first column together with the second row and the second column of Δ are cancelled, the result is -2. This agrees with Eq. A-12.

In the case of reciprocal networks, $\Delta_{12} = \Delta_{21}$, and Eq. A-10 becomes

$$\frac{\Delta_{11}\Delta_{22} - \Delta_{12}^2}{\Delta} = \frac{\Delta_{11}\Delta_{22} - \Delta_{21}^2}{\Delta} = \Delta_{1122} \qquad \text{[A-13]}$$

hyperbolic functions

The basic trigonometric functions are expressed in terms of exponentials having imaginary arguments as follows:

$$\cos \theta = \frac{\epsilon^{j\theta} + \epsilon^{-j\theta}}{2} \qquad \text{[B-1]}$$

$$j \sin \theta = \frac{\epsilon^{j\theta} - \epsilon^{-j\theta}}{2} \qquad \text{[B-2]}$$

$$j \tan \theta = \frac{\epsilon^{j\theta} - \epsilon^{-j\theta}}{\epsilon^{j\theta} + \epsilon^{-j\theta}} \qquad \text{[B-3]}$$

The basic hyperbolic functions are expressed in terms of exponentials with real arguments as follows:

$$\cosh \phi = \frac{\epsilon^{\phi} + \epsilon^{-\phi}}{2} \qquad \text{[B-4]}$$

$$\sinh \phi = \frac{\epsilon^{\phi} - \epsilon^{-\phi}}{2} \qquad \text{[B-5]}$$

$$\tanh \phi = \frac{\epsilon^{\phi} - \epsilon^{-\phi}}{\epsilon^{\phi} + \epsilon^{-\phi}} \qquad \text{[B-6]}$$

where $\cosh \phi$ is the hyperbolic cosine of the angle ϕ, $\sinh \phi$ is the hyperbolic sine, and $\tanh \phi$ is the hyperbolic tangent.

The hyperbolic functions are shown in Fig. B-1. It should be noted that, for large values of ϕ,

$$|\cosh \phi| \cong |\sinh \phi|, \quad \text{and} \quad |\tanh \phi| \cong 1.$$

Tables of the hyperbolic functions are given in Appendix C.

The graphical determination of both the trigonometric and the hy-

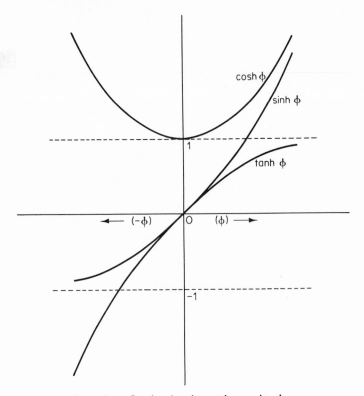

Figure B-1   Graphs of cosh ϕ, sinh ϕ, and tanh ϕ.

perbolic functions is illustrated in Fig. B-2. The significance of $j \sin \theta$ as a quadrature component in Fig. B-2(a) is to be noted.

When $\phi = j\theta$ is substituted in Eqs. B-4 and B-5, the following relations are obtained:

$$\cosh j\theta = \frac{\epsilon^{j\theta} + \epsilon^{-j\theta}}{2} = \cos \theta \qquad \text{[B-7]}$$

$$\sinh j\theta = \frac{\epsilon^{j\theta} - \epsilon^{-j\theta}}{2} = j \sin \theta \qquad \text{[B-8]}$$

Equations B-7 and B-8 give the basic relations between trigonometric and hyperbolic functions, and show that, whereas hyperbolic functions measure real angles, trigonometric functions measure quadrature angles.

The fundamental hyperbolic identities can be derived directly from Eqs. B-4 and B-5, just as the fundamental trigonometric identities can be derived directly from Eqs. B-1 and B-2. Adding Eqs. B-4 and B-5 yields

$$\cosh \phi + \sinh \phi = \epsilon^{\phi} \qquad \text{[B-9]}$$

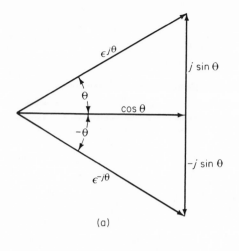

(a)

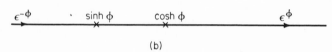

(b)

Figure B-2 Graphical determination of trigonometric and hyperbolic functions.

Squaring Eqs. B-4 and B-5, and subtracting Eq. B-4 from Eq. B-5, yields

$$\cosh^2 \phi - \sinh^2 \phi = \frac{\epsilon^{2\phi} + 2 + \epsilon^{-2\phi}}{4} - \left(\frac{\epsilon^{2\phi} - 2 + \epsilon^{-2\phi}}{4}\right) = 1 \qquad \text{[B-10]}$$

It follows from Eq. B-10 that

$$\cosh \phi = \sqrt{\sinh^2 \phi + 1} \qquad \text{[B-11]}$$

$$\sinh \phi = \sqrt{\cosh^2 \phi - 1} \qquad \text{[B-12]}$$

The substitution of Eq. B-12 in Eq. B-9 gives the following results:

$$\epsilon^\phi = \cosh \phi + \sqrt{\cosh^2 \phi - 1}$$

$$\phi = \ln \left[\cosh \phi + \sqrt{\cosh^2 \phi - 1}\right] \qquad \text{[B-13]}$$

If $\cosh \phi = x$, Eq. B-13 becomes

$$\cosh^{-1} x = \ln \left[x + \sqrt{x^2 - 1}\right] \qquad \text{[B-14]}$$

It also follows from Eqs. B-9 and B-11 that:

$$\sinh^{-1} x = \ln \left[x + \sqrt{x^2 + 1} \right] \qquad \text{[B-15]}$$

The series expansions for cosh ϕ and sinh ϕ follow directly from Eqs. B-4 and B-5, and are given by

$$\cosh \phi = 1 + \frac{\phi^2}{2!} + \frac{\phi^4}{4!} + \cdots \qquad \text{[B-16]}$$

$$\sinh \phi = \phi + \frac{\phi^3}{3!} + \frac{\phi^5}{5!} + \cdots \qquad \text{[B-17]}$$

Equations B-16 and B-17 show that the hyperbolic cosine is an *even* function, and the hyperbolic sine is an *odd* function.

It is seen from Eqs. B-16 and B-17 that

$$\cosh (-\phi) = \cosh \phi \qquad \text{[B-18]}$$
$$\sinh (-\phi) = -\sinh \phi \qquad \text{[B-19]}$$

Equations B-18 and B-19 are analogous to the relations for the trigonometric sine and cosine.

It follows directly from Eq. B-9 that:

$$\epsilon^{\phi_1} = \cosh \phi_1 + \sinh \phi_1 \qquad \text{[B-20]}$$
$$\epsilon^{\phi_2} = \cosh \phi_2 + \sinh \phi_2 \qquad \text{[B-21]}$$

The multiplication of Eq. B-20 by Eq. B-21 yields

$$\epsilon^{\phi_1 + \phi_2} = \cosh (\phi_1 + \phi_2) + \sinh (\phi_1 + \phi_2)$$
$$= \cosh \phi_1 \cosh \phi_2 + \sinh \phi_1 \sinh \phi_2 + \sinh \phi_1 \cosh \phi_2 + \cosh \phi_1 \sinh \phi_2$$
$$\text{[B-22]}$$

The product of two even or two odd functions is an even function. The product of an even and an odd function is an odd function. These relations follow directly from the multiplication of series expansions such as Eqs. B-16 and B-17 and from the fact that the sum of two even or two odd numbers is even, while the sum of an even and an odd number is odd. Equating even and odd functions on both sides of Eq. B-22 gives the following result:

$$\cosh (\phi_1 + \phi_2) = \cosh \phi_1 \cosh \phi_2 + \sinh \phi_1 \sinh \phi_2 \qquad \text{[B-23]}$$
$$\sinh (\phi_1 + \phi_2) = \sinh \phi_1 \cosh \phi_2 + \cosh \phi_1 \sinh \phi_2 \qquad \text{[B-24]}$$

Equations B-23 and B-24 are the addition formulas for the hyperbolic cosine and the hyperbolic sine.

The addition formulas for the corresponding trigonometric functions are found in the same manner by using the relation

$$\epsilon^{j\theta} = \cos\theta + j\sin\theta \qquad [B\text{-}25]$$

and equating real (even) and imaginary (odd) terms.

Hyperbolic functions of complex angles are found from Eqs. B-23 and B-24, with the aid of Eqs. B-7 and B-8. Thus

$$\cosh(\phi + j\theta) = \cosh\phi\cosh j\theta + \sinh\phi\sinh j\theta = \cosh\phi\cos\theta$$
$$+ j\sinh\phi\sin\theta \qquad [B\text{-}26]$$

$$\sin(\phi + j\theta) = \sinh\phi\cosh j\theta + \cosh\phi\sinh j\theta = \sinh\phi\cos\theta$$
$$+ j\cosh\phi\sin\theta \qquad [B\text{-}27]$$

Equations B-26 and B-27 show that the hyperbolic cosine and sine of complex arguments are complex, and are given by

$$\cosh(\phi + j\theta) = \sqrt{\cosh^2\phi\cos^2\theta + \sinh^2\phi\sin^2\theta}\ \underline{/\tan^{-1}\tanh\phi\tan\theta} \quad [B\text{-}28]$$
$$= \sqrt{\sinh^2\phi + \cos^2\theta}\ \underline{/\tan^{-1}\tanh\theta\tan\theta}$$

$$\sinh(\phi + j\theta) = \sqrt{\sinh^2\phi\cos^2\theta + \cosh^2\phi\sin^2\theta}\ \underline{/\tan^{-1}\coth\phi\tan\theta} \quad [B\text{-}29]$$
$$= \sqrt{\sinh^2\phi + \sin^2\theta}\ \underline{/\tan^{-1}\coth\theta\tan\theta}$$

where

$$\coth\phi = \frac{\cosh\phi}{\sinh\phi} \qquad [B\text{-}30]$$

and is the hyperbolic cotangent. The hyperbolic secant (sech ϕ) and cosecant (csch ϕ) are respectively the reciprocals of the hyperbolic cosine and the hyperbolic sine, and are given by

$$\operatorname{sech}\phi = \frac{1}{\cosh\phi} \qquad [B\text{-}31]$$

$$\operatorname{csch}\phi = \frac{1}{\sinh\phi} \qquad [B\text{-}32]$$

When $\phi_1 = \phi_2 = \phi$ in Eqs. B-23 and B-24, the following relations are obtained:

$$\cosh 2\phi = \cosh^2\phi + \sinh^2\phi \qquad [B\text{-}33]$$

$$\sinh 2\phi = 2\sinh\phi\cosh\phi \qquad [B\text{-}34]$$

Two other forms of Eq. B-33 are obtained by use of Eq. B-10. Thus,

$$\cosh 2\phi = \cosh^2 \phi + \cosh^2 \phi - 1 = 2 \cosh^2 \phi - 1 \qquad \text{[B-35]}$$

$$\cosh 2\phi = 1 + \sinh^2 \phi + \sinh^2 \phi = 2 \sinh^2 \phi + 1 \qquad \text{[B-36]}$$

The half-angle formulas for the hyperbolic functions are found by substituting $\phi/2$ for ϕ in Eqs. B-35 and B-36. Thus,

$$\sinh \frac{\phi}{2} = \sqrt{\frac{\cosh \phi - 1}{2}} \qquad \text{[B-37]}$$

$$\cosh \frac{\phi}{2} = \sqrt{\frac{\cosh \phi + 1}{2}} \qquad \text{[B-38]}$$

$$\tanh \frac{\phi}{2} = \sqrt{\frac{\cosh \phi - 1}{\cosh \phi + 1}} \qquad \text{[B-39]}$$

Multiplying both the numerator and denominator on the right-hand side of Eq. B-39 by $(\cosh \phi + 1)$ gives the following result:

$$\tanh \frac{\phi}{2} = \sqrt{\frac{\cosh^2 \phi - 1}{\cosh \phi + 1}} = \frac{\sinh \phi}{\cosh \phi + 1} \qquad \text{[B-40]}$$

Equation B-39 can also be written as

$$\tanh \frac{\phi}{2} = \frac{\cosh \phi - 1}{\sinh \phi} \qquad \text{[B-41]}$$

It follows from Eq. B-9 that:

$$\epsilon^{\phi/2} = \cosh \frac{\phi}{2} + \sinh \frac{\phi}{2} \qquad \text{[B-42]}$$

Hence,

$$\frac{\phi}{2} = \ln \left[\cosh \frac{\phi}{2} + \sinh \frac{\phi}{2} \right] \qquad \text{[B-43]}$$

$$\phi = 2 \ln \left[\cosh \frac{\phi}{2} + \sinh \frac{\phi}{2} \right] \qquad \text{[B-44]}$$

The substitution of Eqs. B-37 and B-38 into Eq. B-44 yields

$$\phi = 2 \ln \left[\sqrt{\frac{\cosh \phi + 1}{2}} + \sqrt{\frac{\cosh \phi - 1}{2}} \right] \qquad \text{[B-45]}$$

Assume now that

$$\theta = \tanh^{-1} x \qquad \text{[B-46]}$$

Then

$$\tanh \theta = x = \frac{\epsilon^\theta - \epsilon^{-\theta}}{\epsilon^\theta + \epsilon^{-\theta}} \qquad \text{[B-47]}$$

It follows from Eq. B-47 that

$$x\epsilon^\theta + x\epsilon^{-\theta} = \epsilon^\theta - \epsilon^{-\theta} \qquad \text{[B-48]}$$

$$\epsilon^{-\theta}(1 + x) = \epsilon^\theta(1 - x) \qquad \text{[B-49]}$$

$$\epsilon^{2\theta} = \frac{1 + x}{1 - x} \qquad \text{[B-50]}$$

$$\theta = \tanh^{-1} x = \frac{1}{2} \ln \left[\frac{1 + x}{1 - x} \right] \qquad \text{[B-51]}$$

tables of exponential and hyperbolic functions

*These tables are reproduced from *Reference Data for Radio Engineers,* Fourth Edition, 1956, with permission of International Telephone and Telegraph Corporation. New York, N.Y.

Hyperbolic sines $[\sinh x = \frac{1}{2}(e^x - e^{-x})]$

x	0	1	2	3	4	5	6	7	8	9	avg diff
0.0	0.0000	0.0100	0.0200	0.0300	0.0400	0.0500	0.0600	0.0701	0.0801	0.0901	100
.1	0.1002	0.1102	0.1203	0.1304	0.1405	0.1506	0.1607	0.1708	0.1810	0.1911	101
.2	0.2013	0.2115	0.2218	0.2320	0.2423	0.2526	0.2629	0.2733	0.2837	0.2941	103
.3	0.3045	0.3150	0.3255	0.3360	0.3466	0.3572	0.3678	0.3785	0.3892	0.4000	106
.4	0.4108	0.4216	0.4325	0.4434	0.4543	0.4653	0.4764	0,4875	0.4986	0.5098	110
0.5	0.5211	0.5324	0.5438	0.5552	0.5666	0.5782	0.5897	0.6014	0.6131	0.6248	116
.6	0.6367	0.6485	0.6605	0.6725	0.6846	0.6967	0.7090	0.7213	0.7336	0.7461	122
.7	0.7586	0.7712	0.7838	0.7966	0.8094	0.8223	0.8353	0.8484	0.8615	0.8748	130
.8	0.8881	0.9015	0.9150	0.9286	0.9423	0.9561	0.9700	0.9840	0.9981	1.012	138
.9	1.027	1.041	1.055	1.070	1.085	1.099	1.114	1.129	1.145	1.160	15
1.0	1.175	1.191	1.206	1.222	1.238	1.254	1.270	1.286	1.303	1.319	16
.1	1.336	1.352	1.369	1.386	1.403	1.421	1.438	1.456	1.474	1.491	17
.2	1.509	1.528	1.546	1.564	1.583	1.602	1.621	1.640	1.659	1.679	19
.3	1.698	1.718	1.738	1.758	1.779	1.799	1.820	1.841	1.862	1.883	21
.4	1.904	1.926	1.948	1.970	1.992	2.014	2.037	2.060	2.083	2.106	22
1.5	2.129	2.153	2.177	2.201	2.225	2.250	2.274	2.299	2.324	2.350	25
.6	2.376	2.401	2.428	2.454	2.481	2.507	2.535	2.562	2.590	2.617	27
.7	2.646	2.674	2.703	2.732	2.761	2.790	2.820	2.850	2.881	2.911	30
.8	2.942	2.973	3.005	3.037	3.069	3.101	3.134	3.167	3.200	3.234	33
.9	3.268	3.303	3.337	3.372	3.408	3.443	3.479	3.516	3.552	3.589	36
2.0	3.627	3.665	3.703	3.741	3.780	3.820	3.859	3.899	3.940	3.981	39
.1	4.022	4.064	4.106	4.148	4.191	4.234	4.278	4.322	4.367	4.412	44
.2	4.457	4.503	4.549	4.596	4.643	4.691	4.739	4.788	4.837	4.887	48
.3	4.937	4.988	5.039	5.090	5.142	5.195	5.248	5.302	5.356	5.411	53
.4	5.466	5.522	5.578	5.635	5.693	5.751	5.810	5.869	5.929	5.989	58
2.5	6.050	6.112	6.174	6.237	6.300	6.365	6.429	6.495	6.561	6.627	64
.6	6.695	6.763	6.831	6.901	6.971	7.042	7.113	7.185	7.258	7.332	71
.7	7.406	7.481	7.557	7.634	7.711	7.789	7.868	7.948	8.028	8.110	79
.8	8.192	8.275	8.359	8.443	8.529	8.615	8.702	8.790	8.879	8.969	87
.9	9.060	9.151	9.244	9.337	9.431	9.527	9.623	9.720	9.819	9.918	96
3.0	10.02	10.12	10.22	10.32	10.43	10.53	10.64	10.75	10.86	10.97	11
.1	11.08	11.19	11.30	11.42	11.53	11.65	11.76	11.88	12.00	12.12	12
.2	12.25	12.37	12.49	12.62	12.75	12.88	13.01	13.14	13.27	13.40	13
.3	13.54	13.67	13.81	13.95	14.09	14.23	14.38	14.52	14.67	14.82	14
.4	14.97	15.12	15.27	15.42	15.58	15.73	15.89	16.05	16.21	16.38	16
3.5	16.54	16.71	16.88	17.05	17.22	17.39	17.57	17.74	17.92	18.10	17
.6	18.29	18.47	18.66	18.84	19.03	19.22	19.42	19.61	19.81	20.01	19
.7	20.21	20.41	20.62	20.83	21.04	21.25	21.46	21.68	21.90	22.12	21
.8	22.34	22.56	22.79	23.02	23.25	23.49	23.72	23.96	24.20	24.45	24
.9	24.69	24.94	25.19	25.44	25.70	25.96	26.22	26.48	26.75	27.02	26
4.0	27.29	27.56	27.84	28.12	28.40	28.69	28.98	29.27	29.56	29.86	29
.1	30.16	30.47	30.77	31.08	31.39	31.71	32.03	32.35	32.68	33.00	32
.2	33.34	33.67	34.01	34.35	34.70	35.05	35.40	35.75	36.11	36.48	35
.3	36.84	37.21	37.59	37.97	38.35	38.73	39.12	39.52	39.91	40.31	39
.4	40.72	41.13	41.54	41.96	42.38	42.81	43.24	43.67	44.11	44.56	43
4.5	45.00	45.46	45.91	46.37	46.84	47.31	47.79	48.27	48.75	49.24	47
.6	49.74	50.24	50.74	51.25	51.77	52.29	52.81	53.34	53.88	54.42	52
.7	54.97	55.52	56.08	56.64	57.21	57.79	58.37	58.96	59.55	60.15	58
.8	60.75	61.36	61.98	62.60	63.23	63.87	64.51	65.16	65.81	66.47	64
.9	67.14	67.82	68.50	69.19	69.88	70.58	71.29	72.01	72.73	73.46	71
5.0	74.20										

If $x > 5$, $\sinh x = \frac{1}{2}(e^x)$ and $\log_{10} \sinh x = (0.4343)x + 0.6990 - 1$, correct to four significant figures.

Hyperbolic cosines $[\cosh x = \frac{1}{2}(e^x + e^{-x})]$

X	0	1	2	3	4	5	6	7	8	9	avg diff
0.0	1.000	1.000	1.000	1.000	1.001	1.001	1.002	1.002	1.003	1.004	1
.1	1.005	1.006	1.007	1.008	1.010	1.011	1.013	1.014	1.016	1.018	2
.2	1.020	1.022	1.024	1.027	1.029	1.031	1.034	1.037	1.039	1.042	3
.3	1.045	1.048	1.052	1.055	1.058	1.062	1.066	1.069	1.073	1.077	4
.4	1.081	1.085	1.090	1.094	1.098	1.103	1.108	1.112	1.117	1.122	5
0.5	1.128	1.133	1.138	1.144	1.149	1.155	1.161	1.167	1.173	1.179	6
.6	1.185	1.192	1.198	1.205	1.212	1.219	1.226	1.233	1.240	1.248	7
.7	1.255	1.263	1.271	1.278	1.287	1.295	1.303	1.311	1.320	1.329	8
.8	1.337	1.346	1.355	1.365	1.374	1.384	1.393	1.403	1.413	1.423	10
.9	1.433	1.443	1.454	1.465	1.475	1.486	1.497	1.509	1.520	1.531	11
1.0	1.543	1.555	1.567	1.579	1.591	1.604	1.616	1.629	1.642	1.655	13
.1	1.669	1.682	1.696	1.709	1.723	1.737	1.752	1.766	1.781	1.796	14
.2	1.811	1.826	1.841	1.857	1.872	1.888	1.905	1.921	1.937	1.954	16
.3	1.971	1.988	2.005	2.023	2.040	2.058	2.076	2.095	2.113	2.132	18
.4	2.151	2.170	2.189	2.209	2.229	2.249	2.269	2.290	2.310	2.331	20
1.5	2.352	2.374	2.395	2.417	2.439	2.462	2.484	2.507	2.530	2.554	23
.6	2.577	2.601	2.625	2.650	2.675	2.700	2.725	2.750	2.776	2.802	25
.7	2.828	2.855	2.882	2.909	2.936	2.964	2.992	3.021	3.049	3.078	28
.8	3.107	3.137	3.167	3.197	3.228	3.259	3.290	3.321	3.353	3.385	31
.9	3.418	3.451	3.484	3.517	3.551	3.585	3.620	3.655	3.690	3.726	34
2.0	3.762	3.799	3.835	3.873	3.910	3.948	3.987	4.026	4.065	4.104	38
.1	4.144	4.185	4.226	4.267	4.309	4.351	4.393	4.436	4.480	4.524	42
.2	4.568	4.613	4.658	4.704	4.750	4.797	4.844	4.891	4.939	4.988	47
.3	5.037	5.087	5.137	5.188	5.239	5.290	5.343	5.395	5.449	5.503	52
.4	5.557	5.612	5.667	5.723	5.780	5.837	5.895	5.954	6.013	6.072	58
2.5	6.132	6.193	6.255	6.317	6.379	6.443	6.507	6.571	6.636	6.702	64
.6	6.769	6.836	6.904	6.973	7.042	7.112	7.183	7.255	7.327	7.400	70
.7	7.473	7.548	7.623	7.699	7.776	7.853	7.932	8.011	8.091	8.171	78
.8	8.253	8.335	8.418	8.502	8.587	8.673	8.759	8.847	8.935	9.024	86
.9	9.115	9.206	9.298	9.391	9.484	9.579	9.675	9.772	9.869	9.968	95
3.0	10.07	10.17	10.27	10.37	10.48	10.58	10.69	10.79	10.90	11.01	11
.1	11.12	11.23	11.35	11.46	11.57	11.69	11.81	11.92	12.04	12.16	12
.2	12.29	12.41	12.53	12.66	12.79	12.91	13.04	13.17	13.31	13.44	13
.3	13.57	13.71	13.85	13.99	14.13	14.27	14.41	14.56	14.70	14.85	14
.4	15.00	15.15	15.30	15.45	15.61	15.77	15.92	16.08	16.25	16.41	16
3.5	16.57	16.74	16.91	17.08	17.25	17.42	17.60	17.77	17.95	18.13	17
.6	18.31	18.50	18.68	18.87	19.06	19.25	19.44	19.64	19.84	20.03	19
.7	20.24	20.44	20.64	20.85	21.06	21.27	21.49	21.70	21.92	22.14	21
.8	22.36	22.59	22.81	23.04	23.27	23.51	23.74	23.98	24.22	24.47	23
.9	24.71	24.96	25.21	25.46	25.72	25.98	26.24	26.50	26.77	27.04	26
4.0	27.31	27.58	27.86	28.14	28.42	28.71	29.00	29.29	29.58	29.88	29
.1	30.18	30.48	30.79	31.10	31.41	31.72	32.04	32.37	32.69	33.02	32
.2	33.35	33.69	34.02	34.37	34.71	35.06	35.41	35.77	36.13	36.49	35
.3	36.86	37.23	37.60	37.98	38.36	38.75	39.13	39.53	39.93	40.33	39
.4	40.73	41.14	41.55	41.97	42.39	42.82	43.25	43.68	44.12	44.57	43
4.5	45.01	45.47	45.92	46.38	46.85	47.32	47.80	48.28	48.76	49.25	47
.6	49.75	50.25	50.75	51.26	51.78	52.30	52.82	53.35	53.89	54.43	52
.7	54.98	55.53	56.09	56.65	57.22	57.80	58.38	58.96	59.56	60.15	58
.8	60.76	61.37	61.99	62.61	63.24	63.87	64.52	65.16	65.82	66.48	64
.9	67.15	67.82	68.50	69.19	69.89	70.59	71.30	72.02	72.74	73.47	71
5.0	74.21										

If $x > 5$, $\cosh x = \frac{1}{2}(e^x)$, and $\log_{10} \cosh x = (0.4343)x + 0.6990 - 1$, correct to four significant figures.

Hyperbolic tangents $\left[\tanh x = (e^x - e^{-x})/(e^x + e^{-x}) = \sinh x/\cosh x\right]$

X	0	1	2	3	4	5	6	7	8	9	avg diff
0.0	.0000	.0100	.0200	.0300	.0400	.0500	.0599	.0699	.0798	.0898	100
.1	.0997	.1096	.1194	.1293	.1391	.1489	.1587	.1684	.1781	.1878	98
.2	.1974	.2070	.2165	.2260	.2355	.2449	.2543	.2636	.2729	.2821	94
.3	.2913	.3004	.3095	.3185	.3275	.3364	.3452	.3540	.3627	.3714	89
.4	.3800	.3885	.3969	.4053	.4136	.4219	.4301	.4382	.4462	.4542	82
0.5	.4621	.4700	.4777	.4854	.4930	.5005	.5080	.5154	.5227	.5299	75
.6	.5370	.5441	.5511	.5581	.5649	.5717	.5784	.5850	.5915	.5980	67
.7	.6044	.6107	.6169	.6231	.6291	.6352	.6411	.6469	.6527	.6584	60
.8	.6640	.6696	.6751	.6805	.6858	.6911	.6963	.7014	.7064	.7114	52
.9	.7163	.7211	.7259	.7306	.7352	.7398	.7443	.7487	.7531	.7574	45
1.0	.7616	.7658	.7699	.7739	.7779	.7818	.7857	.7895	.7932	.7969	39
.1	.8005	.8041	.8076	.8110	.8144	.8178	.8210	.8243	.8275	.8306	33
.2	.8337	.8367	.8397	.8426	.8455	.8483	.8511	.8538	.8565	.8591	28
.3	.8617	.8643	.8668	.8693	.8717	.8741	.8764	.8787	.8810	.8832	24
.4	.8854	.8875	.8896	.8917	.8937	.8957	.8977	.8996	.9015	.9033	20
1.5	.9052	.9069	.9087	.9104	.9121	.9138	.9154	.9170	.9186	.9202	17
.6	.9217	.9232	.9246	.9261	.9275	.9289	.9302	.9316	.9329	.9342	14
.7	.9354	.9367	.9379	.9391	.9402	.9414	.9425	.9436	.9447	.9458	11
.8	.9468	.9478	.9488	.9498	.9508	.9518	.9527	.9536	.9545	.9554	9
.9	.9562	.9571	.9579	.9587	.9595	.9603	.9611	.9619	.9626	.9633	8
2.0	.9640	.9647	.9654	.9661	.9668	.9674	.9680	.9687	.9693	.9699	6
.1	.9705	.9710	.9716	.9722	.9727	.9732	.9738	.9743	.9748	.9753	5
.2	.9757	.9762	.9767	.9771	.9776	.9780	.9785	.9789	.9793	.9797	4
.3	.9801	.9805	.9809	.9812	.9816	.9820	.9823	.9827	.9830	.9834	4
.4	.9837	.9840	.9843	.9846	.9849	.9852	.9855	.9858	.9861	.9863	3
2.5	.9866	.9869	.9871	.9874	.9876	.9879	.9881	.9884	.9886	.9888	2
.6	.9890	.9892	.9895	.9897	.9899	.9901	.9903	.9905	.9906	.9908	2
.7	.9910	.9912	.9914	.9915	.9917	.9919	.9920	.9922	.9923	.9925	2
.8	.9926	.9928	.9929	.9931	.9932	.9933	.9935	.9936	.9937	.9938	1
.9	.9940	.9941	.9942	.9943	.9944	.9945	.9946	.9947	.9949	.9950	1
3.0	.9951	.9959	.9967	.9973	.9978	.9982	.9985	.9988	.9990	.9992	4
4.0	.9993	.9995	.9996	.9996	.9997	.9998	.9998	.9998	.9999	.9999	1
5.0	.9999										

If $x > 5$, $\tanh x = 1.0000$ to four decimal places.

answers to selected problems

1-1 (a) $z_{11} = 9.14$; $z_{12} = 0.1165$; $z_{22} = 14.67$

      (b) $y_{11} = 0.109$; $y_{12} = 0.00087$; $y_{22} = 0.0682$

1-2 (a) $y_{11} = 0.16 - j0.12$; $y_{12} = -(0.08 + j0.04)$ $y_{22} = 0.04 + j0.12$

      (b) Network is not physically realizable.

1-3 (a) $y_{11} = 0$ $Y_A = \quad j0.1$

          $y_{12} = +j0.1$ $Y_B = -j0.1$

          $y_{22} = 0$ $Y_C = \quad j0.1$

      (b) $Z_0 = 10$ ohms   (c) $\dfrac{V_1}{I_2} = -j10$

1-4 $\omega = 10^4$:
$$z_{11} = 337.9 - j149.7$$
$$z_{12} = 328 + j49.3$$
$$z_{22} = 337.9 - j49.7$$

1-5 (a) $A = \dfrac{Z_1 + Z_2}{Z_2}$ $B = \dfrac{Z_1Z_2 + Z_1Z_3 + Z_2Z_3}{Z_2}$

          $C = \dfrac{1}{Z_2}$ $D = \dfrac{Z_2 + Z_3}{Z_2}$

      (c) $\dfrac{V_1}{V_2} = A + \dfrac{B}{Z_L}$

      (d) $\dfrac{A}{C} = Z_1 + Z_2 = z_{11}$

          $\dfrac{1}{C} = Z_2 = z_{12}$

          $\dfrac{D}{C} = Z_2 + Z_3 = z_{22}$

1-6 (a) $k = 0.778$ (b) $Z_1 = -j\omega(0.1)$

      (c) $L_A = \quad 0.878$ henry $Z_2 = j\omega(1.1)$

          $L_B = \quad 0.718$ henry $Z_3 = j\omega(0.90)$

          $L_C = -7.9$ henrys $k_{\max} = 0.707$

          $k \lesssim \quad 0.707$

1-7 *T network*

    $z_{11} = 133.3$ ohms $Z_1 = 33.3$ ohms

    $z_{12} = 100$ ohms $Z_2 = 100$ ohms

    $z_{22} = 200$ ohms $Z_3 = 100$ ohms

    π network

    $y_{11} = 0.012$ mho $Y_A = 0.006$

    $y_{12} = 0.006$ mho $Y_B = 0.006$

    $y_{22} = 0.008$ mho $Y_C = 0.002$

1-8 $R_0 = 500$ ohms

1-13 $\displaystyle Z_0 = \sqrt{\frac{L}{C}}\sqrt{1 - \frac{\omega^2 LC}{4}}$

1-14 $\displaystyle Z_0 = \frac{\sqrt{L/C}}{\sqrt{1 - \dfrac{\omega^2 LC}{4}}}$

1-15 $\displaystyle Z_0 = \sqrt{\frac{L}{C}}\sqrt{1 - \frac{1}{4\omega^2 LC}}$

1-16 $\displaystyle Z_0 = \frac{\sqrt{L/C}}{\sqrt{1 - \dfrac{1}{4\omega^2 LC}}}$

1-17 $\displaystyle Z_0 = \sqrt{\frac{L_1}{C_2}\left(\frac{1 - \dfrac{1}{\omega^2 L_1 C_1}}{1 - \dfrac{1}{\omega^2 L_2 C_2}}\right) - \frac{\omega^2 L_1^2}{4}\left(1 - \frac{1}{\omega^2 L_1 C_1}\right)^2}$

        $\displaystyle = \sqrt{\frac{L_1}{C_2} - \frac{\omega^2 L_1^2}{4}\left(1 - \frac{1}{\omega^2 L_1 C_1}\right)^2}$ when $L_1 C_1 = L_2 C_2$

1-18 $\displaystyle Z_0 = \frac{L_1/C_2}{\sqrt{\dfrac{L_1}{C_2} - \dfrac{\omega^2 L_1^2}{4}\left(1 - \dfrac{1}{\omega^2 L_1 C_1}\right)^2}}$ when $L_1 C_1 = L_2 C_2$

1-19 13. $\displaystyle \cosh\gamma = 1 - \frac{\omega^2 LC}{2}$

      14. $\displaystyle \cosh\gamma = 1 - \frac{\omega^2 LC}{2}$

15. $\cosh \gamma = 1 - \dfrac{1}{2\omega^2 LC}$

16. $\cosh \gamma = 1 - \dfrac{1}{2\omega^2 LC}$

17. $\cosh \gamma = 1 - \dfrac{\omega^2 L_1 C_2}{2}\left(1 - \dfrac{1}{\omega^2 L_1 C_1}\right)^2$ when $L_1 C_1 = L_2 C_2$

18. $\cosh \gamma = 1 - \dfrac{\omega^2 L_1 C_2}{2}\left(1 - \dfrac{1}{\omega^2 L_1 C_1}\right)^2$ when $L_1 C_1 = L_2 C_2$

1-21   (a) $Z_a = R_1$ in parallel with $2C$
        $Z_b = R_1 + 2R_2$ in series with $2L$
        (b) $Z_a = L$ in parallel with $2C_1$
        $Z_b = L$ in series with $C_2/2$.

1-22   (a) $L_1 = L_2$
        Series arm $= L_1$
        Shunt arm $= 2C_2$.
        (b) $L_1 < L_2$
        Series arm $= L_1$

        Shunt arm $= \dfrac{L_2 - L_1}{2}$ in series with $2C_2$.

        (c) $L_1 > L_2$
        Same as (b), but since $L_1 > L_2$, the mutual arm is negative.
        Replace T network of inductances by a transformer. Primary

        and secondary inductances $= \dfrac{L_1 + L_2}{2}$; mutual inductance $=$

        $-\left(\dfrac{L_1 - L_2}{2}\right).$

1-23   (a) $C_1 = C_2$
        shunt arm $= C_1$
        series arm $= 2L$

        (b) $C_1 > C_2$
        shunt arm $= C_1$
        series arm $= 2L$ in parallel with $\dfrac{C_1 - C_2}{2}$

        (c) $C_1 < C_2$
        same as (b), but $\dfrac{C_1 - C_2}{2}$ is negative and not realizable.

1-24   (a) $L_1 = L_2; C_1 = C_2$
        Bridge arm $= 2L$
        Series arm of T network $= C_1$
        Shunt arm of T network $= L_1/2$
            OR

Bridge arm $= C_1/2$
Series arm of T network $= L_1$
Shunt arm of T network $= 2C$

(b) $L_1 < L_2; C_1 > C_2$
Bridge arm $= 2L_1$
Series arm $= C_1$

Shunt arm $= \dfrac{2C_1C_2}{C_1 - C_2}$ in series with $L_2/2$.

OR

Bridge arm $= C_1/2$
Series arm $= L_1$

Shunt arm $= \dfrac{L_2 - L_1}{2}$ in series with $2C_2$

(c) $L_1 > L_2; C_1 < C_2$
same as above, except negative elements appear.

CHAPTER 2

2-1	db loss	2	5	10	20	40	60
	R_a (ohms)	0.115	0.271	0.520	0.820	0.982	0.995
	R_b (ohms)	8.30	3.67	1.93	1.22	1.02	1.01

2-3	db loss	2	5	10	20	40	60
	$R_1/2$ (ohms)	0.115	0.281	0.520	0.820	0.982	0.999
	R_2 (ohms)	4.32	1.64	0.704	0.20	0.019	0.0005

2-4	db loss	2	5	10	20	40	60
	R_1 (ohms)	0.232	0.608	1.42	4.99	50.0	500.0
	$2R_2$ (ohms)	8.74	3.57	1.93	1.22	1.02	1.00

2-5	db loss	0	1	2	3	4	5	6	7	8	9	10
	R_1 (ohms)	0	61	129	206	292	389	498	620	754	913	1080
	R_2 (ohms)	∞	4100	1940	1210	854	642	499	404	331	275	231

2-11   For T network $R_1 = 2R_0 \tanh \dfrac{\alpha}{2};$ $R_2 = R_0 \operatorname{csch} \alpha$

For π network $R_1 = R_0 \sinh \alpha;$ $R_2 = \dfrac{R_0}{2} \coth \dfrac{\alpha}{2}$

CHAPTER 3

3-1 $C_0 = 0.106$ f; $L_\infty = 8.66$ mh
$L_2 = 0.0493$ h; $C_2 = 0.203$ f; $L_4 = 0.00492$ h; $C_4 = 0.226$ f

3-2 $C_0 = 2.6$ f; $L_2 = 0.092$ h; $C_2 = 0.1089$ f

3-3 $L_\infty = 42.8$ mh; $\quad L_1 = 53.5$ mh; $\quad C_1 = 0.0467$ μf

3-4 $L_1 = 210$ mh; $\quad C_1 = 0.0119$ μf
$L_2 = 25.1$ mh; $\quad C_2 = 0.0159$ μf

3-5 $L_2 = 0.394$ h; $\quad L_4 = 0.063$ h; $\quad L_6 = 0.0103$ h
$C_2 = 0.0399$ f; $\quad C_4 = 0.0254$ f; $\quad C_6 = 0.0387$ f

3-6 $C_\infty = 0.104$ f; $\quad L_1 = 0.1$ h; $\quad C_1 = 2.5$ f

3-12 $L = 3.16$ μh; $\quad L_\infty = 0.722$ μh
$C_0 = 0.00183$ μf; $\quad C_2 = 0.00861$ μf; $\quad C_4 = 0.0100$ μf

$$L_2 = 0.187 \text{ } \mu\text{h}; \quad L_4 = 0.081 \text{ } \mu\text{h}$$

3-13 $C_0 = 115$ $\mu\mu$f; $\quad C_2 = 550$ $\mu\mu$f; $\quad L_2 = 1.5$ mh

3-16 $L_1 = 0.00866$ h; $\quad C_1 = 0.053$ f
$L_2 = 0.0796$ h; $\quad C_2 = 0.0218$ f
$L_3 = 0.426$ h; $\quad C_3 = 0.0296$ f

3-17 $C_1 = 0.104$ f; $\quad C_2 = 2.50$ f; $\quad L = 0.10$ h

CHAPTER 4

4-2 $L_1 = 53.4$ mh $\quad C_2 = 0.213$ μf

4-4 $\dfrac{mL_1}{2} = 16$ mh $\quad \left(\dfrac{1-m^2}{4m}\right)L_1 = 14.2$ mh $\quad mC_2 = 0.128$ μf

4-6 $\dfrac{mL_1}{2} = 5.34$ mh $\quad \left(\dfrac{1-m^2}{4m}\right)L_1 = 64$ mh $\quad mC_2 = 0.0425$ μf

CHAPTER 5

5-11 Z_a is a 0.0275 μf capacitor in parallel with a resistor of 940 ohms. Z_b is a 27.5 mh inductor in series with a resistor of 1065 ohms. Unbalanced network can be constructed.

5-12 Z_a is a 185 mh inductor in parallel with a resistor of 940 ohms. Z_b is a 0.185 μf capacitor in series with a resistor of 1065 ohms.

CHAPTER 6

6-2 (a) T: $z_{11} - z_{12} = \dfrac{11}{15}$; $\quad z_{12} = \dfrac{33}{15}$; $\quad z_{22} - z_{12} = \dfrac{33}{15}$

π: $y_{11} + y_{12} = \dfrac{3}{11}$; $\quad y_{12} = \dfrac{3}{11}$; $\quad y_{22} + y_{12} = \dfrac{1}{11}$

(b) T: $z_{11} - z_{12} = \dfrac{17.1}{15}$; $\quad z_{12} = \dfrac{26.9}{15}$

$$\pi: y_{11} + y_{12} = \frac{2.32}{11}; \qquad y_{12} = \frac{3.68}{11}$$

(c) $T: z_{11} - z_{12} = \frac{25.5}{15}; \qquad z_{12} = \frac{40.5}{15}$

$$\pi: y_{11} + y_{12} = \frac{1.55}{11}; \qquad y_{12} = \frac{2.45}{11}$$

From (b)		*From* (c)	
(d) $R_a = \dfrac{17.1}{15};$	$R_b = \dfrac{70.9}{15}$	$R_a = \dfrac{25.5}{15};$	$R_b = \dfrac{106.5}{15}$
$y_a = \dfrac{9.68}{11};$	$y_b = \dfrac{2.32}{11}$	$y_a = \dfrac{4}{11};$	$y_b = \dfrac{1.55}{11}$

6-3 (a) $R_1 = 474.5; \qquad R_2 = 52.7$
(b) $R_{11} = 527.3; \qquad R_{12} = 166.8$

6-4 (a) $L_1 + L_2(1 - a); \qquad aL_2; \qquad aL_2(a - 1)$ (for T network)

$$L_1\left(\frac{a}{a - 1}\right); \qquad aL_1; \qquad \frac{a^2 L_1 L_2}{L_1 + L_2\left(\dfrac{1 - a}{a}\right)} \qquad \text{(for } \pi \text{ network)}$$

(b) $1 \le a \le \dfrac{L_1 + L_2}{L_2}$

	L (henrys) for T network			*L (henrys) for π network*		
(d) $a = 8$	0.2	0.8	5.6	1.03	7.2	28.8
$a = 12$	-0.2	1.2	13.2	0.983	10.8	-64.8

(e) $a = \sqrt{10}$ \qquad\qquad (f) $k = 0.316$

T network			*π network*		
6-5 (a) $\dfrac{C_1 C_2}{C_2 + C_1(1 - a)},$	$\dfrac{C_2}{a},$	$\dfrac{C_2}{a(a - 1)}$	$\dfrac{C_1(a - 1)}{a},$	$\dfrac{C_1}{a},$	$\dfrac{C_2 + C_1(1 - a)}{a^2}$

(b) $1 \le a \le \dfrac{C_1 + C_2}{C_1}$

	C (μf) for T network			*C (μf) for π network*		
(c) $a = 10$:	∞	0.09	0.01	0.09	0.01	0
$a = \sqrt{10}$:	0.1315	0.285	0.1315	0.0684	0.0316	0.0684
$a = 12$:	-0.455	0.075	0.0068	0.0167	0.0835	-0.0765

6-6 (a) $C, L - aM, aM, a^2 L - aM,$ and $\dfrac{C}{a^2}$

(b) $a_{\max} = \dfrac{L}{M}$

6-7 (a) L, $C + C_m\left(\dfrac{1 - a}{a}\right)$, $\dfrac{C_m}{a}$, $\dfrac{C + C_m(1 - a)}{a^2}$, and a^2L

(for π network)

(b) $a_{max} = \dfrac{C + C_m}{C_m}$

6-8 (a) L_1, $\dfrac{C_1C_2}{C_2 + C_1(1 - a)}$, $\dfrac{C_2}{a}$, $\dfrac{C_1C_2}{a[C_2 + C_1(a - 1)]}$, and $a\,L_1$

(for T network)

(b) $a_{max} = \dfrac{C_1 + C_2}{C_1}$

6-10 $\omega^2 = \dfrac{2}{LC}$; $\omega^2 = \dfrac{1}{RrC^2}$

6-11 $G = \dfrac{1}{12R}$; $\omega^2 = \dfrac{1}{3R^2C^2}$

6-12 $\omega^2 = \dfrac{2GR}{LC}$; $\omega^2 = \dfrac{G}{C^2R + 2GLC}$

CHAPTER 8

8-1 (a) $\overline{C} = 0.7060\ \mu f$ (b) $\overline{L} = 91.8\ \mu h$

8-2 (a) $\overline{C} = 0.008\ \mu f$ (b) $\overline{L} = 3.5\ mh$

8-4 100 v

8-5 72,800 v

8-8 (a) 0.0953 in.   (b) 2×10^8 meters per sec

8-9 (a) 1.473 ft   (b) 186,000 miles per sec

8-11 (a) $S = 3$ (b) $V_{min} = 33.3$ v   (c) $I_{max} = 0.33$ amp

8-14 $7.5\ \underline{/-120°}$ v

8-15 $6.0\ \underline{/226°}$ v

8-16 $0.196\ \underline{/-11.3°}$ v

8-17 $8.37\ \underline{/-130°}$ v

8-23 $Z_{ab} = 2Z_0/3$

8-24 20 v

8-25 (a) 0.61 m   (b) 1.356 m   from receiver.

8-26 $f = 10^9$ cps; $Z_r = 990$ ohms

8-28 $v_{ab} = 39.6$ v

CHAPTER 9

9-1 $\alpha = 0.1$; $Z = 293\ \underline{/-42°}$; $u_p = 46,300$ miles per sec

9-2 $\overline{R} = 13.67$ ohms; $\overline{L} = 3.485$ mh; $\overline{C} = 0.00817\ \mu\mathrm{f}$; $\overline{G} = 0$

9-3 $\overline{C} = 0.00685\ \mu\mathrm{f}$; $\overline{R} = 11.65$; $\overline{L}\ 2.88$ mh

9-4   1.47 nepers

9-5 $632\ \underline{/4.3°}$ ohms

9-6 $710\ \underline{/14°}$ ohms

9-7 $Z_{\mathrm{in}} = 300$ ohms

9-9   15.1° v

9-14   28.1 per cent regulation; 91.5 per cent efficiency

9-17 $\overline{R} = 10.3$ ohms; $\overline{L} = 3.60$ mh; $\overline{C} = 0.00815\ \mu\mathrm{f}$;
      $\overline{G} = 4.81\ \mu$mho

9-20 $\alpha = 0.055$; $Z_0 = 445\ \underline{/-13°}$; $u_p = 23{,}800$ miles per sec

CHAPTER 10

10-1   (a) 0.935 m
      (b) 1.56 m
      (c) 2.50 m

10-2   (a) 0.406 m
      (b) 2.09 m
      (c) 2.50 m

10-3   0.520 in.

10-4 $Z_r = 54\ \underline{/-54.05°}$

10-5   60 v;   80 mw

10-6   (a) $Z_r = 0$ (b) $Z_r = 173.2\underline{/90°}$

10-7 $62.7\ \underline{/-56.85°}$

10-8 $18.88\ \underline{/-10.89°}$

10-9   0.199 m;   0.552 m

10-10 $d_s = 0.634$ m; $\ell = 0.187$ m

index